Methods of Statistical Analysis

WILEY PUBLICATIONS IN STATISTICS

Walter A. Shewhart, Editor

Mathematical Statistics

RAO—Advanced Statistical Methods in Biometric Research.

KEMPTHORNE—The Design and Analysis of Experiments.

DWYER—Linear Computations.

FISHER—Contributions to Mathematical Statistics.

WALD—Statistical Decision Functions.

FELLER—An Introduction to Probability Theory and Its Applications, Volume One.

WALD—Sequential Analysis.

HOEL—Introduction to Mathematical Statistics.

Applied Statistics

GOULDEN—Methods of Statistical Analysis, Second Edition.

HALD—Statistical Theory with Engineering Applications.

HALD—Statistical Tables and Formulas.

YOUDEN — Statistical Methods for Chemists.

MUDGETT—Index Numbers.

TIPPETT—Technological Applications of Statistics.

DEMING—Some Theory of Sampling.

COCHRAN and COX—Experimental Designs.

RICE—Control Charts.

DODGE and ROMIG—Sampling Inspection Tables.

Related Books of Interest to Statisticians

HAUSER and LEONARD—Government Statistics for Business Use.

Methods of Statistical Analysis

CYRIL H. GOULDEN
Chief of the Cereal Division
Central Experimental Farm
Ottawa, Canada

SECOND EDITION

New York · John Wiley & Sons, Inc.
London · Chapman & Hall, Limited

Library of Congress Catalog Card Number: 52-9544

PRINTED IN THE UNITED STATES OF AMERICA

Preface

SINCE 1939, THE DATE OF PUBLICATION OF THE FIRST EDITION, many important advances have been made in statistics, necessitating a very complete revision and the introduction of much new material for the present volume. The process has been time-consuming, and new techniques and procedures continually being evolved have made it very difficult to bring the entire book up to date. To make its contribution as valuable as possible in a world of changing statistical techniques, there has been as much emphasis as possible on fundamental principles and basic theory. This knowledge will always be required by the student in order to understand and appreciate new advances.

A book on statistics must necessarily reflect the author's experience and needs in teaching and giving advice to research workers. For this reason, if every teacher were to write a book, the books would all be different and not one of them would be perfectly satisfactory to all the others. In writing a text it is necessary therefore to try to strike an average with respect not only to subject matter but also to methods of presentation and development. The ideas of a number of teaching statisticians have been obtained, and as many of them as possible have been incorporated into the present book.

The subject matter is slanted rather definitely towards the needs of the student who is now, or will eventually be, a research worker. This viewpoint was adopted for two reasons. In the first place it is not likely that the author would be able to write any other kind of book, and in the second place it would seem to meet the needs of the majority of students of science at the present time.

In the development of each procedure an attempt has been made to follow a uniform method. After general statements the algebraic development is given, and this is followed by a completely worked-out example. The teacher may find it expedient to have the students work through the example before they have fully mastered the principles given in the algebraic development. After some familiarity with the numerical procedure is achieved, it is often much easier for them to grasp the fundamental principles involved.

Although the book may be used to a considerable extent as a reference book for methods of analysis, it is not designed entirely for this purpose. The emphasis is on giving detailed methods of analysis which bring out fundamental principles. This means too that the length of a given section or chapter is not necessarily related to its utility. The chapter on the treatment of non-orthogonal data is an example. It is the longest chapter in the book, but it very likely will not be used for reference purposes as much as many of the shorter chapters. Together with the chapter on the analysis of variance, it aims, however, to give the student that knowledge of fundamental principles necessary for a full understanding of the principles of experimental design.

It is difficult to make adequate acknowledgments because of the number of people who have at one time or another been of assistance. Free use has been made of material in other textbooks, particularly in the excellent books by R. A. Fisher, G. W. Snedecor, W. G. Cochran and Gertrude M. Cox, W. A. Shewhart, J. G. Smith and A. J. Duncan, Paul G. Hoel, M. G. Kendall, D. J. Finney, and K. Mather. Professor R. A. Fisher was kind enough to examine and criticize the chapter on basic experimental designs, and Mr. D. J. Finney, the chapter on probit analysis. Mr. G. B. Oakland and Dr. J. W. Hopkins have constantly been consulted on various points. Others have contributed material, and Mrs. J. Sweetland and Miss J. Thomas have struggled successfully with two or three versions of the typescript. Mr. G. Ballantine has checked the figuring on all examples and exercises.

CYRIL H. GOULDEN

Ottawa, Ontario
June, 1952

Contents

1. Introductory Concepts . . . 1
2. Variation, Statistics, and the Frequency Table . . . 15
3. Theoretical Frequency Distributions . . . 27
4. Tests of Significance . . . 47
5. The Analysis of Variance . . . 63
6. Linear Regression Analysis . . . 102
7. Correlation . . . 122
8. Partial and Multiple Regression and Correlation . . . 134
9. The Analysis of Covariance . . . 153
10. Non-Linear Regression . . . 166
11. Basic Experimental Designs . . . 192
12. Factorial Experiments . . . 220
13. Incomplete Block Experiments . . . 257
14. The Treatment of Non-Orthogonal Data . . . 304
15. Goodness of Fit . . . 353
16. Tests of Independence . . . 369
17. The Discriminant Function . . . 378
18. Probit Analysis . . . 394
19. Quality Control and Sampling for Inspection and Verification 418

Appendix . . . 441

Index . . . 459

CHAPTER 1

Introductory Concepts

1. Statistics and the student of science. Statistics is a subject of particular interest to the science student. He will find that it has practical applications in most of the fields in which he is likely to find his life work, and in any event it will help him to a better understanding and appreciation of the phenomena of nature with which he is bound to be in close contact throughout his career. In the first place, statistics helps the student to understand the nature of variability. This is important in practical applications because phenomena observed under one set of conditions are never duplicated exactly under another set of conditions. It is important in research work because the investigator must take into account all the variable factors and attempt to design his experiments and interpret his results accordingly. It is important to industries because the factors causing variability introduce variations in the quality of their output.

In the second place, statistics teaches how to derive general laws from a mass of individual determinations that in themselves are meaningless. On tracing the pattern made by a moving molecule we find that it darts about in varying directions at high velocities. At no particular point can it be said that a certain molecule is going to travel in a given direction at a given velocity. Its behavior as a single molecule is entirely unpredictable. It is well known, however, that as the temperature rises the molecules travel at greater velocities. If the substance under consideration is a gas within a closed chamber, as the temperature rises the molecules bombard the walls of the chamber with increasing force and the pressure on the walls increases accordingly. Pressure determinations show that, within certain limits, the pressure changes are proportional to temperature. In other words, in spite of the vagaries of the movement of individual molecules, their numbers are so large that the effects they produce are uniform and consistent.. This simple example that every student has observed in the laboratory is an illustration of a statistical law. Analogous laws may be derived from experiments although the results may not be as consistent as in the above example. A comparison between two seed treatments is being made. Because of variations in soil and climate the difference between these two treatments with respect to their effect on the yield of the crop may be inconsistent, but if a real difference exists and a sufficient number of comparisons are available this real difference will become evident. The result can then be expressed as a general law because we have confidence that, if the whole experiment is repeated a sufficient number of times, similar results will be obtained.

One of the fundamental functions of statistics is that of expressing, in summary form, facts that are represented by a large number of determinations. Thus the average or mean is often used as the best single value for representing a group. The variability of a group of observations is expressed by the value of the standard deviation. A trend such as the increase in yield with increasing amounts of fertilizer is expressed first in the form of a graph and finally in the form of a regression coefficient. This emphasizes the descriptive value of statistics and its power to condense a large amount of information into a single graph or a single value. In dealing with biological phenomena, where variation is a rule rather than the exception, it is obvious that this phase of statistics has a wide application.

For the student who contemplates advanced study with the object of doing research, the study of statistics will prove a necessity. Some reasons for this will be clear from what has already been stated, but a more pressing reason is that statistical principles are involved in the efficient and economic design of experiments as well as in the interpretation of the results. It is only within recent years that statisticians have been able to make clear, and to have generally accepted, the principle that statistical methods are required in the design of experiments. It was a common occurrence for research workers to consult a statistician after the experiment had been conducted and the data tabulated. In many cases the results proved of little value, and in many others it was found that the experiment could have been performed in an easier way or that it could have provided much more information for a given amount of effort.

Although a large part of this book is taken up with the application of statistics to the design and analysis of experiments, it should not be taken for granted that this is necessarily the most important field for the application of statistics. The principles of statistics and the various theorems with which it deals are common to all applications. Certain specialized procedures may be more common in one field of work than another, but one never knows when they will be found quite applicable in an entirely different field. In the following pages a chapter will be found on the application of the statistical principles of quality control to the manufacturing industry. This is an important branch of statistics and one in which a number of students may find their greatest interest.

One phase of statistics deals with the correct methods for taking samples in order to obtain information on the lot or the population from which the sample is drawn. Such sampling problems are universal. They apply to business, manufacturing, social studies, economics, land evaluation, research experiments, medicine, and a host of other subjects. There is a similarity, for example, in methods of sampling that might be adopted, in one instance in order to conduct a social survey of people in various strata of society, and in the other instance in order to determine the average number of grasshopper eggs in a square foot of soil in a given field.

The general conclusion is that statistical principles have a very wide application, and it is the study of these principles with which the student must be concerned chiefly, rather than techniques of particular value in restricted fields. The student of science in particular has interests in a wide variety of subjects and therefore has a definite need for a knowledge of statistics with special reference to its fundamental principles.

2. Mathematical ideas are fundamental to statistics. There is a good deal of argument concerning the mathematical training a student requires before he undertakes a study of statistics. The statistical methods and discussions in this book do not require a knowledge of advanced mathematics, but they do require a solid foundation in the basic mathematics such as elementary algebra, geometry, and trigonometry. The algebra of probability is particularly important. For purposes of review, a few of the important mathematical ideas are discussed below.

a. Probability. Mathematicians have had lengthy arguments about the definition of probability. For our purpose it is convenient to accept the definition given by Arley and Buch in their *Introduction to the Theory of Probability and Statistics.* This definition is in reality a concept that must be described rather than stated in a few words. Out of a series of n events suppose that n_A of these are of a certain specified class. For example, in driving through farming country each field of grain observed is an event. Of these fields some are wheat and therefore belong to a specific class, the others being oats, barley, etc. Of n fields observed, if n_A are wheat we say that

$$f(A) = \frac{n_A}{n} \qquad 1$$

is the *relative frequency* of A in the series of observations. Now, it can be shown by actual trial in making repeated observations that $f(A)$ is more consistent as n is increased. For small samples there will be wide variations, but for large samples the observed values of $f(A)$ will be closely grouped around some central value. This tendency to grouping as the number of observations is increased may be referred to as the *random law.* The observed values may be interpreted as estimates of some physical constant which is a fixed or "true" value. Quoting from Arley and Buch: "*This physical constant, for which the relative frequencies are experimental values, is called the* **probability** *of the event A . . . and is denoted by P(A).*"

The above definition would not allow us to find the exact value of any probability, but there are circumstances wherein we can deduce probabilities by making certain *postulates* about the conditions. For example, in throwing a coin it is reasonable to assume that heads and tails are equally likely to occur, or more specifically there is no good reason to assume that one is more likely to occur than the other. In a large number of throws it is to be expected, therefore, that the relative frequency of heads will be quite close to 1/2, because approximately one half of the throws will give heads and one half tails. In short, the probability of heads can be deduced from a simple definition

$$P(A) = \frac{n_1}{n_1 + n_2} \tag{2}$$

where $n_1 + n_2$ is all the possible ways in which the event can occur and n_1 is the number of ways in which the specific event A can occur. In this case $n_1 = 1$, $n_2 = 1$, and $P(A) = 1/2$.

In statistical theory it is generally true that it is not necessary to evaluate a probability with exactitude. As an example of a typical statistical problem, consider the testing of a die to determine the extent or existence of a bias. If the die is thrown 1200 times and it is a true die, the expectation is 200 aces. Note that the exact probability of throwing an ace with this particular die is not required. The probability arises as a result of the hypothesis that has been set up that the die is true. The die is then thrown a large number of times, and the agreement between the theoretical and the actual frequency of the occurrence of aces noted. If the result is quite close to the expected result with a true die, the conclusion is that at least with respect to this particular trial there is no evidence of bias. On the other hand, if the results diverge quite widely from expectation, the conclusion is that the die is biased.

b. Basic rules of probability. The first of these may be stated very simply as follows. Let $P(A)$ be the probability of an event A and $P(B)$ the probability of an event B. Then, if the occurrence of one event excludes the occurrence of the other, the probability that either A or B will occur is

$$P(A, B) = P(A) + P(B) \tag{3}$$

Referring to die problems, A may be the occurrence of an ace, and B, a 5. The separate probabilities are $P(A) = 1/6$ and $P(B) = 1/6$. In a single throw if we get an ace the 5 cannot occur, and if we get a 5 the ace cannot occur. Then the probability of turning up an ace or a 5 is $1/6 + 1/6 = 1/3$. This rule can be extended to cover any number of mutually exclusive events. Therefore for 3 events

$$P(A, B, C) = P(A) + P(B) + P(C) \qquad 4$$

Applying this rule to the probability of turning up an ace, 2, 3, 4, 5, or 6, we get

$$P = \tfrac{1}{6} + \tfrac{1}{6} + \tfrac{1}{6} + \tfrac{1}{6} + \tfrac{1}{6} + \tfrac{1}{6} = 1$$

which is the obvious result because one or other of the 6 possible events must happen.

The second general proposition covers events that are not mutually exclusive, as throwing 2 dice and determining the probability of throwing an ace and a 5. Here the 2 events are independent. If the events are A and B, the probability of their occurring together is

$$P(A + B) = P(A) \times P(B) \qquad 5$$

For the dice problem

$$P(1 + 5) = \tfrac{1}{6} \times \tfrac{1}{6} = \tfrac{1}{36}$$

A variation of this problem is encountered when the second event is conditional on the occurrence of the first event. Thus in drawing 2 cards from a pack we might consider the probability of drawing 2 aces. Note that the probability of drawing the first ace is 4/52, and having drawn the ace the probability of drawing a second one is 3/51; therefore the probability of drawing 2 aces is $4/52 \times 3/51 = 12/2652 = 1/221$. The general statement can be made for problems of this type that

$$P = P(\text{first event happens}) \times P(\text{second event happens, given the first})$$

or

$$P = P(A) \times P_A(B) \qquad 6$$

where $P_A(B)$ represents the probability of B conditional on A.

c. Permutations and combinations. Taking the 4 letters *a*, *b*, *c*, *d*, the *permutations* of these letters 2 at a time are *ab*, *ba*, *ac*, *ca*, *ad*, *da*, *bc*, *cb*, *bd*, *db*, *cd*, *dc*. Note that permutations are different if they contain the same letters but in different order. For n things taken r at a time, the total number of permutations is given by

$${}_nP_r = n(n-1)(n-2)\cdots(n-r+1) \qquad 7$$

If all the n things are to be taken, we have

$${}_nP_n = n(n-1)(n-2)\cdots 3 \cdot 2 \cdot 1 \qquad 8$$

The continued product $n(n-1)(n-2) \cdots 3 \cdot 2 \cdot 1$ is known as *factorial* n and is indicated by the symbol $n!$

When the things to be arranged are not all different, as in determining the number of permutations of the 7 letters *aabbbcc*, we note that there are 2 *a*'s, 3 *b*'s, and 2 *c*'s. Then the total number of permutations is

$$\frac{7!}{2!3!2!} = 210$$

If n represents the number of letters and $p, q, r, \cdots$ the number of each kind, the general formula for the total number of permutations taken all together is

$$P = \frac{n!}{p!q!r!} \tag{9}$$

Combinations refer to the groups of things that can be arranged with reference to kind but not to order. Thus all the combinations of the 4 letters a, b, c, d are ab, ac, ad, bc, bd, cd. For n things taken r at a time, the number of combinations represented by $\binom{n}{r}$ is

$$\binom{n}{r} = \frac{n(n-1)(n-2)\cdots(n-r+1)}{r!} = \frac{n!}{r!(n-r)!} \tag{10}$$

The total number of combinations of n different things taken $0, 1, 2, \cdots$ or n at a time is 2^n.

Permutations and combinations are important in working out problems in probability and therefore occur frequently in procedures of mathematical statistics. A simple problem involving permutations is to assume 12 chips in a bowl with the chips numbered from 1 to 12. If 2 chips are drawn at random, what is the probability that the sum of the numbers on the chips will be 5? Two chips can be drawn from 12 in $12(12-2+1) = 12 \times 11$ ways, using equation (7) above. The sum of 5 can be obtained on 2 chips when the numbers are 4 and 1, 3 and 2, 2 and 3, or 1 and 4, making a total of 4 ways. The required probability is then $4/132 = 1/33$.

An important proposition involving combinations comes from considering such problems as the probability of the occurrence of different numbers of heads in tossing n coins. Suppose that 4 coins are thrown. The different numbers of heads and tails possible are obviously 4 heads, 0 tails; 3 heads, 1 tail; 2 heads, 2 tails; 1 head, 3 tails; and 0 heads, 4 tails. To determine the probability of each result it is convenient to consider the 4 coins arranged in a row occupying the positions numbered 1, 2, 3, 4, as shown below. Beginning with zero heads the total number of arrangements is $\binom{4}{0} = 1$. One head can occur in any one of the 4 positions or in $\binom{4}{1} = 4$ ways. Similarly, 2 heads can occur in $\binom{4}{2} = 6$ ways, and so forth for 3 and 4 heads.

One of the possible arrangements of 0, 1, 2, 3, and 4 heads

Position 1	2	3	4	$\binom{n}{r}$	P
0	0	0	0	1	1/16
H	0	0	0	4	1/4
H	H	0	0	6	3/8
H	H	H	0	4	1/4
H	H	H	H	1	1/16
Total				16	1

The probabilities as given in the last column are then easily obtained.

For any similar problem we can write down the probabilities directly. The denominator is 2^n, where n represents the number of coins thrown, and the numerators are

$$1, \binom{n}{n-1}, \binom{n}{n-2}, \cdots, \binom{n}{n-r}, \cdots, \binom{n}{1}, 1 \qquad 11$$

or

$$1, n, \frac{n!}{2!(n-2)!}, \cdots, \frac{n!}{r!(n-r)!}, \cdots, n, 1$$

d. Binomial theorem. This theorem is stated usually in one of the following forms.

$$(q+p)^n = q^n + \binom{n}{n-1} q^{n-1}p + \binom{n}{n-2} q^{n-2}p^2 + \cdots + \binom{n}{n-r} q^{n-r}p^r + \cdots + p^n \qquad 12$$

$$= q^n + nq^{n-1}p + \frac{n(n-1)}{2 \cdot 1} q^{n-2}p^2 + \cdots + \frac{n!}{r!(n-r)!} q^{n-r}p^r + \cdots + p^n \qquad 13$$

This is an extremely useful theorem in probability problems. As a simple example, suppose that p is the probability of the occurrence of an event, and $q = 1 - p$ is the probability of its failure. Then the probability in n trials that the event will occur exactly r times is given by

$$P(r) = \frac{n!}{r!(n-r)!} q^{n-r} p^r \qquad 14$$

which is seen to be the general term of the binomial expansion. In other words the successive terms of the expanded binomial give the probability in n trials of 0, 1, 2, 3, $\cdots$, r, $\cdots$, n occurrences of the event.

Referring to die-throwing problems again, the probability of throwing an ace is 1/6 and of failing to throw an ace is 5/6. Therefore $p = 1/6$ and $q = 5/6$. In throwing 6 dice, the probability of throwing exactly 2 aces is

$$\binom{6}{2}\left(\frac{5}{6}\right)^4\left(\frac{1}{6}\right)^2 = \frac{6!}{2!4!}\left(\frac{5}{6}\right)^4\left(\frac{1}{6}\right)^2 = 0.2009$$

and the probability of throwing either 0, 1, or 2 aces is

$$\left(\frac{5}{6}\right)^6 + \frac{6!}{1!5!}\left(\frac{5}{6}\right)^5\left(\frac{1}{6}\right) + \frac{6!}{2!4!}\left(\frac{5}{6}\right)^4\left(\frac{1}{6}\right)^2 = 0.9378$$

e. Algebraic functions. Every student of statistics should have an understanding of the meaning of functions such as $y = 2x^2$ or $y = e^x$. It is understood here that y takes specific values dependent on the value of x, in which case we may state the proposition that y is a function of x, $y = f(x)$ being the shorthand method of mathematics for condensing the statement. In statistics we deal largely with frequency functions. For example, we may have

$$y = ce^{-u^2} \qquad 15$$

where y is a frequency and is a function of u, and e is the base of the Naperian system of logarithms. The quantity u may itself be a function of another quantity x so that equation (15) written out in full might be

$$y = ce^{-x^2/\sigma} \qquad 16$$

It is expected for a particular problem that σ will be constant, and within those limits y will be strictly a function of x. In a frequency function, x will represent the variate, such as yield of grain or weight of an animal, and so forth. For a given value of x, the frequency function gives the theoretical frequency y. One of our problems in statistics may be to choose a frequency function such that it will fit the experimental data. More often the frequency function serves as a mathematical model on the basis of which tests may be applied to the data of the experiment.

Functions can of course be represented graphically, and Figure 1–1 shows the type of graph that would be obtained for equation (15). There are two important facts represented by such a graph. In the first place, it shows the values of y for given values of u. For example, at $u = -1$, the value of y is 2.4. In the second place, it shows the relation between areas of different parts lying between the curve and the base line. The shaded section, for example, shows the area lying between -1 and $-\infty$. We say $-\infty$ in this case because for this particular equation the curve

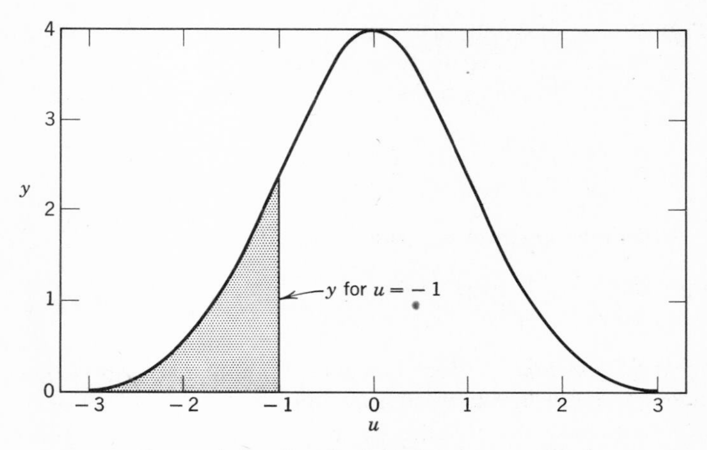

FIGURE 1–1. Graph of the function $y = ce^{-u^2}$.

never actually touches the base line, but this should not cause any confusion. For all practical purposes the area beyond $u = -4$ can be considered as zero. Representing the total area of the curve by unity, the area from $-\infty$ to -1 is a proportion of the whole. In mathematical terms it is referred to as the integral of equation (15) from $-\infty$ to -1.

f. Simultaneous equations. If we have two expressions such as

$$3x + 5y = 22$$

$$7x - 4y = 20$$

they are referred to as a pair of simultaneous equations with two unknowns, x and y. They can be solved by multiplying or dividing the equations by numbers that will make the coefficient of one of the unknowns the same in both equations. For example,

$$7(3x + 5y = 22) = 21x + 35y = 154$$

$$3(7x - 4y = 20) = 21x - 12y = \ \ 60$$

Then, subtracting the second from the first, we have

$$47y = 94$$

and

$$y = 2$$

Substituting 2 for y in one of the equations will then give a new equation which can be solved for x.

It is important to remember that a set of simultaneous equations cannot be solved completely unless there are as many different equations as there are unknowns. We can, however, obtain the relative values of the unknowns if we are lacking only one equation and the terms on the right are zero. For example, we have

$$8x + 5y + 2z = 0$$

$$11x + 2y + 6z = 0$$

Dividing through by x gives

$$8 + 5\frac{y}{x} + 2\frac{z}{x} = 0$$

$$11 + 2\frac{y}{x} + 6\frac{z}{x} = 0$$

and, putting y_1 and z_1 for y/x and z/x, we have

$$5y_1 + 2z_1 = -8$$

$$2y_1 + 6z_1 = -11$$

Solving,

$$15y_1 + 6z_1 = -24$$

$$2y_1 + 6z_1 = -11$$

$$13y_1 = -13$$

$$y_1 = -1$$

Substituting -1 for y_1 in $5y_1 + 2z_1 = -8$, we get

$$-5 + 2z_1 = -8$$

$$2z_1 = -3$$

$$z_1 = -\tfrac{3}{2}$$

The solution of these equations establishes that $y/x = -1$ and $z/x = -3/2$, and therefore that $y/z = y/x \times x/z = (-1) \times (-2/3) = 2/3$.

In some applications this type of solution may be all that is required.

g. Determinants and matrices. Considering the simultaneous equations,

$$a_1x + b_1y = c_1$$

$$a_2x + b_2y = c_2$$

by solving we get

$$x = \frac{b_2c_1 - b_1c_2}{a_1b_2 - a_2b_1}$$

$$y = \frac{a_1c_2 - a_2c_1}{a_1b_2 - a_2b_1}$$

Notice that the denominator is the same for both fractions. It can be represented conveniently by

$$\begin{vmatrix} a_1 & b_1 \\ a_2 & b_2 \end{vmatrix}$$

and in this form is known as a *determinant* of the second order. It can always be set up in the more direct form $a_1b_2 - a_2b_1$ by adding the product of the first diagonal and subtracting the product of the second, where the diagonals are as indicated below.

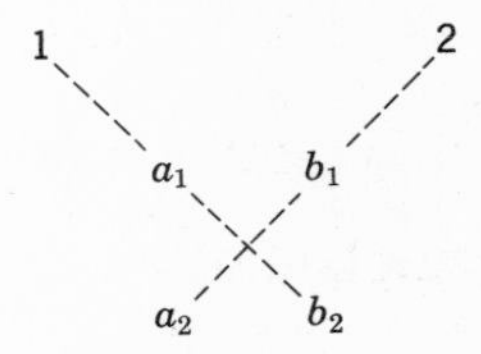

The numerators can also be set up as determinants so that

$$x = \frac{\begin{vmatrix} c_1 & b_1 \\ c_2 & b_2 \end{vmatrix}}{\begin{vmatrix} a_1 & b_1 \\ a_2 & b_2 \end{vmatrix}} \qquad y = \frac{\begin{vmatrix} a_1 & c_1 \\ a_2 & c_2 \end{vmatrix}}{\begin{vmatrix} a_1 & b_1 \\ a_2 & b_2 \end{vmatrix}}$$

17

The positional relations of the symbols in the determinants with the corresponding symbols in the original equations are easily noted, from which the determinants giving the required unknown can be written down directly.

Third-order determinants arise from equations such as

$$a_1x + b_1y + c_1z = d_1$$

$$a_2x + b_2y + c_2z = d_2$$

$$a_3x + b_3y + c_3z = d_3$$

from which it can be shown that

$$x = \frac{\begin{vmatrix} d_1 & b_1 & c_1 \\ d_2 & b_2 & c_2 \\ d_3 & b_3 & c_3 \end{vmatrix}}{\begin{vmatrix} a_1 & b_1 & c_1 \\ a_2 & b_2 & c_2 \\ a_3 & b_3 & c_3 \end{vmatrix}} \qquad 18$$

These can be written down by rule, for it is obvious that in the numerator d replaces the coefficient of the unknown and the denominators are all the same. Thus

$$y = \frac{\begin{vmatrix} a_1 & d_1 & c_1 \\ a_2 & d_2 & c_2 \\ a_3 & d_3 & c_3 \end{vmatrix}}{\begin{vmatrix} a_1 & b_1 & c_1 \\ a_2 & b_2 & c_2 \\ a_3 & b_3 & c_3 \end{vmatrix}} \qquad 19$$

A third-order determinant can also be solved by a simple rule. It can be written as in the diagrams below with two columns repeated. The I diagonals are then added and the J diagonals subtracted.

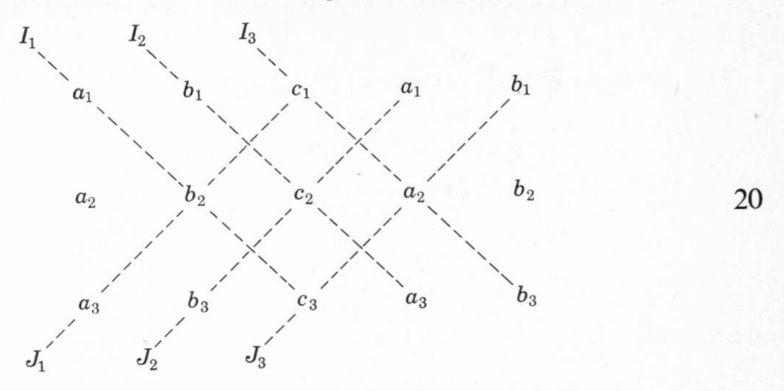

20

Determinants of any order exist, but those of the fourth and higher orders cannot be solved by the simple rules that serve for the second and third order (see appendix).

A set of symbols arranged in the form

$$\begin{pmatrix} a_1 & b_1 & c_1 & d_1 \\ a_2 & b_2 & c_2 & d_2 \\ a_3 & b_3 & c_3 & d_3 \\ a_4 & b_4 & c_4 & d_4 \end{pmatrix} \qquad 21$$

is known as a *matrix*. The term refers merely to a set of symbols arranged in rows and columns and is denoted as a matrix by the large parentheses or by double lines. Also, the number of rows is not necessarily equal to the number of columns. It is very convenient in mathematical writing to be able to refer to a set of symbols as a matrix and for certain systematic arrangements to be able then to represent the whole matrix by one symbol. It must be noted that even when a matrix is square it is not a determinant. However, a square matrix may determine a determinant. Thus for the matrix

$$\begin{pmatrix} a_1 & b_1 \\ a_2 & b_2 \end{pmatrix}$$

we can refer to the determinant of the matrix

$$\begin{vmatrix} a_1 & b_1 \\ a_2 & b_2 \end{vmatrix}$$

3. Exercises.

1. Give three examples wherein the making of a single measurement supplies very little useful information.

2. Calculate the probabilities:

(*a*) That in a single throw a coin will turn up "heads."

(*b*) That in throwing 2 coins they will both turn up "heads."

3. Show how you would conduct an experiment to get some idea of the "trueness" of a coin with respect to turning up "heads" and "tails."

4. Calculate the probability of obtaining the following cards in drawing 3 cards from a complete pack of 52.

(*a*) An ace, a jack, and a deuce.

(*b*) Ace, jack, and 2 of spades.

5. In drawing 5 cards from one pack what is the probability of drawing the ace, king, queen, jack, and 10 of one suit.

6. Find the following permutations and combinations.

(*a*) Permutations of 15 things, 3 at a time.

(*b*) Permutations of 6 things, 6 at a time.

(*c*) Combinations of 15 things, 3 at a time.

(*d*) Combinations of 5 things, 5 at a time.

7. In how many different ways can a committee of 5 men be made up from a group of 16?

8. In throwing 8 coins at once, the number turning up heads may be 0, 1, 2, . . ., 8. Determine the probability of throwing 0, 1, 2, or 3 heads.

CHAPTER 2

Variation, Statistics, and the Frequency Table

1. Variation. The need for the statistical method arises from the variability of the material with which we have to deal. Illustrations of variation are abundant in the biological field. Everyone is familiar with the fact that not all the apples on a tree are the same size, that not every acre of grain produces the same number of bushels, that not all men are the same height, that not all animals of the same group gain equally on equal amounts of food, and so forth. It is possible to cite a great many other examples of a similar nature.

Since variability exists, it is obvious that a problem arises in attempting to define the characteristics of groups. It could be said that, since the characteristics to be measured are subject to variability, it is not possible to establish figures that are of any value in describing the group; but that is clearly absurd, as such measures are continually being employed with considerable confidence. It is the purpose of statistics to define the best methods of describing the characteristics of groups of individuals and to demonstrate how such descriptions can be subjected to objective tests of their reliability. Generally speaking, the method is to prepare tables and graphs, to calculate statistics, and to apply tests of significance.

2. Populations. It is difficult to define exactly what is meant by the term population in the statistical sense, but it is somewhat easier to give examples. If we were trying to determine the average income of the male citizens of Canada, the population we have in mind is strictly speaking a population of incomes and not a population of male citizens. Such populations are referred to as finite populations as distinguished from infinite populations which form the background of our thinking in the development of mathematical statistics. To quote R. A. Fisher [2]: "The idea of infinite populations distributed in a frequency distribution in respect of one or more characters is fundamental to all statistical work."

One of the principal objectives of statistics is to draw inferences with respect to populations by the study of groups of individuals drawn at random that are referred to as *samples*.

3. Samples. As pointed out above, the purpose of drawing samples is to obtain information about the populations from which they are drawn. This information will be of real value only if the sample is drawn in such a way that the results obtained are unbiased. In the usual course of events this is ensured by drawing the sample at random; i.e., in making up the sample each individual in the population has an equal chance of being included. The size of the sample varies, depending on expense, convenience, accuracy required, and many other factors. In fact, sampling is the subject of much discussion in statistical literature, and an excellent book on the whole subject has been written by W. Edwards Deming [1] to which the student should refer for a detailed discussion of many sampling problems.

4. Arithmetic mean. The arithmetic mean is our first sample of a *statistic*. It is called a statistic because it is calculated from a sample and for our purpose is used to estimate the mean of the population from which the sample is drawn. It is necessary in studying statistics to keep in mind this important proposition with respect to all statistics calculated from samples. Thus, the yield of a variety of wheat as taken from a number of plots in an experimental field is not of particular interest in itself as it is merely an estimate of what the variety would yield if grown over a large area under similar conditions.

For a sample of N variates where X_i represents any one variate, the mean $\bar{X}$ is given by

$$\bar{X} = \frac{X_1 + X_2 + X_3 + \cdots + X_i + \cdots + X_N}{N}$$

which for the sake of abbreviation is written

$$\bar{X} = \frac{\sum_{i=1}^{N} (X_i)}{N} \qquad 1$$

Applying the short formula means simply that the summation of the quantities is understood and that we do not need to write them all out and connect them with plus signs. The expression $\sum_{i=1}^{N} (X_i)$ shows that N values are summated; but the simpler form $\Sigma(X)$ may be used when the number of values summed is obvious.

One of the most interesting properties of the mean is that the sum of the deviations of all the individual variates from the mean is zero. This may be shown as follows, with X_i representing an individual variate, and $x_i = (X_i - \bar{X})$ an individual deviation.

$$\Sigma(x_i) = (X_1 - \bar{X}) + (X_2 - \bar{X}) + \cdots + (X_i - \bar{X}) + \cdots + (X_N - \bar{X})$$
$$= (X_1 + X_2 + \cdots + X_i + \cdots + X_N) - N\bar{X}$$

and since

$$N\bar{X} = \frac{N(X_1 + X_2 + \cdots + X_i + \cdots + X_N)}{N} \qquad 2$$

it is clear that $\Sigma(x_i) = 0$. Using the summation sign in order to shorten the algebra,

$$\Sigma(x_i) = \Sigma(X_i - \bar{X}) = \Sigma(X) - N\bar{X}$$

and since

$$N\bar{X} = \frac{N\Sigma(X)}{N}$$

it is again clear that $\Sigma(x_i) = 0$.

Another interesting property of the mean is that the sum of the squares of the deviations from the mean, $\Sigma(X_i - \bar{X})^2 = \Sigma(x_i)^2$, is less than the sum of the squares of the deviation from any other value. This can be stated formally as follows.

$$\Sigma(X_i - \bar{X})^2 = \Sigma(X_i - M)^2 - N(\bar{X} - M)^2 \qquad 3$$

Thus, if M is substituted for $\bar{X}$, the sum of the squares of the deviations is increased by $N(\bar{X} - M)^2$.*

5. Standard deviation. In taking the mean of a sample to represent the sample as a whole, it should be clear that the reliability of this mean will depend on the degree of variation among the individual variates that make

---

* Let $M = \bar{X} \pm \Delta$.
Then

$$\Sigma(X_i - M)^2 = \Sigma(X_i - \bar{X} \pm \Delta)^2 = \Sigma[(X_i - \bar{X}) \pm \Delta]^2$$
$$= \Sigma(X_i - \bar{X})^2 \pm 2\Delta\Sigma(X_i - \bar{X}) + N\Delta^2$$

From (2) above it is known that $\Sigma(X_i - \bar{X}) = 0$, and in the expression $2\Delta\Sigma(X_i - \bar{X})$ each deviation is multiplied by 2Δ, which is constant, and consequently the entire expression equals zero. Finally

$$\Sigma(X_i - M)^2 = \Sigma(X_i - \bar{X})^2 + N\Delta^2$$
$$= \Sigma(X_i - \bar{X})^2 + N(\bar{X} - M)^2$$

which is equivalent to (3) in the text.

up the sample. If there is no variation, the mean represents the whole sample perfectly; but, as the variation becomes greater, the single value of the mean is less and less descriptive of the entire group, and it becomes necessary, in order to describe the sample more completely, to have some measure of variability. The average deviation from the mean might suggest itself, but the sum of the deviations from the mean is zero (Section 4), and from this it follows that the average of the deviations is also zero. We cannot deal with a statistic that is always zero, and the only alternative is to disregard signs and take the mean of the absolute deviations, but a statistic of this type does not lend itself readily to algebraic manipulation.

Other measures of variability that might be selected could be based on the values of $\Sigma(X_i - \bar{X})^2$, $\Sigma(X_i - \bar{X})^3$, $\Sigma(X_i - \bar{X})^4$, and so forth. The even powers would always be positive, and the odd powers could be positive, zero, or negative. In making the selection the first point to note is that, the higher the power of the deviations, the greater the effect of individual outlying deviations. When this is taken into consideration together with the fact that it is not desirable to complicate the computations any more than is necessary, the value of $\Sigma(X_i - \bar{X})^2$ has been universally selected as the basis of a standard measure of variability. This is the standard deviation represented by the symbol s', given by

$$s' = \sqrt{\frac{\Sigma(X_i - \bar{X})^2}{N}} = \sqrt{\frac{\Sigma(x_i)^2}{N}} \qquad 4$$

The direct method of calculating the standard deviation is to determine all the deviations from the mean, square them, summate, divide by N, and then extract the square root. When there are several variates in the sample and especially when the deviations contain decimal figures, a much shorter method is available. The main part of the work is to find the sum of squares of the deviations, and it can be shown very easily that

$$\Sigma x_i^2 = \Sigma X_i^2 - \frac{(\Sigma X_i)^2}{N} \qquad 5$$

This formula is particularly applicable in machine calculation and is now employed almost exclusively in statistical laboratories.

It is necessary here to consider a point that is very important in the practical application of statistical methods. The mean of a sample may be taken as the best possible estimate of the *mean* of the population from which the sample is drawn. The reason for this is that the mean is not a biased statistic. It is the best estimate of the population mean in the sense that, if we have a large group of means from samples of equal size and determine their average, this value will be the same as if we determined the mean of the whole collection of individuals without regard to their arrangement into groups. Now, for the population being sampled it follows that the mean and the standard deviation for this population are fixed values and hence may be called *parameters*. If the mean of the parent population is denoted by μ, then $\bar{X}$, the mean of the sample, is an unbiased estimate of the parameter μ. Similarly, denoting the standard deviation of the population by σ, what is calculated from the sample should be an unbiased estimate of this parameter. Actually this estimate is not the root-mean-square deviation defined above. This arises in part from the fact that, if μ is the mean of the population, the unbiased estimate of σ^2 is given by

$$\frac{\Sigma(X_i - \mu)^2}{N} \qquad 6$$

but μ is not known, and we must substitute $\bar{X}$, the mean of the sample. From (3) above it is obvious that

$$s'^2 = \frac{\Sigma(X_i - \bar{X})^2}{N} = \frac{\Sigma(X - \mu)^2}{N} - (\bar{X} - \mu)^2 \qquad 7$$

In other words s'^2 will be smaller than $\Sigma(X - \mu)^2/N$ by a quantity equal to $(\bar{X} - \mu)^2$. Further algebraic development of this idea leads to the proof that an unbiased estimate of σ^2 is given by

$$s^2 = \frac{\Sigma(X_i - \bar{X})^2}{N - 1} \qquad 8$$

A simple proof of this point based on mathematical expectation is given by Hoel [3].

It might be assumed that an unbiased estimate would then be given by

$$s = \sqrt{\frac{\Sigma(X_i - \bar{X})^2}{N - 1}} \qquad 9$$

but in actual fact this has a slight bias, and this bias can be removed completely only if we know that the population is normally distributed as defined in Chapter 3. The formulas for giving unbiased estimates of σ are

$$\hat{\sigma} = s' \sqrt{\frac{2}{N}} \frac{\left(\frac{N-2}{2}\right)!}{\left(\frac{N-3}{2}\right)!} \quad \text{or} \quad s \sqrt{\frac{2}{N-1}} \frac{\left(\frac{N-2}{2}\right)!}{\left(\frac{N-3}{2}\right)!} \qquad 10$$

where $\hat{\sigma}$ means the estimated value of σ. Actually we frequently employ s as an unbiased estimate of σ because the bias is generally not large enough to be important.

It should be noted that the symbolism adopted here restricts the Greek letters to population parameters and the Latin letters to statistics that are estimates of the parameters. This is followed throughout where possible.

The divisor $(N - 1)$ in (8) above is known as the number of degrees of freedom (DF) in the sample that are available for estimating the standard deviation. The N degrees of freedom originally available in the sample is reduced by 1 because 1 statistic, $\bar{X}$, was itself calculated from the sample and applied in determining the estimate of the standard deviation.

6. Standard error of a mean. It is obvious that sample means will vary from sample to sample, and the degree of variation will be related to the degree of variation among the individual variates. The general relation between the variation of individual variates and that of means of samples is given by

$$s_{\bar{X}} = \frac{s}{\sqrt{N}} \qquad 11$$

where $s_{\bar{X}}$ is the standard error of the mean of a sample, s is the standard deviation for the sample as a whole, and N is the number in the sample. In other words, if s is taken as the estimate of the standard deviation of the parent population, $s/\sqrt{N}$ is the estimate of the standard deviation of a population of means of samples of size N drawn from the same population. The standard error of a mean is therefore inversely proportional to the square root of the number in the sample.

7. Variance. The term variance is now used very extensively in connection with the statistical analysis of the results from experiments. The student should therefore be familiar with it from the first. The variance of a population is merely the square of the standard deviation and therefore would ordinarily be represented by the symbol σ^2. Similarly, the unbiased estimate of σ^2, commonly referred to as the mean square deviation, would be represented by s^2.

Like the standard deviation the variance is a measure of variability but its particular value in statistical analysis is discussed in detail in Chapter 5, The Analysis of Variance.

8. Frequency table. The frequency table shows, for the sample studied, the frequencies with which the variates fall into certain clearly defined classes. If the sample is small the frequency table will ordinarily not be necessary, but for large or moderately large samples it is usually desirable to begin the reduction of the data with a table of this kind. The frequency table provides the values for easy graphical representation, and from it such statistics as the mean and standard deviation may be calculated with much greater ease than from the original set of individual values.

9. Setting up a frequency table. The first task is to decide on the class values. This will depend on the accuracy required in the computation of statistics from the table, the range of variation (which is, of course, the difference between the lowest and highest value of the sample), the number in the sample or total frequency, and the facility with which these classes can be handled in computation. In the first place, the greater the number of classes, the greater the accuracy of the calculations made from the table. But there is a limit to the number of classes we can handle conveniently, and these two opposing factors must be balanced. A good general rule is to make the class interval not more than one-quarter of the standard deviation. Of course we do not as a rule know the standard deviation before the table is drawn up, but it is possible to make a rough estimate of its value from the range of variation. Tippett [5] has published detailed tables on the relation between the range of variation and the standard deviation, and these have been summarized in a short table prepared by Snedecor [4]. The values in Table 2–1 were taken from

TABLE 2–1

VALUES OF RANGE DIVIDED BY THE STANDARD DEVIATION FOR SAMPLE SIZES FROM 20 TO 1000

Number in Sample	Range/σ	Number in Sample	Range/σ
20	3.7	200	5.5
30	4.1	300	5.8
50	4.5	400	5.9
75	4.8	500	6.1
100	5.0	700	6.3
150	5.3	1000	6.5

Snedecor's table after rounding off the figures to two significant digits. Suppose that we have a sample of 500 and the range of variation is 0.25 to $2.63 = 2.38$. The expected standard deviation will then be $2.38/6.1$, and a suitable interval will be $\frac{1}{4}(2.38/6.1) = 0.098$. It is more convenient to have an odd number for a class interval than an even one, since then the mid-point of the interval does not require one more decimal place than we have in the values that define the class range. In the example above we should probably decide on an interval of 0.11.

In making up the classes it is usual to begin with the lower boundary of the first class slightly below the lowest value, so that the classes and mid-points would finally be set up somewhat as follows.

Class Range	Class Value, or Mid-Point of Class Range
0.19–0.29	0.24
0.30–0.40	0.35
0.41–0.51	0.46
0.52–0.62	0.57
etc.	etc.

These class ranges assume that values such as 0.296 having an additional decimal point will not occur. If 0.296 should occur, it would be put in the class 0.30 to 0.40.

By following the above rules we ensure a sufficient degree of accuracy in any statistics that are calculated from the frequency table; but, if the table is required mainly for the preparation of a graph as described below, this method may give classes that are too small, in that some of the classes may have very low frequencies or none at all. It is desirable then to make the class interval from one-half to one-third of the standard deviation.*

Sorting is greatly facilitated by writing the value of each variate on cards of a convenient size for handling. If the class ranges are written out on cards and arranged in order on a table, the sorting can then be done rapidly, and on completing the distribution it is easy to run through the piles and obtain a check on the work. It is important to have perfect accuracy at this point, as a misplaced card may give a great deal of trouble at a later stage. The frequency table is made up finally by entering the frequencies opposite the corresponding class values.

Table 2–2 is a sample of a frequency table. It represents data on the areas of 500 bull sperms. The areas are given in arbitrary units. The

---

* In statistical literature one may encounter references to Sheppard's corrections for grouping. These are designed to remove bias from certain statistics that are calculated from grouped data instead of from the individual values. Thus in calculating $\Sigma(X - \bar{X})^2/N$ it has been shown that the bias is positive and equal approximately to 1/12 of the square of the class interval. In the tests for abnormality described in Chapter 3 and in certain other specific calculations it is preferable to make the adjustments, but in general practice they are ignored and in many tests of significance it is best to omit them altogether.

It is important to note that Sheppard's corrections are for removing a definite bias and that they do not make up for general inaccuracies introduced by having groups that are too large. Also they do not remove the bias completely but tend to rectify the results.

standard deviation for this sample is 2.58; therefore in order to have a high degree of accuracy in the calculations the class interval should have been about 0.6. However, this additional accuracy was not required, and the class interval selected was 1.0. Note the agreement between the

TABLE 2–2

FREQUENCY TABLE FOR AREAS IN ARBITRARY UNITS OF 500 BULL SPERMS

Class Range	Frequency	Class Range	Frequency
0.6–1.5	5	8.6–9.5	69
1.6–2.5	6	9.6–10.5	54
2.6–3.5	10	10.6–11.5	35
3.6–4.5	25	11.6–12.5	22
4.6–5.5	44	12.6–13.5	12
5.6–6.5	61	13.6–14.5	4
6.6–7.5	68	14.6–15.5	1
7.6–8.5	83	15.6–16.5	1

range and the standard deviation as given in Table 2–1. Here the range is approximately 0.6 to 16.5 = 15.9. From Table 2–1 the standard deviation should be approximately 15.9/6.1 = 2.61.

10. Graphical representation of a frequency table. Frequency tables are usually represented by graphs of two types. The more common one

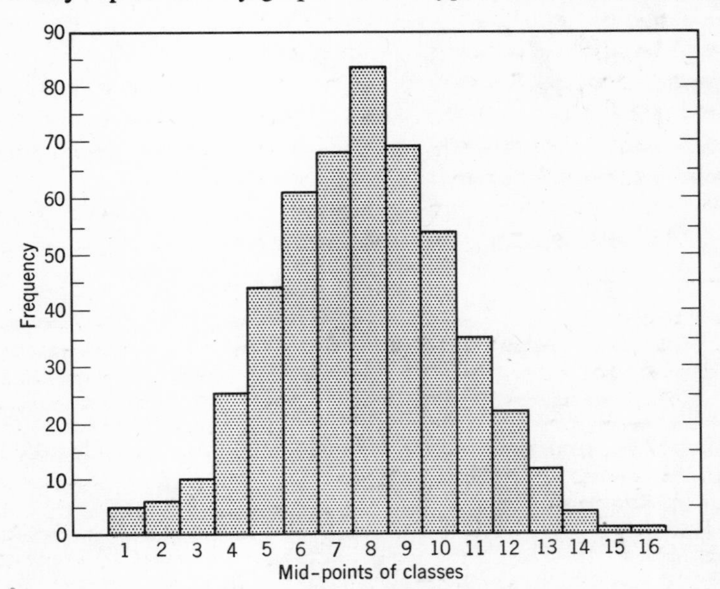

FIGURE 2–1. Histogram for areas of 500 bull sperms.

is the histogram. It is a diagrammatic presentation of a frequency table in which the class values are represented on the horizontal axis and the frequencies by vertical columns erected in their appropriate positions on the horizontal axis. As an example the histogram for the data of Table 2–2 is shown in Figure 2–1.

The other type of graph is referred to as a frequency polygon. A straight line is erected for each frequency at the mid-point of the corresponding class value, and the ends of these connected in series by straight lines. It does not give so accurate a picture as the histogram but may be better than the histogram for a comparison of two distributions on the same graph.

11. Calculation of the mean and standard deviation from a frequency table. The first step is to add two more columns to the frequency table, as indicated in the small example given below. The mean is then given by

$$\bar{X} = \frac{\Sigma(f_i X_i)}{N} \tag{12}$$

and the standard deviation by

$$s = \sqrt{\frac{\Sigma\,(f_i X_i^2) - [\Sigma(f_i X_i)]^2/N}{N-1}} \tag{13}$$

Class Value	Frequency	Frequency Multiplied by Class Value	Frequency Multiplied by Square of Class Value
X_i	f_i	$f_i X_i$	$f_i X_i^2$
1	2	2	2
2	4	8	16
3	7	21	63
4	6	24	96
5	1	5	25
Total	$20 = N$	$60 = \Sigma(f_i X_i)$	$202 = \Sigma(f_i X_i^2)$

It will be remembered that the numerator of the standard deviation contains $\Sigma(x^2)$, and it has been obtained here from the identity given in (5).

Very frequently the class values are numbers containing 2 to 4 digits, in which case a great deal of labor can be saved by replacing them for calculation by the series of natural numbers 1, 2, 3, 4, · · ·, etc. The calculations then give a standard deviation and a mean that may be represented by $\bar{X}''$ and s'', respectively. These can be converted into the true values by means of the following identities.

$$\bar{X} = (\bar{X}'' - 1)c + X_1 \qquad 14$$

$$s = s''c \qquad 15$$

where c is the true class interval and X_1 is the first true class value.

When the number of classes is fairly large, the work can be further reduced by working with an arbitrary origin that is close to the mean. The table can be set up as follows, where actual numerical classes are selected for illustration.

X_i	u_i	f_i	$f_i u_i$	$f_i u_i^2$
18	-2	.	.	.
21	-1	.	.	.
24	0	.	.	.
27	1	.	.	.
30	2	.	.	.
		N	$\Sigma f_i u_i$	$\Sigma f_i u_i^2$

Here X_0 the arbitrary origin $= 24$. Note that

$$X_i = cu_i + X_0$$

Then

$$\bar{X} = c\bar{u} + X_0 \qquad 16$$

where $\bar{u} = \Sigma f_i u_i / N$. The standard deviation is given by

$$c\sqrt{\frac{\Sigma f_i(u_i - \bar{u})^2}{N - 1}} \qquad 17$$

where

$$\Sigma f_i(u_i - \bar{u})^2 = \Sigma f_i u_i^2 - \frac{(\Sigma f_i u_i)^2}{N}$$

12. Coefficient of variability. The term coefficient of variability is applied to the standard deviation when it is expressed in percentage of the mean of the sample. It is a statistic of limited application, owing to the difficulty of determining its reliability by statistical methods. The formula is

$$C \text{ (Coefficient of variability)} = s\left(\frac{100}{\bar{X}}\right) \qquad 18$$

13. Exercises.

1. Substitute the natural numbers 1, 2, 3, · · ·, 16 for the class values of Table 2–2 and calculate the mean and standard deviation. Convert calculated to actual values, by means of formulas 14 and 15.

$\bar{X}'' = 7.852. \quad \bar{X} = 7.902. \quad s'' = 2.578. \quad s = 2.578.$

2. Table 2–3 gives the yields in grams of 400-square-yard plots of barley. Set up a frequency table and histogram for these yields. Make the class interval 11 and the first class 14 to 24.

Calculate the mean and standard deviation from your frequency table.

$\bar{X}'' = 13.06. \quad \bar{X} = 151.69. \quad s'' = 2.862. \quad s = 31.49.$

3. Prove the identity:

$$\Sigma(x^2) = \Sigma(X^2) - \frac{(\Sigma X)^2}{N}$$

TABLE 2–3

YIELDS IN GRAMS OF 400-SQUARE-YARD PLOTS OF BARLEY

185	162	136	157	141	130	129	176	171	190	157	147	176	126	175	134	169	189	180	128
169	205	129	117	144	125	165	170	153	186	164	123	165	203	156	182	164	176	176	150
216	154	184	203	166	155	215	190	164	204	194	148	162	146	174	185	171	181	158	147
165	157	180	165	127	186	133	170	134	177	109	169	128	152	165	139	146	144	178	188
133	128	161	160	167	156	125	162	128	103	116	87	123	143	130	119	141	174	157	168
195	180	158	139	139	168	145	166	118	171	143	132	126	171	176	115	165	147	186	157
187	174	172	191	155	169	139	144	130	146	159	164	160	122	175	156	119	135	116	134
157	182	209	136	153	160	142	179	125	149	171	186	196	175	189	214	169	166	164	195
189	108	118	149	178	171	151	192	127	148	158	174	191	134	188	248	164	206	185	192
147	178	189	141	173	187	167	128	139	152	167	131	203	231	214	177	161	194	141	161
124	130	112	122	192	155	196	179	166	156	131	179	201	122	207	189	164	131	211	172
170	140	156	199	181	181	150	184	154	200	187	169	155	107	143	145	190	176	162	123
189	194	146	22	160	107	70	84	112	162	124	156	138	101	138	141	143	135	163	183
99	118	150	151	83	136	171	191	155	164	98	136	115	168	130	111	136	129	122	120
179	172	192	171	151	142	193	174	146	180	140	137	138	194	109	120	124	126	126	147
115	148	195	154	149	139	163	118	126	127	139	174	167	175	179	172	174	167	142	169
122	163	144	147	123	160	137	161	122	101	158	103	119	164	112	57	94	106	132	122
164	142	155	147	115	143	68	184	183	167	160	138	191	133	160	156	122	111	153	148
103	131	180	142	191	175	146	181	111	110	154	176	168	175	175	146	148	167	106	123
121	154	148	91	93	74	113	79	131	119	96	80	97	98	106	107	69	86	94	129

REFERENCES

1. W. Edwards Deming, *Some Theory of Sampling*, John Wiley and Sons, New York, 1950.
2. R. A. Fisher, *Statistical Methods for Research Workers*, Oliver and Boyd, Edinburgh and London, 10th ed., 1948.
3. Paul G. Hoel, *Introduction to Mathematical Statistics*, John Wiley and Sons, New York, 1947.
4. G. W. Snedecor, *Statistical Methods*, Iowa State College Press, Ames, Iowa, 4th ed., 1946.
5. L. H. C. Tippett, *Biometrika*, **17**, 386, 1926.

CHAPTER 3

Theoretical Frequency Distributions

1. Characteristics of one actual distribution of a biological variate. In Chapter 2 was shown the histogram obtained when the results were graphed for the frequency table for 500 bull sperms. Now, if 10,000 sperms had been measured instead of 500, the class interval could have been made much smaller, and, keeping the base line the same length, the ends of the columns would present the appearance almost of a smooth curve. Carrying this reasoning to its logical conclusion, we decide that the areas of bull sperms in an infinitely large population could be represented by such a curve. This is actually the picture we have in mind in applying statistical methods to any population of a continuous variate. Discontinuous variables can be represented in an infinite population by a histogram only.*

Having noted the manner in which at least one biological variable is distributed, it is of interest to inquire as to the theoretical conditions from which such a distribution would arise. This leads to a consideration of the mode of action of the causes of variation. The developing sperm is clearly influenced by a number of factors that may affect its ultimate size. As it is developing from the meiotic tissue of the glands there are innumerable minor factors that can influence size, some acting to make the sperm larger and others to make it smaller. As a basis for arriving at a clue to the manner in which these factors act, it is useful to assume that they all act with equal intensity, and then to come to some conclusion concerning

---

* A continuous variate x is one that theoretically can take any value whatever in a given range $a \leq x \leq b$, which may be finite or infinite. The yield of a plot of wheat, for example, could be 160.1 grams, and, if we measured it very accurately it might be 160.0912 grams. In theory any number of decimal places can be taken, and consequently there is no logical reason why the yield of the plot cannot take any value within the range from zero to some positive value. In other words, the yield is a variate that can vary continuously.

An example of a discontinuous variate would be the number of black balls in the selection of 10 balls from an urn, or the number of heads with brown chaff in 100 heads selected at random from a plot of wheat. Such variates can obviously take only certain fixed values and are correctly referred to as discontinuous.

the theoretical distribution that will be generated. The procedure is one of mathematical derivation from the assumption that there are a large number of factors acting with equal intensity. It leads to the distribution that is commonly referred to as the *normal distribution*. The approach here is purely mathematical, and the biological student will probably be more interested in setting up and determining the type of distribution generated by actual trial.

2. Experimental derivation of a normal distribution. On examining a set of random numbers such as those given by Tippett [7] and Fisher

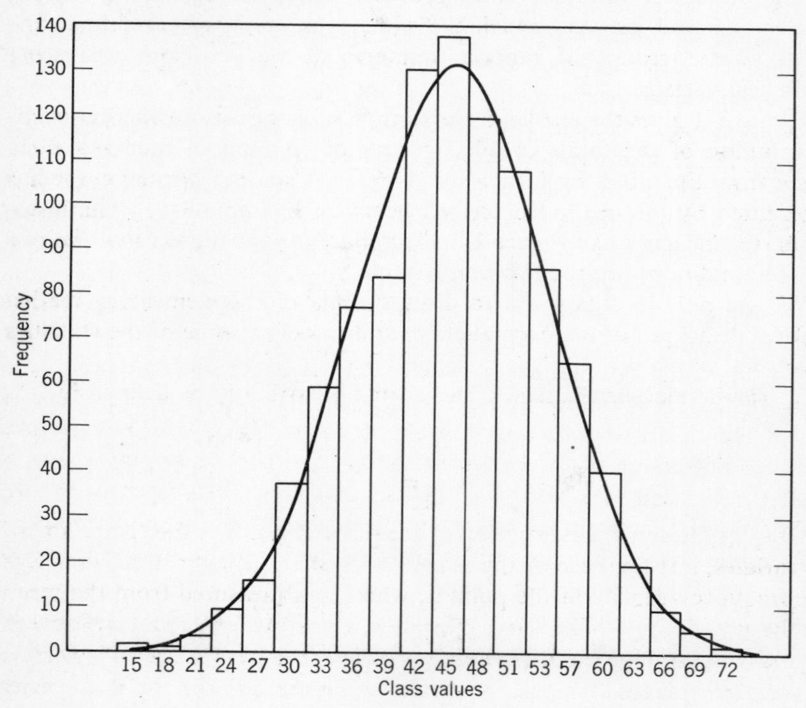

FIGURE 3–1. Histogram and fitted normal curve for the totals of 1000 groups of random digits.

and Yates [2] we note that, if taken in groups of 10, the totals for the groups will vary from 0 to 90. A zero total can be obtained, however, only when we select 10 zeros, and a total of 90 only when we select 10 nines. Since the probability of selecting a zero in taking 1 digit at random from the table is 0.1, the probability of selecting 10 zeros in taking a group of 10 at random is $0.1^{10} = 0.000\,000\,000\,1$. The probability of selecting 10 nines will, of course, be the same as that of selecting 10 zeros. It is obvious, however, that a total such as 45 can be obtained from a large number of combinations of digits, and therefore in selecting groups of 10 digits at random this total will occur with much greater frequency than a 0 or a 90. Thus the numbers in the middle of the range will occur with greatest frequency and the others with lesser frequency as we approach the limits.

The conditions set up here are comparable in a rough way to those affecting biological variates. Each digit may be regarded as a cause, and the total of a group as the ultimate effect of the operation of these causes on the biological variate. Thus, provided our assumptions are reasonable, we should get very much the same type of distribution from the totals of the groups of random numbers as we get from measuring biological variates.

Figure 3–1 gives the results in the form of a histogram for the frequency distribution of the totals of 1000 groups of 10 random numbers each, taken from the tables by Fisher and Yates. A smooth normal curve has been fitted by the method described below in Example 3–1. The histogram is sufficiently like Figure 2–1 to support the conclusion that the two sets of conditions are roughly comparable.

We are now in a position to discuss some of the elementary mathematical principles of the normal curve and to define some of the statistics involved.

3. The normal distribution. The normal distribution is defined by

$$Y = \frac{N}{\sigma\sqrt{2\pi}} e^{-\,{}^1\!/_2(x/\sigma)^2} \qquad 1$$

where σ is the standard deviation of the population, N is the total number of variates, e is the base of the Napierian system of logarithms, and Y is the frequency density at the point x, where x is measured from the mean of the population. The curve expresses, therefore, the relation between Y and x, with Y as the dependent variable. Figure 3–2 shows a normal curve superimposed on the histogram of Figure 2–1 for the frequencies of areas of bull sperms.

Equation (1) may be written

$$Y\left(\frac{\sigma}{N}\right) = \frac{e^{-\,{}^1\!/_2(x/\sigma)^2}}{\sqrt{2\pi}} \qquad 2$$

and, putting Z for $Y(\sigma/N)$, we have

$$Z = \frac{e^{-\,{}^1\!/_2(x/\sigma)^2}}{\sqrt{2\pi}} \qquad 3$$

Now for values of $x/\sigma < -6$ or > 6 the values of Z are extremely small; therefore in practice we can obtain all the information we require about Z if it is tabulated for x/σ from 0 to 6, proceeding by intervals of 0.01. These are given in Sheppard's Tables of the Probability Integral and are published in Pearson's *Tables for Statisticians and Biometricians*, Part 1 (in abbreviated form in Table A–2). For the actual population with

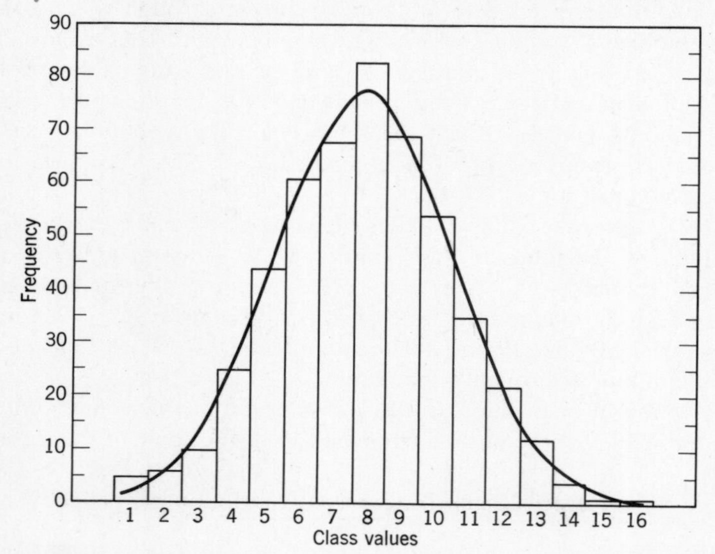

FIGURE 3–2. Normal curve superimposed on histogram of Figure 2–1.

which we are dealing, values of Z can then be transformed to Y by multiplying by cN/σ, where c is the class interval. In other words, for a particular population for which N and σ are known, we can proceed with a set of tables of Z to plot the theoretical smooth normal curve.

A smooth curve plotted by the above method is an estimate of the form of the infinite population from which the sample was drawn; but what is often required is the theoretical frequency distribution corresponding to the actual frequency distribution of the sample. That is, we require the theoretical normal frequencies for the arbitrarily chosen class values of the actual distribution. For this purpose, if N is taken as 1, equation (1) becomes

$$Y = \frac{e^{-\frac{1}{2}(x/\sigma)^2}}{\sigma\sqrt{2\pi}} \qquad 4$$

which can be integrated from $x/\sigma = -\infty$ to $x/\sigma =$ any assigned value. This gives the area under that portion of the curve, which is represented usually by $\frac{1}{2}(1 + \alpha)$ in Sheppard's Tables of the Probability Integral.

The integration is started at $x/\sigma = -\infty$ because the normal curve never actually touches the base line, although, at $x/\sigma = -6$, Y is an exceedingly small value. The reason for indicating the area by $\frac{1}{2}(1 + \alpha)$ or $\frac{1}{2} + \frac{1}{2}\alpha$ will be seen from an examination of Figure 3–3. For any assigned value of x/σ the area within the limits of $\pm x/\sigma$ is represented by α. Therefore, if the total area of the curve is 1, the area from $x/\sigma = -\infty$ to $x/\sigma =$ any

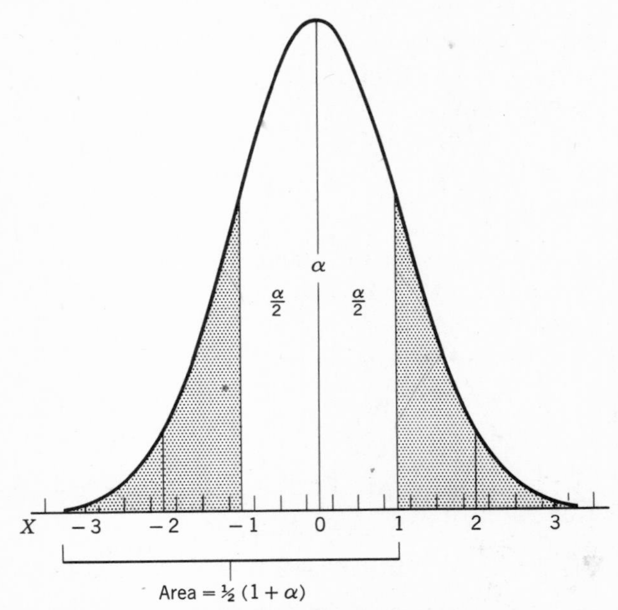

FIGURE 3–3. Normal curve showing ordinates at $x/\sigma = +1$ and -1. The unshaded area is α, and the shaded area is $(1 - \alpha)$.

assigned value is $\frac{1}{2} + \frac{1}{2}\alpha$. The application of this method to a practical example is given below under Section 4.

4. Fitting a normal curve. Fitting a normal curve is demonstrated by means of Example 3–1, below.

Example 3–1. The calculations necessary to fit a normal curve to an actual frequency distribution and to determine the normal frequencies corresponding to the actual frequencies are given in Table 3–1. The data are for the transparencies of 400 red blood cells taken from a patient suffering from primary anemia [4]. The transparency is taken as the ratio of the total light passing through the cell to the area of the cell in cross section. For this distribution $\bar{X} = 7.06$ and $s'' = 2.45$, the latter figure is to take the place of σ.

The calculations can best be described by considering each column of the table. These have been numbered at the head of the table for convenient reference.

Column 1. The class ranges are as described in Chapter 2. Note that unit class intervals have been substituted for the actual class intervals in order to simplify the arithmetic. After the class ranges are set up, the actual frequencies may be entered as in column 10, but they do not enter into the calculations at this stage.

Column 2. In order to be sure of the meaning of the term class limits,* refer to any histogram as in Figure 2–1, Chapter 2. The limits correspond with the lines bordering the columns of the histogram.

The mean of the sample is placed in the range in which it falls. In this case the mean is 7.06 and must be placed opposite the class range 6.6 to 7.5. The remaining limits are then entered by passing in both directions from the mean. The class in which the mean falls will require the entering of two limits, but for each of the others we enter only the one farthest from the mean.

Column 3. The deviation of the class limit from the mean.

Column 4. Values in the same line in the previous column, divided by the standard deviation which is calculated from the formula

$$\sqrt{\frac{\Sigma(X - \bar{X})^2}{N}}$$

where the deviations $(X - \bar{X})$ are based on the unit class interval.

Column 5. Values of Z from Table A–2 of ordinates of the normal curve.

Column 6. Corresponding Z values multiplied by N/s''. The complete formula is cN/s'', but c is equal to 1.

Column 7. Values of $\frac{1}{2}(1 + \alpha)$ from Table A–1.

Column 8. Corresponding values of $\frac{1}{2}(1 + \alpha)$ multiplied by N.

Column 9. Differences between consecutive values in column 8, beginning at the ends and working towards the center. In the central class the two differences are added. This column must total to N, providing a check on the work.

Column 10. The actual frequencies.

---

* Note that these class limits are not exact; e.g., between the class ranges 0.6 to 1.5, and 1.6 to 2.5, the exact class limit will be 1.55. Omitting the 0.05 in each class simplifies the work and makes a negligible change in the calculated ordinates and frequencies.

TABLE 3–1

CALCULATION OF ORDINATES FOR FITTING A NORMAL CURVE, AND THEORETICAL FREQUENCIES

(1) Class Range	(2) Class Limit	(3) d	(4) $\frac{d}{s''}$	(5) Z	(6) $Y = Z\left(\frac{N}{s''}\right)$	(7) $\frac{1}{2}(1+\alpha)$	(8) $\frac{N}{2}(1+\alpha)$	(9) Theoretical Normal Frequency	(10) Actual Frequency
		9.56	3.90	0.0002	0.03	1.0000	400.00	0.08	
		8.56	3.49	0.0009	0.15	0.9998	399.92	0.32	
		7.56	3.08	0.0035	0.57	0.9990	399.60	1.08	
0.6– 1.5		6.56	2.68	0.0110	1.80	0.9963	398.52	3.16	4
1.6– 2.5	1.5	5.56	2.27	0.0303	4.95	0.9884	395.36	7.92	11
2.6– 3.5	2.5	4.56	1.86	0.0707	11.54	0.9686	387.44	16.84	17
3.6– 4.5	3.5	3.56	1.45	0.1394	22.76	0.9265	370.60	30.28	29
4.6– 5.5	4.5	2.56	1.04	0.2323	37.92	0.8508	340.32	44.76	43
5.6– 6.5	5.5	1.56	0.64	0.3251	53.08	0.7389	295.56	59.16	56
	6.5	0.56	0.23	0.3885	63.43	0.5910	236.40		
6.6– 7.5	7.06	0.00	0.00	0.3989	65.12	0.5000	200.00	64.96	58
	7.5	0.44	0.18	0.3925	64.08	0.5714	228.56		
7.6– 8.5	8.5	1.44	0.59	0.3352	54.72	0.7224	288.96	60.40	63
8.6– 9.5	9.5	2.44	1.00	0.2420	39.51	0.8413	336.52	47.56	61
9.6–10.5	10.5	3.44	1.40	0.1497	24.44	0.9192	367.68	31.16	25
10.6–11.5	11.5	4.44	1.81	0.0775	12.65	0.9649	385.96	18.28	20
11.6–12.5	12.5	5.44	2.22	0.0339	5.53	0.9868	394.72	8.76	9
12.6–13.5	13.5	6.44	2.63	0.0126	2.06	0.9957	398.28	3.56	4
13.6–14.5		7.44	3.04	0.0039	0.64	0.9988	399.52	1.24	
		8.44	3.44	0.0011	0.18	0.9997	399.88	0.36	
		9.44	3.85	0.0002	0.03	0.9999	399.96	0.08	
		10.44	4.26	0.0000	0.00	1.0000	400.00	0.04	
							Total	400	400

5. Types of abnormality. The types of variation from the normal of frequency distributions may be divided roughly into three classes. These are:

a. Skewness. The degree of skewness of a distribution is indicated approximately by

$$\text{Skewness} = \frac{\text{Mean} - \text{Mode}}{\sigma}$$

where the mode is the position on the base line or X ordinate of a perpendicular line drawn to the maximum point of the curve. This measure is obviously zero for the normal distribution, as the curve is symmetrical and the mean and the mode coincide. When the mode is greater than the mean, we have negative skewness, and, when less than the mean, positive skewness. For negative skewness note that the tail of the curve is extended to the left, and, for positive skewness, to the right.

b. Flatness. In flat curves the shoulders are filled out more fully than in the normal curve and the tails are depleted.

c. Peakedness. For peaked curves the center is higher and more pointed than the normal and the tails are extended.

In certain distributions we may have skewness as well as flatness or peakedness, as indicated by *b* and *c* in Figure 3–4, which illustrates some common types of abnormality.

6. Measures of abnormality. An approximate measure of skewness can be obtained by the method described in Section 5, but a much more

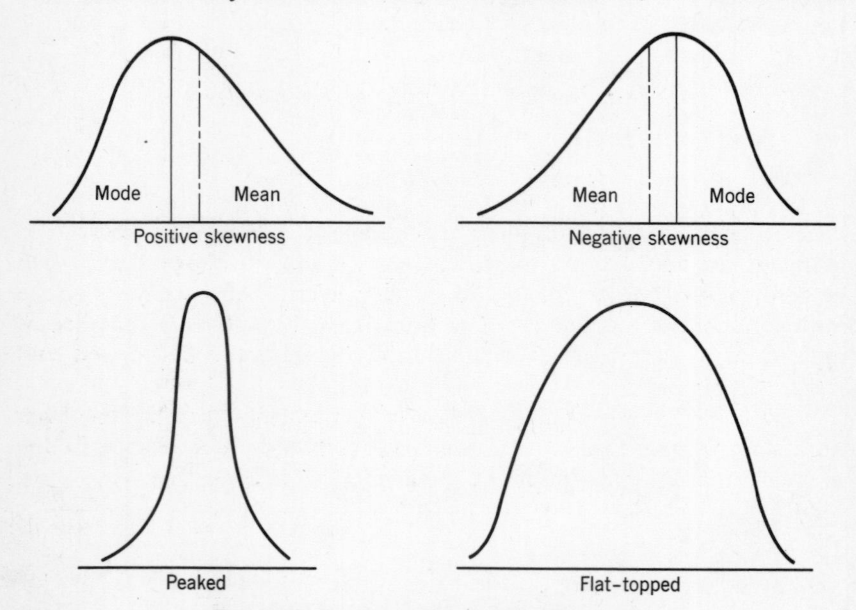

FIGURE 3–4. Illustrating types of abnormality.

efficient measure is obtained by calculating statistics that are determined by the values of the *moments* of the sample. The *k*th moment of a distribution with respect to a particular origin *m* is given by $[\Sigma(X-m)^k]/N$. Thus the second moment about the mean as origin will be $[\Sigma(X-\bar{X})^2]/N$.

The moments up to the fourth power are convenient indications of deviations from normality. For example, if the distribution is symmetrical, the moments about the mean will be zero for the odd powers, and, if the tails are extended, this will tend to make the even high-power moments larger than for a normal distribution.

For the calculation of the moments about the mean as origin it is most convenient to obtain first the series of quantities indicated below.

$$a_1 = \frac{\Sigma(X)}{N} \qquad a_2 = \frac{\Sigma(X^2)}{N} \qquad a_3 = \frac{\Sigma(X^3)}{N} \qquad a_4 = \frac{\Sigma(X^4)}{N} \qquad 5$$

Then the moments are

First moment $\nu_1 = a_1$

Second moment $\nu_2 = a_2 - a_1^2$

Third moment $\nu_3 = a_3 - 3a_1a_2 + 2a_1^3$ (6)

Fourth moment $\nu_4 = a_4 - 4a_1a_3 + 6a_1^2a_2 - 3a_1^4$

Two measures of distribution type based on the moments are

$$\alpha_3 = \frac{\nu_3}{\nu_2^{3/2}} \qquad \alpha_4 = \frac{\nu_4}{\nu_2^2} \qquad (7)$$

(These are frequently referred to as $\sqrt{\beta_1}$ and β_2.) Since the odd power moments are zero for a symmetrical distribution, it follows that α_3 will be zero for the normal or any other symmetrical distribution. For the normal curve $\alpha_4 = 3$, and any deviations from this value are regarded as indications of abnormality. If $\alpha_4 < 3$ the distribution is flat-topped, and if $\alpha_4 > 3$ it is peaked.

For the measurement of the departure of frequency distributions from normality, R. A. Fisher [1] calculates a set of values related to the moments that he refers to as the *k* statistics. These are given by

$$k_1 = \nu_1$$

$$k_2 = \left(\frac{N}{N-1}\right)\nu_2$$

$$k_3 = \left[\frac{N^2}{(N-1)(N-2)}\right]\nu_3 \qquad (8)$$

$$k_4 = \frac{N^2}{(N-1)(N-2)}\left[\frac{(N+1)\nu_4 - 3(N-1)\nu_2^2}{N-3}\right]$$

Two of the *k* statistics, k_2 and k_4, require correction for the interval of grouping of the frequency distribution. For a unit interval the corrected values are given by

$$k'_2 = k_2 - \tfrac{1}{12} \qquad k'_4 = k_4 + \tfrac{1}{120} \qquad (9)$$

Corrections for other intervals will not be necessary as it is always possible to use a unit interval for purposes of calculation.

For the k statistics, the measures of curve type comparable to α_3 and α_4 are

$$g_1 = \frac{k_3}{(k'_2)^{3/2}} \qquad g_2 = \frac{k'_4}{(k'_2)^2} \tag{10}$$

These are considered to be estimates from the samples studied of the population parameters γ_1 and γ_2.

The standard errors of g_1 and g_2 are

$$s_{g_1} = \sqrt{\frac{6N(N-1)}{(N-2)(N+1)(N+3)}} \tag{11}$$

$$s_{g_2} = \sqrt{\frac{24N(N-1)^2}{(N-3)(N-2)(N+3)(N+5)}} \tag{12}$$

The student should note that g_2 tends to a value of 0 and α_4 tends to a value of 3, as the curve approaches the normal.

For normal distributions both g_1 and g_2 are zero. g_1 is a measure of symmetry and has the same sign as (mean − mode). Figure 3–4 illustrates positive and negative skewness as indicated by positive and negative values of g_1. A positive value of g_2 indicates a peaked curve, and a negative value a flat-topped curve. These two types are also illustrated in Fig. 3–4.

The calculation of the k statistics and the measures of skewness, g_1 and g_2, is illustrated in Example 3–2.

Example 3–2. Table 3–2 gives the frequency distribution for this example and the preliminary calculations. Note that the deviations are taken from an arbitrary origin of 5. It is not essential that an arbitrary origin be employed, but it makes possible a decided reduction in the work, especially when the number of classes in the frequency table is fairly large. In the formulas given above for a_1, a_2, a_3, and a_4, X is replaced by d, the deviation from the assumed mean.

From the k statistics, g_1 and g_2 are calculated as follows.

$$g_1 = \frac{0.697\,258}{(2.426\,63)^{3/2}} = +\,0.1844 \qquad s_{g_1} = 0.226$$

$$g_2 = \frac{0.1094}{(2.4266)^2} = +\,0.0186 \qquad s_{g_2} = 0.451$$

TABLE 3–2

CALCULATION OF k STATISTICS USING AN ASSUMED MEAN

x	f	Deviation (d) from Assumed Mean	fd	fd^2	fd^2	fd^4
1	1	− 4	− 4	16	− 64	256
2	6	− 3	− 18	54	− 162	486
3	13	− 2	− 26	52	− 104	208
4	25	− 1	− 25	25	− 25	25
5	30					
6	22	1	22	22	22	22
7	9	2	18	36	72	144
8	5	3	15	45	135	405
9	2	4	8	32	128	512
$\Sigma(d) \cdots \Sigma(d^4)$ ($N = 113$)			− 10	282	2	2058
a_1, a_2, a_3, a_4			− 0.088 495 6	2.495 58	0.017 699 1	18.2124
				− 0.007 83	0.662 543 5	0.0063
					− 0.001 386 1	0.1173
						− 0.0001
$^*\nu_2, \nu_3, \nu_4$				2.487 75	0.678 856 5	18.3359
k_2, k_3, k_4				2.509 96	0.697 258 3	0.1011
Corrections				− 0.083 33		0.0083
k'_2, k_3, k'_4				2.426 63	0.697 258 3	0.1094

7. Distribution of means of samples. In Section 5 it was noted that α_3 and α_4 are measures of the degree of abnormality in actual frequency distributions. In connection with these statistics there is a well-known theorem of mathematical statistics that has an important bearing on the distribution of the means of samples. This theorem states that, if we draw samples of size N from any population and determine the frequency distribution of the means of the samples, the values $\alpha_{3\bar{X}}$ and $\alpha_{4\bar{X}}$ for this distribution will be given by

$$\alpha_{3\bar{X}} = \frac{\alpha_3}{\sqrt{N}} \qquad \alpha_{4\bar{X}} = \frac{\alpha_4 - 3}{N} + 3$$

where α_3 and α_4 are values for the population sampled. Thus, regardless of any abnormalities that may exist in the parent population, the

* To determine figures for ν_2, ν_3, and ν_4, refer to formula (6).

distribution of the means of samples drawn from that population will tend towards normality.* It can be shown that, even for populations having definitely skewed distributions, the means of samples for which n is as small as 4 are for all practical purposes normally distributed. Shewhart [5] performed the experiment of drawing 1000 samples of 4 each from 2 abnormal populations. One of these was rectangular, and the other one right-triangular. In both cases the distributions of means of the samples of 4 closely approximated the normal distribution. In this connection Shewhart states: "Such evidence, supported by more rigorous analytical methods beyond the scope of our present discussion, leads us to believe that in almost all cases in practice we may establish sampling limits for averages of samples of 4 or more, upon the basis of normal law theory."

This brings our attention back to the near normal distribution of Section 2 that was obtained by taking totals of samples of 10 digits drawn at random from a table of random numbers. Random numbers have an essentially rectangular distribution, that is, the top of the curve is flat, and, since the range of the digits is limited to 0 to 9, the theoretical values of α_3 and α_4 can be deduced. These work out to $\alpha_3 = 0$ and $\alpha_4 = 2.01$. For the distribution of totals of 10 numbers we should have therefore $\alpha_3 = 0$ and $\alpha_4 = [(2.01 - 3)/10] + 3 = 2.90$. The value of α_4 obtained experimentally was 2.88.

8. The binomial distribution. The binomial distribution is one of the most useful distributions for dealing with discontinuous variates. It may be defined in practical terms as follows: In a segregating population of wheat plants, if the probability of the occurrence of an awned plant is p, and the probability of the occurrence of an awnless plant is q, then the theoretical distribution of awnless and awned plants in a large number of samples of size n will be given by the successive terms of the expanded binomial $(q + p)^n$. Assuming $q = 1/4$ and $p = 3/4$, on expanding the binomial $(1/4 + 3/4)^6$ (see Section 2*d*, Chapter 1), where each sample is made up of 6 plants, we get

$$(\tfrac{1}{4})^6 + 6(\tfrac{1}{4})^5(\tfrac{3}{4}) + 15(\tfrac{1}{4})^4(\tfrac{3}{4})^2 + 20(\tfrac{1}{4})^3(\tfrac{3}{4})^3 + 15(\tfrac{1}{4})^2(\tfrac{3}{4})^4 + 6(\tfrac{1}{4})(\tfrac{3}{4})^5 + (\tfrac{3}{4})^6$$

---

* This is not strictly true, as there are certain theoretical distributions for which not all the moments may exist. These distributions are not very likely to be models for the actual distributions of biological variates and so are not considered to be important in deriving the general law stated above with respect to the means of samples. It must be remembered, however, that occasional distributions occur that are very abnormal, and consequently the reduction in abnormality for means of samples may be quite slow as the size of the sample is increased.

which is a little easier to calculate if it is put into the form

$$(\tfrac{1}{4})^6 + 6 \times 3(\tfrac{1}{4})^6 + 15 \times 3^2(\tfrac{1}{4})^6 + 20 \times 3^3(\tfrac{1}{4})^6 + 15 \times 3^4(\tfrac{1}{4})^6 + 6 \times 3^5(\tfrac{1}{4})^6 + 3^6(\tfrac{1}{4})^6$$

Using logarithms, the terms are calculated as follows:

$$\text{Log term } 1 = \log (\tfrac{1}{4})^6 = 6 \log (\tfrac{1}{4})$$

$$\text{Log term } 2 = \log 6 + \log 3 + 6 \log (\tfrac{1}{4})$$

$$\text{Log term } 3 = \log 15 + 2 \log 3 + 6 \log (\tfrac{1}{4})$$

etc.

It is convenient first to write down 6 log (1/4) and log 3. Here we have

$$6 \log (\tfrac{1}{4}) = \bar{4}.387\,640\,0$$

$$\log 3 = 0.477\,121\,3$$

In the next step the logs and antilogs of the terms are written as follows.

Awned Plants in Sample of 6	Log Term	Antilog Term or Probability
0	$\bar{4}.387\,640\,0$	0.000 244
1	$\bar{3}.642\,912\,6$	0.004 395
2	$\bar{2}.517\,973\,9$	0.032 959
3	$\bar{1}.120\,033\,9$	0.131 836
4	$\bar{1}.472\,216\,5$	0.296 631
5	$\bar{1}.551\,397\,8$	0.355 957
6	$\bar{1}.250\,367\,8$	0.177 979

A direct method of calculating the terms of a binomial expansion which is done on the machine and does not require logarithms is given by Snedecor [6]. It is illustrated below for the expansion of $(1/4 + 3/4)^6$.

Awned Plants	$(q)^{n-r} = (0.25)^{n-r}$	$p^r = (0.75)^r$	$\binom{n}{r}$	Term
0	0.000 244		1	0.000 244
1	0.000 977	0.75	6	0.004 396
2	0.003 906	0.562 5	15	0.032 957
3	0.015 625	0.421 875	20	0.131 836
4	0.062 5	0.316 406	15	0.296 631
5	0.25	0.237 305	6	0.355 958
6		0.177 979	1	0.177 979

We start with 0.25 in the last line but one and multiply successively by 0.25, writing down the product at each stage. Similarly, the powers of 0.75 are calculated successively and put in, beginning with the second line.

The third column is $n!/r!(n-r)!$. Multiplying the figures in the second, third, and fourth columns gives the term value in the fifth column.

Another procedure adapted to machine work arises from the fact that, beginning with q^n and multiplying successively by (p/q), we obtain

$$q^n, q^{n-1}p, q^{n-2}p^2, q^{n-3}p^3, \cdots$$

and if these are multiplied by the corresponding value of $\binom{n}{r}$ we have the terms of the expanded binomial. It is convenient to obtain q^n either by logarithms or by continuous multiplication on the machine. For the same example the calculations are

Awned Plants	$q^n\left(\frac{p}{q}\right)^r$		Term
0	0.000 244 141	× 1	= 0.000 24
1	0.000 732 423	× 6	= 0.004 39
2	0.002 197 27	× 15	= 0.032 96
3	0.006 591 81	× 20	= 0.131 84
4	0.019 775 4	× 15	= 0.296 631
5	0.059 326 2	× 6	= 0.355 96
6	0.177 979	× 1	= 0.177 98

We can now make a practical application of this distribution. If p and q are the correct probabilities for a given population, it is easy to determine the probability, in taking a random sample of 6 plants, of obtaining 2 awned plants or fewer. This is obviously the sum of the probabilities of obtaining 0, 1, and 2 awned plants, which works out to 0.038. In taking 1000 samples of 6 plants the expected number of samples containing 2 awned plants or fewer is 38.

The mean and standard deviation of a binomial distribution can be worked out in the same manner as for any frequency distribution. Thus, assuming that there are 1000 samples of 6 plants, the theoretical distribution would be as follows.

Awned Plants in Sample X	Frequency f
0	0.2
1	4.4
2	33.0
3	131.8
4	296.6
5	356.0
6	178.0
Total	1000

$$\Sigma(X) = (0 \times 0.2) + (1 \times 4.4) + \cdots + (6 \times 178.0) = 4500.2$$

$$\text{Mean awned plants per sample} = \frac{4500.2}{1000} = 4.50$$

$$\Sigma(X^2) = (0.2 \times 0^2) + (4.4 \times 1^2) + \cdots + (178.0 \times 6^2) = 21,376.2$$

$$\frac{[\Sigma(X)]^2}{1000} = \frac{(4500.2)^2}{1000} = 20,251.8$$

Then

$$\Sigma(x^2) = 21,376.2 - 20,251.8 = 1124.4$$

and

$$\sigma = \sqrt{\frac{1124.4}{1000}} = 1.06$$

Actually in this example we are measuring two parameters of a theoretical distribution for which p, q, and n are known. Since p and n completely define a binomial distribution, the mean and standard deviation must be related to them mathematically. Therefore, by mathematical derivation it can be proved that

$$\bar{X} = pn \qquad 13$$

where $\bar{X}$ stands for the mean number of occurrences per sample of the event for which the probability is p. It can also be shown that the standard deviation is given by

$$\sigma = \sqrt{pqn} \qquad 14$$

Applying these formula to the example above, we have

$$\bar{X} = (\tfrac{3}{4})\, 6 = 4.5$$

$$\sigma = \sqrt{\tfrac{3}{4} \times \tfrac{1}{4} \times 6} = 1.06$$

As would be expected, the agreement with the direct calculations is perfect.

It will of course be understood that in certain applications the values of p and q are unknown, in which case the direct method as illustrated first would enable us to obtain estimates of the values of p and q from the data.

When n is small the effect of the values of p and q on the terms of the expanded binomial is fairly clear. When p and q are equal the terms are symmetrical, but when p and q are not equal the distribution is skewed.

A very good picture of the effect of p, q, and n on the shape of the binomial distribution can be obtained from the formulas for α_3 and α_4 appropriate to the binomial. These are

$$\alpha_3 = \frac{q-p}{\sqrt{pqn}} \qquad \alpha_4 = 3 + \frac{1-6pq}{npq} \tag{15}$$

We note first that $\alpha_3 = 0$ when $p = q$, and that its value increases as p and q differ. However, regardless of the difference between p and q, α_3 becomes quite small as n increases. A study of α_4 reveals that variations in p, q, and n make relatively small changes in its value, but when there is a marked difference between p and q, and n is small, there is a tendency for the distribution to be flat-topped.

If we set up a histogram for a binomial distribution where $n = 9$, there are 10 classes and 10 columns in the histogram. On the same length of base line, a histogram for $n = 29$ will have 30 columns, and the columns will be $^1/_3$ the width of those for the example with $n = 9$. Continuing to increase n and erecting histograms on the same base line, it is clear that the tops of the histograms will tend towards a continuous curve. Actually, as n increases, the binomial distribution approaches and merges into the normal distribution that we have already studied.

9. The Poisson distribution. The Poisson distribution is a theoretical distribution of great practical importance. It can be illustrated best by a specific example.

Suppose that a carload of wheat is being sampled and that each sample consists of 1 pound or approximately 16,000 seeds. There are seeds of ragweed in the wheat, and each sample is examined carefully in order to determine the number of ragweed seeds per pound. If the actual number of ragweed seeds per pound in the entire carload is 3, then, if a number of samples are taken, a variation in number of ragweed seeds around this figure will be expected. It will be apparent from our study of the binomial distribution that the theoretical frequency of weed seeds per sample of 16,000 would be given by

$$(q + p)^{16,000}$$

where p is the probability of the occurrence of a weed seed and q is the probability of non-occurrence. It should be noted, however, that in two respects this differs markedly from the type of problem to which the binomial distribution was applied. In the first place the number in the sample is very large, and in the second place the probability p is very small. When we have these conditions, it can be shown mathematically that the consecutive terms of the distribution can be expressed by the following.

$$e^{-m}\left(1, m, \frac{m^2}{2!}, \cdots, \frac{m^r}{r!}, \cdots\right) \qquad 16$$

where e is the base of the Napierian system of logarithms and m is the mean number of occurrences of the event per sample. This is commonly known as the Poisson distribution. In more detail it may be referred to as the Poisson exponential limit to the binomial.

One of the most useful properties of the Poisson distribution is that the variance is equal to the mean. For this reason a Poisson distribution is completely specified by the mean, and consequently in the expression above for the terms of the distribution the mean is the only parameter given.

It is of interest to note also the effect of p and n on the shape of the Poisson distribution. Since

$$\alpha_3 = \frac{1}{\sqrt{np}} \qquad \text{and} \qquad \alpha_4 = 3 + \frac{1}{np} \qquad 17$$

it is obvious that as p decreases we have greater skewness, and as n increases the distribution approaches symmetry. The formula for α_4 shows that its value will never be less than 3; therefore the distribution never becomes flatter than the normal. As the quantity np becomes appreciable, the degree of peakedness of the curve becomes very small.

Examples to which the Poisson distribution may be applied can in most cases be determined by the nature of the sampling problem. In the example given, the probability of obtaining a weed seed in selecting any one seed at random from the carlot is quite small, but the actual number of weed seeds in a 1-pound sample is appreciable. Since the mean is given by pn where n is the number in the sample, the conditions under which a Poisson distribution should be obtained can be defined as follows. The probability of the occurrence of the event must be quite small, but n must be large enough so that pn is an appreciable quantity. For example, suppose that there are approximately 10,000 heads of wheat per plot in a series of 200 plots. On examining the plots it is noted that a small proportion of heads are killed by wheat stem maggots. Counts show that the mean number of injured heads per plot is 6. Since $pn = 6$, we can determine that $p = 6/10{,}000$, and it is immediately obvious that the distribution of injured heads will follow the Poisson distribution.

Applications of the Poisson distribution are important in many sampling procedures. Further applications are given in a later chapter, but it will be of interest at this point to consider the application of the Poisson distribution to seed sampling. Suppose that a farmer has a quantity of seed which has 3 weed seeds to the pound. What is the probability that a 1-pound sample of seed taken from the bulk lot will contain 6 or more weed seeds, 5 per pound being the tolerance limit? This, in other words, is the probability that the farmer's seed will be rejected on the basis of the results from the examination of the 1-pound sample. In order to solve this problem we must set up the theoretical distribution for the case in which $m = 3$. This has been done for us and is available in Pearson's *Tables for Statisticians and Biometricians*. On looking up the table and entering under $m = 3$, the following values are found.

Number of Weed Seeds per Sample	Probability of Occurrence
0	0.050
1	0.149
2	0.224
3	0.224
4	0.168
5	0.101
6	0.050
7	0.022
8	0.008
9	0.003
10	0.001
11	0.000
Total	1.000

Letting P = probability of acceptance of a sample and $Q = 1 - P$ = probability of rejection, we note that Q is the sum of the probabilities of obtaining 6, 7, 8, or more weed seeds per sample. This is 0.084, and hence $P = 0.916$. Thus, if 5 is the tolerance limit for seed of a certain class and a single 1-pound sample is taken, the probability that the lot will be rejected is 0.084. Another way of stating this proposition is to say that the probability of rejection is about 1 : 12; or, if a large number of such samples is presented for inspection, the expectation is that only 1 out of 12 will be rejected.

10. Exercises.

1. Calculate the ordinates (Y) and the theoretical normal frequencies for the frequency distribution from the exercises of Chapter 2. Totaling the theoretical frequencies will provide a check on the work.

2. Make a histogram for the actual frequencies of Exercise 1, and plot over this graph the smooth curve arising from connecting the end points of the ordinates.

3. Put equation (1) of Section 3 equal to

$$Y = Ce^{-\,{}^1/_2(x/\sigma)^2}$$

and show how σ affects the shape of the curve.

4. If the mean of a population is 21.65 and $\sigma = 3.21$, find the probability that a variate taken at random will be greater than 28.55 or less than 14.75. *P = 0.0316.*

5. If, for the population of Exercise 4, the standard deviation of the mean of a sample of 400 variates is $\sigma/\sqrt{400}$, find the probability that the mean of a sample taken at random will fall outside the limits 21.33 to 21.97. *P = 0.045.*

6. Test the following distributions for departure from normality.

(*a*)	*X*	1	2	3	4	5	6	7	8	9	10	11	12	13	14	15	16
	f	1	57	185	217	177	126	87	54	30	20	14	11	13	5	1	2
(*b*)	*X*	1	2	3	4	5	6	7	8	9	10	11	12	13	14	15	16
	f	2	3	4	5	7	11	17	30	50	34	21	10	7	5	2	2
(*c*)	*X*	1	2	3	4	5	6	7	8	9	10	11	12	13	14	15	16
	f	1	7	13	19	23	26	27	28	26	24	22	17	14	9	4	1

(*a*) $g_1 = 1.360$, $g_2 = 2.143$. (*b*) $g_1 = -\,0.327$, $g_2 = 0.939$.
(*c*) $g_1 = 0.107$, $g_2 = -\,0.766$.

7. Suppose that you have a bag of beans of which 20% are black and the remainder white. Determine the probability in drawing a single sample of 8 beans that it will contain 6 or more white beans. *P = 0.7969.*

8. A sample of 1000 seeds of wheat is drawn from a supply and grown in order to observe the proportion of off-type plants. If the supply contains exactly 3 off-types per 1000 plants, determine the probability that 3 off-types will be found in the test.

9. Table 3–3 gives the frequency table for 1000 totals of 10 random digits. Calculate the mean and standard deviation, taking an assumed mean at 45.

$\bar{X} = 45.32$. $s = 9.148$.

TABLE 3–3

FREQUENCY TABLE FOR 1000 TOTALS OF 10 RANDOM DIGITS

Class Range	Frequency	Class Range	Frequency
14–16	2	44–46	137
17–19	1	47–49	119
20–22	3	50–52	104
23–25	9	53–55	86
26–28	16	56–58	64
29–31	37	59–61	40
32–34	56	62–64	18
35–37	77	65–67	9
38–40	86	68–70	5
41–43	130	71–73	1

REFERENCES

1. R. A. Fisher, *Statistical Methods for Research Workers*, Oliver and Boyd, Edinburgh and London, 10th ed., 1948.
2. R. A. Fisher and F. Yates, *Statistical Tables*, Oliver and Boyd, Edinburgh and London, 3rd ed., 1949.
3. Paul G. Hoel, *Introduction to Mathematical Statistics*, John Wiley and Sons, New York, 1947.
4. A. Savage, C. H. Goulden, and J. M. Isa, *Can. J. Research*, **12**, 803–811, 1935.
5. W. A. Shewhart, *Economic Control of Quality of Manufactured Product*, D. Van Nostrand Co., New York, 1931.
6. G. W. Snedecor, *Statistical Methods*, Iowa State College Press, Ames, Iowa, 4th ed., 1946.
7. L. H. C. Tippett, *Random Sampling Numbers*, Cambridge University Press, Cambridge, 1927.

CHAPTER 4

Tests of Significance

One of the most important functions of the statistical method is to provide "tests of significance." The quoted phrase may express a concrete and definite idea on first reading, but on further thought it becomes necessary to clarify its meaning and particularly to define what is meant by a test of significance in the statistical sense. The word significance has a meaning in every-day usage that in only a broad sense is similar to its meaning in the statistical phrase.

Suppose that we have a coin and that there is some question as to whether or not it is unbiased, i.e., whether or not there is an equal probability on throwing the coin of its turning up heads or tails. The first thought that suggests itself is to throw the coin a number of times and note what happens. If we carry out a trial and there is a preponderance of heads or tails, we have some evidence to the effect that the coin is biased. However, without further analysis this experiment leaves us in a very unsatisfactory state of mind because we do not know what preponderance of heads or tails indicates definitely that the coin is biased, nor do we know what variation from the expected equality of heads and tails can be expected even if the coin is true. It is at this point that we draw on our knowledge of mathematics and at the same time adopt a logical procedure that keeps our thinking clear.

1. Logic of tests of significance. Suppose that a coin thrown 16 times gives 13 heads and 3 tails. The first process of developing a logical test of significance is to ask the question: How frequently will such a result be obtained if the coin is unbiased? With a true coin the probability of heads (p) equals the probability of tails (q), where $p + q = 1$. The distribution of heads and tails should be given therefore by the expansion of the binomial $(p + q)^{16} = (1/2 + 1/2)^{16}$. Expanding to get the first 5 terms, we have

Number of heads	16	15	14	13	12
Probability (P)	0.000 015	0.000 244	0.001 831	0.008 545	0.027 771

and the probability of getting 13 or more heads in throwing a true coin 16 times is the sum of the first four terms,

$$0.000\,015 + 0.000\,244 + 0.001\,831 + 0.008\,545 = 0.011$$

The result observed would occur with a true coin only about once in 100 trials, where each trial represents 16 throws. That it should occur the first time in an actual throw would seem to cast considerable doubt on the trueness of the coin.

It should now be clear that we have at our disposal, from our knowledge of the theoretical distribution of heads and tails for a true coin, a definite measuring stick with which to judge the significance of results with an actual coin. If the theoretical distribution gives $P = 0.4$, it is obvious that the result obtained is not in any way unusual and that there is no evidence of bias. On the other hand, if $P = 0.001$, we would be reasonably certain that the coin is not true.

This brings us to a consideration of values of P. At what level shall we say a result is significant? In order to answer this question the most realistic approach is to consider the results obtained with a large number of trials with unbiased coins. Let us decide that if $P \leq 0.05$ we shall consider the coin biased, but if $P > 0.05$ we shall classify it as unbiased. Now in 1000 trials with a true coin it is expected that 50 will give values of $P \leq 0.05$. Thus in 5% of the trials we shall classify the coin as biased when it is actually unbiased. If we are prepared to be wrong in 5% of the trials a level of P equal to 0.05 is satisfactory, but if we do not wish to be wrong as often as this it is necessary to use a lower value.

At this point we should not fall into the error of deciding that a very low value of P is the most desirable one, on the assumption that it will reduce errors of judgment. The reason for this is that one important factor has not yet been taken into account. In actual practice we are very unlikely to be testing a large series of perfect coins. In order that there shall be some point in making the tests it must be assumed that there are at least some bad coins present, and the object of the tests is to eliminate them. It should be obvious then that there are two kinds of errors that can be made. Owing to the pertinent suggestion of J. Neyman and E. S. Pearson [7], these are referred to as errors of the *first kind* and errors of the *second kind*. We make an error of the first kind when a good coin is classified as bad, and an error of the second kind when a bad coin is classified as good. Now let us see how the significance level affects the proportion of the two kinds of errors.

A simple way of demonstrating the effect of using different levels of significance is to assume that the coins being tested consist of true coins for which $p = q = 1/2$, and bad coins for which $p = 0.8$ and $q = 0.2$. Figure 4–1 shows the theoretical distribution of heads for the two types of coins. Let us assume arbitrarily that the level of significance is taken at $P = 0.038$, representing the trial wherein 12 or more heads are obtained in 16 throws. The distributions for $(0.5 + 0.5)^{16}$ and $(0.8 + 0.2)^{16}$ are shown in Figure 4–1. The single-hatched area of the distribution for good coins representing 3.8% of the total is shown at the lower left of the figure. This represents the percentage of good coins that are called bad. The double-hatched area represents the percentage of bad coins that are called good. The effect of changing the level of significance will

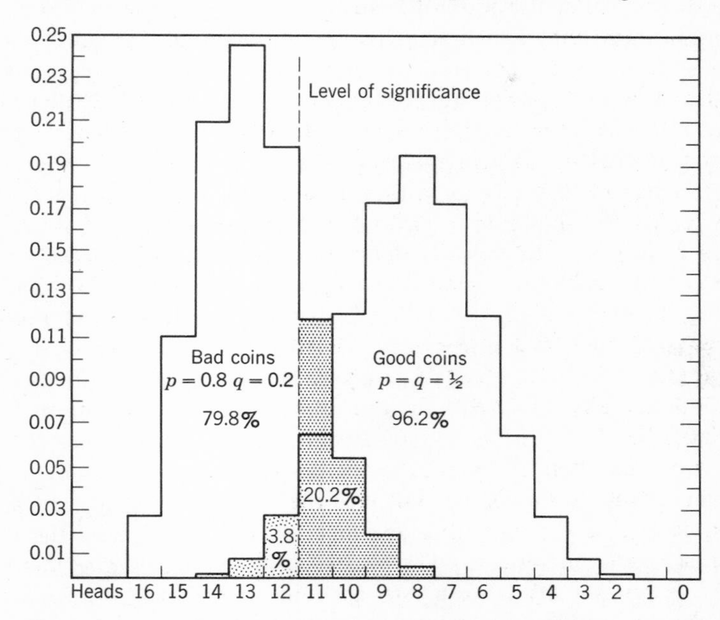

FIGURE 4–1. Distribution of heads, in 16 throws of 2 types of coins.

now be obvious. If we move it to the right to include one more column, only 8.2% of the bad coins will be considered good but 10.5% of the good coins will be considered bad. Moving the line one column to the left gives 40.2% of the bad coins classified as good and 1.1% of the good coins classified as bad. This can be summarized very conveniently as follows.

Level of Significance, Heads per 16 Throws	Percentage of Good Coins Classified as Bad	Percentage of Bad Coins Classified as Good	Total Error
15: $P = 0.0003$	0.03	85.9	85.9
14: $P = 0.002$	0.2	64.8	65.0
13: $P = 0.011$	1.1	40.2	41.3
12: $P = 0.038$	3.8	20.2	24.0
11: $P = 0.105$	10.5	8.2	18.7
10: $P = 0.227$	22.7	2.7	25.4
9: $P = 0.402$	40.2	0.7	40.9

For this particular example there is a point of minimum error at $P = 0.105$, but this does not tell the whole story. The result would be different if the bad coins were represented by a distribution of $(0.7 + 0.3)^{16}$ and would be a very complex affair if there were a wide range of bad coins differing in amount of bias. Furthermore there is the question of the seriousness of the two kinds of error. In certain cases an error of the first kind may be more serious than an error of the second kind, and hence we would require a lower value of P, for our level of significance. When errors of the second kind are more important, we would require a higher value of P.

Serious thought on this subject leads to conservatism in setting levels of significance. In any event it is clear that setting too low a value of P will increase errors of the second kind. This is a most important generalization and should not be lost sight of in any applications of tests of significance. As a general working rule a value of P equal to 0.05 is considered satisfactory. It is usually referred to as the 5% level of significance.

2. A test for bias in either direction. In the preceding discussion of testing coins the question asked was: "Is the coin biased such that heads turn up more frequently than is expected?" In other words we did not ask the simpler question: "Is the coin biased?" The latter would involve testing for a bias towards the production of either heads or tails. To answer this question it is necessary to determine the frequency for a good coin of obtaining a result as bad or worse than that observed. Thus, if we get 13 heads and 3 tails, the result at the other end of the scale representing a similar degree of bias would be 3 heads and 13 tails. The frequency of results as bad or worse than the one observed would be given by adding the theoretical frequencies at both ends of the distribution. In this example, since the distribution is symmetrical, it is simply a matter of doubling the frequency for 13 or more heads, so we get $P = 0.022$.

It will be recognized that the simpler question with respect to the existence or non-existence of a bias is the more general one, and therefore in tests of significance it is usually the type of question asked. There is no difficulty involved here in deciding how to get the correct value of P if one is clear as to the question being asked. Lack of understanding on this point has, however, caused a good deal of confusion.

3. Tests of significance involving the distribution of *t*. In experimental procedure, the making of surveys, etc., the tests of significance to be made are considerably more complicated from the theoretical standpoint than the one we have just described in connection with the testing of coins. The actual performance of these tests is not difficult, however, owing to a great deal of the theoretical work having been done in advance and tables prepared for the purpose. At this stage in our study of statistics we are concerned chiefly with the underlying logic of the test and shall approach it from that standpoint.

Suppose that the results given in Table 4–1 of the yields in plot tests of 2 varieties of wheat are brought into the statistical laboratory and we are asked to examine the data and come to some conclusion as to whether or not the 2 varieties are essentially different in yielding ability.

TABLE 4–1

YIELDS OF 2 WHEAT VARIETIES AT 12 STATIONS

Station	1	2	3	4	5	6	7	8	9	10	11	12
Variety X_1	24.4	27.9	28.2	19.8	23.1	22.9	25.6	28.7	26.2	25.7	37.0	31.5
Variety X_2	17.5	15.1	21.6	18.2	21.6	13.7	24.8	27.8	25.2	19.2	34.0	25.2

In the first place we know from previous study that the yields of wheat varieties are most likely to be normally distributed. Furthermore an examination of the literature on the distribution of the yields of grain from field plots can be made and further evidence obtained that there is a definite tendency towards normality in the distribution of a variate of this type. In any event we know that the means of samples of 12 variates will be approximately normally distributed, regardless of the kind of distribution of the population from which the sample is drawn. It can be assumed safely therefore that, if we obtain a large number of samples of 12 yields each of either variety X_1 or variety X_2, the means of these samples will be normally distributed.

The logical hypothesis to set up for testing is that the mean difference between the 2 varieties is zero. We picture therefore, arising from our hypothesis, a very large normal distribution of the differences $\bar{X}_1 - \bar{X}_2$ about a mean of zero. Then from our knowledge of the normal distribution (Chapter 3, Section 3) we know that, having the mean (μ) and the standard deviation of this distribution (σ_{md}), where the subscripts indicate that it is a standard deviation of a mean difference, we can determine the probability of obtaining a value of $\bar{X}_1 - \bar{X}_2$ as great or greater than the one observed. For example, if the standard deviation $\sigma_{md} = 2$, and $\bar{X}_1 - \bar{X}_2 = 4$, the ratio of these two quantities, which is merely a measure of $\bar{X}_1 - \bar{X}_2$ in terms of the standard deviation, is equal to 2, and tables of the probability integrals of the normal curve give for this ratio $\frac{1}{2}(1 + \alpha) = 0.9773$. Therefore the probability of obtaining a positive value of $\bar{X}_1 - \bar{X}_2$ as great or greater than the one observed is $1 - 0.9773 = 0.0227$.

When we apply this method to an actual example, however, it is obvious

that we do not have the pertinent facts for making the test outlined. It will be remembered that our mental picture arising from the hypothesis is a normally distributed population about a mean of zero with a given standard deviation σ_{md}. It would be necessary to know this standard deviation in order to make the test work perfectly. In other words, knowing the standard deviation, we could draw a large number of samples, each one giving us a value of $\bar{X}_1 - \bar{X}_2$. We could then find the ratio $(\bar{X}_1 - \bar{X}_2)/\sigma_{md}$ for each sample and by means of the tables find a value of P which would be the probability of obtaining a value of $\bar{X}_1 - \bar{X}_2$ as great or greater than the one observed. On checking through the results for a large series of samples for which the hypothesis is true, we should find that we had obtained values of $P \leq 0.05$ for 5% of the samples. This would be exactly in accord with theory and would prove that the test is correct. However, we do not know σ_{md}, and any test made must be based on an estimate of σ_{md} determined from the sample.

The first problem is to decide on a method of estimating σ_{md}, and this involves estimating σ for the population of individual values from which the samples are drawn and equating this to an estimate of σ_{md}. A logical decision is to pool the estimates of σ obtained from the 2 samples. Representing estimates of σ by s, we have, from sample 1,

$$s_1^2 = \frac{\Sigma(X_1 - \bar{X}_1)^2}{n-1} = \frac{\Sigma x_1^2}{n-1} \tag{1}$$

and for sample 2

$$s_2^2 = \frac{\Sigma(X_2 - \bar{X}_2)^2}{n-1} = \frac{\Sigma x_2^2}{n-1} \tag{2}$$

Now the estimate of the standard deviation of a difference

$$s_d^2 = \frac{\Sigma[(X_1 - X_2) - (\bar{X}_1 - \bar{X}_2)]^2}{n-1} = \frac{\Sigma[(X_1 - \bar{X}_1) - (X_2 - \bar{X}_2)]^2}{n-1}$$

$$= \frac{\Sigma(x_1 - x_2)^2}{n-1} \tag{3}$$

On expanding the last expression we have

$$s_d^2 = \frac{\Sigma x_1^2}{n-1} + \frac{\Sigma x_2^2}{n-1} - 2\,\frac{\Sigma(x_1 x_2)}{n-1} \tag{4}$$

$$= s_1^2 + s_2^2 - 2\,\frac{\Sigma(x_1 x_2)}{n-1} \tag{5}$$

and we see that s_d^2 is equal to the sum of the variances for X_1 and X_2 less a quantity depending on $\Sigma(x_1 x_2)$, the sum of the products of the deviations from the mean of the variates in the 2 samples. More information on this quantity will be given in our study of regression and correlation, but for the present it is sufficient to point out that, as we take pairs of values of x_1 and x_2, if they tend to be both positive or both negative, the sum of products will be a positive quantity. On the other hand, if positive values of one variable are usually associated with negative values of the other variable, the sum of products will be negative. There is the intermediate situation where about half of the positive values of x_1 will be obtained with negative values of x_2, and the other half with positive values of x_2. The negative values of x_1 will be similarly divided, and the resulting sum of products will be close to zero. The latter situation is described by saying that the 2 variables are independent.

In our example the yields come from pairs of plots at a series of stations, and if we examine the deviations of each yield from the mean of the variety it is noted that positive and negative deviations tend to occur together. This means that the sum of products $\Sigma(x_1x_2)$ will be a definite positive quantity and therefore should be taken into account in equation 5. We can calculate s_d^2 from equation (4), but it is more convenient to make use of the relation

$$\Sigma(x_1 - x_2)^2 = \Sigma(X_1 - X_2)^2 - \frac{[\Sigma(X_1 - X_2)]^2}{n} \quad . \quad 6$$

in order to determine the numerator for the calculation of s_d^2 from equation (3).

The differences $X_1 - X_2$, are

6.9 12.8 6.6 1.6 1.5 9.2 0.8 0.9 1.0 6.5 3.0 6.3

and their total or $\Sigma X_1 - \Sigma X_2 = 57.1$. We then have

$$\Sigma(x_1 - x_2)^2 = 437.85 - \frac{57.1^2}{12} = 166.15$$

and

$$s_d^2 = \frac{166.15}{11} = 15.105$$

Also

$$s_{md}^2 = \frac{s_d^2}{n} = \frac{15.105}{12} = 1.2588$$

And

$$s_{md} = \sqrt{1.2588} = 1.12$$

Having made an estimate of s_{md} we can calculate the ratio $(\bar{X}_1 - \bar{X}_2)/s_{md}$. This is known as the statistic t. The question we then have to ask is whether or not this ratio can replace $(\bar{X}_1 - \bar{X}_2)/\sigma_{md}$ for the probability calculations. This is easily answered. σ_{md} is a population parameter and is therefore constant from sample to sample. On the other hand, s_{md} is estimated from the sample and will vary. It is a statistic and is subject to the usual sampling variations and has a distribution all its own. We note particularly that if n is large the values of s_{md} will be quite consistent, whereas if n is small the variations in s_{md} will be proportionately greater. This would indicate that if n is large the error involved in replacing σ_{md} with s_{md} will be negligible, but if n is small the error may be appreciable. Actually what we require for a solution of this problem is the sampling distribution of t for different values of n. If we knew this, we could determine for any given problem the probability of obtaining, when the hypothesis is true, a value of t as great or greater than the one observed.

This problem was first solved by "Student" [9] in 1908, and he published tables of the distribution of Z which is a statistic closely related to t and from which tests of significance could be made. Fisher [2] gave the distribution of t and supplied a formal proof which covered the distribution of Z.

The first point to be noted in connection with tables of probability based on the distribution of t is that in theory there is a different distribution for each value of $n - 1$, the degrees of freedom available for estimating σ^2. To cover the entire field $n - 1$ tables would be required, where $n - 1$ could take any value from 1 to ∞. This is clearly impossible, but on examining the distribution we note that beyond $n - 1 = 30$ there is very little change and from that point on it is satisfactory to use a table of t based on $n - 1 = \infty$.

In order to cover the whole field, however, 30 tables would be required, each as large as the tables of the probability integral for the normal curve. This would also be an enormous task. It has been abbreviated by Fisher [3] and Fisher and Yates [5] through the preparation of tables giving values of t through the range of $n - 1 = 1$ to 30, and then for 40, 60, 120, and ∞, for given values of P. The values of P are those in which we are chiefly interested in making tests of significance, such as 0.01, 0.05, and 0.10.

Returning now to the numerical example, we find that

$$t = \frac{\bar{X}_1 - \bar{X}_2}{s_{md}} = \frac{4.76}{1.12} = 4.25$$

On looking up Table A–3, we observe that, for $n - 1 = 11$, the value of t for $P = 0.01$ is 3.11, and since our t is greater than this we know that

P is less than 0.01. There are definite indications that the 2 varieties are really different in yielding ability.

Summarizing the procedure for applying the t test to the mean difference of a series of paired variates, we have

$$s_d^2 = \frac{\Sigma(x_1 - x_2)^2}{n - 1} \qquad 7$$

where

$$\Sigma(x_1 - x_2)^2 = \Sigma(X_1 - X_2)^2 - \frac{(\Sigma X_1 - \Sigma X_2)^2}{n} \qquad 8$$

$$s_{md}^2 = \frac{s_d^2}{n} \qquad 9$$

$$t = \frac{\bar{X}_1 - \bar{X}_2}{s_{md}} = (\bar{X}_1 - \bar{X}_2)\sqrt{\frac{n(n-1)}{\Sigma(x_1 - x_2)^2}} \qquad 10$$

The table of t is entered for $n - 1$ degrees of freedom.

4. Application of the *t* test when the variates are not paired. The example given above was for a series of pairs of plots, and in working out a method of estimating s_{md}^2 we noted that it was necessary to take into consideration the value of $\Sigma(x_1x_2)$ which enters into the equation. When the variates are not paired, this term can be disregarded because it follows that, if the variates X_1 and X_2 are drawn independently, the positive and negative products x_1x_2 will cancel out. We have then the simple equation

$$s_d^2 = s_1^2 + s_2^2 \qquad 11$$

There are two variations of this case: (1) where the number of variates in the 2 samples are equal, or $n_1 = n_2$; and (2) where $n_1 \neq n_2$. For these variations the formula for estimating s_{md}^2 are slightly different.

(1) Variates not paired, $n_1 = n_2 = n$.

$$s_d^2 = \frac{\Sigma x_1^2 + \Sigma x_2^2}{2(n - 1)} \qquad 12$$

$$s_{md}^2 = \frac{s_d^2}{n} + \frac{s_d^2}{n} = s_d^2\left(\frac{2}{n}\right) \qquad 13$$

$$t = \frac{\bar{X}_1 - \bar{X}_2}{s_{md}} = (\bar{X}_1 - \bar{X}_2)\sqrt{\frac{n(n-1)}{\Sigma x_1^2 + \Sigma x_2^2}} \qquad 14$$

And for calculation we use

$$\Sigma x_1^2 = \Sigma X_1^2 - \frac{(\Sigma X_1)^2}{n} \quad \text{and} \quad \Sigma x_2^2 = \Sigma X_2^2 - \frac{(\Sigma X_2)^2}{n} \qquad 15$$

In entering tables of t, note that the degrees of freedom here are $2(n - 1)$.

(2) Variates not paired, $n_1 \neq n_2$.

$$s_d^2 = \frac{\Sigma x_1^2 + \Sigma x_2^2}{n_1 + n_2 - 2} \qquad 16$$

$$s_{md}^2 = s_d^2 \left(\frac{n_1 + n_2}{n_1 n_2}\right) \qquad 17$$

$$t = \frac{\bar{X}_1 - \bar{X}_2}{s_{md}} = (\bar{X}_1 - \bar{X}_2) \sqrt{\frac{n_1 n_2 (n_1 + n_2 - 2)}{(n_1 + n_2)(\Sigma x_1^2 + \Sigma x_2^2)}} \qquad 18$$

In entering tables of t, the degrees of freedom are $n_1 + n_2 - 2$.

The test applied to sets of variates that are not paired is based on the assumption that the samples arise from populations having the same variance and that the differences observed between s_1^2 and s_2^2 are due to random sampling only. Putting this another way, what we actually wish to test is the significance of the difference between the means, but what we are actually testing is the significance of t, the ratio of the mean difference to the pooled standard deviations. This test can apply strictly to the mean difference only if the standard deviations can be assumed to be the same in the populations sampled. A method of dealing with the situation where the standard deviations can be assumed different is to apply what is known as the Behrens-Fisher test, tables for which are given by Fisher and Yates [5]. In the great majority of examples it is somewhat simpler to apply approximate tests as indicated below.

a. When $n_1 = n_2 = n$, it is usually sufficient to assume that the variates are paired, in which case only $n - 1$ degrees of freedom are available for estimating t. The value of t required for significance is increased accordingly.

b. When $n_1 \neq n_2$, an approximation suggested by Cochran and Cox [1] is quite satisfactory. We calculate

$$s_1^2 = \frac{\Sigma x_1^2}{n_1 - 1} \qquad s_2^2 = \frac{\Sigma x_2^2}{n_2 - 1} \qquad 19$$

$$s_{\bar{X}_1}^2 = \frac{s_1^2}{n_1} = w_1 \qquad s_{\bar{X}_2}^2 = \frac{s_2^2}{n_2} = w_2 \qquad 20$$

Then, if $\bar{X}_1 - \bar{X}_2 = d$ is the mean difference,

$$t = \frac{d}{\sqrt{w_1 + w_2}} \qquad 21$$

And the t value required for significance at a given level is given by

$$t' = \frac{t_1 w_1 + t_2 w_2}{w_1 + w_2} \qquad 22$$

where t_1 is the 5% point value for $n_1 - 1$ degrees of freedom and t_2 for $n_2 - 1$ degrees of freedom. This method is demonstrated in Example 4–2.

5. Example 4–1. Application of t test when variates are not paired. The data of Section 3 can serve to illustrate the methods of calculation.

First we have

$$\Sigma x_1^2 = 24.4^2 + 27.9^2 + \cdots + 31.5^2 - \frac{321.0^2}{12}$$

$$= 8806.30 - 8586.75 = 219.55$$

$$\Sigma x_2^2 = 17.5^2 + 15.1^2 + \cdots + 25.2^2 - \frac{263.9^2}{12}$$

$$= 6168.91 - 5803.60 = 365.31$$

$$s_d^2 = \frac{219.55 + 365.31}{22} = 26.5845$$

$$s_{md}^2 = 26.5845\left(\frac{2}{12}\right) = 4.4308$$

$$t = \frac{26.75 - 21.99}{4.43} = 1.07$$

Here we have 22 degrees of freedom for the estimation of t; therefore we look up t at the 5% point for 22 degrees of freedom. We find this to be 2.08, and hence according to this test the difference observed is not significant. In comparison to the test made in Section 4, the difference is due to our not taking into consideration, in calculating s_d^2, the third term on the right of equation (4). This has increased s_d^2 to the point where t is no longer significant. The result illustrates the value of correct design and analysis of an experiment. In the first place, the pairing of comparisons wherever possible should be adopted as a method of reducing error. In the second place, when comparisons have been paired, it is essential that the correct method of analysis be followed.

A further point is that, when pairing of comparisons is not expected to reduce the error, there is a loss of precision from pairing in that fewer degrees of freedom are available for estimating t and a larger value of t is required for a given degree of significance.

6. Example 4–2. Application of the t test when $n_1 \neq n_2$ and the variances of the 2 populations are assumed different. The following data are from J. A. Anderson's *Protein Survey of Western Canadian Wheat, 1950 Crop.* The figures in the first row represent 8 values at random from a large series of protein determinations for individual stations in Saskatchewan (sample 1). The second row represents a similar series of 14 values from Manitoba (sample 2).

Sample 1	15.1	14.3	11.5	14.5	15.4	12.5	14.6	16.6						
Sample 2	12.2	12.5	11.2	12.6	11.0	11.6	12.0	12.5	11.8	12.4	11.5	12.0	11.6	12.7

$$\Sigma X_1 = 114.5 \qquad \bar{X}_1 = 14.31$$

$$d = 14.31 - 11.97 = 2.34$$

$$\Sigma X_2 = 167.6 \qquad \bar{X}_2 = 11.97$$

$$\Sigma x_1^2 = 1657.13 - \frac{(114.5)^2}{8} = 18.35$$

$$s_1^2 = \frac{18.35}{7} = 2.6214 \qquad s_{\bar{X}_1}^2 = \frac{2.6214}{8} = 0.328$$

$$\Sigma x_2^2 = 2010.20 - \frac{(167.6)^2}{14} = 3.79$$

$$s_2^2 = \frac{3.79}{13} = 0.2915 \qquad s_{\bar{X}_2}^2 = \frac{0.2915}{14} = 0.021$$

$$t = \frac{2.34}{\sqrt{0.328 + 0.021}} = 3.97$$

$$t_1 = 2.36 \qquad t_2 = 2.16$$

$$t' = \frac{2.36 \times 0.328 + 2.16 \times 0.021}{0.328 + 0.021} = 2.35$$

Since t is well beyond the approximate 5% point value of 2.35, the difference in protein content can be considered significant.

In this example there is a very decided difference in the mean squares for the 2 samples. The ratio is 2.6214/0.2915 = 9.0. In Chapter 5, which deals with the analysis of variance, it is shown that a test of significance can be applied to this ratio. The 5% point for this ratio can be shown to be 2.84, and the 1% point 4.44. Therefore here we have quite definite evidence of a difference in the variances of the 2 populations sampled and full justification for the more exact test. With the ordinary method we would have taken the 5% point of t for 20 degrees of freedom, which is 2.09, so it is evident that the more exact test requires a greater difference between the means for a given level of significance.

7. The null hypothesis. The t test of Section 3 involved our setting up the hypothesis that the difference between the variety yields is normally distributed about a mean of zero. Professor R. A. Fisher has aptly termed this the null hypothesis. It is a very simple concept and should cause no confusion. In testing a coin our null hypothesis is that the coin is unbiased. For an unbiased coin we can say that the distribution of heads is given by the expansion of the binomial $(1/2 + 1/2)^n$, where n is the number of throws. Thus the null hypothesis is the basis for our deduction of the theoretical distribution. It should be kept clearly in mind that the theoretical distribution has nothing to do with the actual distribution obtained but flows directly from the null hypothesis.

All tests of significance require that a hypothesis be set up. The second consideration is that the theoretical distribution generated by the hypothesis be known. If the distribution is unknown, it may be possible to derive it by mathematical methods. The third step is to compare the result obtained with the theoretical frequency of such results according to the hypothesis and come to some conclusion as to its statistical significance.

8. Fiducial limits. The null hypothesis is only one of an infinite number of hypotheses that can be set up. For example, in the test made in Section 3 we could have set up the hypothesis that the difference between the varieties is normally distributed around a mean of 3.00. Putting $\bar{X}_1 - \bar{X}_2 = d$, the null hypothesis involves calculating t from the formula

$$\pm t = \frac{d - 0}{s_{md}} \qquad 23$$

The hypothesis that the mean is 3.00 would involve calculating t from

$$\pm t = \frac{d - 3.00}{s_{md}}$$

In other words, the general formula for t is

$$\pm t = \frac{d - m}{s_{md}} \qquad 24$$

where any value whatever can be given to m according to the hypothesis required.*

The question now arises as to what use can be made of the above generalization. Professor R. A. Fisher has made the extremely valuable suggestion that, in addition to tests of the null hypothesis, further information can be gained by an application of formula (24) to determine 2 values of m such that the calculated t is equal to the t in the table at a given percentage point. These values of m are known as the *fiducial limits*. For example, using the data of Section 3,

$$\pm t = \frac{4.76 - m}{1.12}$$

giving

$$m_1 = 4.76 + 1.12t$$

$$m_2 = 4.76 - 1.12t$$

Then, if t at the 5% point for 11 degrees of freedom is 2.20,

$$m_1 = 4.76 + 2.20 \times 1.12 = 7.22$$

$$m_2 = 4.76 - 2.20 \times 1.12 = 2.30$$

The meaning of these fiducial limits is made clear by noting that, if we select for m any values equal to or greater than 7.22, the value of P obtained from the t test will be ≤ 0.05. Similarly any value of m equal to or less than 2.30 will yield a $P \leq 0.05$. Stating this proposition in another way, any values of m within the range 2.30 to 7.22 will not differ significantly from 4.76 at the 5% level. Any values outside the range 2.30 to 7.22 will differ significantly from 4.76 at the 5% level. We have therefore reasonably good assurance that the true mean difference between the variety yields lies between 2.30 and 7.22.

It is desirable in connection with interpreting the meaning of fiducial limits to picture, drawing a large number of samples, as in testing 2 varieties, and determining the fiducial limits from each sample. It is to be expected, of course, that the fiducial limits will change from sample to sample, but in 95% of such determinations the fiducial limits calculated will be expected to contain the true mean. It is of value to picture a

* It might be more correct to say that the general formula for t is

$$\pm t = \frac{\bar{X} - M}{s_{\bar{X}}}$$

In (24), d is the variable corresponding to $\bar{X}$ and s_{md} corresponds to $s_{\bar{X}}$, so the formulas are really identical.

vertical line representing the true mean. The fiducial limits for 1 sample can then be represented by a horizontal line. In plotting the limits for each sample, it is to be expected that, if we calculate the limits at the 5% point, 95% of them will cross the vertical line representing the true mean.

The student should be warned against making the statement that, with respect to the above problem, it has been determined that the probability is 0.05 that the true mean lies between 2.30 and 7.22. The true mean is a parameter of a population and has therefore a fixed value, and we cannot make any exact probability statement with respect to where the true mean lies.

9. Exercises.

1. The figures below are for protein tests of the same variety of wheat grown in 2 districts. The average in district 1 is 12.74, and in district 2 is 13.03. Test the significance of the difference between the 2 averages. Do you consider it necessary in this example to make the more exact test described in Sections 5 and 6?

Protein Results

District 1	12.6	13.4	11.9	12.8	13.0		
District 2	13.1	13.4	12.8	13.5	13.3	12.7	12.4

$t = 1.04$, $P = 0.3$, approximately.

2. Mitchell [6] conducted a paired feeding experiment with pigs on the relative value of limestone and bonemeal for bone development. The results are given in Table 4–2 below.

TABLE 4–2

ASH CONTENT IN PERCENTAGE OF SCAPULAS OF PAIRS OF PIGS FED ON LIMESTONE AND BONEMEAL

Pair	Limestone	Bonemeal
1	49.2	51.5
2	53.3	54.9
3	50.6	52.2
4	52.0	53.3
5	46.8	51.6
6	50.5	54.1
7	52.1	54.2
8	53.0	53.3
Mean	50.94	53.14

Determine the significance of the difference between the means in two ways: (1) by assuming that the values are paired, and (2) by assuming that the values are not paired. On the basis of your results, discuss the effect of pairing.

(1) Paired: $t = 4.42$, P = less than 0.01.
(2) Unpaired: $t = 2.48$, P = approximately 0.02

3. In a wheat variety test the mean difference between 2 varieties was found to be 4.5 bushels per acre. The standard error (s_{md}) was 1.5 bushels per acre. Determine the fiducial limits at the 5% point for the mean difference.

Note. Since a large number of tests were made, t can be taken as 1.96.

Fiducial limits, 1.56 to 7.44.

REFERENCES

1. W. G. Cochran and Gertrude M. Cox, *Experimental Designs*, John Wiley and Sons, New York, 1950.
2. R. A. Fisher, Applications of "Student's" Distribution, *Metron*, **5**, 3–17, 1925. Expansion of "Student's" integral in powers of $n-1$, *Metron*, **5**, 22–32, 1925.
3. R. A. Fisher, *Statistical Methods for Research Workers*, Oliver and Boyd, Edinburgh and London, 10th ed., 1948.
4. R. A. Fisher, *The Design of Experiments*, Oliver and Boyd, Edinburgh and London, 4th ed., 1947.
5. R. A. Fisher and F. Yates, *Statistical Tables*, Oliver and Boyd, Edinburgh and London, 3rd ed., 1949.
6. H. H. Mitchell, *Proc. Am. Soc. Animal Production*, **23**, 63–72, 1930.
7. J. Neyman and E. S. Pearson, *Trans. Roy. Soc. London*, **A, 31**, 289–337, 1933.
8. G. W. Snedecor, *Statistical Methods*, Iowa State College Press, Ames, Iowa, 4th ed., 1946.
9. "Student," *Biometrika*, **6**, 1, 1908.

CHAPTER 5

The Analysis of Variance

1. Definition. Basically the *analysis of variance* is a simple arithmetical method of sorting out the components of variation in a given set of results. In order to understand this it is essential to know what is meant by components of variation.

Whenever there is heterogeneity of variation more than one component is present. Suppose that we have 1 group of men drawn from a population in which the people are all of the same race and the variable studied is height in inches. A frequency distribution is drawn up and found to be approximately normal. There is good reason to assume, therefore, that variation in this group is approximately homogeneous. The same would apply to a group of women studied in the same manner. However, if data from the 2 groups are mixed to form a new group, a second component of variation is brought in, namely the difference between the means of the 2 groups. This difference would be large enough so that the frequency distribution for the combined groups would probably show 2 peaks or modes. Carrying the analogy further, a third group might consist of boys from 13 to 15 years of age, and a fourth group girls of a similar age. When all 4 groups are combined the frequency distribution might appear reasonably normal, but we know that 2 components of variation are actually present, one representing variation within the groups and another between the groups. The arithmetical procedure of the analysis of variance enables us to sort out and evaluate the components of variation for such mixed populations.

The complete analysis of variance actually performs a dual role. In the first place we have the sorting out and estimation of the variance components, and in the second place it provides for tests of significance. The sorting-out process is purely mechanical and can be applied in all cases, but the reliability of the estimates of variance so obtained is dependent to some extent on the manner in which the data are collected. This is a difficult point to explain before the details of the methods of analysis have been made clear, so it is deferred to a later section. The consideration of tests of significance, however, can be taken up concurrently with a description of the method of analysis and the theory on which it is built.

2. Fundamental principles. In Chapter 2, Section 4, we stated the relation between the standard deviation of a population and that of means of samples of size n. In terms of variance this is expressed as

$$n\sigma_{\bar{X}}^2 = \sigma^2 \qquad 1$$

where n is the number in each sample, $\sigma_{\bar{X}}^2$ is the variance of the means, and σ^2 is the variance of the population from which the samples are drawn. From this expression a very simple but important deduction can be made. Having drawn a series of samples of size n we can in any event calculate a mean square V_i for any one sample, and each of these can be taken as an estimate of the population variance (σ^2). Furthermore, we can calculate $V_{\bar{X}}$ from the means of the samples, and from equation (1) above it is clear that $nV_{\bar{X}}$ can also be taken as an estimate of σ^2.

In order to clarify the above ideas we shall represent the series of samples by symbols as follows

Sample			*Variates*		*Mean*
1	X_{11}	X_{12} · · ·	X_{1j} · · ·	X_{1n}	$\bar{X}_1$
2	X_{21}	X_{22} · · ·	X_{2j} · · ·	X_{2n}	$\bar{X}_2$
i	X_{i1}	X_{i2} · · ·	X_{ij} · · ·	X_{in}	$\bar{X}_i$
k	X_{k1}	X_{k2} · · ·	X_{kj} · · ·	X_{kn}	$\bar{X}_k$

where there are k samples of n variates each. To give the symbols a concrete meaning it can be supposed that kn rats are divided at random into k samples. Then X_{11} is the weight of the first rat in the first sample. Also, X_{ij} is the weight of the jth rat in the ith sample.

For each sample we calculate

$$V_i = \frac{\sum_{j=1}^{n} (x_{ij}^2)}{n-1} \qquad 2$$

where x_{ij} represents a single deviation $(X_{ij} - \bar{X}_i)$ from the sample mean. Since each of these is an unbiased estimate of σ^2, the series can be averaged to provide a single estimate. Thus

$$V = \frac{\sum_{i=1}^{k} (V_i)}{k} = \frac{\sum_{i=1}^{k} \sum_{j=1}^{n} (x_{ij}^2)}{k(n-1)} \qquad 3$$

which amounts to summing all the sums of squares of deviations from sample means and dividing by the total number of degrees of freedom available within samples.

To find $nV_{\bar{X}}$ we take

$$nV_{\bar{X}} = \frac{n\sum_{i=1}^{k}(\bar{X}_i - \bar{X})^2}{k-1} \qquad 4$$

where $\bar{X}$ is the general mean, or average of all sample means.

If the variates in all samples are drawn at random, both V and $nV_{\bar{X}}$ are unbiased estimates of σ^2, but they are of course not equally reliable since V is based on $k(n-1)$ degrees of freedom and $nV_{\bar{X}}$ on only $k-1$ degrees of freedom. The random arrangement ensures that any one rat has an equal chance of being included in any sample. It should be clear, therefore, that the only factor affecting the values of both V and $nV_{\bar{X}}$ is the variability of the population from which the samples are drawn.

It will be of interest to apply this proposition to actual figures. The figures below have been placed at random into 5 groups of 5.

Group	Variates					Mean
1	29	45	14	25	11	24.8
2	44	38	48	31	31	38.4
3	16	29	29	18	46	27.6
4	37	11	31	28	44	30.2
5	50	12	19	20	28	25.8

Calculating V from formula 3 but applying short cuts explained in a later section, we get

$$V = \frac{3006.80}{20} = 150.34$$

Then

$$nV_{\bar{X}} = \frac{594.96}{4} = 148.74$$

The agreement here is better than would ordinarily be expected. The purpose of the calculations is merely to show the meaning of the algebraic symbols in terms of actual figures. In a large series of such samples we would, however, expect to get very close agreement between V and $nV_{\bar{X}}$.

Our chief interest in the proposition outlined above lies in the situation that is created when the population is not homogeneous, as in the example mentioned in Section 1 where the variance due to the means is affected by fundamental differences between the groups. With groups of rats, each group may have been given a different ration. The conditions causing variation within the groups will be due to the original variation in the population, but the means of the samples will vary additionally owing to the differences in the rations. With symbols the situation can be represented as follows.

Sample	Variates			Sample Mean	Mean Square
1	$X_{11} + Y_1$	$X_{12} + Y_1 \cdots$	$X_{1n} + Y_1$	$\bar{X}_1 + Y_1$	V_1
2	$X_{21} + Y_2$	$X_{22} + Y_2 \cdots$	$X_{2n} + Y_2$	$\bar{X}_2 + Y_2$	V_2
⋮	⋮	⋮	⋮	⋮	⋮
k	$X_{k1} + Y_k$	$X_{k2} + Y_k \cdots$	$X_{kn} + Y_k$	$\bar{X}_k + Y_k$	V_k

Note that in sample 1 each variate value consists of a part X, as in the case where all variates are drawn at random, plus a portion Y, which is constant for each variate. Thus the mean of sample 1 is $\Sigma X_1/n + nY_1/n = \bar{X}_1 + Y_1$. Since Y is constant for any one sample, it does not affect the value of V_i. Algebraically, we have for sample 1

$$V_1 = \frac{\sum_1^n [(X_1 + Y_1) - (\bar{X}_1 + Y_1)]^2}{n-1} = \frac{\sum_1^n (X - \bar{X}_1)^2}{n-1} = \frac{\sum_1^n (x^2)}{n-1} \qquad 5$$

Therefore V based on all samples will be the same as if the Y factor did not exist.

Examination of the new mean square for sample means shows that it is definitely affected by differences among the values of Y. We shall represent it by $V'_{\bar{x}}$.

$$V'_{\bar{x}} = \frac{\sum_1^k [(\bar{X}_i + Y_i) - (\bar{X} + \bar{Y})]^2}{k-1} = \frac{\sum_1^k [(\bar{X}_i - \bar{X}) + (Y_i - \bar{Y})]^2}{k-1}$$

$$= \frac{\sum_1^k (\bar{X}_i - \bar{X})^2}{k-1} + \frac{\sum_1^k (Y_i - \bar{Y})^2}{k-1} + \frac{2\sum_1^k (\bar{X}_i - \bar{X})(Y_i - \bar{Y})}{k-1}$$

$$= V_{\bar{x}} \qquad + V_Y \qquad + \frac{2\sum_1^k (\bar{X}_i - \bar{X})(Y_i - \bar{Y})}{k-1} \qquad 6$$

$V'_{\bar{x}}$ consists now of $V_{\bar{x}} + V_Y$ plus the additional quantity which is a sum of products of deviations. Now the part of the differences between the sample means and the general mean represented by $(\bar{X}_i - \bar{X})$ arises purely from random sampling and would bear no relation to corresponding values of $(Y_i - \bar{Y})$. Therefore, we can assume that for a large series of samples this sum of products will be zero. We are left then with

$$V'_{\bar{X}} = V_{\bar{X}} + V_Y \qquad 7$$

or

$$nV'_{\bar{X}} = nV_{\bar{X}} + nV_Y$$

and conclude that for such a series of samples $nV'_{\bar{X}}$ will tend to be greater than $nV_{\bar{X}}$ by an amount equal to nV_Y.

The numerical example above can be adjusted to show how the algebraic statement works out. For example, we shall take $Y_1 = 0$, $Y_2 = +2$, $Y_3 = 0$, $Y_4 = 0$, and $Y_5 = -2$. Then the figures are

Group	Variates					Mean
1	29	45	14	25	11	24.8
2	46	40	50	33	33	40.4
3	16	29	29	18	46	27.6
4	37	11	31	28	44	30.2
5	48	10	17	18	26	23.8

We get

$$V = \frac{3006.80}{20} = 150.34 \quad \text{as before}$$

$$V'_{\bar{X}} = \frac{886.97}{4} = 221.74$$

The latter is considerably inflated over the previous figure of 148.74, showing the effect of Y.

In an actual experiment we do not know the value of $V_{\bar{X}}$ because we do not have a set of figures showing the random variation only. All we have are the final figures containing both X and Y. We know, however, that V is a good estimate of $nV_{\bar{X}}$; therefore from (7)

$$nV_Y = nV'_{\bar{X}} - V \qquad 8$$

gives a good estimate of the portion of the total variance due to means that can be attributed to the Y effects arising from the treatments applied to the samples. Here we have

$$221.74 - 150.34 = 71.40$$

This procedure is known as estimating the variance component due to treatments and represents one of the important functions of the analysis of variance.

The same general principles hold when the data are classified in two ways, as in a simple replicated experiment with a series of treatments. The data may be arranged in a table as follows.

		Treatment			
		1	2	$\cdots$ n	
Replicate	1	X_{11}	X_{12}	$\cdots$ X_{1n}	$\bar{R}_1$
	2	X_{21}	X_{22}	$\cdots$ X_{2n}	$\bar{R}_2$
	$\vdots$	$\vdots$	$\vdots$	$\vdots$	$\vdots$
	r	X_{r1}	X_{r2}	$\cdots$ X_{rn}	$\bar{R}_r$
		$\bar{T}_1$	$\bar{T}_2$	$\cdots$ $\bar{T}_n$	M

Here X_{11} represents the yield of treatment 1 in replicate 1. This table may be regarded as made up of r samples of n each, or n samples of r each. Thus, if the variates were all drawn at random from a population with variance σ^2 and simply arranged as above in rows and columns, we could make an estimate of this variance in three ways: (1) from the means of the rows, (2) from the means of the columns, and (3) from the residual mean square not affected by rows and columns.

In order to clarify this point it is convenient to represent each yield by $X + Y + Z$ instead of by X alone. Then Y is the portion representing the replicates and Z the portion representing the treatments.

The same reasoning as was applied to the example of k samples of n each will then show that an estimate of the population variance from the means of the replicates gives

$$nV'_{\bar{R}} = nV_{\bar{R}} + nV_Y \qquad 9$$

and from the means of the treatments

$$rV'_{\bar{T}} = rV_{\bar{T}} + rV_Z \qquad 10$$

In (9) nV_Y is that portion of the mean square for replicates that is due to real variation among the replicates and not to random variation from plot to plot. Also in (10) rV_Z is the component of the mean square due only to treatments.

When each variate is represented by $(X + Y + Z)$, where Y_1 will be the contribution due to replicate 1 and Z_1 the contribution due to treatment 1, the first variate can be represented by $(X_{11} + Y_1 + Z_1)$. Then, in order to obtain an estimate of random variation only it should be noted that

$$(X_{11} + Y_1 + Z_1 - M) - [(\bar{X}_{R1} + Y_1 + \bar{Z}) - M] \\ - [(\bar{X}_{T1} + \bar{Y} + Z_1) - M] \qquad 11$$

where M is the general mean, $\bar{X}_{R1}$ the mean of the replicate containing X_{11}, and $\bar{X}_{T1}$ the mean of the treatment containing X_{11}, can be simplified to

$$(X_{11} - \bar{X}) - (\bar{X}_{R1} - \bar{X}) - (\bar{X}_{T1} - \bar{X}) \qquad 12$$

since $M = \bar{X} + \bar{Y} + \bar{Z}$. This shows that, for an individual deviation from the general mean, if the deviations due to replicate and treatment means are subtracted, the remaining portion represents random variation only. It shows how a mean square can be calculated that will be an estimate of σ^2 in that all effects due to replicates and treatments are removed. The method of making the actual calculations will be demonstrated in later sections.

3. The test of significance. In Section 2 it was noted that, owing to treatment effects, the mean square $V'_{\bar{X}}$ estimated from the treatment or sample means tends to be larger than V, the estimate of the variance, owing to random sampling variations. V is referred to as the error variance and $nV'_{\bar{X}}$ as the treatment variance.

A situation of this kind calls for our being able to make some sort of probability statement with respect to the result obtained. This would be possible if the theoretical distribution of such a ratio as $nV'_{\bar{X}}/V$ could be determined. This problem was solved when R. A. Fisher [12] gave the required theoretical distribution of $z = \frac{1}{2} \log_e (V_1/V_2)$, where V_1 and V_2 are independent estimates of the same variance and are based on n_1 and n_2 degrees of freedom respectively. Here we are concerned with $nV'_{\bar{X}}$ and V, the first based on $k - 1$ and the latter on $k(n - 1)$ degrees of freedom. The ratio is

$$\frac{nV'_{\bar{X}}}{V} = \frac{nV_{\bar{X}}}{V} + \frac{nV_Y}{V} \qquad 13$$

and since $nV_{\bar{X}}$ tends to be equal to V, the ratio amounts to*

$$\frac{nV'_{\bar{X}}}{V} = 1 + \frac{nV_Y}{V} \qquad 14$$

The test of significance in effect determines, therefore, the extent to which nV_Y/V differs from zero.

---

* The mean value of a ratio of two mean squares is actually $n_2/(n_2 - 2)$ and is therefore always slightly greater than 1. It is close enough to unity in the general case to enable us to say that (14) is approximately true.

Complete tables for making tests of significance would be very cumbersome as there is a different distribution for each pair of values of n_1 and n_2. This difficulty is overcome in the tables prepared by Fisher [14] and Fisher and Yates [16] by means of a series of selected values of n_1 and n_2 and a complete table for each probability level. Snedecor [23] gives Fisher's tables in the form of V_1/V_2, the variance ratio, to which he gave the symbol F. Fisher and Yates [16] give tables for both z and F. The probability levels selected are those in which we are ordinarily interested in making tests of significance, such as 0.01, 0.05, and 0.10.

In the numerical example given above

$$F = \frac{221.74}{150.34} = 1.47$$

The mean square in the numerator is estimated from 4 degrees of freedom and that in the denominator from 20 degrees of freedom. Looking up Table A–6 and entering under $n_1 = 4$ and $n_2 = 20$, we find that the value of F at the 5% point is 2.87. It would be concluded that the variance component V_Y is not significantly greater than zero.

4. Orthogonality. We have seen from Section 2 that variation among the treatment means represented by $\bar{X}_i + Y_i$ does not have any effect on V, the mean square arising from variation among the variates but within samples. When this is the relation between two mean squares, we say that they are orthogonal. Orthogonality is a mathematical term that has very much the same meaning as independence. Two effects in an experiment that can be estimated separately and not entangled in any way are orthogonal to each other. Strictly speaking, it cannot always be said that two effects are orthogonal without making a mathematical analysis, but there are certain general rules that will not lead us astray unless they are applied without careful thought to complex situations. This can be made clear by means of a simple demonstration. An experiment consists of 4 treatments in 3 replications, and after operating the experiment we are able to make a table of results as follows.

		Treatment				
		A	B	C	D	Replicate Mean
	1	X_{A1}	X_{B1}	X_{C1}	X_{D1}	$\bar{R}_1$
Replicate	2	X_{A2}	X_{B2}	X_{C2}	X_{D2}	$\bar{R}_2$
	3	X_{A3}	X_{B3}	X_{C3}	X_{D3}	$\bar{R}_3$
Variety mean		$\bar{T}_A$	$\bar{T}_B$	$\bar{T}_C$	$\bar{T}_D$	G

On examining this table it is clear that one plot of each variety occurs in each replicate. Now suppose that treatment A gives much higher yields than the others. This will have no effect on the variation among the replicates because treatment A occurs in each. Similarly, if replicate 1 gives much higher yields than the others, this will not affect variation among the treatments. We can say quite safely that mean squares representing treatments and replicates are therefore orthogonal. Picturing the opposite situation, suppose that A is much the highest yielding treatment but the plot of A in replicate 1 is missing. This would tend to decrease $\bar{R}_1$ as compared to $\bar{R}_2$ and $\bar{R}_3$, and the treatment and replicate effects as represented by $\bar{T}_A$, $\bar{T}_B$, $\bar{T}_C$, $\bar{T}_D$, and $\bar{R}_1$, $\bar{R}_2$, $\bar{R}_3$ would no longer be orthogonal.

5. Partitioning of sums of squares and degrees of freedom. Suppose that we have a table of results as follows.

		Treatment 1	2	3 ⋯	n	Replicate Total
Replicate	1	X_{11}	X_{12}	X_{13} ⋯	X_{1n}	R_1
	2	X_{21}	X_{22}	X_{23} ⋯	X_{2n}	R_2
	⋮	⋮				⋮
	r	X_{r1}	X_{r2}	X_{r3} ⋯	X_{rn}	R_r
Treatment Total		C_1	C_2	C_3 ⋯	C_n	G = Grand Total

For any one observation, say X_{11}, we can write

$$(X_{11} - \bar{X}) = (X_{11} - \bar{R}_1) + (\bar{R}_1 - \bar{X})$$

where $\bar{X}$ is the general mean and $\bar{R}_1$ is the mean of replicate 1. Then

$$(X_{11} - \bar{X})^2 = (X_{11} - \bar{R}_1)^2 + (\bar{R}_1 - \bar{X})^2 + 2(X_{11} - \bar{R}_1)(\bar{R}_1 - \bar{X})$$

and, summating over replicate 1,

$$\sum_1^n (X - \bar{X})^2 = \sum_1^n (X - \bar{R}_1)^2 + n(\bar{R}_1 - \bar{X})^2 + 2(\bar{R}_1 - \bar{X}) \sum_1^n (X_1 - \bar{R}_1)$$

The last term is zero because it contains $\sum_1^n (X_1 - \bar{R}_1)$, which must be zero because it is a sum of deviations from a mean. The second last term contains $(\bar{R}_1 - \bar{X})$ which is constant, and therefore in summating it is merely taken n times. Eliminating the last term, we have

$$\sum_1^n (X - \bar{X})^2 = \sum_1^n (X - \bar{R}_1)^2 + n(\bar{R}_1 - \bar{X})^2$$

Now, if we repeat this for each replicate and summate over the whole experiment, we get

$$\sum_{1}^{rn}(X-\bar{X})^2 = \sum_{1}^{r}\sum_{1}^{n}(X-\bar{R}_r)^2 + n\sum_{1}^{r}(\bar{R}_r-\bar{X})^2 \qquad 15$$

This is a very important equation in that it shows how the total sum of squares can be partitioned into one part representing deviations from the mean within replicates and another part representing deviations of the replicate means from the general mean. Simply by extending the algebra we can show that, if a deviation of X_{11} from the general mean is written as

$$(X_{11}-\bar{X}) = (\bar{R}_1-\bar{X}) + (\bar{C}_1-\bar{X}) + [(X_{11}-\bar{X})-(\bar{R}_1-\bar{X})-(\bar{C}_1-\bar{X})]$$
$$= (\bar{R}_1-\bar{X}) + (\bar{C}_1-\bar{X}) + (X-\bar{R}_1-\bar{C}_1+\bar{X})$$

then the total sum of squares can be partitioned into

$$\sum_{1}^{rn}(X-\bar{X})^2 = n\sum_{1}^{r}(\bar{R}-\bar{X})^2 + r\sum_{1}^{n}(\bar{C}-\bar{X})^2 + \sum_{1}^{rn}(X-\bar{R}_i-\bar{C}_j+\bar{X})^2 \qquad 16$$

Total = Replicates + Treatments + Random variation

where i runs from 1 to r and j from 1 to n.

The degrees of freedom can be partitioned in a similar manner. Adjustment for the mean takes up 1 degree of freedom; therefore a total of $rn-1$ are available for partitioning. Taking $r-1$ degrees of freedom for replicates and $n-1$ for treatments leaves

$$(rn-1)-(r-1)-(n-1) = (r-1)(n-1)$$

for random variations. The equation for degrees of freedom corresponding to (16) is therefore

$$rn-1 = (r-1) \quad + (n-1) \quad + (r-1)(n-1)$$

Total = Replicates + Treatments + Random variations

The complete analysis of variance is most conveniently set up in tabular form as shown below, where we now substitute the term error for random variation.

	Sum of Squares	Degrees of Freedom	Mean Square
Replicates	$n\Sigma(\bar{R}-\bar{X})^2$	$r-1$	$nV'_{\bar{R}}$
Treatments	$r\Sigma(\bar{C}-\bar{X})^2$	$n-1$	$rV'_{\bar{C}}$
Error	$\Sigma(X-\bar{R}-\bar{C}+\bar{X})^2$	$(r-1)(n-1)$	V
Total	$\Sigma(X-\bar{X})^2$	$rn-1$	

This form is convenient for tabulation and for making tests of significance. An F value for replicates or for treatments can be calculated from

$$F_r = \frac{nV'_{\bar{R}}}{V} \qquad F_c = \frac{nV'_{\bar{C}}}{V}$$

For F_r the degrees of freedom are $(r-1)$ and $(r-1)(n-1)$, and for treatments they are $(n-1)$ and $(r-1)(n-1)$.

The calculations are best carried out as in the formulas given below.

Total $$\sum_1^{nr}(X-\bar{X})^2 = \sum_1^{nr}(X^2) - \frac{G^2}{rn} \qquad (17)$$

Replicates $$n\sum_1^{r}(\bar{R}-\bar{X})^2 = \frac{\sum_1^{r}(R^2)}{n} - \frac{G^2}{rn} \qquad (18)$$

Treatments $$r\sum_1^{n}(\bar{C}-\bar{X})^2 = \frac{\sum_1^{n}(C^2)}{r} - \frac{G^2}{rn} \qquad (19)$$

Error = Total − Replicates − Treatments

The entire procedure, including tests of significance, is given in Example 5–1.

6. Example 5–1. Twofold classification of variates. In a swine feeding experiment, Dunlop [10] obtained the results given in Table 5–1. The three rations, A, B, and C, differed in the substances providing the vitamins. The animals were in 4 groups of 3 each, the grouping being on the basis of litter and initial weight. For our purpose we shall assume that the grouping is merely a matter of replication.

TABLE 5–1

GAINS IN WEIGHT OF SWINE FED ON RATIONS A, B, C

Ration	I	II	III	IV	Total
A	7.0	16.0	10.5	13.5	47.0
B	14.0	15.5	15.0	21.0	65.5
C	8.5	16.5	9.5	13.5	48.0
Total	29.5	48.0	35.0	48.0	160.5

The form of the analysis is

	SS	DF
Rations		2
Groups		3
Error		6
Total		11

Calculating the sums of squares, we have

$$\text{Total} = 2316.75 - (160.5)^2/12 = 2316.75 - 2146.69 = 170.06$$

$$\text{Rations} = (47.0^2 + 65.5^2 + 48.0^2)/4 - 2146.69 = 54.12$$

$$\text{Groups} = (29.5^2 + \cdot \cdot \cdot + 48.0^2)/3 - 2146.69 = 87.73$$

$$\text{Error} = 170.06 - 54.12 - 87.73 = 28.21$$

This gives us an analysis of variance as follows.

	SS	DF	MS	*F*	5% Point
Rations	54.12	2	27.06	5.75	5.14
Groups	87.73	3	29.24	6.22	4.76
Error	28.21	6	4.702		
Total	170.06	11			

The mean square for rations is just significant. The meaning of the significance of the mean square for groups depends on the manner in which the classification into groups has been made. We have assumed here that the groups are merely replications, in which case the error mean square is a result of variations within groups not due to the rations. It is, therefore, valid to consider this mean square as an error with which the others can be compared. The group mean square, since it results from the plan of the experiment, is an expression of error control. If the arrangement had been other than in groups, we would have had a simple classification into within and between rations. The mean square for within rations would have been much larger than it is according to the present arrangement, and consequently the experiment would have been less precise.

7. Experimental error. In previous discussions the variates have been presented by symbols such as $X_{11} + Y_1 + Z_1$, where X_{11} is that portion due entirely to random variability, and our problem in the analysis of variance was to isolate the mean square resulting from this random variability from other mean squares resulting from the effects of treatments, replicates, etc. This mean square due to random variability is commonly referred to as the mean square for experimental error. In other words, it represents in an experiment that portion of the total variability that is beyond control. If the previous discussions have been followed carefully, it will be obvious that the experimental error is the logical measuring stick for making tests of significance of other mean squares, because, if the mean square tested is not inflated by any real effect in the experiment, it must tend to be equal to the experimental error.

In spite of the apparent simplicity of the analysis of variance as applied to experimental data, there is often much confusion in connection with the correct expression for error in tests of significance. In other words, it is not always clear what constitutes a valid error for a given test.

8. Selecting a valid error. Significance is a relative and not an absolute term. Differences are found to be significant or insignificant in relation to variability arising from a source arbitrarily selected according to the interpretation to be put on the result. In this connection the experimenter should understand clearly the concept of tests of significance as based on the testing of a given hypothesis. *The hypothesis selected for test decides what is a valid error.* To make these points clear let us assume that an experiment is being conducted involving chemical determinations on 2 kinds of material being compared. The method is to draw 20 samples from each material. In the laboratory each sample is split and analyzed in duplicate. The form of the analysis of variance may be set up as follows.

	DF	Expected Value of MS	MS in an Actual Experiment
Materials (A and B)	1	σ_t^2	s_t^2
Variability among A samples	19	σ_a^2 } σ_s^2	s_s^2
Variability among B samples	19	σ_b^2 } σ_s^2	
Between duplicates	40	σ_e^2	s_e^2
Total	79		

It may be assumed, as in most studies of this sort, that σ_a^2 and σ_b^2 are of the same magnitude and may be combined to form a single variance σ_s^2 representing the variability due to sampling. The hypothesis under test in this example is that the materials are identical. When this hypothesis is true, the expected value of σ_t^2 is σ_s^2. In other words, variation due to the samples will be the only factor contributing to the random difference between the two means. Turning to σ_s^2, if the samples do not contribute any variability, the expected value is equal to σ_e^2. Thus, in an actual experiment where samples and materials contribute to the total variability and where the contribution due to real differences between the materials is equal to σ_p^2 and that due to real differences between samples is equal to σ_q^2, we have

$$\begin{aligned} \sigma_t^2 &= \sigma_p^2 + \sigma_q^2 + \sigma_e^2 \\ \sigma_s^2 &= \sigma_q^2 + \sigma_e^2 \\ \sigma_e^2 &= \sigma_e^2 \end{aligned}$$

This fundamental relation can be applied to solve the problem of whether s_s^2 or s_e^2 should be the error term in making a test of the significance of s_t^2. The existence of a difference between A and B is perhaps important in some industrial process, and we will suppose that A gives a higher and more favorable result than B. Now, if either of these 2 materials is used, the results obtained will be subject to a sampling error because this sampling error reflects the fact that the material is not entirely uniform. Furthermore, a high degree of refinement in laboratory technique may have made σ_e^2 very small. It follows, therefore, that our estimate of σ_e^2 as an error would be erroneous as it does not give a measure of the random fluctuations to which results with either of the materials would be subject in actual practice. This is, of course, provided that σ_s^2 is actually greater than σ_e^2. Owing to the design of the experiment, the expected value of σ_s^2 is equal to or greater than σ_e^2, but in exceptional cases the estimated values obtained in an experiment may give $s_e^2 > s_s^2$. We would then be able to accept s_e^2 as a valid error.

A question sometimes asked in connection with an experiment of this kind is: Why make the determinations in duplicate if the results are not applied in the test of significance? To answer this we should note again that

$$F = \frac{s_t^2}{s_s^2} = \frac{s_p^2 + s_q^2 + s_e^2}{s_q^2 + s_e^2}$$

and, the smaller we make s_e^2, the more sensitive the experiment will be in testing for differences between the materials. It is important, therefore, to have a measure of this source of error. That portion of the error represented by s_q^2 may be beyond our control in that it represents variability of the material, but it is quite conceivable that s_e^2 may be considerably reduced by improvements in laboratory technique and the sensitivity of the test increased. As a general rule, in experiments of this type s_q^2 is larger than s_e^2, which is the same as saying that real variability due to sampling usually exists. It is a common practice to make the test of significance given by

$$F = \frac{s_s^2}{s_e^2}$$

in order to decide this point. It would, of course, be impossible to make the test if we did not have some measure of σ_e^2.

9. Interactions. It will have been noted that the methods of the analysis of variance are particularly appropriate for data that may be classified in two ways as into treatments and replicates. Actually the method can be applied to data classified simultaneously in several ways. For example, we may have 3 treatments each at 2 levels (e.g., 3 fertilizers each at 2 rates), and the whole experiment may be replicated 4 times. The data could then be set up in four 3×2 tables, 1 for each replicate, giving a threefold classification. Our chief interest, however, in a situation of this kind is in the 2×3 table which can be made up of the 6 treatment totals. Suppose that the table is as follows.

		Treatment			
		A	*B*	*C*	
Level	1				T_1
	2				T_2

Looking at this table from the standpoint of degrees of freedom, we see that out of the total of 5 there is only 1 for levels and 2 for treatments. The other 2 degrees of freedom must represent an effect due to the treatments but not reflected in the marginal totals. It must therefore represent something due to the relation between the treatments and the levels. This effect is commonly referred to as an interaction. To demonstrate the characteristics of an interaction it is most convenient to examine a 2×2 table. We shall assume that there are 2 treatments at 2 levels in 3 replicates, providing a table of results as follows.

		Treatment		
		A	*B*	
Level	1	4	8	$12 = T_1$
	2	8	12	$20 = T_2$
		12	20	$32 = G$
		$= T_A$	$= T_B$	

The general method of analysis given in equations (17), (18), and (19) can be followed, but the discussion can be simplified by applying 2 new formulas for sums of squares.

1. *Sum of squares for 2 totals such as T_1 and T_2.*

$$\frac{T_1^2 + T_2^2}{n} - \frac{(T_1 + T_2)^2}{2n} = \frac{(T_1 - T_2)^2}{2n} \qquad 20$$

where n is the number of individual determinations in each total.

2. *Sum of squares for the interaction in a 2 × 2 table.* Let the sub-totals in the table be represented in the following manner.

	A	B
1	t_{1A}	t_{1B}
2	t_{2A}	t_{2B}

The interaction sum of squares is given by

$$\frac{[(t_{1A} + t_{2B}) - (t_{2A} + t_{1B})]^2}{2n} \qquad 21$$

where the numerator is merely the square of the difference between the diagonal totals.

In the example we have

$$\text{Treatments (SS)} = \frac{(12 - 20)^2}{12} = 5.33$$

$$\text{Levels (SS)} = \frac{(12 - 20)^2}{12} = 5.33$$

$$\text{Interaction (SS)} = \frac{(16 - 16)^2}{12} = 0$$

and on examining the nature of the sub-totals it is obvious that the interaction sum of squares must be zero if the responses of the treatments are the same for both levels. In terms of symbols

	A	B
1	a	b
2	$a + x$	$b + x$

where x is the increase in response due to level 2 as compared to level 1. It follows that $(a + b + x) - (a + x + b) = 0$, and the interaction sum of squares $= 0$.

Considering the responses in two directions, we could represent the table algebraically by

	A	B
1	a	$a + x$
2	$a + y$	$a + x + y$

where x represents the response due to B as compared to A, and y the response of 2 as compared to 1. Then

$$a + (a + x + y) - [(a + y) + (a + x)] = 0$$

and the interaction sum of squares $= 0$.

Let us examine the situation when the responses are not equal. For example, we have the results

	A	B
1	6	4
2	8	12

in which B gives a much greater response to the increased quantity of treatment than A. Here we have

$$\text{Treatments (SS)} = \frac{(14 - 16)^2}{12} = 0.33$$

$$\text{Levels (SS)} = \frac{(10 - 20)^2}{12} = 8.33$$

$$\text{Interaction (SS)} = \frac{(18 - 12)^2}{12} = 3.00$$

and the interaction is appreciable.

It is of interest to note that the additive type of response is the only one that gives a zero interaction. A proportional response does not. For example, when the relation is

	A	B
1	a	b
2	$a + \frac{a}{x}$	$b + \frac{b}{x}$

the interaction sum of squares $= [(b - a)/x]^2/2n$, from which it is obvious that the interaction will not be zero unless $a = b$. However, if the values are transformed to logarithms, it can be shown easily that the interaction becomes zero.

10. Interactions of higher order. As more factors in an experiment are introduced, interactions of a higher order result. For example, in addition to the 2 treatments at 2 levels, each set may be applied at 2 different dates. With replicates we would then have a fourfold classification. The treatment totals may be set up in three tables.

Date 1

Level	A	B
1		
2		

Date 2

Level	A	B
1		
2		

Dates 1 and 2

Level	A	B
1		
2		

For each date we have

	DF
Treatments	1
Levels	1
2-factor interaction	1

and, taking into consideration the dates, there will be 1 degree of freedom for the dates and 1 each for the interaction of the above 3 effects with dates, making a complete allotment of the 9 degrees of freedom as follows.

	DF
Dates	1
Treatments	1
Levels	1
2-factor interaction (treatments × levels)	1
2-factor interaction (dates × treatments)	1
2-factor interaction (dates × levels)	1
3-factor interaction (dates × treatments × levels)	1

The meaning of a 3-factor interaction is most easily interpreted in relation to simple interactions. If the 2-factor interactions (treatments × levels) are equal for the 2 dates, the 3-factor interaction = 0. This can be proved easily by inserting figures and calculating sums of squares. The 3-factor interaction measures, therefore, the extent to which a 2-factor interaction for any 2 factors varies with the third factor.

A 3-factor interaction for 2 × 2 tables may be calculated by a simple extension of the geometrical method used for the simple interaction. In the diagram below, the dotted lines show the method of obtaining the necessary totals.

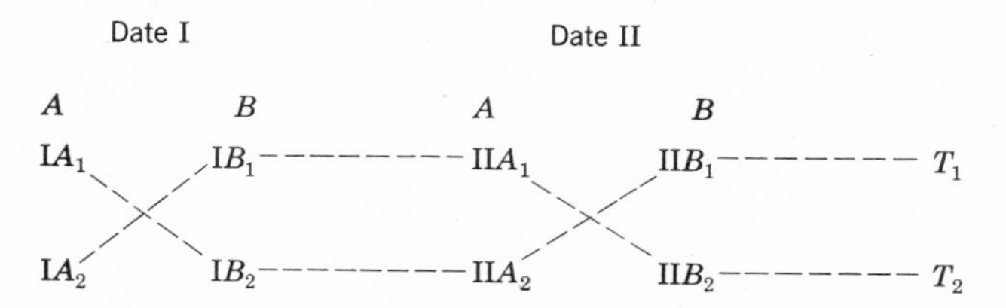

In terms of symbols

$$T_1 = \mathrm{I}A_1 + \mathrm{I}B_2 + \mathrm{II}A_2 + \mathrm{II}B_1$$

$$T_2 = \mathrm{I}A_2 + \mathrm{I}B_1 + \mathrm{II}A_1 + \mathrm{II}B_2$$

Then the sum of squares is

$$\frac{(T_1 - T_2)^2}{2n}$$

where n is again the number of individual variates entering into each total, such as T_1.

Having seen how 3-factor interactions can be obtained from threefold classifications, it follows that with a fourth factor we will have a 4-factor interaction, and so on for each factor added. It is clear, however, that high-order interactions, at least any interaction of an order higher than the 3-factor, is not of much practical significance. In the first place they are rarely significant statistically, and in the second place they are too complex for any practical interpretation. It will be seen, as we progress with the study of experimental design, that it is frequently desirable to sacrifice high-order interactions in the design of the experiment in order to obtain more accuracy for the study of main effects and simple interactions.

11. Methods of calculating sums of squares. After mastering the general principles of the analysis of variance, the student requires a knowledge of methods of calculating sums of squares. The following are some of the methods that give the sums of squares for most experiments, in a systematic and compact form.

a. Total for a set of n variates, $X_1, X_2, X_3 \cdots X_i \cdots X_n$.

$$\sum_{i=1}^{n}(x^2) = \sum_{i=1}^{n}(X^2) - \frac{\left[\sum_{i=1}^{n}(X)\right]^2}{n} \qquad 22$$

The term $\sum_{i=1}^{n}(X^2)$ is known as the raw sum of squares, and the term $\left[\sum_{i=1}^{n}(X)\right]^2 / n$ is frequently referred to as the correction term (abbreviated C.T.). Since $\sum_{i=1}^{n}(X)$ is merely the grand total, it is convenient to refer to it as G.

b. For a set of k groups where each group is made up of n variates.

$$n\sum_{1}^{k}(\bar{X}_i - \bar{X})^2 = \frac{\sum_{1}^{k}[\Sigma(X_i)]^2}{n} - \frac{\left[\sum_{1}^{kn}(X)\right]^2}{kn} \qquad 23$$

c. For a set of k groups where the number of variates is not the same for each group. If the series of totals and the numbers in each is represented as follows.

Total	ΣX_1	ΣX_2	$\Sigma X_3 \cdots$	$\Sigma X_j \cdots$	ΣX_k	Grand total $= G$
Number	n_1	n_2	n_3	$\cdots n_j$	$\cdots n_k$	Grand total $= N$

the sum of squares is given by

$$\frac{(\Sigma X_1)^2}{n_1} + \frac{(\Sigma X_2)^2}{n_2} + \cdots + \frac{(\Sigma X_j)^2}{n_j} + \cdots + \frac{(\Sigma X_k)^2}{n_k} - \frac{G^2}{N} \qquad 24$$

Notice that this is a general formula and reduces to the one given in (*b*) above if the numbers in each total are equal.

d. In $(2 \times n)$*-fold tables.* Suppose that the table is as follows.

		Treatment							
		1	2	3	$\cdots$	i	$\cdots$	n	
Level	I	X_1	X_2	X_3	$\cdots$	X_i	$\cdots$	X_n	ΣX
	II	Y_1	Y_2	Y_3	$\cdots$	Y_i	$\cdots$	Y_n	ΣY
		$X_1 + Y_1$	$X_2 + Y_2$	$X_3 + Y_3$	$\cdots$	$X_i + Y_i$	$\cdots$	$X_n + Y_n$	$G = \Sigma(X_i + Y_i)$
		$X_1 - Y_1$	$X_2 - Y_2$	$X_3 - Y_3$	$\cdots$	$X_i - Y_i$	$\cdots$	$X_n - Y_n$	$S = \Sigma(X_i - Y_i)$ $= \Sigma X_i - \Sigma Y_i$

Setting out the sums of squares required, we have

	DF
Treatments	$n - 1$
Levels	1
Interaction	$n - 1$
Total	$2n - 1$

Instead of 2 levels we may have I and II representing replicates, in which case the third term will be an error.

The total sum of squares is obtained from

$$\Sigma X^2 + \Sigma Y^2 - \frac{G^2}{2n} \qquad 25$$

which is merely an application of (*a*) above.

For levels

$$\frac{(\Sigma X - \Sigma Y)^2}{2n} \qquad 26$$

For treatments

$$\frac{\Sigma(X_i + Y_i)^2}{2} - \frac{G^2}{2n} \qquad 27$$

Then for the interaction or error term we can follow two courses. First, we can subtract treatments and levels from the total, obtaining the error as a difference. Second, we can calculate the third term directly, from

$$\frac{\Sigma(X_i - Y_i)^2}{2} - \frac{(\Sigma X - \Sigma Y)^2}{2n} \qquad 28$$

where the term on the right is the same as in (26).

It should be noted that these formulas are based on there being a single variate in each cell. If the above experiment had been operated with r replicates, r would have appeared in the denominator of each term. Thus the last formula would have been

$$\frac{\Sigma(X_i - Y_i)^2}{2r} - \frac{(\Sigma X - \Sigma Y)^2}{2rn} \tag{29}$$

Also the total sum of squares given above is the total for $2n - 1$ degrees of freedom in the table. The grand total sum of squares will be

$$\Sigma(X^2) + \Sigma(Y^2) - \frac{G^2}{2rn} \tag{30}$$

where X and Y here are individual variates and not sub-totals.

e. In an $(m \times n)$-fold table. Suppose that there are n columns and m rows in the table.

		Column				
		1	2	$\cdots$	n	
Row	1	X_{11}	X_{12}	$\cdots$	X_{1n}	T_{R1}
	2	X_{21}	X_{22}	$\cdots$	X_{2n}	T_{R2}
	$\vdots$	$\vdots$	$\vdots$		$\vdots$	$\vdots$
	m	X_{m1}	X_{m2}	$\cdots$	X_{mn}	T_{Rm}
		T_{C1}	T_{C2}	$\cdots$	T_{Cn}	G

Setting up the outline of sums of squares and degrees of freedom, we have

SS	DF
Columns	$n - 1$
Rows	$m - 1$
Interaction ($C \times R$)	$(n - 1)(m - 1)$
Total	$mn - 1$

Then

$$\text{Total sum of squares} = \Sigma X^2 - \frac{G^2}{mn}.$$

$$\text{Columns} = \frac{\Sigma(T_C^2)}{m} - \frac{G^2}{mn}$$

$$\text{Rows} = \frac{\Sigma(T_R^2)}{n} - \frac{G^2}{mn}$$

$$\text{Interaction} = \Sigma X^2 - \frac{\Sigma T_C^2}{m} - \frac{\Sigma T_R^2}{n} + \frac{G^2}{mn}$$

The last line is the same as subtracting the sums of squares for rows and columns from the total. If the experiment is replicated r times, r will appear in the denominator of all the above expressions. Also the total sum of squares given above will be the total for the sub-totals of the table representing $mn - 1$ degrees of freedom. The grand total sum of squares will be

$$\Sigma X^2 - \frac{G^2}{rmn}$$

where X here is an individual variate and not a sub-total.

f. Three-factor interactions. Assuming that there are 3 factors A, B, and C each at more than 1 level, a general method for calculating 3-factor interactions is to obtain the 2-factor interaction for any 2 factors, for each level of the third. The sum of these less the 2-factor interaction for all levels of the third factor combined gives the 3-factor interaction. Thus there are always three tables to be formed. For example, if A, B, and C are each at 2 levels, we have

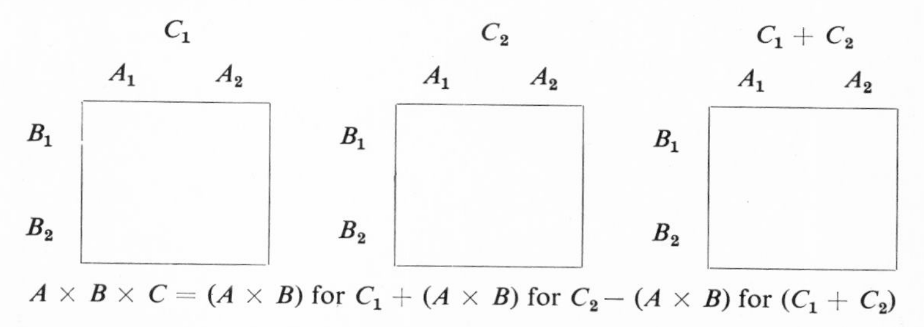

$$A \times B \times C = (A \times B) \text{ for } C_1 + (A \times B) \text{ for } C_2 - (A \times B) \text{ for } (C_1 + C_2)$$

In certain cases there are simplifications. For example, in a $2 \times 2 \times 2$ experiment the 3-factor interaction can be determined directly by obtaining 2 totals as indicated diagrammatically below. This procedure was given on

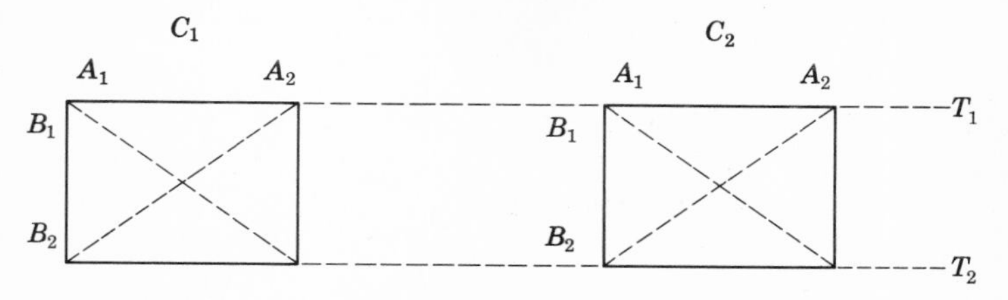

page 81 but is repeated here for the convenience of having all calculation methods in one place. If the totals are T_1 and T_2, the sum of squares is

$$\frac{(T_1 - T_2)^2}{2n} \qquad 31$$

where n is the number of variates entering into each total.

There is also a simplification that can be employed in the calculation of 3-factor interactions for $3 \times 3 \times 3$ experiments. Supposing that the factors are N, P, and K, each at 3 levels, we would have three tables as follows.

	K_1				K_2				K_3		
	P				P				P		
	1	2	3		1	2	3		1	2	3
1	111	121	131	1	112	122	132	1	113	123	133
N 2	211	221	231	2	212	222	232	2	213	223	233
3	311	321	331	3	312	322	332	3	313	323	333

Each table enables us to calculate the interaction $N \times P$ for 1 level of K.

Note first that a 3×3 table can be divided into 2 sets of diagonal totals as in the squares below.

3 × 3 Table

11	12	13
21	22	23
31	32	33

I Diagonals	*J* Diagonals
$11 + 22 + 33 = I_1$	$11 + 32 + 23 = J_1$
$21 + 32 + 13 = I_2$	$21 + 12 + 33 = J_2$
$31 + 12 + 23 = I_3$	$31 + 22 + 13 = J_3$

The 4 degrees of freedom for interaction in a 3×3 table can be partitioned into 2 for the I totals and 2 for the J totals. The sums of squares would be

$$I \text{ (totals)} \qquad \frac{I_1^2 + I_2^2 + I_3^2}{3n} - \frac{G^2}{9n}$$

$$J \text{ (totals)} \qquad \frac{J_1^2 + J_2^2 + J_3^2}{3n} - \frac{G^2}{9n} \qquad 32$$

where G is the grand total and each sub-total in the square consists of n individual determinations.

From the three tables of data we can write down first a set of I totals for each. For example,

$$111 + 221 + 331 = A_1 \qquad 112 + 222 + 332 = B_1 \qquad 113 + 223 + 333 = C_1$$
$$211 + 321 + 131 = A_2 \qquad 212 + 322 + 132 = B_2 \qquad 213 + 323 + 133 = C_2$$
$$311 + 121 + 231 = A_3 \qquad 312 + 122 + 232 = B_3 \qquad 313 + 123 + 233 = C_3$$

From the I totals another I set and a J set can be written. Thus

I Set	J Set
$A_1 + B_2 + C_3 = I_1$	$A_1 + B_3 + C_2 = J_1$
$A_2 + B_3 + C_1 = I_2$	$A_2 + B_1 + C_3 = J_2$
$A_3 + B_1 + C_2 = I_3$	$A_3 + B_2 + C_1 = J_3$

Starting again from the beginning, we first write down the J totals from each table.

$$111 + 231 + 321 = A'_1 \qquad 112 + 232 + 322 = B'_1 \qquad 113 + 233 + 323 = C'_1$$
$$211 + 121 + 331 = A'_2 \qquad 212 + 122 + 332 = B'_2 \qquad 213 + 123 + 333 = C'_2$$
$$311 + 221 + 131 = A'_3 \qquad 312 + 222 + 132 = B'_3 \qquad 313 + 223 + 133 = C'_3$$

and these will also yield an I' and a J' set.

I' Set	J' Set
$A'_1 + B'_2 + C'_3 = I'_1$	$A'_1 + B'_3 + C'_2 = J'_1$
$A'_2 + B'_3 + C'_1 = I'_2$	$A'_2 + B'_1 + C'_3 = J'_2$
$A'_3 + B'_1 + C'_2 = I'_3$	$A'_3 + B'_2 + C'_1 = J'_3$

Each of the above sets of 3 totals will give a sum of squares corresponding to 2 degrees of freedom for the 3-factor interaction, and summing these for the 4 sets completes the calculation.

This principle will be employed again in the discussion of experimental design. It is sufficient to note here that the sums of squares arising from the 4 sets of totals are orthogonal. Therefore the 8 degrees of freedom for the 3-factor interaction $N \times P \times R$ is broken up into 4 pairs that are mutually orthogonal.

12. Partitioning of sums of squares into components corresponding to individual degrees of freedoms. One of the results of the analysis of variance technique is that the experimenter may be inclined to assume that the establishment of significant differences among the treatments is a sufficient conclusion. Actually this may be only preliminary to learning more about the differences and the characteristic effects of the treatments. A useful technique for breaking down the sum of squares for treatments into individual components arises from the procedure described by Fisher [13], Yates [24], and Cochran and Cox [8] for partitioning the sums of squares into orthogonal components, each representing a single degree of freedom.

The components arise from what are known as linear functions of the treatment totals. For example, with 5 treatment totals T_1, T_2, T_3, T_4, and T_5, one linear function would be

$$z = T_1 + T_2 - T_3 - T_4 + (0 \times T_5) \tag{33}$$

In general

$$z = l_1 T_1 + l_2 T_2 + \cdots + l_k T_k \tag{34}$$

where there are k totals, and in such linear functions a characteristic requirement for our purpose is that

$$l_1 + l_2 + \cdots + l_k = 0 \tag{35}$$

In equation (33), for example, $1 + 1 - 1 - 1 + 0 = 0$.

For such linear functions of the treatments the corresponding sum of squares is z^2/D, where

$$D = r(l_1^2 + l_2^2 + \cdots + l_k^2) \tag{36}$$

and r is the number of replications.

After writing any one such linear function representing 1 degree of freedom, it is obvious that other similar functions must exist for the remaining degrees of freedom. These functions can be written down by a rule based on the following. Any 2 linear functions, such as

$$\begin{aligned} z_1 &= l_{11} T_1 + l_{12} T_2 + \cdots + l_{1k} T_k \\ z_2 &= l_{21} T_1 + l_{22} T_2 + \cdots + l_{2k} T_k \end{aligned} \tag{37}$$

are said to be orthogonal if

$$l_{11} l_{21} + l_{12} l_{22} + \cdots + l_{1k} l_{2k} = 0 \tag{38}$$

Applying this to equation (33) above, we have

$$z_1 = T_1 + T_2 - T_3 - T_4 + (0 \times T_5)$$

and

$$z_2 = T_1 - T_2 + (0 \times T_3) + (0 \times T_4) + (0 \times T_5)$$

is an equation such that the sum of the coefficients = 0, and the sum of the products of the coefficients for z_1 and z_2

$$(1 \times 1) + (1 \times -1) = 0$$

It is thus proved that the two comparisons are orthogonal.

Returning to equation (33), the following 4 linear functions can be shown to be orthogonal. The coefficients are written opposite each function for convenience in obtaining the sum of products.

(1)	$\frac{1}{2}T_1 + \frac{1}{2}T_2 - T_3$	$\frac{1}{2} + \frac{1}{2} - 1 + 0 + 0 = 0$
(2)	$T_4 - T_5$	$0 + 0 + 0 + 1 - 1 = 0$
(3)	$2T_1 + 2T_2 + 2T_3 - 3T_4 - 3T_5$	$2 + 2 + 2 - 3 - 3 = 0$
(4)	$T_1 - T_2$	$1 - 1 \quad = 0$

It will be found that the sum of products for all pairs of functions is zero; hence it can be assumed that the functions are orthogonal.

The corresponding sums of squares are as follows, where the divisors are given by equation (36), and it is assumed that we have 4 replicates.

(1) $$\frac{z_1^2}{D_1} = \frac{[\frac{1}{2}(T_1 + T_2) - T_3]^2}{6}$$

(2) $$\frac{z_2^2}{D_2} = \frac{(T_4 - T_5)^2}{8}$$

(3) $$\frac{z_3^2}{D_3} = \frac{[2(T_1 + T_2 + T_3) - 3(T_4 + T_5)]^2}{120}$$

(4) $$\frac{z_4^2}{D_4} = \frac{(T_1 - T_2)^2}{8}$$

Using actual figures, let

$$T_1 = 1652$$
$$T_2 = 1579$$
$$T_3 = 347$$
$$T_4 = 317$$
$$T_5 = 151$$

Then

$$(1) = \frac{[\frac{1}{2}(1652 + 1579) - 347]^2}{6} = 268{,}182.0$$

$$(2) = \frac{(317 - 151)^2}{8} = 3{,}444.5$$

$$(3) = \frac{[2(1652 + 1579 + 347) - 3(317 + 151)]^2}{120} = 275{,}712.5$$

$$(4) = \frac{(1652 - 1579)^2}{8} = 666.1$$

Total $= 548{,}005.1$

Calculating the total sum of squares for treatments in the usual way,

$$\frac{1652^2 + 1579^2 + 347^2 + 317^2 + 151^2}{4} - \frac{4046^2}{20} = 548{,}005.2$$

shows that the arithmetic of partitioning is correct.

Since the comparisons discussed here represent individual degrees of freedom, it is obvious that, if the standard errors of the comparisons based on the means can be obtained, an application of the t test will give a measure of their significance. The general rule for calculating the standard error is

$$s_z = s\sqrt{\frac{l_1^2}{r_1} + \frac{l_2^2}{r_2} + \cdots + \frac{l_k^2}{r_k}} \qquad 39$$

where s is the root mean square in the error line of the analysis of variance. Suppose, for example, that the t test is to be applied to comparison (3). Using the means gives

$$2(413.0 + 394.8 + 86.8) - 3(79.2 + 37.8) = 1438.2$$

Let

$$s = 54.7$$

Then

$$s_z = 54.7\sqrt{\frac{2^2 + 2^2 + 2^2 + 3^2 + 3^2}{4}} = 150$$

And

$$t = \frac{1438.2}{150} = 9.59$$

It should be noted that r is not always the same for all treatments as in a factorial experiment where there may be a control for each level of the treatments.

13. Example 5–2. Selecting a valid error. A series of 5 wheat varieties was grown at 4 stations, and baking tests were made on the flour. A sample of each variety was taken from each station and milled into flour. Two loaves were baked from each sample. The error of determination was given, therefore, by the differences between the volumes of the duplicate loaves.

To determine the form that the analysis of variance will take, note first that there must be a station mean square represented by 3 degrees of freedom, and a variety mean square represented by 4 degrees of freedom. There must also be an interaction effect which may be regarded as the differential response of the varieties at the different stations. The rule for finding the degrees of freedom for an interaction is to multiply the degrees of freedom for the interacting factors. The interaction mean square (MS) must therefore be represented by $3 \times 4 = 12$ degrees of

TABLE 5–2

DUPLICATE LOAF VOLUMES FOR 5 VARIETIES OF WHEAT GROWN AT 4 STATIONS (LOAF VOLUMES IN CC. − 500)/10

		Station								
		I		II		III		IV		Total
	1	7.5	4.5	15.5	14.0	16.5	14.5	19.0	18.6	110.1
	2	12.5	13.2	20.0	18.5	15.0	14.0	23.8	24.4	141.4
Variety	3	7.0	1.0	10.0	8.0	15.5	14.0	17.8	18.5	91.8
	4	1.5	2.0	13.0	15.0	8.5	9.0	14.8	16.6	80.4
	5	28.0	29.0	19.5	16.0	10.5	12.0	22.0	24.8	161.8
Total		106.2		149.5		129.5		200.3		585.5

freedom. There is a total of 40 determinations, so there is a total of 39 degrees of freedom. The remaining 20 degrees of freedom must represent the error of duplicate determinations. We have a check on this because there are 20 pairs of loaves, and, since each pair gives us 1 degree of freedom, there must be 20 in all. The final form of the analysis is:

MS	DF
Stations	3
Varieties	4
Interaction (varieties × stations)	12
Error	20
Total	39

To obtain the sums of squares another table is required. This table, shown below, gives the values of $(X_1 - X_2)$ and $(X_1 + X_2)$, where X_1 and X_2 are taken to represent the paired values.

		I	II	III	IV
	1	3.0	1.5	2.0	0.4
	2	− 0.7	1.5	1.0	− 0.6
$X_1 - X_2$	3	6.0	2.0	1.5	− 0.7
	4	− 0.5	− 2.0	− 0.5	− 1.8
	5	− 1.0	3.5	− 1.5	− 2.8

		I	II	III	IV	Total
	1	12.0	29.5	31.0	37.6	110.1
	2	25.7	38.5	29.0	48.2	141.4
$X_1 + X_2$	3	8.0	18.0	29.5	36.3	91.8
	4	3.5	28.0	17.5	31.4	80.4
	5	57.0	35.5	22.5	46.8	161.8
Total		106.2	149.5	129.5	200.3	585.5

In outlining the form of the analysis for these data, the first logical division is into

	DF
Between pairs	19
Within pairs	20

The first of these may be calculated from the table of $(X_1 - X_2)$ and the second from the table of $X_1 + X_2$ as follows.

$$\text{Between pairs} = \frac{1}{2}\,\Sigma(X_1 + X_2)^2 - \frac{[\Sigma(X)]^2}{N}$$

where N is 40, the total number of observations.

$$\text{Within pairs} = \tfrac{1}{2}\Sigma(X_1 - X_2)^2$$

This will be the error term of the analysis.

The sum of squares and degrees of freedom for between pairs now have to be divided into

	DF
Stations	3
Varieties	4
Interaction (varieties × stations)	12

The calculations are

$$\text{Total} \quad = 10{,}329.73 - \frac{585.5^2}{40} = 1759.47$$

$$\text{Error} \quad = \tfrac{1}{2}(93.33) = 46.67$$

$$\text{Between pairs} = \frac{20{,}566.13}{2} - \frac{585.5^2}{40}$$

$$= 10{,}283.06 - 8570.26 = 1712.80$$

$$\text{Stations} \quad = \frac{90{,}519.03}{10} - 8570.26 = 481.64$$

$$\text{Varieties} \quad = \frac{73{,}186.61}{8} - 8570.26 = 578.07$$

$$\text{Interaction} \quad = 1712.80 - 481.64 - 578.07 = 653.09$$

The analysis of variance is as follows.

	SS	DF	MS
Stations	481.64	3	160.5
Varieties	578.07	4	144.5
Interaction (varieties × stations)	653.09	12	54.42
Error	46.67	20	2.334
Total	1759.47		

Seeing that the four component sums of squares add to the total as calculated provides a good check on the work.

It now has to be decided whether to use the mean square from the duplicate loaf volumes or the interaction mean square to test the significance of the differences between stations and varieties. If the purpose of the experiment is to determine which of the varieties will give the highest loaf volume over the whole area that the stations sample, it will be necessary to make the comparison of the variety mean square with the interaction mean square because in this light the stations are merely replications of the experiment. The error from duplicate loaf volumes will give an indication merely of the accuracy of the laboratory technique. If it is large it will reduce the significance of the differences because it raises the value of the interaction variance.

On comparing the variety mean square with the interaction mean square, we get an F value of 2.66; and, since the 5% point is 3.26, it must be concluded that, considering the whole area being sampled, the differences in loaf volume are not significant. In other words, the variation in the order of the mean loaf volumes of the varieties, from station to station, is so great that the differences between the means for the whole area may easily be accounted for by this variation.

The interaction mean square is very much higher than that arising from differences between duplicate loaf volumes. This means that the laboratory error is not an appreciable factor affecting the precision of the results in this experiment.

Since variety tests are conducted in replicated plots at each station, it follows that, if loaf-volume determinations had been made on each plot, another measure of error could have been obtained. This error would have measured the variation due to soil heterogeneity; and, if the variety mean square for the whole area was significant when compared to the pooled error due to soil heterogeneity, this would indicate that in general at each station the differences between the means of the varieties were greater than could be accounted for by such sampling variation. This would not, however, alter our conclusion based on the test in which the interaction is the error.

14. Example 5–3. Threefold classification of variates. In testing out a machine for molding the dough in experimental baking, Geddes et al. [17] employed 3 adjustments of the machine, designated *A*, *B*, and *C*, and tried them out on a series of 5 flours baked according to 2 formulas. The loaf-volume data are given in Table 5–3.

TABLE 5–3

LOAF-VOLUME RESULTS IN A TEST OF A MACHINE FOR MOLDING THE DOUGH (LOAF VOLUME IN CC. – 500)/10

Formula	Machine Setting	Flour					Total
		1	2	3	4	5	
Simple	*A*	9.4	2.6	12.3	4.6	13.5	42.4
	B	9.6	3.1	13.0	4.3	13.8	43.8
	C	9.6	2.7	12.4	1.8	13.0	39.5
	Flour sub-total	28.6	8.4	37.7	10.7	40.3	125.7
Bromate	*A*	13.7	21.6	19.4	13.5	24.5	92.7
	B	12.7	22.6	20.6	10.4	24.3	90.6
	C	12.6	21.8	20.9	6.8	23.2	85.3
	Flour sub-total	39.0	66.0	60.9	30.7	72.0	268.6
	Flour Total	67.6	74.4	98.6	41.4	112.3	394.3

When the form of the analysis is worked out and compared to those that have been worked out previously, we find an additional complication. The 6 rows in Table 5–3 represent 2 classifications, but for the present we shall consider them as 6 classes, giving us a simple twofold classification. The form of the analysis is then

	DF
Flours	4
Classes	5
Interaction (flours × classes)	20
Total	29

But the 5 degrees of freedom for classes must be split up into

	DF
Machine settings (*ABC*)	2
Formulas (*SB*)	1
Interaction (*ABC* × *SB*)	2

Hence the interaction in the first analysis is an interaction of the above 3 factors with the flours. Realizing this, we can then write out the form of the analysis in full.

	DF
Flours (1 · · · 5)	4
Machine settings (*ABC*)	2
Formulas (*SB*)	1
Interaction (*ABC* × *SB*)	2
Interaction (1 · · · 5 × *ABC*)	8
Interaction (1 · · · 5 × *SB*)	4
Interaction (1 · · · 5 × *ABC* × *SB*)	8
Total	29

The last interaction is known as a 3-factor interaction. In this example it represents the degree to which the interaction of (*ABC* × *SB*) is different for the different flours. If the interaction (*ABC* × *SB*) is the same for each flour, the 3-factor interaction will be zero.

To determine the sums of squares for the components set out above it is necessary to set up three calculation tables as below:

Machine Setting	Flour					Total
	1	2	3	4	5	
A	23.1	24.2	31.7	18.1	38.0	135.1
B	22.3	25.7	33.6	14.7	38.1	134.4
C	22.2	24.5	33.3	8.6	36.2	124.8
Total	67.6	74.4	98.6	41.4	112.3	394.3

Formula	Flour					Total
	1	2	3	4	5	
S	28.6	8.4	37.7	10.7	40.3	125.7
B	39.0	66.0	60.9	30.7	72.0	268.6
S + *B*	67.6	74.4	98.6	41.4	112.3	394.3
S − *B*	− 10.4	− 57.6	− 23.2	− 20.0	− 31.7	− 142.9

Formula	Machine Setting			Total
	A	*B*	*C*	
S	42.4	43.8	39.5	125.7
B	92.7	90.6	85.3	268.6
S + *B*	135.1	134.4	124.8	394.3
S − *B*	− 50.3	− 46.8	− 45.8	− 142.9

The calculations are

Total $= 6618.43 - \dfrac{394.3^2}{30} = 6618.43 - 5182.42 = 1436.01$

Flours $(1 \cdots 5) = (34{,}152.33/6) - 5182.42 = 509.64$

Settings $(ABC) = (51{,}890.41/10) - 5182.42 = 6.62$

Formulas $(SB) = (268.6 - 125.7)^2/30 = 680.68$

Interaction $(ABC \times SB) = [\Sigma(S - B)^2/10] - 680.68 = (6817.97/10) - 680.68 = 1.12$

Interaction $(1 \cdots 5 \times ABC)$

Total for table $= (11{,}436.57/2) - 5182.42 = 535.86$

Flours $(1 \cdots 5) = 509.64$

Settings $(ABC) = 6.62$

Remainder $(1 \cdots 5 \times ABC) = 19.60$

Interaction $(1 \cdots 5 \times SB) = [\Sigma(S - B)^2/6] - 680.68 = (5369.05/6) - 680.68 = 214.16$

Interaction $(1 \cdots 5 \times ABC \times SB) =$ Remainder $= 4.19$

The analysis of variance when set up in detail is as follows.

	SS	DF	MS	F	5% Point
Flours $(1 \cdots 5)$	509.64	4	127.4	243.1	3.84
Formulas (SB)	680.68	1	680.7	1299.0	5.32
Interaction $(1 \cdots 5 \times SB)$	214.16	4	53.54	102.2	3.84
Settings (ABC)	6.62	2	3.31	6.31	4.46
Interaction $(ABC \times SB)$	1.12	2	0.560	1.07	4.46
Interaction $(1 \cdots 5 \times ABC)$	19.60	8	2.450	4.68	3.44
Interaction $(1 \cdots 5 \times ABC \times SB)$	4.19	8	0.524		
Total	1436.01	29			

It is of interest to make a detailed study of Example 5–3 from the standpoint of the selection of a valid error. Note first that the determinations were not made in duplicate so that there is no real measure of the error in the technique. In the second place it must be remembered that the primary object of the experiment is to study the differences in the loaf volumes due to the different settings of the machine and the differential responses due to these same settings. For this reason the analysis of variance has been separated into two portions. The three effects in the first group are of no particular interest, as previous experience would have enabled the cereal chemists to predict that just such results would be obtained. The separation of these three effects into one group is not a result of the data obtained in the experiment but was preconceived, and it was decided before the experiment was operated that this would be done.

Considering the variance due to the settings, the first question to be asked is whether or not it should be tested against a variance representing pure laboratory error or against one of the 2-factor interactions. It should not be tested against ($ABC \times SB$) because in actual practice either the simple or the bromate formula will be used. Actually there are two questions to be answered here, and there are answers appropriate to both. If the effect of the settings is considered in relation to results with a series of different flours, the correct error would be the (flours $\times$ settings) interaction. The result would indicate no significance for the effect of settings. If the effect of settings is to be judged on a series of loaves from the same flour, the correct error would be the 3-factor interaction in that it most nearly represents laboratory error.

The F values and their 5% points are given in the analysis, and with their aid the results may be summarized very quickly. The flour and formula differences as well as the interaction between them are very large in comparison to the experimental error and may be dismissed with that statement. The primary interest in the experiment is in the settings of the machine and the interaction of the settings with the other factors. The settings are significant in relation to experimental error, and a glance at the totals indicates that this must be due to the fact that the C setting gives a somewhat lower loaf volume than A or B. The interaction of ABC with the formulas S and B is not significant, indicating that the differences between the settings are reasonably consistent for both methods of baking. The interaction of the flours with the settings is significant, and we can conclude that the results with the flours are to a certain extent changed by the machine settings. From an inspection of the results this would seem to be due to flour 4, as the B and C settings depress the loaf volume for this flour to a greater extent than for the others.

15. Limitations of the analysis of variance. Cochran [7] has stated that "the analysis of variance depends on the assumptions that the treatment and environment effects are additive and that the experimental errors are independent in the probability sense, have equal variance, and are normally distributed." It will be recalled that in Section 2 an individual result was represented by the symbols $X + Y + Z$, where X is the part due to random variation, Y the part due to replicate, and Z the part due to treatment. It is necessary only that the X be independently and normally distributed with a mean of zero and variance σ^2 in order for the F test to hold. A correlation between experimental errors may exist under certain conditions. Actually in field experiments the errors of adjacent plots are distinctly correlated in that they tend to vary together. This difficulty is very largely overcome in field experiments by a process of randomization which is illustrated in later chapters. Inequality of variances arise frequently. In Chapter 11 one experiment is described in which this occurs, and methods are illustrated for obtaining more accurate tests of significance than in the straightforward application of the analysis of variance. Lack of normality in data also occurs frequently, and a brief outline is given below on methods of transforming data to some other scale such that a closer approach to normality is obtained.

16. Transformations. These are described below with reference to common types of data requiring transformation.

a. Small whole numbers. Suppose that we are making counts of the number of insects per square foot of soil where the concentration of insects is quite low. The count for a number of individual square feet may be zero, and the maximum may be around 10. The most appropriate transformed variate is $\sqrt{X}$, where X is the actual count. When zeros occur, it is advisable to take $\sqrt{\frac{1}{2} + X}$ as the transformed variate.

b. Fractions or percentages. Percentages are particularly likely to show deviations from the normal distribution. As a matter of fact, it will be clear from Chapter 3 that the distribution expected is the binomial. When $p \neq q$, it is obvious that the distribution will be skewed. When p is equal or nearly equal to q, the distribution is sufficiently symmetrical to be treated as normal. A good working rule is to transform percentages unless nearly all the data lie between 30 and 70%. The appropriate transformation is to the angle for which the sine is the square root of the percentage to be transformed. This is known as the inverse sine transformation for which tables are given by Fisher and Yates [16], Bliss [3, 4], and Snedecor [23]. When a series of experiments are analyzed singly and then thrown together in one analysis, it is obvious that the transformation must be made throughout, regardless of the range.

c. Whole number counts with a wide range. Referring again to insect counts in soil, if the concentration is high, counts in certain squares may be very high. Imagine a soil treatment for insect control where with an effective treatment the counts range from 5 to 20, whereas with an ineffective treatment they may range from 100 to 10,000. In such cases there is usually a proportional relation between the mean and the standard deviation. The appropriate transformation is to the logarithm of the count. Here, again, when zeros are encountered, it is advisable to add 1 to each number before taking the logarithm.

Generally speaking, in examining data it is worth while to watch for skew distributions, unequal variances, and other abnormalities with a view to making appropriate corrections or transformations before proceeding with the analysis. Further details on this subject can be obtained in *Biometrics* of March, 1947, in which a whole issue by Churchill Eisenhardt,

W. G. Cochran, and M. S. Bartlett is devoted to explaining the theoretical requirements of the analysis of variance, the consequences of abnormality in data, and appropriate transformations.

17. Exercises.

1. Table 5–4, taken from data by Crampton and Hopkins [9], shows the gains in weight of pigs in a comparative feeding trial. The 5 lots of pigs represent 5 different treatments, and there were 10 pigs in each lot. Make an analysis of variance for the data, and test the significance of the treatment differences.

TABLE 5–4

GAINS OF PIGS IN A COMPARATIVE FEEDING TRIAL

Replicate	Lot I	Lot II	Lot III	Lot IV	Lot V
1	165	168	164	185	201
2	156	180	156	195	189
3	159	180	189	186	173
4	167	166	138	201	193
5	170	170	153	165	164
6	146	161	190	175	160
7	130	171	160	187	200
8	151	169	172	177	142
9	164	179	142	166	184
10	158	191	155	165	149

The error mean square in this experiment works out to 243.6.

2. In agronomic trials of varieties of cereal crops it is desirable to conduct the trials at various points in the area under consideration and to carry them on for a period of 2 or more years. Immer et al. [20] have given data on barley yields at several stations in Minnesota over a period of 2 years. Table 5–5 shows the yields at 3 stations for 2 years for 6 varieties. Analyze the results.

Note that the blocks are numbered 1, 2, and 3, but this does not mean that block 1 at University Farm has any relation to block 1 at Waseca or any other station. Consequently the sum of squares and degrees of freedom for blocks are worked out at each station and lumped together in the final analysis. A common error that beginners make in sorting out the degrees of freedom for an experiment of this kind is to regard the blocks as a factor occurring at 3 levels, and thus they have such expressions in their analysis as these:

Blocks × Stations

Blocks × Years

Blocks × Stations × Years

etc.

These expressions obviously have no meaning as the block numbers do not represent definite levels that are uniform at all stations. The correct procedure is therefore to calculate the block sum of squares for each experiment and add all these sums of squares together in order to show them in the final analysis.

TABLE 5–5

YIELDS IN BUSHELS PER ACRE OF 6 VARIETIES OF BARLEY GROWN AT 3 STATIONS IN EACH OF 2 YEARS

Block	Manchuria	Glabron	Svansota	Velvet	Trebi	Peatland	Station	Year
1	29.2	44.6	33.9	36.7	41.2	38.5	University Farm	1931
2	25.0	39.1	39.4	41.0	31.9	29.6		
3	26.8	45.5	32.1	42.0	36.6	30.2		
1	19.7	28.6	20.1	20.3	19.3	22.3	University Farm	1932
2	31.4	38.3	30.8	27.5	22.4	30.8		
3	29.6	43.5	31.4	32.6	45.5	31.1		
1	47.5	55.4	44.5	56.9	63.9	41.2		
2	52.2	53.4	46.0	40.6	63.8	51.5	Waseca	1931
3	46.9	56.8	51.5	53.2	63.8	53.0		
1	40.8	44.4	41.0	44.6	53.5	39.8		
2	29.4	34.9	41.1	41.4	44.2	39.2	Waseca	1932
3	30.2	33.9	33.4	26.2	50.0	29.1		
1	24.0	27.5	26.5	27.2	42.1	24.7		
2	24.7	25.5	21.5	28.0	42.5	29.5	Morris	1931
3	33.6	33.3	29.3	23.2	46.7	35.4		
1	29.6	36.6	27.1	35.9	40.0	35.7		
2	34.1	34.3	35.7	33.9	46.9	41.9	Morris	1932
3	39.4	34.5	42.3	46.7	53.0	52.0		

The following values for the sums of squares will assist in checking the calculations:

Total	*11,504.61*
Varieties	*1,566.58*
Varieties × Stations × Years	*230.52*

3. Prove that $\sum_{1}^{n}(x^2) = \sum_{1}^{n}(X^2) - [\Sigma(X)]^2/n$.

Find the 5% points of F for the following values of n_1 and n_2.

n_1	n_2	n_1	n_2
3	51	16	39
6	43	18	215
4	92	17	19
12	195	36	28
7	36	28	154
11	64	53	42

4. Table 5–6 gives a portion of the data given by Jones [22] on wire-worm counts. Convert the data to $\sqrt{\frac{1}{2} + X}$ and perform an analysis of variance. Calculate means for the treatments and reconvert to counts. Use square roots accurate to two decimal places.

TABLE 5–6

Wire-Worm Counts for 5 Treatments in an Experiment with 3 Replicates

Replicate 1	*P*	*O*	*N*	*K*	*M*
	3	2	5	1	4
Replicate 2	*M*	*K*	*O*	*N*	*P*
	6	0	6	4	4
Replicate 3	*O*	*M*	*K*	*P*	*N*
	4	9	1	6	5

Treatment mean square = 1.0133.

REFERENCES

1. M. S. Bartlett, *J. Roy. Stat. Soc. Suppl.*, **3**, 68–78, 1936.
2. M. S. Bartlett, *Biometrics*, **3**, 39–52, 1947.
3. C. I. Bliss, *Plant Protect.*, (*U. S. S. R.*), **12**, 67–77, 1937.
4. C. I. Bliss, *Ohio J. Sci.*, **38**, 9–12, 1938.
5. W. G. Cochran, *Empire J. Exptl. Agr.*, **6**, 157–175, 1938.
6. W. G. Cochran, *Ann. Math. Stat.*, **11**, 335–347, 1940.
7. W. G. Cochran, *Biometrics*, **3**, 22–38, 1947.
8. W. G. Cochran and Gertrude M. Cox, *Experimental Designs*, John Wiley and Sons, New York, 1950.
9. E. W. Crampton and J. W. Hopkins, *J. Nutrition*, **8**, 329–339, 1934.
10. G. Dunlop, *J. Agr. Sci.*, **25**, 445–459, 1935.
11. Churchill Eisenhardt, *Biometrics*, **3**, 1–21, 1947.
12. R. A. Fisher, *Proc. Int. Math. Congress*, Toronto, 1924, pp. 805–813.
13. R. A. Fisher, *The Design of Experiments*, Oliver and Boyd, Edinburgh and London, 1935.
14. R. A. Fisher, *Statistical Methods for Research Workers*, Oliver and Boyd, Edinburgh and London, 10th ed., 1948.
15. R. A. Fisher and W. Mackenzie, *J. Agr. Sci.*, **13**, 311–320, 1923.
16. R. A. Fisher and F. Yates, *Statistical Tables*, Oliver and Boyd, Edinburgh and London, 3rd ed., 1949.
17. W. F. Geddes et al., *Can. J. Research*, **4**, 421–482, 1921.
18. C. H. Goulden, *Sci. Agr.*, **11**, 681–701, 1931.
19. C. H. Goulden, *Cereal Chem.*, **9**, 239–260, 1932.
20. F. R. Immer et al., *J. Am. Soc. Agron.*, **26**, 403–419, 1934.
21. J. O. Irwin, *J. Roy. Stat. Soc.*, **94**, 284–300, 1931.
22. A. W. Jones, *J. Agr. Research*, **54**, 123–134, 1937.
23. G. W. Snedecor, *Statistical Methods*, Iowa State College Press, Ames, Iowa, 4th ed., 1946.
24. F. Yates, The Design and Analysis of Factorial Experiments, *Imp. Bur. Soil Sci. Tech. Commun.*, 35, 1937.

CHAPTER 6

Linear Regression Analysis

1. General observations. In the previous discussions emphasis was placed on the variations that occur in any one variable, such as the yield of plots of wheat, the weight of animals, the count of diseased plants per plot, or the volume of loaves of bread. The present chapter deals chiefly with the joint variation of two variables, and particularly with the situation where the variation of one variable is sensibly dependent on variation in the second variable. Thus one variable is said to be dependent and the other one independent. We might have the two variables, rainfall and yield. It is well known that rainfall affects yields, so rainfall would be considered the independent variable, and yield, the dependent.

In Chapter 5 we had some contact with problems of this type. For example, the yields of plots on which different levels of fertilizer have been applied actually present a regression problem, where yield is the dependent variable, and amount of fertilizer, the independent. In an actual trial we might have results somewhat as follows.

					Mean
Quantity of fertilizer, pounds per acre	100	200	300	400	250
Yield of wheat, bushels per acre	19	24	27	30	25

The results can be graphed as in Figure 6–1.

The first point that strikes us about this result is the fairly uniform increase in yield with uniform increases in amount of fertilizer. This is a practical way of describing the effect in terms of yield and fertilizer. In statistical language, however, we would say that the response of wheat yield to quantity of fertilizer appears to be linear, i.e., can be represented by a straight line. The next thought is that if the relation between the two variables is linear it can be represented by an equation of the form $Y = a + bX$, where Y is yield and X is quantity of fertilizer. The term a represents the origin of the line or the value of Y for $X = 0$, and b represents the slope of the line. Thus b is the increase in Y for a unit of increase in X.

2. Derivation of the regression equation. The situation outlined in Section 1 immediately poses the question of how to set up the required equation. There is a good deal of elegant theory involved in this, and for an excellent exposition of the whole subject the student is referred to Chapter 6 of *Statistical Methods* by G. W. Snedecor [5]. Here we shall be satisfied with the statement that the most suitable equation for the average problem is the one for which the sum of squares of the deviations from the straight line is a minimum. We shall take the regression line to be fitted as $Y_e = a + bX$, where the subscript indicates that Y is an estimated quantity. There is a definite reason for selecting this particular

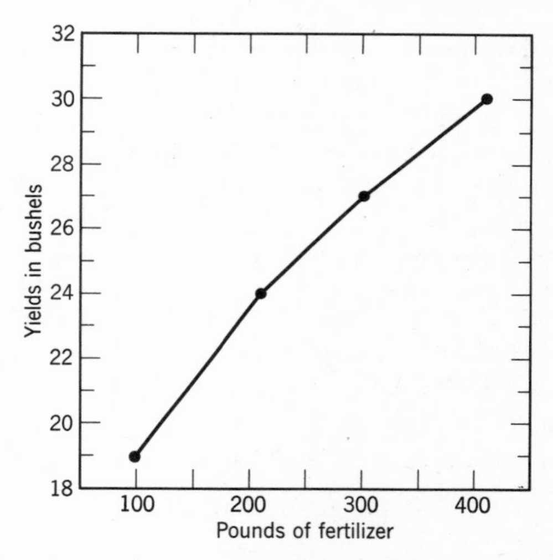

FIGURE 6–1. Graph showing relation between yield and quantity of fertilizer.

straight-line equation. In the first place, by putting in the constant a, the position of the line on the Y axis is allowed to take any value required and does not have to pass through any particular point on the Y axis. Thus, if $X = 0$, $Y_e = a$. If we had put $Y_e = bX$, then the line would have been forced to pass through the origin of Y and X. The values of the constants a and b are to be such that the sum of squares of the errors of estimation will be a minimum. Figure 6–2 illustrates the situation for one pair of variates, Y and X. We see that $y = y_e + y_d$, where y_e represents the deviation of Y_e from $\bar{Y}$, and y_d the deviation of Y from the regression line. The regression line to be fitted is $Y_e = a + bX$, but it is quite permissible to transform Y and X to deviations from their respective means, whence the regression equation becomes $Y_e - \bar{Y} = a' + b'(X - \bar{X})$, or $y_e = a' + b'x$, using the prime notation for a and b because we do not know at this stage if they will be the same as in $Y_e = a + bX$. The sum of squares to be minimized $= \Sigma(Y - Y_e)^2 = \Sigma y_d^2$. From

Figure 6–2, $y_d = (y - y_e)$, and therefore, on substituting for y_e, we have $y_d = (y - a' - b'x)$.

The sum of squares to be minimized is $\Sigma(y - a' - b'x)^2 = f$. Differentiating with respect to a', we have*

$$\frac{df}{da'} = -2\Sigma(y - a' - b'x) = -2\Sigma y + 2na' + 2b'\Sigma x$$

and then with respect to b',

$$\frac{df}{db'} = -2x\Sigma(y - a' - b'x) = -2\Sigma xy + 2a'\Sigma x + 2b'\Sigma x^2$$

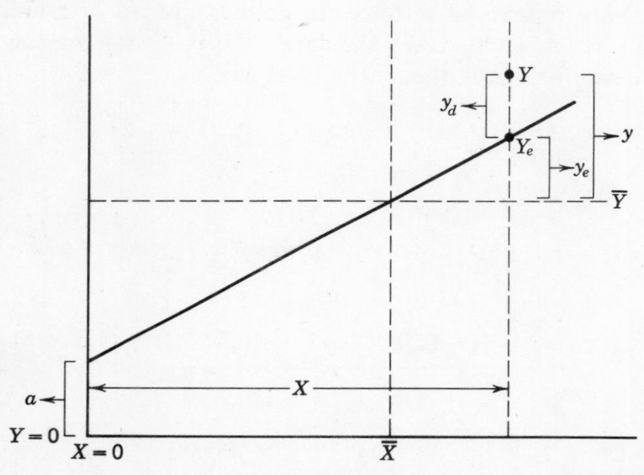

FIGURE 6–2. Illustrating deviations from regression and deviations from the general mean of Y, for one pair of variates of X and Y.

where n represents the number of pairs of variates. Putting both derivatives equal to zero, we get the two equations

$$\Sigma y = a'n + b'\Sigma x \qquad 1$$

$$\Sigma xy = a'\Sigma x + b'\Sigma x^2 \qquad 2$$

These are known as the *normal equations*, which we have derived here by the method of *least squares*. Then, since Σy and Σx are equal to zero, $a' = 0$, and

$$b' = \frac{\Sigma(xy)}{\Sigma x^2} \qquad 3$$

* Students not familiar with differential calculus must take it for granted that equations (1) and (2) do result from minimizing the sum of squares for deviations from the regression line.

The statistic b' is commonly referred to as the regression coefficient. The regression equation is $y_e = b'x$, and, if we substitute $Y_e - \bar{Y}$ for y_e, and $X - \bar{X}$ for x,

$$Y_e = \bar{Y} + b'(X - \bar{X}) \quad \text{or} \quad \bar{Y} + b'x$$

and

$$Y_e = (\bar{Y} - b'\bar{X}) + b'X \qquad 4$$

which can be put in the general form $Y_e = a + bX$, where $a = \bar{Y} - b'\bar{X}$.

It will be of interest to calculate the regression equation for the example of wheat yields and fertilizer, but we shall first perform an operation on the values of X that will reduce the work. This is merely to divide each X by 100, giving weights of fertilizer in pounds instead of hundreds of pounds. This is known as *coding* the data. Then, setting out the results in terms of deviations from the means gives us

x	-1.5	-0.5	0.5	1.5
y	-6	-1	2	5

Then

$$\Sigma x^2 = (-1.5)^2 + (-0.5)^2 + (0.5)^2 + (1.5)^2 = 5.0$$

and

$$\Sigma xy = (-1.5) \times (-6) + (-0.5) \times (-1) + (0.5 \times 2) + (1.5 \times 5) = 18.0$$

giving

$$b = \frac{18}{5} = 3.6$$

This tells us that, according to the regression equation, the expected increase in yield for 100 pounds of fertilizer is 3.6 bushels. The actual equation is

$$Y_e = 25 + 3.6(X - 2.5)$$

or

$$Y_e = 25 - (3.6 \times 2.5) + 3.6X = 16.0 + 3.6X$$

In order to draw the line on the graph only two points are required. Taking

$$16.0 + 3.6 \times 1 = 19.6$$

$$16.0 + 3.6 \times 4 = 30.4$$

two points are obtained from which the line can be placed on the graph in the correct position. Note that the regression equation passes through $\bar{X}$, $\bar{Y}$, providing a check on the calculations.

3. Goodness of fit of regression line. Reference to Figure 6–3 will show that y_i, the deviation of an individual variate Y_i from its mean $\bar{Y}$, is made up of two parts, y_{di} and y_{ei}. Thus

$$y_i = y_{di} + y_{ei}$$

and

$$\Sigma(y^2) = \Sigma(y_d + y_e)^2 = \Sigma y_d^2 + \Sigma y_e^2 + 2\Sigma(y_e y_d) \qquad 5$$

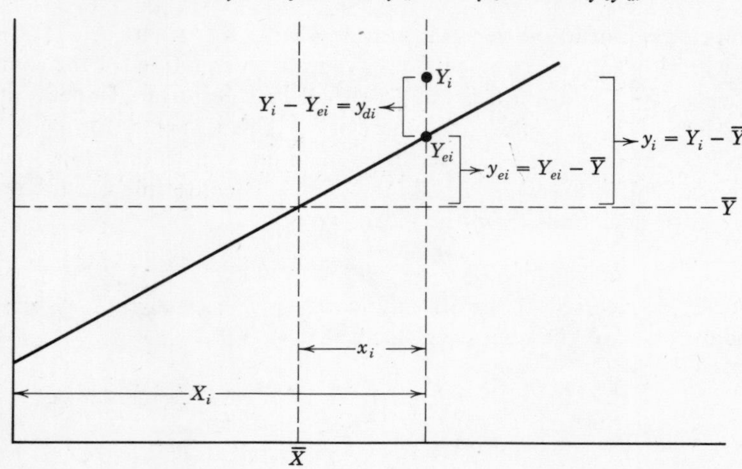

FIGURE 6–3. Illustrating the origin of sums of squares for deviations from regression, and deviations of estimated value from the general mean.

From the regression equation $Y_e = \bar{Y} + bx$ we get $Y_e - \bar{Y} = bx$ or $y_e = bx$. From the graph we know that $y_d = y - y_e = y - bx$. Therefore

$$\Sigma(y_d y_e) = \Sigma(y - bx)bx = b\Sigma xy - b^2\Sigma x^2$$

From equation (3) it is seen that we can substitute $b\Sigma x^2$ for Σxy, and it is then obvious that

$$\Sigma(y_d y_e) = 0 \qquad 6$$

Thus the third term on the right in (5) vanishes, and we have

$$\Sigma y^2 = \Sigma y_e^2 + \Sigma y_d^2 \qquad 7$$

which is a very important generalization. It shows that the total sum of squares of Y can be partitioned into one part representing regression and a second part representing deviations from regression.

The next step is to decide on the degrees of freedom to be associated with each sum of squares. The clue is given by the number of statistics calculated from the sample in order to obtain $\Sigma(y_e^2)$, which in turn is wholly dependent on the regression equation, $y_e = bx$. The regression coefficient is the one additional statistic required to define this equation; therefore $\Sigma(y_e^2)$ is represented by 1 degree of freedom. This gives us the basis for setting up an analysis of variance as follows.

	SS	DF	MS
Total	$\Sigma(y^2)$	$n-1$	
Regression	$\Sigma(y_e^2)$	1	V_e
Deviations from regression	$\Sigma(y_d^2)$	$n-2$	V_d

A test of significance is then given by calculating $F = V_e/V_d$ and noting the 5% point of F for 1 and $n - 2$ degrees of freedom. This amounts to testing whether or not b differs significantly from zero.

The significance of b can be tested directly by means of the t test. Let

$$s_e = \sqrt{\frac{\Sigma(y_d^2)}{n-2}} \qquad 8$$

where s_e is referred to as the standard error of estimate. Then the standard error of the regression coefficient is

$$s_b = \frac{s_e}{\sqrt{\Sigma(x^2)}} = \sqrt{\frac{\Sigma(y_d^2)}{(n-2)\Sigma(x^2)}} \qquad 9$$

and

$$t = \frac{b}{s_b} \qquad 10$$

It is easily verified that the two tests of significance are identical since $F = t^2$ when the mean square tested is estimated from 1 degree of freedom.

4. Fiducial limits of the regression coefficient. The general expression for t in testing a regression coefficient is

$$\pm t = \frac{(b-\beta)}{s_b} \qquad 11$$

where β is the regression coefficient of any hypothetical population that we choose to take. In other words, we can take $\beta = 0$ in the ordinary test of significance which involves the hypothesis that b has arisen by random sampling from a population in which $\beta = 0$. This allows us to set up fiducial limits for b. Thus

$$\beta = b \pm ts_b \qquad 12$$

and to obtain the fiducial limits at the 5% point we take

$$l_1 = b - t_{0.05}s_b \qquad l_2 = b + t_{0.05}s_b \qquad 13$$

where $t_{0.05}$ is the value of t given in the tables for $p = 0.05$ and degrees of freedom equal to $n - 2$.

5. Standard error of estimated Y. The term standard error of estimate should not lead one to think that it is to be applied to the accuracy of an estimate of Y. The standard error of estimate applies specifically, as we have seen in applying the t test, to variation in the regression coefficient. It may be necessary, however, to make a test of significance or set up fiducial limits for Y_e. From the regression equation $Y_e = \bar{Y} + bx$ it can be seen that the mean square of Y depends upon variation in $\bar{Y}$ and bx for which the separate mean squares are s_e^2/n and $(s_e^2/\Sigma x^2)x^2$, and these must be added to obtain the mean square for Y, giving

$$s_{Y_e}{}^2 = \frac{s_e{}^2}{n} + \left(\frac{s_e{}^2}{\Sigma x^2}\right) x^2 = s_e{}^2 \left(\frac{1}{n} + \frac{x^2}{\Sigma x^2}\right) \qquad 14$$

For purposes of calculation it is convenient to put

$$s_{Y_e}{}^2 = \frac{\Sigma(y_d{}^2)}{n-2}\left(\frac{1}{n} + \frac{x^2}{\Sigma x^2}\right) \qquad 15$$

From this equation is it clear that $s_{Y_e}{}^2$ is a minimum when $x = (X - \bar{X}) = 0$, that is, when the value of X for which Y_e is being predicted is equal to its mean. As X varies from its mean, the mean square of Y_e increases.

The regression line represents estimates of values of Y for given values of X in the population sampled, and the standard error as given in (14) may be used to set up fiducial limits on both sides of the regression line. It is quite another problem to select a given X and use the regression equation to predict the corresponding Y. For example, a regression problem may involve studying the regression of weight on age for pigs. For pigs of a given age X_1 we may predict by means of the regression equation that their average weight would be Y_1. This is a problem of estimation for the population, and to set up fiducial limits the standard error required would be that of equation (14). Now if we wish to select an individual pig of age X_1 and make an estimate of its weight, the answer would again be Y_1, but the error of such an estimate is greater and is given by

$$s'_{Y_e} = s_e{}^2 \left(1 + \frac{1}{n} + \frac{x^2}{\Sigma x^2}\right) \qquad 16$$

6. Linear regression when both variables are subject to error. In the example described above it was assumed that the data were taken from an experiment involving different levels of application of a fertilizer. Probably the more usual case is to have a series of pairs of values of the two variates X and Y, and it is required to determine the regression line for predicting Y from X. For this situation it should be noted that the assumption is that X can be measured without error. Suppose that X is percentage disease infection and Y is yield and the data are obtained from a series of plots. It is assumed that the percentage infection on each plot can be determined accurately, and generally this is close enough to being true not to influence the value of the regression coefficient. However, if we estimate the percentage of disease by means of a small sample, there will be a definite error in determining X and the regression coefficient will be biased accordingly.

In this connection Yates [7] makes the following statement. "Errors in the independent variates do not affect the validity of the ordinary tests of significance, provided that only differences from zero are being tested, and the coefficients as ordinarily evaluated will always be the best coefficients for the purpose of prediction from subsequent observations subject to similar errors." He points out further that errors in the independent variable introduce a bias which generally reduces the absolute value of the regression coefficient. Therefore a value of b that is biased cannot strictly be compared with a theoretical population value β if the dependent variable is subject to error. This would naturally affect the theory of setting up fiducial limits. The general problem of dealing with and making tests of significance when the dependent variable is subject to error is fairly complex, so it is not feasible to describe it in detail here. For a complete discussion and methods of fitting, refer to Deming [1].

7. Calculation of linear regressions for ungrouped data. The simplest situation occurs when there is a series of pairs of values of X and Y. We might have, for example,

$$\begin{matrix} X_1 & X_2 & X_3 \cdots X_i \cdots X_n \\ Y_1 & X_2 & X_3 \cdots Y_i \cdots Y_n \end{matrix}$$

and wish to obtain the regression equation $Y_e = a + bx$. Ordinarily we would not group the data unless we have about 50 or more pairs. A suitable method of calculation is to obtain directly from the paired values ΣX, ΣY, and ΣXY. Then we calculate

$$\Sigma x^2 = \Sigma X^2 - \frac{(\Sigma X)^2}{n}$$

$$\Sigma y^2 = \Sigma Y^2 - \frac{(\Sigma Y)^2}{n}$$

$$\Sigma xy = \Sigma XY - \frac{(\Sigma X)(\Sigma Y)}{n}$$

and finally

$$b = \frac{\Sigma xy}{\Sigma x^2}$$

A test of significance can be made from the analysis of variance where the corresponding sums of squares and degrees of freedom are

$$\Sigma y^2 = \frac{(\Sigma xy)^2}{\Sigma x^2} + \Sigma(y_d^2) \qquad 17$$

$$n - 1 = \quad 1 \quad + (n - 2) \qquad 18$$

If we wish to set up fiducial limits for b we determine s_b as in formulas (8) and (9), and proceed as in Section 4.

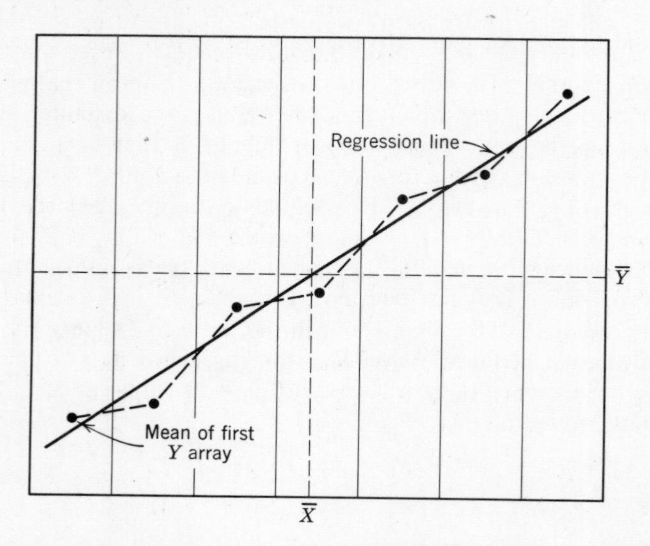

FIGURE 6–4. Graph of means of arrays from a regression table.

8. Linear regression for data arranged in a regression table. A regression analysis can always be carried through by the method described in Section 7, but when there are more than 50 pairs it is more convenient to arrange the data in a table similar to Table 6–1. There is another advantage in setting up a table of this kind as it enables us to make a test of the significance of deviations from linear regression.

Representing the regression table diagrammatically as in Figure 6–4, we can then show an enlarged section of one of the arrays of Y, as in Figure 6–5, together with a single observation. Then y can be broken up into $y_p + y_d + y_e$, where y_p is the deviation of an individual observation from the mean of the array, y_d is the deviation from regression of the mean of an array, and y_e is the deviation of the regression line from the mean of Y. It may be proved easily* that the total sum of squares and degrees of freedom can be expressed as

$$\sum_{1}^{N} y^2 = \sum_{1}^{q} n_p y_e^2 + \sum_{1}^{q} n_p y_d^2 + \sum_{1}^{q}\sum_{1}^{n_p} y_p^2 \qquad 19$$

$$N - 1 = 1 + (q - 2) + (N - q) \qquad 20$$

$$\text{Total} = \text{Regression} + \text{Deviations} + \text{Error}$$

where n_p is the frequency in a Y array, q is the number of arrays, and N is the total number of pairs of observations. From these expressions it

---

* In one array

$$\sum_{1}^{n_p} y^2 = \sum_{1}^{n_p} (y_p + y_t)^2 = \sum_{1}^{n_p} y_p^2 + n_p y_t^2 + 2\sum_{1}^{n_p} y_p y_t$$

and, since y_t is constant for the array, and $\sum_{1}^{n_p} y_p = 0$, it follows that

$$\sum_{1}^{n_p} y_p y_t = 0. \quad \text{Then}$$

$$\sum_{1}^{n_p} y^2 = \sum_{1}^{n_p} y_p^2 + n_p y_t^2$$

Over all q arrays where $\sum_{1}^{q} n_p = N$

$$\sum_{1}^{N} y^2 = \sum_{1}^{q}\sum_{1}^{n_p} y_p^2 + \sum_{1}^{q} n_p y_t^2$$

which is a familiar expression of the analysis representing the sum of squares for total within, and between arrays. The corresponding degrees of freedom are

$$N - 1 = (N - q) + (q - 1)$$

It remains to show that the sum of squares for between arrays can be broken up into two parts, representing linear regression and deviations from linear regression.

Over all arrays

$$\sum_{1}^{q} n_p y_t^2 = \sum_{1}^{q} n_p (y_d + y_e)^2 = \sum_{1}^{q} n_p y_d^2 + \sum_{1}^{q} n_p y_e^2 + 2\sum_{1}^{q} n_p (y_d y_e)$$

which is equivalent to equation (5), Section 3, and would reduce to that equation if n_p were constant for all arrays. Therefore $\sum_{1}^{q} n_p (y_d y_e) = 0$, and the complete expression for sums of squares with corresponding degrees of freedom is as given in (19) and (20).

can be seen that a test of significance can be made either for regression or deviations from regression.

It is recommended that in a regression analysis the tests of significance as outlined be performed first. If the mean square for linear regression is not significant, there is no object in fitting a straight line. If the mean square for deviations from regression is significant, the indications are that some function other than that of a straight line will give a better fit.

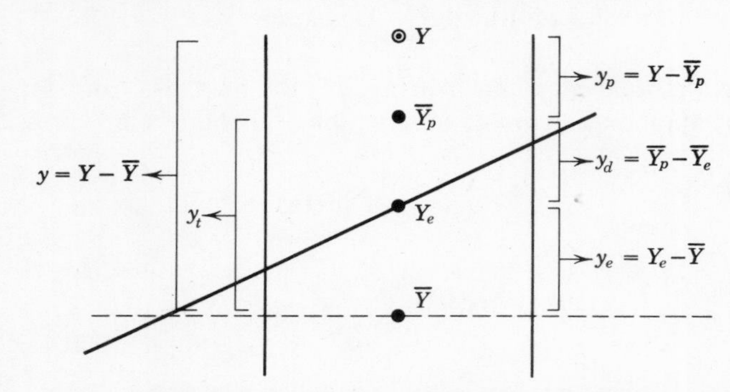

FIGURE 6–5. Section of regression graph showing deviation of individual variate from the mean of Y, broken down into three parts.

This is of course true even if the mean square for linear regression is also significant.

9. Calculations for a regression table. The easiest way to learn how to do the calculations is to follow through Example 6–2. This example explains also how to proceed in setting up the table itself.

In many examples the labor of calculation can be reduced by coding the data. This involves either subtracting a uniform quantity from the values of each individual variate or dividing by a constant quantity, or in certain cases both devices may be employed at the same time. Suppose that the actual values are as given below on the left; the values on the right are examples of how the coding may be carried out.

Uncoded		Coded		
X	Y	X	Y	
2402	2785	240	278	Dividing by 10 and rounding off last figure
		40	78	Subtracting 200
198	196	8	6	Subtracting 190
195	193	5	3	
256	274	56	74	Subtracting 200, but in general avoid negative
229	198	29	−2	values if a machine is available for calculation

10. Example 6–1. Regression analysis on a series of paired values. In a hypothetical example the values for 10 pairs of variates are as given below.

X	9	8	7	7	6	4	3	3	1	2	$\Sigma X = 50$	$\bar{X} = 5.0$
Y	7	9	7	8	7	3	6	1	2	2	$\Sigma Y = 52$	$\bar{Y} = 5.2$

To find the sums of squares of both sets of variates and the sums of products, we proceed as follows.

$$\Sigma XY = (9 \times 7) + (8 \times 9) + \cdots + (2 \times 2) = 321$$

$$\frac{\Sigma X \Sigma Y}{N} = \frac{50 \times 52}{10} = 260$$

$$\text{Difference} = \Sigma xy = 61$$

$$\Sigma Y^2 = 7^2 + 9^2 + \cdots + 2^2 = 346$$

$$\frac{(\Sigma Y)^2}{N} = \frac{(52)^2}{10} = 270.4$$

$$\text{Difference} = \Sigma y^2 = 75.6$$

$$\Sigma X^2 = 9^2 + 8^2 + \cdots + 2^2 = 318$$

$$\frac{(\Sigma X)^2}{N} = \frac{(50)^2}{10} = 250$$

$$\text{Difference} = \Sigma x^2 = 68$$

Then the sum of squares for linear regression is

$$\frac{(\Sigma xy)^2}{\Sigma x^2} = \frac{(61)^2}{68} = 54.72$$

We can then set up the analysis of variance.

	SS	DF	MS	F
Regression	54.72	1	54.72	20.97
Error or deviations from regression	20.88	8	2.610	
Total	75.60	9		

Since the regression is very significant, we proceed to obtain the regression coefficient given by

$$b_{yx} = \frac{\Sigma xy}{\Sigma x^2} = \frac{61}{68} = 0.8971$$

and the regression equation is

$$Y_e = (\bar{Y} - b\bar{X}) + bX$$

$$= (5.2 - 0.8971 \times 5.0) + 0.8971X$$

$$= 0.7145 + 0.8971X$$

The fiducial limits of b_{yx} at the 5% point are given by

$$l_1 = b - t_{0.05}s_b \qquad l_2 = b + t_{0.05}s_b$$

where $s_b = \sqrt{20.88/(8 \times 68)} = 0.1959$ and $t_{0.05}$ is 2.31, the value of t at the 5% point for $n_1 = 1$ and $n_2 = 8$. Here we have

$$l_1 = 0.8971 - 2.31 \times 0.1959 = 0.4446$$

$$l_2 = 0.8971 + 2.31 \times 0.1959 = 1.3496$$

The standard error of estimates of yield for different levels of fertilizer can be determined from equation (15). In general

$$s_{Ye}^2 = \frac{20.88}{8}\left(\frac{1}{10} + \frac{x^2}{68.00}\right) = 0.2610 + 0.0384x^2$$

Then for $x = 0$ $\qquad s_{Ye} = \sqrt{0.2610} = 0.511$

$x = 2$ $\qquad s_{Ye} = \sqrt{0.4146} = 0.644$

$x = 4$ $\qquad s_{Ye} = \sqrt{0.8754} = 0.936$

From these calculations it is evident that there is a much greater possibility of error in estimating values of Y near the ends of the regression line.

11. Example 6–2. Regression analysis for a large series of paired values set up in a regression table. When dealing within a large number of variates, it is convenient to make up a frequency table in order to summarize the data and reduce the labor of calculating the mean and standard deviation. Similarly, in regression studies, for a large series of paired values, it is desirable to make up a table that combines the frequency tables of the two variates. In the next chapter we shall see also that this table is of value for calculating the correlation coefficient.

To prepare the table it is convenient to copy the paired values on cards of a size that can be handled easily. Thus if we decided to make up a table for the carotene data of Table 6–4, the cards for the first three pairs would be as follows.

First Card		Second Card		Third Card	
X	1.18	X	2.13	X	1.41
Y	2.39	Y	3.11	Y	2.15

After deciding on the class values as outlined in Chapter 2, Section 9, distribute the cards for one of the variables, preferably Y, and then distribute each pile for the second variable. As each pile is distributed the frequencies can be entered in the appropriate cell of the table.

Table 6–1 was prepared in the above manner for readings on the transparency and area of 400 red blood cells from a normal patient (Savage et al. [4]). The transparency values are in arbitrary units based on deflections of a galvanometer operated by a photoelectric cell. Notice that in the margins the actual class values have been replaced by a series of natural numbers beginning with 1. This is a form of coding which reduces the labor of calculation.

After setting up the regression table it is convenient to set up a table similar to Table 6–2 for entering values to be used later. For the column headed "Totals, Y Arrays" proceed to obtain the totals for each array as follows, where the first array of Y is the distribution of the Y variates that fall in the first class for X.

First array $(1 \times 7) + (2 \times 4) = 15$

Second array $(2 \times 8) + (2 \times 7) + (3 \times 6) + (1 \times 3) = 51$

etc.

The total for this column is obviously ΣY. In the same way obtain the totals for the X arrays and ΣX. There are two columns headed ΣXY, the object being to calculate ΣXY in two ways in order to have a complete check on the calculations. The entries in the first ΣXY column are obtained by multiplying the totals for the Y arrays by the corresponding class values of X. In the second ΣXY column multiply the totals for the X arrays by the corresponding class values of Y. We have to calculate also ΣY^2 and ΣX^2, the method being the same as outlined in Chapter 2 for any frequency distribution. If a calculating machine is available, it is most convenient to summate these as we multiply frequencies by squares of corresponding class values. ΣXY may also be obtained by a process of continuous multiplication and summation on the machine, and in that case the individual entries as in Table 6–2 can be omitted.

In this example we have

$$\Sigma XY = 18{,}345.0000 \qquad \Sigma Y^2 = 27{,}509.0000 \qquad \Sigma X^2 = 13{,}337.0000$$

$$\frac{\Sigma X \Sigma Y}{N} = 17{,}679.5325 \qquad \frac{(\Sigma Y)^2}{N} = 25{,}808.4225 \qquad \frac{(\Sigma X)^2}{N} = 12{,}111.0025$$

$$\Sigma xy = 665.4675 \qquad \Sigma y^2 = 1{,}700.5775 \qquad \Sigma x^2 = 1{,}225.9975$$

At this stage we may omit the calculations leading to the test of the significance of deviations from regression, in which case the regression analysis can be set up directly after calculating the sum of squares for regression given by

$$\text{SS (regression)} = \frac{(\Sigma xy)^2}{\Sigma x^2} = \frac{(665.47)^2}{1226.00} = 361.22$$

Analysis of Variance

	SS	DF	MS
Regression	361.22	1	361.22
Error	1339.36	398	3.3652
Total	1700.58	399	

The F value is very large, so its calculation can be omitted.

The regression coefficient is given by

$$b = \frac{\Sigma xy}{\Sigma x^2} = \frac{665.47}{1226.00} = 0.5428$$

and the regression equation is

$$\begin{aligned} Y_e &= (\bar{Y} - b_{yx}\bar{X}) + bX \\ &= (8.0325 - 0.5428 \times 5.5025) + 0.5428X \\ &= 5.0457 + 0.5428X \end{aligned}$$

If a graph is required, calculate two values of Y_e, preferably for $X = 1$ and $X = 12$, and locate the regression line accordingly. The standard error of b_{yx} is given by

$$s_b = \sqrt{\frac{3.3652}{1226.00}} = \sqrt{0.002745} = 0.0524$$

The fiducial limits of b_{yx} at the 5% point are

$$l_1 = 0.5428 - 1.97 \times 0.0524 = 0.4396$$

$$l_2 = 0.5428 + 1.97 \times 0.0524 = 0.6460$$

In order to make a test of deviations from regression we require the total of the last column of Table 6–2. Each entry in this column is the square of the total for a Y array, divided by the corresponding frequency. Thus

$$75.00 = \frac{15^2}{3} \qquad 325.12 = \frac{51^2}{8} \qquad \text{etc.}$$

This gives the sum of squares for between arrays as follows. See equation (19).

$$\Sigma n_p Y_d^2 = 26{,}181.23$$

$$\frac{(\Sigma Y)^2}{N} = 25{,}808.42$$

$$\Sigma n_p y_d^2 = 372.81$$

The complete analysis can then be set up.

	SS	DF	MS
Regression	361.22	1	361.2
Deviations from regression	11.59	10	1.159
Error	1327.77	387	3.431
Total	1700.58		

The deviations from regression are less than expectation, so there is no object in calculating a value of F.

The depression in deviations from regression can in fact be shown to be statistically significant. The ratio 3.431/1.159 = 2.96 exceeds the 5% point for 387 and 10 degrees of freedom. Such a result should lead the experimenter to a closer examination of the data in order to find the reason for the unusually close fit of the means of the arrays to the straight line. In this example, since we have only the bare figures and no details of the experiment, we can only conclude that the close fit may be merely a random occurrence.

It should be pointed out here that, had the deviations from regression proved significant, the method of setting up of the fiducial limits for b would not have been quite appropriate since the sum of squares used for

TABLE 6–1

DATA FOR REGRESSION OF TRANSPARENCY (Y) ON AREA (X) FOR 400 HUMAN BLOOD CELLS

	Frequency X	3	8	36	65	96	90	53	31	10	4	3	1	400 = n
14	0.691–0.720										1			1
13	0.661–0.690													0
12	0.631–0.660				1	1	3	1	1				1	8
11	0.601–0.630			1	3	3	6	5	4	2	2	3		29
10	0.571–0.600			4	5	13	16	11	12	3	1			65
9	0.541–0.570			4	8	14	21	15	6	3				71
8	0.511–0.540		2	4	13	29	21	12	3	2				86
7	0.481–0.510	1	2	6	10	17	10	4	4					54
6	0.451–0.480		3	5	8	8	8	4						36
5	0.421–0.450			5	12	7	2							26
4	0.391–0.420	2		3	3	3	3	1						15
3	0.361–0.390		1	3	1	1			1					7
2	0.331–0.360													0
1	0.301–0.330			1	1									2
	Actual classes	27–29	30–32	33–35	36–38	39–41	42–44	45–47	48–50	51–53	54–56	57–59	60–62	Frequency Y
	Coded classes	1	2	3	4	5	6	7	8	9	10	11	12	

TABLE 6–2

CALCULATIONS FOR REGRESSION ANALYSIS, DATA OF TABLE 6–1

Y	Frequency Y	X	Frequency X	Totals, Y Arrays	$\Sigma(XY)$	Totals, X Arrays	$\Sigma(XY)$	SS Between Arrays
1	2	1	3	15	15	7	7	75.00
2	0	2	8	51	102	0	0	325.12
3	7	3	36	238	714	28	84	1,573.44
4	15	4	65	465	1,860	63	252	3,326.54
5	26	5	96	750	3,750	110	550	5,859.38
6	36	6	90	759	4,554	169	1,014	6,400.90
7	54	7	53	464	3,248	268	1,876	4,062.19
8	86	8	31	285	2,280	465	3,720	2,620.16
9	71	9	10	95	855	420	3,780	902.50
10	65	10	4	46	460	403	4,030	529.00
11	29	11	3	33	363	204	2,244	363.00
12	8	12	1	12	144	54	648	144.00
13	0					0		
14	1					10	140	
	400		400	3,213	18,345	2,201	18,345	26,181.23
	n		n	ΣY	ΣXY	ΣX	ΣXY	$\Sigma np(Y_d^2)$

the error term included deviations from regression. With the present analysis the procedure of obtaining fiducial limits for b would be to use the error mean square 3.431. Thus

$$s = \sqrt{\frac{3.431}{1226.00}} = 0.0529$$

Then

$$l_1 = 0.5428 - 1.97 \times 0.0529 = 0.4386$$

$$l_2 = 0.5428 + 1.97 \times 0.0529 = 0.6740$$

Since the deviations from regression are not significant, the fiducial limits agree closely with those obtained previously.

12. Exercises.

1. Table 6–3 gives the results obtained in an experiment with 25 wheat varieties on the number of days from seeding to heading and the number of days from seeding to maturity. Calculate the regression equation for the regression of days to mature on days to head, and test the significance of the regression coefficient. Code the data before beginning your calculations by subtracting 50 from the days to head and 85 from the days to mature. Find the fiducial limits at the 5% point of the regression coefficient, and decide as to the practicability of substituting days to head for days to mature, on the basis of the data provided by this sample.

Regression coefficient = 105.23/125.68 = 0.8373 (coded data).

TABLE 6–3

DATA ON DAYS TO HEAD AND DAYS TO MATURE OF 25 WHEAT VARIETIES

Variety	Days to Head	Days to Mature	Variety	Days to Head	Days to Mature
1	60.0	94.4	14	58.2	92.4
2	53.6	89.0	15	58.0	91.6
3	59.0	94.0	16	59.4	94.0
4	61.8	95.4	17	55.4	90.8
5	53.8	88.2	18	61.6	95.2
6	57.8	93.4	19	63.0	97.2
7	57.8	93.6	20	60.2	94.6
8	58.4	92.0	21	61.6	96.0
9	57.8	92.8	22	57.6	92.6
10	59.0	93.4	23	60.8	95.4
11	59.2	93.8	24	61.2	94.4
12	59.0	92.8	25	58.2	94.0
13	58.6	94.2			

TABLE 6–4

CAROTENE CONTENT OF FLOUR AND WHOLE WHEAT FOR 139 VARIETIES

Variety	Carotene in Flour	Carotene in Wheat	Variety	Carotene in Flour	Carotene in Wheat	Variety	Carotene in Flour	Carotene in Wheat
1	2.39	1.18	48	1.71	1.16	95	1.97	1.33
2	3.11	2.13	49	1.93	1.14	96	1.83	1.14
3	2.15	1.41	50	1.81	1.30	97	2.00	1.51
4	1.96	1.42	51	1.89	1.32	98	1.96	1.28
5	2.02	1.50	52	1.65	1.32	99	2.00	1.33
6	1.76	1.25	53	1.93	1.28	100	2.02	1.32
7	2.10	1.65	54	2.12	1.48	101	1.78	1.17
8	2.12	1.24	55	2.25	1.50	102	1.83	1.10
9	2.28	1.48	56	1.92	1.42	103	1.93	1.22
10	1.86	1.35	57	2.25	1.66	104	2.14	1.44
11	2.60	1.58	58	2.25	1.63	105	2.15	1.54
12	2.11	1.45	59	1.65	1.18	106	2.13	1.46
13	2.30	1.74	60	1.63	1.14	107	1.97	1.40
14	1.80	1.42	61	1.70	1.22	108	1.83	1.11
15	2.00	1.45	62	1.61	1.20	109	2.10	1.40
16	2.05	1.87	63	1.83	1.33	110	1.84	1.19
17	2.09	2.00	64	1.60	1.13	111	1.98	1.39
18	2.33	1.65	65	1.37	0.92	112	2.31	1.60
19	2.29	1.64	66	1.96	1.20	113	2.29	1.53
20	2.30	1.62	67	1.88	1.26	114	2.15	1.45
21	1.97	1.55	68	1.92	1.34	115	1.96	1.44
22	2.36	1.68	69	1.89	1.04	116	1.98	1.40
23	1.73	1.32	70	1.99	1.26	117	1.89	1.30
24	1.72	1.47	71	1.82	0.98	118	2.08	1.33
25	1.70	1.53	72	2.12	1.31	119	2.00	1.42
26	1.63	1.50	73	2.16	1.16	120	2.06	1.44
27	1.93	1.48	74	2.14	1.04	121	1.96	1.36
28	1.50	1.25	75	1.63	0.88	122	2.07	1.38
29	1.77	1.33	76	2.76	1.91	123	2.24	1.51
30	1.60	1.40	77	2.07	1.20	124	2.15	1.38
31	2.31	1.49	78	1.67	1.07	125	1.83	1.18
32	2.17	1.42	79	2.78	1.80	126	1.84	1.20
33	2.10	1.35	80	3.40	2.02	127	2.03	1.45
34	2.90	1.58	81	3.67	2.10	128	1.87	1.05
35	2.17	1.50	82	2.41	1.61	129	2.24	1.44
36	2.15	1.40	83	2.23	1.38	130	2.14	1.06
37	2.01	1.40	84	3.07	1.93	131	2.13	1.10
38	2.35	1.67	85	2.22	1.44	132	2.03	0.98
39	2.34	1.62	86	2.55	1.58	133	2.25	1.31
40	2.00	1.47	87	2.12	1.39	134	2.33	1.08
41	2.18	1.55	88	1.94	1.27	135	2.01	1.14
42	2.47	1.73	89	1.95	1.41	136	1.89	1.41
43	2.25	1.62	90	1.59	1.08	137	3.00	2.20
44	1.77	1.39	91	2.00	1.30	138	2.16	1.73
45	1.68	1.34	92	1.77	1.22	139	2.29	1.61
46	2.46	1.29	93	1.98	1.26			
47	1.86	1.28	94	1.97	1.30			

2. Table 6–4 contains data on the carotene content determined by two methods for 139 wheat varieties. By one method carotene was determined on the whole wheat, and by the other method, on the flour. The figures for carotene in the wheat are lower than for carotene in the flour, which is of course the reverse of the actual condition. This was due to a different method of extraction for the whole wheat which gave lower but relative results.

Make out cards, one for each pair of values, and prepare a regression table, letting the flour carotene represent the dependent variable Y. In order to reduce the labor of calculation make the classes fairly large; for example, let the first class for X be 0.85 to 0.95, and the first class for Y be 1.33 to 1.49. Also do not forget to replace the actual class values by the natural numbers, beginning at 1, before going ahead with the calculations. Determine the regression equation, and prepare a regression graph.

$b_{yx} = 438.39/665.96 = 0.6583$ *(coded data).*

3. Prove (*a*) $\Sigma xy = \Sigma XY - \dfrac{\Sigma X \Sigma Y}{n}$

$$(b)\quad \Sigma(Y - Y_e)^2 = \Sigma y^2 - b_{yx}^2 \Sigma x^2$$
$$= \Sigma y^2 - b \Sigma xy$$

REFERENCES

1. W. Edwards Deming, *Statistical Adjustment of Data*, John Wiley and Sons, New York, 1943.
2. M. Ezekiel, *Methods of Correlation Analysis*, John Wiley and Sons, New York, 2nd ed., 1941.
3. R. A. Fisher, *Statistical Methods for Research Workers*, Oliver and Boyd, London and Edinburgh, 10th ed., 1948.
4. A. Savage, C. H. Goulden, and J. M. Isa, *Can. J. Research*, **12**, 803–811, 1935.
5. G. W. Snedecor, *Statistical Methods*, Iowa State College Press, Ames, Iowa, 4th ed., 1946.
6. L. H. C. Tippett, *The Methods of Statistics*, Williams and Norgate, London, 1931.
7. F. Yates, *Proc. Roy. Soc. Edinburgh*, **59**, 184–194, Session 1938–39.

CHAPTER 7

Correlation

1. Covariation. This term is very expressive of the fundamental situation regarding two variables, from which the methods of correlation arise. In the previous chapter it was pointed out that, when two variables are so related that one may logically be considered as dependent on the other, the methods of regression are completely applicable to an analysis of this relation; but, when the two variables cannot be considered as dependent and independent, regression methods are not fully satisfactory. Suppose that a study is to be made of the relation between the heights of brothers and sisters. It would not be logical to consider the height of one member of the pair as being dependent on the height of the other, yet we may be fairly certain that the two variables are in some way related, and wish to measure the relation and be able to compare it in some logical manner with other similar relations. The question most frequently asked with respect to two such variables is: To what extent do the heights of brother and sister vary together? Thus we have the term *covariation*, and the conventional statistic for the measurement of covariation is the *correlation coefficient*.

2. Definition of correlation. Table 7–1 presents three sets of figures that may be taken as measurements on 2 variables which we shall designate

TABLE 7–1

THREE SAMPLES OF PAIRED VARIATES ILLUSTRATING THE PHENOMENON OF CORRELATION

Set 1	X_1	7	7	1	6	5	3	8	9	3	1	Total = 50
	X_2	5	9	6	1	3	1	9	4	6	8	Total = 52
Set 2	X_1	9	8	7	7	6	5	3	3	1	1	Total = 50
	X_2	9	9	8	6	6	5	4	3	1	1	Total = 52
Set 3	X_1	1	1	3	3	5	6	7	7	8	9	Total = 50
	X_2	9	9	8	6	6	5	4	3	1	1	Total = 52

as X_1 and X_2. On examining these, it will be noted that the relation between X_1 and X_2 is different in each. In set 2 high values of X_1 are associated with high values of X_2, and in set 3 high values of X_1 are associated with low values of X_2. In both sets there is an obvious relation, but one is the reverse of the other. In set 1, on the other hand, the 2 variables do not appear to be related. These sets may be regarded as samples from infinite parent populations of paired variables. In the population from which set 2 is drawn, whenever a pair of variates is selected at random,

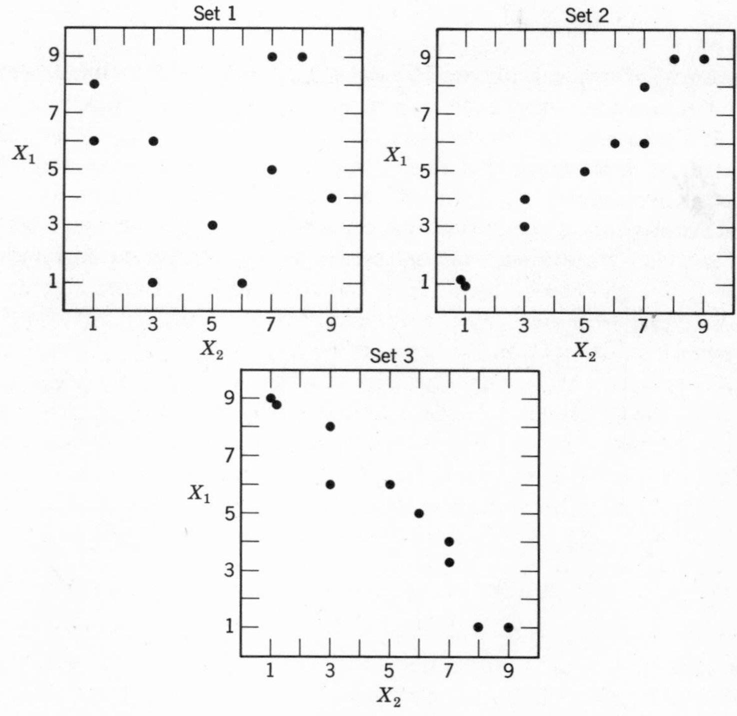

FIGURE 7–1. Scatter diagrams for data of Table 7–1.

we expect to find, if the pair contains a high value of X_1, that a high value of X_2 will be associated with it. In the population represented by the sample in set 3, it is to be expected that high values of X_1 will be found associated with low values of X_2. These two opposite situations are referred to as positive and negative correlation. Set 1 represents still another situation. High values of X_1 do not appear to be associated with either high or low values of X_2. In other words, it is to be expected that in the parent populations the 2 variables vary independently. A graphical picture of the results with these 3 samples is given in Figure 7–1. Each sample is represented by what is usually known as a *dot* or *scatter diagram*. The values of X_1 are represented as ordinates and the values of X_2 as abscissas, so that each pair can be represented by a dot on the diagram. The final result is a figure that represents in a general way, by the scatter of the dots, the relation between the 2 variables. For set 1 the dots are scattered more or less uniformly over the whole surface. For sets 2 and 3 there is a definite relation between the variables, as shown by the tendency for the dots to arrange themselves in a straight line along the diagonals of the square. We are reminded here of the regression graphs of the previous chapter. The difference is that we are now studying not the effect of one variable on the other, but rather the degree to which the variables vary together owing presumably to influences that are common to both. If such measurements represent heights of brothers and sisters, it is apparent that this common influence might be the similarity of their genes.

3. Measurement of correlation. Figure 7–2 illustrates the shape of the swarm in a correlation surface for three different degrees of correlation.

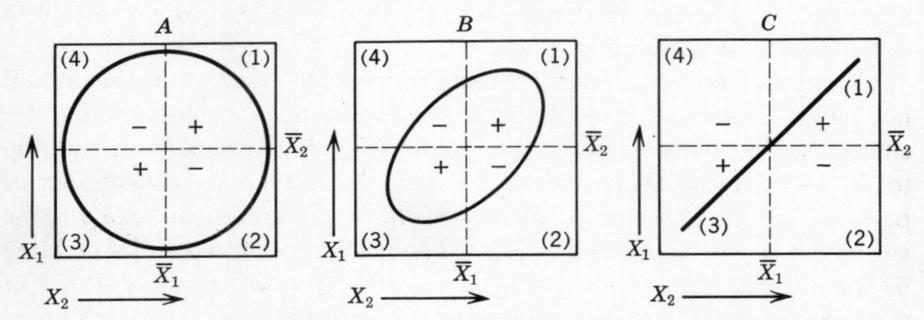

FIGURE 7–2. Correlation surfaces showing variation in shape of swarm with increasing correlation.

The circular swarm at *A* represents zero correlation; in *C* the swarm falls entirely on the diagonal and must represent perfect correlation; *B* shows a condition between the other two extremes. Now each surface is divided into quadrants by lines erected at the positions of the means, and in each quadrant are plus and minus signs representing the signs of the products of the X_1 and X_2 deviations from their means. Thus in the upper right-hand quadrant (1) the deviations of X_1 and X_2 are both positive so that the product of the deviations is positive. Therefore products are positive in quadrants (1) and (3) and negative in (2) and (4). Now it is obvious in *A* that the plus and minus products will cancel each other and the sum will be zero. In *C* all the products will be positive so that their sum will be a maximum. In *B* the condition is intermediate between *A* and *C*. The plus products are greater than the negative products; hence we have a positive but not a perfect correlation.

Let us consider now the sets of figures in Table 7–1. On calculating the sum of products $\Sigma x_1 x_2$ for each set, we find agreement with the theory outlined above. To carry out these calculations we make use of the identity

$$\Sigma x_1 x_2 = \Sigma X_1 X_2 - \frac{\Sigma X_1 \Sigma X_2}{n} \qquad 1$$

where ΣX_1 is the sum of the X_1 values, ΣX_2 is the sum of the X_2 values, and n is the number of pairs. The calculations come out as follows

	$\Sigma X_1 X_2$	$\frac{\Sigma X_1 \Sigma X_2}{n}$	$\Sigma x_1 x_2$
Set 1	262	260	2
Set 2	335	260	75
Set 3	186	260	– 74

The result is in perfect agreement with the theory that the sum of products is a measure of correlation.

The sum of products is an absolute measure of correlation, but it will not serve as a relative measure because it is dependent on factors that are characteristic of the data for the individual variables and have nothing to do with the correlation between them. It depends on the number of pairs of variates measured, on the units of measurement, and on the variability of both variables. The first objection is overcome by dividing by the degrees of freedom, giving $\Sigma x_1 x_2/(n-1)$ which we now define as the *covariance*. It can be represented by the symbol u_{12}. To overcome the other difficulties we express the variates in what is known as standard measure. If a variate is represented by X, in standard measure it is

$$d = \frac{X - \bar{X}}{s_X} = \frac{x}{s_X}$$

where s_X is the standard deviation of the sample. Thus we have finally

$$r_{12} = \frac{\Sigma(x_1/s_1)(x_2/s_2)}{n-1} = \frac{\Sigma(x_1 x_2)/(n-1)}{s_1 s_2} = \frac{u_{12}}{s_1 s_2} \qquad 2$$

Another formula, giving the variances of X_1 and X_2 in place of their standard deviations, is

$$r_{12} = \frac{\Sigma(x_1 x_2)/(n-1)}{\sqrt{v_1 v_2}} \qquad 3$$

where v_1 is the variance of X_1, and v_2 is the variance of X_2. Since the regression coefficient

$$b_{12} = \frac{\Sigma x_1 x_2}{\Sigma x_2^2} = \frac{\Sigma x_1 x_2/(n-1)}{\Sigma x_2^2/(n-1)} = \frac{u_{12}}{v_2}$$

and

$$b_{21} = \frac{u_{12}}{v_1}$$

formula (3) shows also that

$$r_{12}^2 = \frac{u_{12}}{v_2} \times \frac{u_{12}}{v_1} = b_{12}b_{21}$$

and

$$r_{12} = \sqrt{b_{12}b_{21}} \qquad 4$$

The correlation coefficient is therefore the geometric mean of the two regression coefficients.

4. Range and interpretation of the correlation coefficient. If we take

$$d_1 = \frac{x_1}{s_1} \qquad \text{and} \qquad d_2 = \frac{x_2}{s_2}$$

the correlation coefficient can be written neatly as

$$r_{12} = \frac{\Sigma(d_1 d_2)}{n-1} \qquad 5$$

and we can then prove very easily that*

$$r_{12} = 1 - \frac{\Sigma(d_1 - d_2)^2}{2(n-1)} \qquad 6$$

---

* Expanding the term on the right in (6), we have

$$r_{12} = 1 - \frac{\Sigma d_1^2}{2(n-1)} + \frac{\Sigma d_2^2}{2(n-1)} - \frac{\Sigma d_1 d_2}{n-1}$$

Now

$$\frac{\Sigma d_1^2}{2(n-1)} = \frac{\Sigma(x_1/s_1)^2}{2(n-1)} = \frac{\Sigma x_1^2}{2s_1^2(n-1)} = \frac{1}{2}$$

because $s_1^2 = \Sigma x_1^2/(n-1)$. Similarly

$$\frac{\Sigma d_2^2}{2(n-1)} = \frac{1}{2}$$

Then

$$r_{12} = 1 - \left(\frac{1}{2} + \frac{1}{2} - \frac{\Sigma d_1 d_2}{n-1}\right) = \frac{\Sigma(d_1 d_2)}{n-1}$$

and also that

$$r_{12} = -1 + \frac{\Sigma(d_1 + d_2)^2}{2(n-1)} \qquad 7$$

Equation (6) shows us that, since $\Sigma(d_1 - d_2)^2$ cannot be less than 0, r_{12} will have a maximum value of $+1$. Equation (7) shows that r_{12} will have a minimum value of -1. Therefore, in general

$$1 \geq r_{12} \geq -1 \qquad 8$$

which defines the complete range of values that the correlation coefficient can take.

The relation between correlation and linear regression can be extended from that given in Section 3 by reverting to the equation for the sums of squares of the dependent variable as given in Chapter 6, Section 3. The fundamental equation, considering X_1 as the dependent variable, is

$$\Sigma x_1^2 = \Sigma x_{1d}^2 + \Sigma x_{1e}^2 \qquad 9$$

where x_{1d} represents a deviation of a value of X_1 from the regression line defined by $x_{1e} = b_{12}x_2$, and x_{1e} represents the value of x_1 estimated by the regression equation. The regression coefficient b_{12} is of course given by $\Sigma x_1 x_2/\Sigma x_2^2$.

Since $x_{1e} = b_{12}x_2$, it follows that

$$\Sigma x_{1e}^2 = b_{12}^2 \Sigma x_2^2$$

Substituting $\Sigma x_1 x_2/\Sigma x_2^2$ for b_{12}, we have

$$\Sigma x_{1e}^2 = \frac{(\Sigma x_1 x_2)^2}{\Sigma x_2^2}$$

and, since $r_{12}^2 = (\Sigma x_1 x_2)^2/\Sigma x_1^2 \Sigma x_2^2$, by definition

$$\Sigma x_{1e}^2 = r_{12}^2 \Sigma x_1^2$$

The equation for sums of squares can then be written

$$\Sigma x_1^2 = \Sigma x_{1d}^2 + r_{12}^2 \Sigma x_1^2 \qquad 10$$

$$= (1 - r_{12}^2)\Sigma x_1^2 + r_{12}^2 \Sigma x_1^2 \qquad 11$$

for which the corresponding degrees of freedom are

$$n - 1 = \quad (n-2) \quad + \quad 1$$

This leads to an analysis of variance giving a test of significance of r_{12}. Obviously

$$F = \frac{r_{12}^2(n-2)}{1 - r_{12}^2} \qquad 12$$

and this is exactly the same value as is obtained if we calculate F in order to test the regression coefficient. This analysis shows that essentially the correlation coefficient is a measure of linear regression.

The relation of the correlation coefficient to linearity of regression can be illustrated further by dealing with equation (9) in a somewhat different manner. If we substitute $r_{12}^2\Sigma x_1^2$ for Σx_{1e}^2, we have

$$r_{12}^2\Sigma x_1^2 = \Sigma x_1^2 - \Sigma x_{1d}^2 \qquad 13$$

and

$$r_{12}^2 = 1 - \frac{\Sigma x_{1d}^2}{\Sigma x_1^2} \qquad 14$$

Similarly, by substituting $(1 - r_{12}^2)\Sigma x_1^2$ for Σx_{1d}^2, we can get

$$r_{12}^2 = \frac{\Sigma x_{1e}^2}{\Sigma x_1^2} \qquad 15$$

We note first from (14) that r_{12}^2 will approach a maximum value of 1 as the sum of squares for deviations from regression approaches zero. Equation (15) shows that r_{12}^2 is merely a ratio of the sum of squares for regression to the total. The latter is a very useful concept since it can be taken as the beginning of a generalized concept of correlation representing any type of regression. Thus, if a more complex equation representing a curve is fitted, we would have a series of estimated values of X_1 lying on a curve. Extending our concept of r for linear regressions, we would be able to put

$$r'_{12}{}^2 = \frac{\Sigma x'_{1e}{}^2}{\Sigma x_1^2}$$

where $\Sigma x'_{1e}{}^2$ would now represent the sum of squares for the regression of the curved line. Such coefficients are usually called *indices of curvilinear correlation.*

Equation (11) is of particular importance in interpreting a value of a correlation coefficient. The sum of squares for the dependent variable is split up into two portions, one part representing deviations from regression which is proportional to $1 - r_{12}^2$, and one part representing regression which is proportional to r_{12}^2. An approximate but valuable concept is to assume that r_{12}^2 measures the importance of a correlation. For example, we may have a coefficient $r_{12} = 0.90$ measuring the relation between yield and soil moisture, and by a different method of treating the plots we are able to raise this to 0.95. The increase in r_{12}^2 is $0.95^2 - 0.90^2 = 0.0925$. If the initial coefficient had been 0.40 and it is increased to 0.50, the difference is still 0.09; therefore at this level an increase of 0.1 is of no more importance than an increase of 0.05 at the higher level.

5. Sampling distribution of the correlation coefficient. Suppose that we have a population in which the correlation coefficient $\rho_{12} = 0$ (the symbol

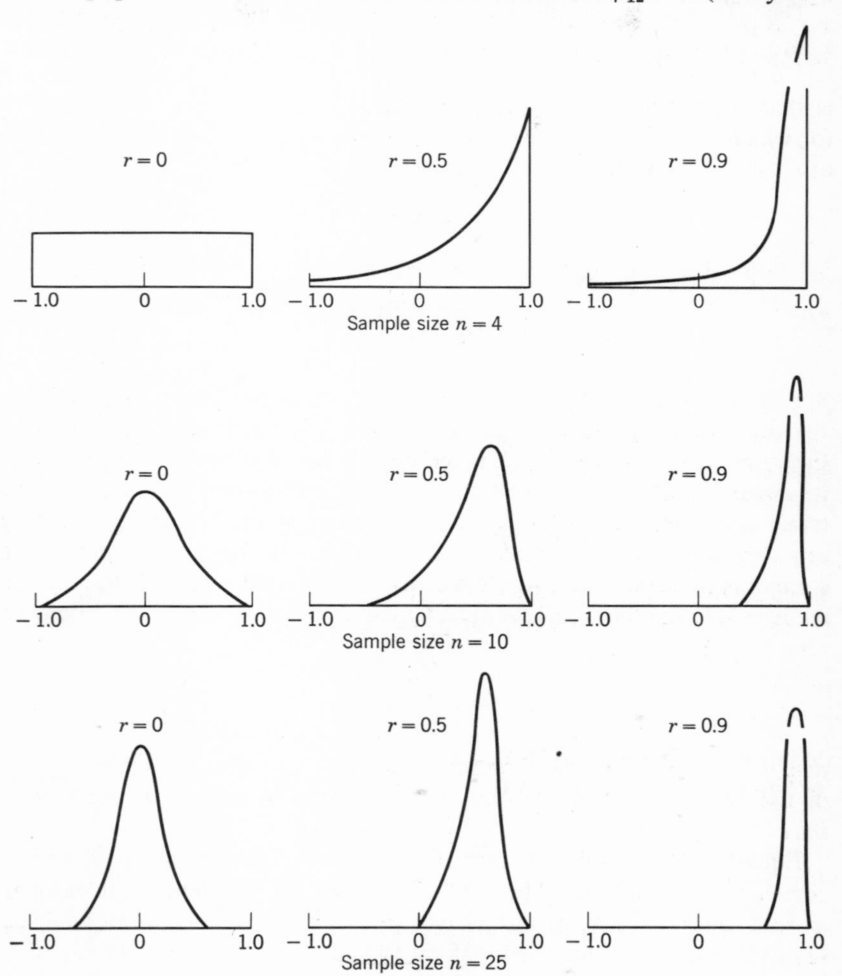

FIGURE 7–3. Distribution of the correlation coefficient for different values of ρ and for different sample sizes.

ρ_{12} replaces r_{12} because it is the population parameter of which r_{12} is an estimate), and we take a large series of samples and determine r_{12} for each. If the values of r_{12} are set up in a frequency distribution, we shall find that the distribution is symmetrical although it approaches normality only when the samples are large. On the other hand, if $\rho_{12} = 0.8$, the distribution of r_{12} will be decidedly skewed. Figure 7–3, which is adapted from Shewhart [3], illustrates this phenomenon not only for different values of ρ but for different sizes of samples.

The nature of the distribution of r is important in making tests of significance and determining fiducial limits. The usual test of significance based on the distribution of t is not affected because our null hypothesis is that ρ_{12} is zero in the population sampled. Assuming a population for which ρ_{12} is zero, we wish to find the probability of obtaining a value of r_{12} equal to or greater than the one observed. We determine

$$t = \frac{r_{12}\sqrt{n-2}}{\sqrt{1 - r_{12}^2}} \qquad 16$$

which is equivalent to $r_{12}/s_{r_{12}}$ where $s_{r_{12}}$ is the standard error of r_{12}. We should note here that $t = \sqrt{F}$, as determined from the analysis of variance. From the tables of t we then find the corresponding value of P for $n - 2$ degrees of freedom. This test works successfully because the distribution of t as determined from a series of values of r_{12} taken from a population in which $\rho_{12} = 0$ behaves in a typical fashion and in accordance with theory.

However, if $\rho_{12} = 0.8$, the distribution of t calculated from the samples will not be in agreement with the distribution on which the tables are based owing to the skewness of the distribution of r_{12}. The t distribution is not satisfactory, therefore, for a test based on

$$\pm t = \frac{r_{12} - \rho_{12}}{s_{r_{12}}}$$

unless $\rho_{12} = 0$. It follows also that the distribution of t is not suitable for setting up fiducial limits for r_{12} unless ρ_{12} is equal to or close to zero.

In order to overcome this difficulty, R. A. Fisher [1] has developed a transformation of r to a statistic z which is approximately normally distributed. We determine

$$z = \frac{1}{2}\log_e\left(\frac{1+r}{1-r}\right) \qquad 17$$

and

$$s_z = \frac{1}{\sqrt{n-3}} \qquad 18$$

Then

$$\pm t = \frac{z - \zeta}{s_z} \qquad 19$$

giving

$$l_1 = z - t_{0.05}s_z$$

$$l_2 = z + t_{0.05}s_z$$

and, on transforming l_1 and l_2 back to values of r, we have the fiducial limits at the 5% point. The value of t in these tests arises from assuming the degrees of freedom to be infinite. Accordingly a table of the normal deviate will give the same result as the table of t.

The z transformation is also useful for testing differences between correlation coefficients. Thus

$$s_{z_1-z_2} = \sqrt{\frac{1}{n_1 - 3} + \frac{1}{n_2 - 3}} \qquad 20$$

where n_1 and n_2 are the numbers of pairs of variates in the samples from which the two correlations were determined. Then

$$t = \frac{z_1 - z_2}{s_{z_1-z_2}} \qquad 21$$

In making a test of this kind it should be remembered that the two values of the correlation coefficients must not in themselves be correlated. For example, we might calculate the correlation coefficient for insect damage and yield in a series of plots, taking portions at random from each plot for the determinations. Then, if a similar correlation coefficient is obtained at a later date by sampling the *same set of plots*, the two coefficients will be related and the test described here will not apply. However, if the correlations are obtained from two entirely different sets of plots, the coefficients can be regarded as independent and the test is valid.

When pairs of correlations or linear regressions are in themselves correlated and it is necessary to make tests of significance of differences, a method has been developed by Yates [5] which is quite satisfactory. The reference will be found at the end of this chapter. For the simple case where we have one value of X_1 and two sets of values of the independent variate X_2 and X_3, and r_{12} and r_{13} are to be compared, it is satisfactory to determine a new variate $X_4 = (X_2 - X_3)$ and correlate X_1 with X_4. Yates discusses this problem in the paper cited as well as the more difficult one where there are two sets of both variables, X'_1 and X'_2 as well as X_1 and X_2, and it is known that the correlations or regressions are correlated.

6. Calculation of the correlation coefficient. If the student has worked through the methods of calculating the regression coefficient given in Chapter 6, it will be obvious that these methods can be applied to the calculation of the correlation coefficient. For the regression coefficient we required merely Σxy and Σx^2, whereas for the correlation coefficient we require in addition Σy^2. In terms of the symbols of this chapter we need

$$\Sigma x_1x_2 = \Sigma X_1X_2 - \frac{\Sigma X_1 \Sigma X_2}{n}$$

$$\Sigma x_1^2 = \Sigma X_1^2 - \frac{(\Sigma X_1)^2}{n}$$

$$\Sigma x_2^2 = \Sigma X_2^2 - \frac{(\Sigma X_2)^2}{n}$$

These can be determined directly from the paired values if there are about 50 pairs or less, but for more than 50 it is usually desirable to set up a regression table as in Chapter 6.

7. Exercises.

1. The figures in Table 7–2 are physics and English marks* for home economics students at the University of Manitoba. Determine the correlation coefficient for the relation between the marks in the two subjects. Calculate by the direct method, and test the significance of the coefficient. *$r = +0.634$. $t = 5.67$.*

TABLE 7–2

MARKS IN PHYSICS AND ENGLISH OF 50 STUDENTS IN HOME ECONOMICS AT THE UNIVERSITY OF MANITOBA

Student	Physics	English	Student	Physics	English	Student	Physics	English
1	20	21	18	26	29	35	23	26
2	25	26	19	24	27	36	26	27
3	24	27	20	19	26	37	22	21
4	22	24	21	25	25	38	26	25
5	27	27	22	18	20	39	23	21
6	26	28	23	20	24	40	29	26
7	26	24	24	23	24	41	23	19
8	32	26	25	22	20	42	20	19
9	22	24	26	23	26	43	23	30
10	27	26	27	31	27	44	33	32
11	22	23	28	24	25	45	21	19
12	22	25	29	28	30	46	28	30
13	22	24	30	25	28	47	24	21
14	29	30	31	26	32	48	26	28
15	26	30	32	24	25	49	24	22
16	24	28	33	27	30	50	30	25
17	25	29	34	28	30			

* By courtesy of the Registrar, University of Manitoba.

2. Determine the correlation coefficient for days to head and days to mature of 25 wheat varieties, for the data of Table 7–3. Find the fiducial limits at the 5% point for this coefficient. *$r = +0.946$. $l_1 = 0.916$. $l_2 = 0.972$.*

TABLE 7–3

DAYS TO HEAD AND DAYS TO MATURE OF 25 VARIETIES OF WHEAT

Variety	Days To Head	Days To Mature	Variety	Days To Head	Days To Mature
1	60.0	94.4	14	58.2	92.4
2	53.6	89.0	15	58.0	91.6
3	59.0	94.0	16	59.4	94.0
4	61.8	95.4	17	55.4	90.8
5	53.8	88.2	18	61.6	95.2
6	57.8	93.4	19	63.0	97.2
7	57.8	93.6	20	60.2	94.6
8	58.4	92.0	21	61.6	96.0
9	57.8	92.8	22	57.6	92.6
10	59.0	93.4	23	60.8	95.4
11	59.2	93.8	24	61.2	94.4
12	59.0	92.8	25	58.2	94.0
13	58.6	94.2			

REFERENCES

1. R. A. Fisher, *Statistical Methods for Research Workers*, Oliver and Boyd, Edinburgh and London, 10th ed., 1948.
2. Paul G. Hoel, *Introduction to Mathematical Statistics*, John Wiley and Sons, New York, 1947.
3. W. A. Shewhart, *Economic Control of Quality of Manufactured Product*, D. Van Nostrand Co., New York, 1931.
4. G. W. Snedecor, *Statistical Methods*, Iowa State College Press, Ames, Iowa, 4th ed., 1946.
5. F. Yates, *Proc. Roy. Soc. Edinburgh*, **59**, 1938–39.

CHAPTER 8

Partial and Multiple Regression and Correlation

1. The partial and multiple regression problem. In many regression problems the investigator is concerned purely with the effect of one variable on another. Suppose that a new method has been developed for determining the protein content of grain and that this method is to be compared with an older and thoroughly tested method known to give very accurate results. The two methods are tried out on a large series of samples, and the regression is determined for the results by the old method on those for the new method. The object here is to see how closely the protein content of a sample can be predicted from results obtained by the new method. It does not matter in this example whether the new method actually measures protein or some other characteristic closely associated with protein. A high degree of accuracy in prediction is all that is required.

In examples of a different nature we may be intimately concerned with the effect of more than one independent variable on the dependent variable, and total relations as given by simple regression coefficients may not give satisfactory information. Suppose that we find that the regression of yield of wheat on rainfall is represented by an increase of 1 bushel for every tenth of an inch of rainfall. Can we conclude from this that a given increase in rainfall will always cause a given increase in yield? The answer is no, because yield may be influenced by another factor, such as temperature, which may be different for another set of data obtained under different conditions. Also there may be a significant regression of rainfall on temperature, and it is difficult to decide whether the yield increases observed are due to one factor or to a combination of both factors.

What we require in examples of this sort is a measure of the relation between two variables when the other variable is constant. This is the purpose of partial regression and correlation methods.

2. Partial regression methods. As simple or total regression is based on the derivation of a regression equation of the form

$$Y_e = a + bX$$

so partial regression is based on a regression equation of the form

$$Y_e = a + b_1X_1 + b_2X_2 + \cdots + b_pX_p \qquad 1$$

where there are p independent variables and the regression coefficients $b_1, b_2, \cdots, b_p$ are referred to as partial regression coefficients. The equation is actually an equation of *multiple* regression as it represents a method of predicting values of Y from individual values of the p variables with which we are concerned.

Changing to deviations from the mean, equation (1) becomes

$$y_e = b_1x_1 + b_2x_2 + \cdots + b_px_p \qquad 2$$

and the error in estimating a single value of Y will be

$$y - b_1x_1 - b_2x_2 - \cdots - b_px_p \qquad 3$$

Following the same procedure as for simple regression, our problem is to find values of $b_1, b_2, \cdots, b_p$ that will make the sum of the squares of the errors of estimation a minimum. Thus it is required to minimize

$$\Sigma(y - b_1x_1 - b_2x_2 - \cdots - b_px_p)^2 \qquad 4$$

and this leads by the method of least squares to p simultaneous equations, which are given below for 3 independent variables, and can be extended easily for the number of independent variables required.

$$\begin{aligned} b_1\Sigma x_1^2 + b_2\Sigma x_1x_2 + b_3\Sigma x_1x_3 &= \Sigma x_1y \\ b_1\Sigma x_1x_2 + b_2\Sigma x_2^2 + b_3\Sigma x_2x_3 &= \Sigma x_2y \qquad 5 \\ b_1\Sigma x_1x_3 + b_2\Sigma x_2x_3 + b_3\Sigma x_3^2 &= \Sigma x_3y \end{aligned}$$

The solution of these equations gives the values of b_1, b_2, b_3 to be inserted in the prediction equation

$$y_e = b_1x_1 + b_2x_2 + b_3x_3$$

It should be noted that the partial regression coefficients are represented in the equation by an abbreviated notation. Thus to write b_1 in full we should write $b_{y1\cdot23}$, showing that this is a partial regression coefficient for Y on X_1, with the variables X_2 and X_3 held constant.

3. Meaning of partial regression. Although we have said that the regression coefficient $b_{y1\cdot23}$ represents the regression of Y on X_1 with X_2 and X_3 held constant, it is possible to put this relation in a more direct form. Suppose that we have 2 independent variables X_1 and X_2 and wish to obtain the partial regression coefficient $b_{y1\cdot2}$. We can determine the simple regression equations

$$y_e = b_{y2}x_2 \qquad \text{and} \qquad x_{1e} = b_{12}x_2$$

From the first equation we can obtain a series of estimated values of Y. Then from the second equation we can get a series of estimated values of X_1. The deviations of the actual values of Y and X_1 from the respective regression lines represented by

$$u = y - b_{y2}x_2 \qquad \text{and} \qquad v = x_1 - b_{12}x_2$$

are both independent of X_2; hence the required regression coefficient will be b_{uv}. This can be taken as the starting point in the derivation of partial regression methods. It leads by substitution and algebraic manipulation to the values of b obtained by solving the normal equations. Thus $b_{uv} = b_{y1 \cdot 2}$. This procedure can be built up for the derivation of regression equations with p independent variables.

4. Calculation of partial regression coefficients. It is obvious that equations (5) can be solved by a direct application of elementary methods involving successive elimination of the unknowns. These can be found in any good text on algebra. A tabular method for the solution of the normal equations, known as the Doolittle method, is very convenient, and more recently Dwyer [2] has summarized and related all available methods and has presented what is referred to as the abbreviated Doolittle solution. Since this method reduces time and labor to the minimum, we shall use it here. The work is given in Example 8–1.*

5. Example 8–1. Calculation of partial regression coefficients. The following data were obtained in a study of the relation between quality characteristics of wheat flour. Data were taken on 139 strains of wheat. The characteristics studied were loaf volume (Y), protein content (X_1), flour yield (X_2), and crumb color score (X_3). In this example loaf volume is taken as the dependent variable. This is not quite satisfactory in connection with crumb color, as actually it is variations in the loaf volume that influence color and bring about the correlation, and not the variations in color that affect the volume.

$$\Sigma(x_1 y) = 694.96 \qquad \Sigma(y^2) = 1142.45 \qquad \Sigma(x_1 x_2) = -20.834$$

$$\Sigma(x_2 y) = 79.648 \qquad \Sigma(x_1^2) = 947.17 \qquad \Sigma(x_1 x_3) = 272.76$$

$$\Sigma(x_3 y) = 407.00 \qquad \Sigma(x_2^2) = 414.23 \qquad \Sigma(x_2 x_3) = -354.00$$

$$\Sigma(x_3^2) = 630.00$$

---

* Crout [1] has demonstrated a method that appears to give maximum abbreviation. It is demonstrated in the Appendix.

TABLE 8–1

Calculation of Partial Regression Coefficients

Line					Line				
1	947.17	− 20.834	272.76	694.96	1	a_{11}	a_{21}	a_{31}	a_{Y1}
2		414.23	− 354.00	79.648	2		a_{22}	a_{32}	a_{Y2}
3			630.00	407.00	3			a_{33}	a_{Y3}
4	947.17	− 20.834	272.76	694.96	4	a_{11}	a_{21}	a_{31}	a_{Y1}
5	1.0	− 0.021 996	0.287 97	0.733 72	5	1.0	b_{21}	b_{31}	b_{Y1}
6		413.77	− 348.00	94.934	6		$a_{22\cdot1}$	$a_{32\cdot1}$	$a_{Y2\cdot1}$
7		1.0	− 0.841 05	0.229 44	7		1.0	$b_{32\cdot1}$	$b_{Y2\cdot1}$
8			258.77	286.72	8			$a_{33\cdot12}$	$a_{Y3\cdot12}$
9			1.0	1.1080	9			$b_{33\cdot12}$	$b_{Y3\cdot12}$
10	0.440 19	1.1613	1.1080		10	$b_{Y1\cdot23}$	$b_{Y2\cdot13}$	$b_{Y3\cdot12}$	

Check:

$$(947.17 \times 0.440\,19) + (-\,20.834 \times 1.1613) + (272.76 \times 1.1080) = 694.96$$

Instructions

Line	
1 to 3	Enter sums of squares and products.
4	Copy line 1.
5	Divide each entry in line 4 by a_{11}.
6	$a_{22\cdot1} = a_{22} - a_{21}b_{21}$ $a_{32\cdot1} = a_{32} - a_{31}b_{21}$ $a_{Y2\cdot1} = a_{Y2} - a_{Y1}b_{21}$
7	Divide each entry in line 6 by $a_{22\cdot1}$.
8	$a_{33\cdot12} = a_{33} - a_{31}b_{31} - a_{32\cdot1}b_{32\cdot1}$ $a_{Y3\cdot12} = a_{Y3} - a_{Y1}b_{31} - a_{Y2\cdot1}b_{32\cdot1}$
9	Divide each entry in line 8 by $a_{33\cdot12}$.
10	Reverse solution.

$b_{Y3\cdot12}$ copied from line 9

$$b_{Y2\cdot13} = b_{Y2\cdot1} - b_{32\cdot1}b_{Y3\cdot12}$$

$$b_{Y1\cdot23} = b_{Y1} - b_{31}b_{Y3\cdot12} - b_{21}b_{Y2\cdot13}$$

Check:

$$a_{11}b_{Y1\cdot23} + a_{21}b_{Y2\cdot13} + a_{31}b_{Y3\cdot12} = a_{Y1}$$

The sum of squares for regression is given by

$$b_1\Sigma x_1y + b_2\Sigma x_2y + b_3\Sigma x_3y$$

in which $b_{Y1\cdot23}$ is abbreviated to b_1, etc. The figures are

$$(0.44019 \times 694.96) + (1.1613 \times 79.648) + (1.1080 \times 407.00)$$

$$305.91 \quad + \quad 92.50 \quad + \quad 450.96 \quad = 849.37$$

The normal equations corresponding to equations (5) are

$$b_1(947.17) + b_2(-20.834) + b_3(272.76) = 694.96$$

$$b_1(-20.834) + b_2(414.23) + b_3(-354.00) = 79.648$$

$$b_1(272.76) + b_2(-354.00) + b_3(630.00) = 407.00$$

To solve these equations we shall set them up as in Table 8–1. The portion of the table on the right represents the known values in terms of symbols in which the notation is in accordance with Dwyer [2]. Below the table are line-by-line instructions for carrying through the calculations. The calculations in Table 8–1 enable us to set up an analysis of variance for the multiple regression.

	SS	DF		MS
Regression	849.37	3	p	283.12
Deviations from regression	293.08	135	$n-p-1$	2.1710
Total	1142.45	138	$n-1$	

Since the value of F will be very large, there is no object in going farther with this test. It will be more informative to study the significance and possibly the fiducial limits of the partial regression coefficients. The method is given in Section 8.

It should be noted that the multiple correlation coefficient is given by

$$r_{Y \cdot 123} = \sqrt{\frac{849.37}{1142.45}} = 0.8622$$

and its test of significance is given by the analysis of variance above.

6. Calculation of partial regression coefficients for different sets of values of the dependent variable. It happens frequently in a partial regression analysis that the investigator has more than one set of values of the dependent variable. In an example given by Fisher [3] of the effect of longitude, latitude, and altitude on yield, these would remain the same for a given set of locations, but the yield would change each year. It is desirable in such circumstances to be able to calculate sets of partial regression coefficients with minimum labor. Fisher [3] has shown how this can be done by the calculation from the dependent variables of a set of statistics commonly known as the Gauss multipliers. There are other important applications of the Gauss multipliers that we shall refer to later.

The proposition is illustrated by setting up the normal equations in the form given below, for 3 independent variables. The student can very easily take these as a basis for writing the equations for more than 3 independent variables.

$$\begin{aligned} c_{11}\Sigma x_1^2 + c_{12}\Sigma x_1x_2 + c_{13}\Sigma x_1x_3 &= 1 \\ c_{11}\Sigma x_1x_2 + c_{12}\Sigma x_2^2 + c_{13}\Sigma x_2x_3 &= 0 \\ c_{11}\Sigma x_1x_3 + c_{12}\Sigma x_2x_3 + c_{13}\Sigma x_3^2 &= 0 \end{aligned} \qquad 6$$

$$\begin{aligned} c_{21}\Sigma x_1^2 + c_{22}\Sigma x_1x_2 + c_{23}\Sigma x_1x_3 &= 0 \\ c_{21}\Sigma x_1x_2 + c_{22}\Sigma x_2^2 + c_{23}\Sigma x_2x_3 &= 1 \\ c_{21}\Sigma x_1x_3 + c_{22}\Sigma x_2x_3 + c_{23}\Sigma x_3^2 &= 0 \end{aligned} \qquad 7$$

$$\begin{aligned} c_{31}\Sigma x_1^2 + c_{32}\Sigma x_1x_2 + c_{33}\Sigma x_1x_3 &= 0 \\ c_{31}\Sigma x_1x_2 + c_{32}\Sigma x_2^2 + c_{33}\Sigma x_2x_3 &= 0 \\ c_{31}\Sigma x_1x_3 + c_{32}\Sigma x_2x_3 + c_{33}\Sigma x_3^2 &= 1 \end{aligned} \qquad 8$$

The solution of these equations gives the matrix of multipliers:

$$\begin{matrix} c_{11} & c_{12} & c_{13} \\ c_{21} & c_{22} & c_{23} \\ c_{31} & c_{32} & c_{33} \end{matrix} \qquad \text{where } c_{21} = c_{12}, \text{ etc.}$$

and the regression coefficients can then be obtained from

$$\begin{aligned} b_1 &= c_{11}\Sigma x_1y + c_{12}\Sigma x_2y + c_{13}\Sigma x_3y \\ b_2 &= c_{12}\Sigma x_1y + c_{22}\Sigma x_2y + c_{23}\Sigma x_3y \\ b_3 &= c_{13}\Sigma x_1y + c_{23}\Sigma x_2y + c_{33}\Sigma x_3y \end{aligned} \qquad 9$$

This shows that for any one set of values of Y we have to obtain merely Σx_1y, Σx_2y, and Σx_3y.

This method is applied in Example 8–2 to obtain the same set of regression coefficients as in Example 8–1.

7. Example 8–2. Calculation of partial regression coefficients using the Gauss multipliers. The three sets of normal equations given in (6), (7), and (8) can be solved simultaneously in tabular form with the abbreviated Doolittle technique. The procedure is shown in Table 8–2. The same rules of calculation apply as in Table 8–1, but a further table of symbols with instructions is given for convenient reference.

TABLE 8–2

CALCULATION OF GAUSS MULTIPLIERS—ABBREVIATED DOOLITTLE SOLUTION

1	947.17	– 20.834	272.76	1.0	0	0
2		414.23	– 354.00	0	1.0	0
3			630.00	0	0	1.0
4	947.17	– 20.834	272.76	1.0	0	0
5	1.0	– 0.021 996	0.287 97	0.001 055 8	0	0
6		413.77	– 348.00	0.021 996	1.0	0
7		1.0	– 0.841 05	0.000 053 160	0.002 416 8	0
8			258.77	– 0.269 47	0.841 05	1.0
9			1.0	– 0.001 041 3	0.003 250 2	0.003 864 4
10				0.001 337 6	– 0.000 822 67	– 0.001 041 3
11					0.005 150 4	0.003 250 2
12						0.003 864 4

Check:

$(0.001\,337\,6 \times 947.17) + (-0.000\,822\,67 \times -20.834) + (-0.001\,041\,3 \times 272.76) = 1.0000$

Regression coefficients can now be obtained using equations (9).

$$b_1 = (0.001\,337\,6 \times 694.96) + (-\,0.000\,822\,67 \times 79.648) + (-\,0.001\,041\,3 \times 407.00) = 0.4402$$

$$b_2 = (-\,0.000\,822\,67 \times 694.96) + (0.005\,150\,4 \times 79.648) + (0.003\,250\,2 \times 407.00) = 1.1613$$

$$b_3 = (-\,0.001\,041\,3 \times 694.96) + (0.003\,250\,2 \times 79.648) + (0.003\,864\,4 \times 407.00) = 1.1080$$

The significance of the regression coefficients can be determined by the t test, using the formula for the standard error given in equation (10), Section 8. From the analysis of variance, Example 8–1, we have $s^2 = 2.1710$; thus $s = 1.473$.

$$s_{b_1} = 1.473\sqrt{0.001\,337\,6} = 0.0539$$

$$s_{b_2} = 1.473\sqrt{0.005\,150\,4} = 0.1057$$

$$s_{b_3} = 1.473\sqrt{0.003\,864\,4} = 0.0916$$

TABLE 8–3

CALCULATION OF GAUSS MULTIPLIERS—INSTRUCTIONS FOR USE OF ABBREVIATED DOOLITTLE SOLUTION

1	a_{11}	a_{21}	a_{31}	1.0	0	0
2		a_{22}	a_{32}	0	1.0	0
3			a_{33}	0	0	1.0
4	a_{11}	a_{21}	a_{31}	d_{11}	0	0
5	1	b_{21}	b_{31}	e_{11}	0	0
6		$a_{22\cdot 1}$	$a_{32\cdot 1}$	$d_{11\cdot 1}$	$d_{12\cdot 1}$	0
7		1.0	$b_{32\cdot 1}$	$e_{11\cdot 1}$	$e_{12\cdot 1}$	0
8			$a_{33\cdot 12}$	$d_{11\cdot 12}$	$d_{12\cdot 12}$	$d_{13\cdot 12}$
9			1.0	$e_{11\cdot 12}$	$e_{12\cdot 12}$	$e_{13\cdot 12}$
10				c_{11}	c_{12}	c_{13}
11					c_{22}	c_{23}
12						c_{33}

Instructions

Line	
1, 2, 3	Enter sums of squares and products.
4	Copy line 1.
5	Divide each entry in line 4 by a_{11}.
6	$a_{22\cdot 1} = a_{22} - a_{21}b_{21}$ $a_{32\cdot 1} = a_{32} - a_{31}b_{21}$ $d_{11\cdot 1} = 0 - d_{11}b_{21}$ etc.,
7	Divide each entry in line 6 by $a_{22\cdot 1}$.
8	$a_{33\cdot 12} = a_{33} - a_{31}b_{31} - a_{32\cdot 1}b_{32\cdot 1}$ $d_{11\cdot 12} = 0 - d_{11}b_{31} - d_{11\cdot 1}b_{32\cdot 1}$ etc., for $d_{12\cdot 12}$ and $d_{13\cdot 12}$.
9	Divide each entry in line 8 by $a_{33\cdot 12}$.
10, 11, 12	$c_{11} = d_{11}e_{11} + d_{11\cdot 1}e_{11\cdot 1} + d_{11\cdot 12}e_{11\cdot 12}$

$$
\begin{aligned}
c_{11} &= d_{11}e_{11} + d_{11\cdot 1}e_{11\cdot 1} + d_{11\cdot 12}e_{11\cdot 12} \\
c_{12} &= d_{11\cdot 1}e_{12\cdot 1} + d_{11\cdot 12}e_{12\cdot 12} \\
c_{13} &= d_{11\cdot 12}e_{13\cdot 12} \\
c_{22} &= d_{12\cdot 1}e_{12\cdot 1} + d_{12\cdot 12}e_{12\cdot 12} \\
c_{23} &= d_{12\cdot 12}e_{13\cdot 12} \\
c_{33} &= d_{13\cdot 12}e_{13\cdot 12}
\end{aligned}
$$

8. Testing the significance of partial regression coefficients. The Gauss multipliers provide an easy method for determining the standard errors of partial regression coefficients. These are given by

$$s_{b_1} = s\sqrt{c_{11}}$$

$$s_{b_2} = s\sqrt{c_{22}} \qquad 10$$

$$s_{b_3} = s\sqrt{c_{33}}$$

where

$$s = \sqrt{\frac{\Sigma(Y - Y_e)^2}{n - p - 1}} \qquad 11$$

p is the number of independent variables, and $\Sigma(Y - Y_e)^2$ is most easily obtained from

$$\Sigma(Y - Y_e)^2 = \Sigma y^2 - b_1\Sigma x_1 y - b_2\Sigma x_2 y - b_3\Sigma x_3 y \qquad 12$$

The standard error of a difference between two regression coefficients can also be expressed in terms of the multipliers. Thus, for the difference between $b_{y1\cdot 2\ldots n}$ and $b_{y2\cdot 1\ldots n}$ the standard error is

$$s\sqrt{c_{11} + c_{22} - 2c_{12}} \qquad 13$$

A further application is in determining the standard error of an estimated value of Y such as Y_{e1}. For 3 independent variables, the standard error of Y_e is given by

$$\text{SE} = s\sqrt{\frac{1}{n} + c_{11}x_1^2 + c_{22}x_2^2 + c_{33}x_3^2 + 2c_{12}x_1x_2 + 2c_{13}x_1x_3 + 2c_{23}x_2x_3} \qquad 14$$

where x_1, x_2, and x_3 are the deviations from the means of the particular values for which Y is estimated. Again, as in Chapter 6, it should be pointed out that the estimated Y is an estimate of the population value of Y for a given set of values of X_1, X_2, and X_3.

9. Deletion of a variable. After completing a regression or correlation analysis, we may inquire as to the results that would be obtained if a certain variable had been omitted. An easy technique is available if the Gauss multipliers have been obtained. It involves the calculation of a new matrix according to the formulas given below. These formulas are a little cumbersome to express in general terms and are therefore given for specific cases that can be adapted to the general case. rc_{11} represents a value in the reduced matrix.

Variables Y, X_1, X_2, X_3: to delete X_3,

$$rc_{11} = c_{11} - \frac{c_{13}^2}{c_{33}} \qquad rc_{12} = c_{12} - \frac{c_{13}c_{23}}{c_{33}} \qquad rc_{22} = c_{22} - \frac{c_{23}^2}{c_{33}} \qquad 15$$

Variables Y, X_1, X_2, X_3: to delete X_2,

$$rc_{11} = c_{11} - \frac{c_{12}^2}{c_{22}} \qquad rc_{13} = c_{13} - \frac{c_{12}c_{23}}{c_{22}} \qquad rc_{33} = c_{33} - \frac{c_{23}^2}{c_{22}} \qquad 16$$

The calculations required to delete X_2 from Example 8–2 are given in Example 8–3. The same formulas can be applied to a matrix of Gauss multipliers arising from a correlation analysis.

10. Example 8–3. Deletion of X_2 from regression analysis for Y, X_1, X_2, and X_3.

$$rc_{11} = 0.001\,337\,6 - \frac{(-\,0.000\,822\,67)^2}{0.005\,150\,4} = 0.001\,206\,2$$

$$rc_{13} = -\,0.001\,041\,3 - \frac{(-\,0.000\,822\,67 \times 0.003\,250\,2)}{0.005\,150\,4} = -\,0.000\,522\,15$$

$$rc_{33} = 0.003\,864\,4 - \frac{(0.003\,250\,2)^2}{0.005\,150\,4} = 0.001\,813\,3$$

Check:

$$(0.001\,206\,2 \times 947.17) + (-\,0.000\,522\,15 \times 272.76) = 1.000\,05$$

$$b_1 = c_{11}\Sigma x_1 y + c_{13}\Sigma x_3 y$$

$$= (0.001\,206\,2 \times 694.96) + (-\,0.000\,522\,15 \times 407.00) = 0.625\,74$$

$$b_3 = c_{13}\Sigma x_1 y + c_{33}\Sigma x_3 y$$

$$= (-\,0.000\,522\,15 \times 694.96) + (0.001\,813\,3 \times 407.00) = 0.375\,14$$

Check:

$$(0.625\,74 \times 947.17) + (0.375\,14 \times 272.76) = 695.00$$

$$\text{SS regression} = b_1\Sigma x_1 y + b_3\Sigma x_3 y$$

$$= (0.625\,74 \times 694.96) + (0.375\,14 \times 407.00) = 587.55$$

$$r_{Y\cdot 13} = \sqrt{\frac{587.55}{1142.45}} = 0.7171 \quad \text{etc.}$$

11. Partial and multiple correlation. Referring to Section 3 above, we note that for 2 independent variables, X_1 and X_2, the simple regression equations

$$y_e = b_{y2}x_2 \qquad \text{and} \qquad x_{1e} = b_{12}x_2$$

provide a series of estimated values of y for each value of x_2 and a similar series of estimated values of x_1. The deviations of the actual values of y and x_1 from the respective regression lines are independent of x_2. Representing these by

$$u = y - b_{y2}x_2 \qquad \text{and} \qquad v = x_1 - b_{12}x_2$$

r_{uv} is a partial correlation coefficient and can be represented symbolically by $r_{Y1.2}$.

In general, in correlation analysis we are not so much concerned with the distinction between dependent and independent variables as we are in regression analysis; therefore we shall refer to the variates as X_1, X_2, X_3, etc., where the relation with regression problems is such that X_1 is taken as the variable corresponding to Y. For the normal equations we have therefore, with 4 variables and 3 unknowns,

$$\begin{aligned} b'_{12\cdot34} + r_{23}b'_{13\cdot24} + r_{24}b'_{14\cdot23} &= r_{12} \\ r_{23}b'_{12\cdot34} + b'_{13\cdot24} + r_{34}b'_{14\cdot23} &= r_{13} \\ r_{24}b'_{12\cdot34} + r_{34}b'_{13\cdot24} + b'_{14\cdot23} &= r_{14} \end{aligned} \qquad 17$$

where in the subscripts, $1 = X_1$, $2 = X_2$, $3 = X_3$, $4 = X_4$, or in correspondence with regression analysis, $1 = Y$, $2 = X_1$, $3 = X_2$, $4 = X_3$.

These equations are derived from (5). The regression coefficients are distinguished by a prime because they are actually *standard* regression coefficients. In other words, they are made standard with respect to the standard deviations of the variables involved. Thus

$$\begin{aligned} b'_{12\cdot34} &= b_{12\cdot34}\sqrt{\frac{\Sigma x_2^2}{\Sigma x_1^2}} \\ b'_{13\cdot24} &= b_{13\cdot24}\sqrt{\frac{\Sigma x_3^2}{\Sigma x_1^2}} \end{aligned} \qquad 18$$

The methods of calculating partial correlation coefficients are similar to those for calculating regression coefficients. The basic procedure is to solve the normal equations for the standard regression coefficients and then obtain the partial correlation coefficients from the relation

$$r_{12\cdot34\cdots p} = \sqrt{b'_{12\cdot34\cdots p}\, b'_{21\cdot34\cdots p}} \qquad 19$$

From the normal equations in (17) it is obvious that the solution of one set of equations giving $b'_{12\cdot34}$, $b'_{13\cdot24}$, and $b'_{14\cdot23}$ will not enable us to calculate any correlation coefficients, as to give us $r_{12\cdot34}$, $r_{13\cdot24}$, and $r_{14\cdot23}$ we require in addition $b'_{21\cdot34}$, $b'_{31\cdot24}$, and $b'_{41\cdot23}$. These can be obtained by rearranging the equations and solving again, continuing with such rearrangements until all possible values of the standard regression coefficients have been obtained, but the whole problem is greatly simplified by the calculation of a matrix of multipliers which is the inverse of the r matrix. Thus the calculations with the r matrix on the left below gives the c' matrix as shown on the right.

$$\begin{matrix} r_{11} & r_{12} & r_{13} & r_{14} \\ r_{12} & r_{22} & r_{23} & r_{24} \\ r_{13} & r_{23} & r_{33} & r_{34} \\ r_{14} & r_{24} & r_{34} & r_{44} \end{matrix} \qquad \begin{matrix} c'_{11} & c'_{12} & c'_{13} & c'_{14} \\ c'_{12} & c'_{22} & c'_{23} & c'_{24} \\ c'_{13} & c'_{23} & c'_{33} & c'_{34} \\ c'_{14} & c'_{24} & c'_{34} & c'_{44} \end{matrix} \qquad 20$$

From the c' matrix any of the partial regression or correlation coefficients can be calculated. Thus, it can be shown that

$$b_{12\cdot34} = -\frac{c'_{12}}{c'_{11}} \qquad b_{21\cdot34} = -\frac{c'_{12}}{c'_{22}} \qquad \text{etc.}$$

from which it follows that

$$r_{12\cdot34} = -\frac{c'_{12}}{\sqrt{c'_{11}c'_{22}}} \qquad \text{etc.}$$

$$r_{23\cdot14} = -\frac{c'_{23}}{\sqrt{c'_{22}c'_{33}}} \qquad 21$$

The significance of a partial correlation coefficient is tested by the calculation of t from

$$t = \frac{r}{\sqrt{1-r^2}}\sqrt{n-p-1} \qquad 22$$

where r is the coefficient being tested, n is the number in the sample, and p is the number of independent variates.

In Example 8–4 the abbreviated Doolittle method is used to obtain the matrix of multipliers for a problem with 6 variables.

12. Example 8–4. Calculation of partial and multiple correlation coefficients. The total correlation coefficients in Table 8–4 were obtained in a study [5] of the effect of the physical characteristics of wheat on the yield and quality of flour.

TABLE 8–4

SIMPLE CORRELATION COEFFICIENTS FOR THE RELATIONS BETWEEN 6 VARIABLES

	2	3	4	5	6
1	– 0.4589	– 0.5612	– 0.3947	– 0.3123	0.6412
2		0.3114	0.0429	0.2861	– 0.3190
3			– 0.0655	0.1467	– 0.4462
4				0.1882	– 0.3511
5					– 0.3092

1 = yield of flour
2 = percentage of bran frost
3 = percentage of heavy frost
4 = percentage immaturity
5 = percentage of green kernels
6 = weight per bushel

Tables 8–5 and 8–6 together with the line-by-line instructions give the complete details of the calculations. Further abbreviations in the method are given in the Appendix.

13. Interpretation and significance of multiple correlation coefficients. We have noted that the multiple regression equation is

$$y_e = b_1x_1 + b_2x_2 + \cdots + b_px_p$$

where the dependent variable is Y and the independent variables are $X_1, X_2, \cdots, X_p$. The greater the prediction power of this equation, the closer the agreement between the actual and predicted values of y. Hence the prediction power of the equation should be measured by the simple correlation r_{yy_e}. This actually is the multiple correlation coefficient, $r_{Y\cdot 12}$, and obviously its minimum value is zero and its maximum value is $+1$. It does not have a range from -1 to $+1$ as in the case of a simple correlation between two variables.

In the analysis of the sums of squares of Y we have

$$\Sigma y^2 = \Sigma(Y - Y_e)^2 + \Sigma(Y_e - \bar{Y})^2$$

or

$$\Sigma y^2 = \Sigma y_d^2 + \Sigma y_e^2$$

as in the case of simple correlation, but the corresponding degrees of freedom in this case are

$$n - 1 = (n - p - 1) + p$$

TABLE 8–5

ABBREVIATED DOOLITTLE SOLUTION FOR STANDARD REGRESSION AND PARTIAL CORRELATION COEFFICIENTS

1	1.0000	− 0.4589	− 0.5612	− 0.3947	− 0.3123	0.6412	1.0	0	0	0	0	0
2		1.0000	0.3114	0.0429	0.2861	− 0.3190	0	1.0	0	0	0	0
3			1.0000	− 0.0655	0.1467	− 0.4462	0	0	1.0	0	0	0
4				1.0000	0.1882	− 0.3511	0	0	0	1.0	0	0
5					1.0000	− 0.3092	0	0	0	0	1.0	0
6						1.0000	0	0	0	0	0	1.0
7	1.0	− 0.4589	− 0.5612	− 0.3947	− 0.3123	0.6412	1.0	0				
8	1.0	− 0.4589	− 0.5612	− 0.3947	− 0.3123	0.6412	1.0	0				
9		0.7894	0.0539	− 0.1382	0.1428	− 0.0248	0.4589	1.0	0			
10		1.0	0.0683	− 0.1751	0.1809	− 0.0314	0.5813	1.2668	0			
11			0.6814	− 0.2776	− 0.0383	− 0.0847	0.5299	− 0.0682	1.0	0		
12			1.0	− 0.4074	− 0.0562	− 0.1243	0.7777	− 0.1001	1.4676	0		
13				0.7069	0.0743	− 0.1369	0.6909	0.1473	0.4074	1.0	0	
14				1.0	0.1051	− 0.1937	0.9774	0.2084	0.5763	1.4146	0	
15					0.8667	− 0.0948	0.1865	− 0.2002	0.0134	− 0.1051	1.0	0
16					1.0	− 0.1094	0.2152	− 0.2310	0.0155	− 0.1213	1.1538	0
17						0.5407	− 0.4067	0.0296	0.2047	0.1822	0.1094	1.0
18						1.0	− 0.7522	0.0547	0.3786	0.3370	0.2023	1.8494
19	0.4067	− 0.0296	− 0.2047	− 0.1822	− 0.1094		2.7002	0.6069	1.0248	0.8177	0.1329	− 0.7522
20	− 0.1130	0.1913	− 0.0484	0.0718		− 0.1720		1.3522	− 0.0071	0.2426	− 0.2250	0.0547
21	− 0.5492	− 0.1630	− 0.4324		0.0567	− 0.2264			1.7801	0.6437	0.0569	0.3786
22	− 0.5757	0.0040		− 0.3616	− 0.0320	− 0.2127				1.4888	− 0.0844	0.3370
23	− 0.4488		0.0052	− 0.1794	0.1664	− 0.0404					1.1759	0.2023
24		− 0.2248	− 0.3795	− 0.3028	− 0.0492	0.2786						1.8494
25								− 0.318	− 0.467	− 0.408	− 0.074	0.337
26									0.005	− 0.171	0.178	− 0.034
27										− 0.395	− 0.039	− 0.209
28											0.064	− 0.203
29		$r_{1.23456} = 0.678$										− 0.137

TABLE 8–6

Calculation of Partial and Multiple Correlation Coefficients*

1	a_{11}	a_{21}	a_{31}	a_{41}	a_{51}	a_{61}	1	0	0	0	0	0
2		a_{22}	a_{32}	a_{42}	a_{52}	a_{62}	0	1	0	0	0	0
3			a_{33}	a_{43}	a_{53}	a_{63}	0	0	1	0	0	0
4				a_{44}	a_{54}	a_{64}	0	0	0	1	0	0
5					a_{55}	a_{65}	0	0	0	0	1	0
6						a_{66}	0	0	0	0	0	1
7	a_{11}	a_{21}	a_{31}	a_{41}	a_{51}	a_{61}	d_{11}	0				
8	1	b_{21}	b_{31}	b_{41}	b_{51}	b_{61}	e_{11}	0				
9		$a_{22\cdot 1}$	$a_{32\cdot 1}$	$a_{42\cdot 1}$	$a_{52\cdot 1}$	$a_{62\cdot 1}$	$d_{11\cdot 1}$	$d_{12\cdot 1}$	0			
10		1	$b_{32\cdot 1}$	$b_{42\cdot 1}$	$b_{52\cdot 1}$	$b_{62\cdot 1}$	$e_{11\cdot 1}$	$e_{12\cdot 1}$	0			
11			$a_{33\cdot 2}$	$a_{43\cdot 2}$	$a_{53\cdot 2}$	$a_{63\cdot 2}$	$d_{11\cdot 2}$	$d_{12\cdot 2}$	$d_{13\cdot 2}$	0		
12			1	$b_{43\cdot 2}$	$b_{53\cdot 2}$	$b_{63\cdot 2}$	$e_{11\cdot 2}$	$e_{12\cdot 2}$	$e_{13\cdot 2}$	0		
13				$a_{44\cdot 3}$	$a_{54\cdot 3}$	$a_{64\cdot 3}$	$d_{11\cdot 3}$	$d_{12\cdot 3}$	$d_{13\cdot 3}$	$d_{14\cdot 3}$	0	
14				1	$b_{54\cdot 3}$	$b_{64\cdot 3}$	$e_{11\cdot 3}$	$e_{12\cdot 3}$	$e_{13\cdot 3}$	$e_{14\cdot 3}$	0	
15					$a_{55\cdot 4}$	$a_{65\cdot 4}$	$d_{11\cdot 4}$	$d_{12\cdot 4}$	$d_{13\cdot 4}$	$d_{14\cdot 4}$	$d_{15\cdot 4}$	0
16					1	$b_{65\cdot 4}$	$e_{11\cdot 4}$	$e_{12\cdot 4}$	$e_{13\cdot 4}$	$e_{14\cdot 4}$	$e_{15\cdot 4}$	0
17						$a_{66\cdot 5}$	$d_{11\cdot 5}$	$d_{12\cdot 5}$	$d_{13\cdot 5}$	$d_{14\cdot 5}$	$d_{15\cdot 5}$	$d_{16\cdot 5}$
18						$b_{66\cdot 5}$	$e_{11\cdot 5}$	$e_{12\cdot 5}$	$e_{13\cdot 5}$	$e_{14\cdot 5}$	$e_{15\cdot 5}$	$e_{16\cdot 5}$
19	b'_{61}	b'_{62}	b'_{63}	b'_{64}	b'_{65}		c'_{11}	c'_{12}	c'_{13}	c'_{14}	c'_{15}	c'_{16}
20	b'_{51}	b'_{52}	b'_{53}	b'_{54}		b'_{56}		c'_{22}	c'_{23}	c'_{24}	c'_{25}	c'_{26}
21	b'_{41}	b'_{42}	b'_{43}		b'_{45}	b'_{46}			c'_{33}	c'_{34}	c'_{35}	c'_{36}
22	b'_{31}	b'_{32}		b'_{34}	b'_{35}	b'_{36}				c'_{44}	c'_{45}	c'_{46}
23	b'_{21}		b'_{23}	b'_{24}	b'_{25}	b'_{26}					c'_{55}	c'_{56}
24		b'_{12}	b'_{13}	b'_{14}	b'_{15}	b'_{16}						c'_{66}
25							r_{11}	r_{12}	r_{13}	r_{14}	r_{15}	r_{16}
26	$r^2_{1\cdot 23456} = a_{61}b_{61} + a_{62\cdot 1}b_{62\cdot 1} + a_{63\cdot 2}b_{63\cdot 2}$							r_{22}	r_{23}	r_{24}	r_{25}	r_{26}
27	$+ a_{64\cdot 3}b_{64\cdot 3} + a_{65\cdot 4}b_{65\cdot 4}$								r_{33}	r_{34}	r_{35}	r_{36}
28										r_{44}	r_{45}	r_{46}
29											r_{55}	r_{56}
30												r_{66}

* Subscripts have been abbreviated, thus $b_{65\cdot 4} = b_{65\cdot 1234}$.

Instructions for Calculation of the Inverse Matrix Yielding Standard Partial Regression Coefficients and Partial Correlation Coefficients

Line	
1 to 6	Enter known values for normal equations.
7	Repeat line 1.
8	Divide each item through by a_{11}.
9	$a_{22\cdot1} = a_{22} - a_{21}b_{21},\ a_{32\cdot1} = a_{32} - a_{31}b_{21},\ a_{42\cdot1} = a_{42} - a_{41}b_{21}, \cdots,$ $d_{12\cdot1} = 1 - 0 \times b_{21}$
10	Divide line 9 by $a_{22\cdot1}$.
11	$a_{33\cdot2} = a_{33} - a_{31}b_{31} - a_{32\cdot1}b_{32\cdot1},\ a_{43\cdot2} = a_{43} - a_{41}b_{31} - a_{42\cdot1}b_{32\cdot1}, \cdots,$ $d_{13\cdot2} = 1 - 0 \times b_{32\cdot1}$
12	Divide line 11 by $a_{33\cdot2}$.
13	$a_{44\cdot3} = a_{44} - a_{41}b_{41} - a_{42\cdot1}b_{42\cdot1} - a_{43\cdot2}b_{43\cdot2},\ a_{54\cdot3} = a_{54} - a_{51}b_{41} - a_{52\cdot1}b_{42\cdot1} - a_{53\cdot2}b_{43\cdot2}, \cdots,\ d_{14\cdot3} = 1 - 0 \times b_{53\cdot2}$
14 to 18	Complete calculations following systematic procedure outlined above.

19

$$c'_{11} = d_{11}e_{11} + d_{11\cdot1}e_{11\cdot1} + d_{11\cdot2}e_{11\cdot2} + \cdots + d_{11\cdot5}e_{11\cdot5}$$
$$c'_{12} = d_{11\cdot1}e_{12\cdot1} + d_{11\cdot2}e_{12\cdot2} + \cdots + d_{11\cdot5}e_{12\cdot5}$$
$$c'_{13} = d_{11\cdot2}e_{13\cdot2} + \cdots + d_{11\cdot5}e_{13\cdot5}$$

etc.

(Omit calculation of regression coefficients at this stage.)

20

$$c'_{22} = d_{12\cdot1}e_{12\cdot1} + d_{12\cdot2}e_{12\cdot2} + d_{12\cdot3}e_{12\cdot3} + \cdots + d_{12\cdot5}e_{12\cdot5}$$
$$c'_{23} = d_{12\cdot2}e_{13\cdot2} + d_{12\cdot3}e_{13\cdot3} + \cdots + d_{12\cdot5}e_{13\cdot5}$$

etc.

21

$$c'_{33} = d_{13\cdot2}e_{13\cdot2} + d_{13\cdot3}e_{13\cdot3} + \cdots + d_{13\cdot5}e_{13\cdot5}$$

etc.

22 to 24 Complete calculation of multipliers.

25

$$r_{12\cdot3456} = \frac{-c'_{12}}{\sqrt{c'_{11}c'_{22}}} \qquad r_{13\cdot2456} = \frac{-c'_{13}}{\sqrt{c'_{11}c'_{33}}} \qquad \text{etc.}$$

26

$$r_{23\cdot1456} = \frac{-c'_{23}}{\sqrt{c'_{22}c'_{33}}} \qquad r_{24\cdot1356} = \frac{-c'_{24}}{\sqrt{c'_{22}c'_{44}}} \qquad \text{etc.}$$

27 to 30 Complete calculation of partial correlation coefficients.

Return to line 19 $b'_{61} = \dfrac{-c'_{16}}{c'_{66}},\ b'_{62} = \dfrac{-c'_{26}}{c'_{66}}, \cdots, b'_{16} = \dfrac{-c'_{16}}{c_{11}}$

For these calculations, first obtain reciprocals of $c_{11}, c_{22}, \cdots, c_{66}$ and multiply these systematically by numerators to obtain the required quotients. A complete check is obtained by repeating the calculation of the partial coefficients from $r_{12\cdot3\cdots6} = \sqrt{b'_{12} \cdot b'_{21}}$, etc.

where p is the number of independent variables. A test of significance of the multiple regression equation or of the multiple correlation coefficient is given by calculating

$$F = \frac{\Sigma y_e^2}{p} \times \frac{n - p - 1}{\Sigma y_d^2} \qquad 23$$

and the table of F is entered under $n - p - 1$ degrees of freedom.

When the correlations only are known, F can be calculated from

$$F = \frac{r^2_{1\cdot 23 \cdots p}}{1 - r_{1\cdot 23 \cdots p}} \left(\frac{n - p - 1}{p} \right) \qquad 24$$

This arises from the fact that

$$r^2_{1\cdot 23 \cdots p} = \frac{\Sigma y_e^2}{\Sigma y^2} \qquad 25$$

and

$$1 - r^2_{1\cdot 23 \cdots p} = \frac{\Sigma y_d^2}{\Sigma y^2} \qquad 26$$

Putting (26) into the form

$$r^2_{1\cdot 23 \cdots p} = 1 - \frac{\Sigma y_d^2}{\Sigma y^2} \qquad 27$$

is also of value in an interpretation of the multiple correlation coefficient. As the deviations from regression approach zero, the coefficient approaches $+1$.

14. Special applications. The analysis of variance provides a test of the significance of the additional information obtained in calculating multiple correlation coefficients. This principle was applied by Geddes and Goulden [4] in a practical problem in cereal chemistry. Correlations were first determined between loaf volume of wheat flour and the percentage of protein. In later studies the protein was separated into two portions, peptized and non-peptized, and with these two portions as variables the multiple correlation for their combined effect on loaf volume was calculated. If the proportions of the two kinds of protein have an important effect on loaf volume, the multiple correlation should be significantly higher than the simple correlation for total protein and loaf volume. A method of comparing the two correlations would determine, therefore, the practical significance, for purposes of predicting flour quality, of knowing the amounts of peptized and non-peptized protein in addition to the total protein.

If we let X_1 represent loaf volume, X_2 the peptized protein, X_3 the non-peptized protein, and X_p the total protein, the corresponding simple and multiple correlation coefficients are r_{1p} and $r_{1\cdot 23}$. The total protein is, of course, $(X_2 + X_3)$, the sum of the two fractions.

Assuming these correlations to be determined from 20 pairs of values, the sums of squares representing deviations from the regression function are proportional to $(1 - r^2_{1p})$ and $(1 - r^2_{1\cdot 23})$, respectively, and the corresponding degrees of freedom are 18 and 17. The effect of bringing in more variables to estimate X_1 as in multiple regression is to decrease the sum of squares due to deviations from the regression function, but for each additional variable introduced 1 degree of freedom is lost, and unless the reduction of the sum of squares is more than proportional to the loss in degrees of freedom there is no gain in precision. An analysis may therefore be set up as follows:

	SS	DF	MS
Deviations, regression of X_p on X_1	$1 - r^2_{1p}$	18	
Deviations, regression of X_2 and X_3 on X_1	$1 - r^2_{1\cdot 23}$	17	(1)
Additional degree of freedom	$(1 - r^2_{1p}) - (1 - r^2_{1\cdot 23})$	1	(2)

Applying the F test to the mean squares (1) and (2), taking (1) as the error, we can determine the significance of the gain in information due to the addition of another variable.

In one actual experiment for a series of 20 flours from No. 2 Northern wheat, $r_{1p} = 0.511$ and $r_{1\cdot 23} = 0.732$. The analysis gives

SS		DF	MS	F	1% Point
$1 - r^2_{1p}$	0.738 879	18			
$1 - r^2_{1\cdot 23}$	0.464 176	17	0.027 30		
Difference	0.274 703	1	0.274 7	10.06	8.40

15. Exercises.

1. R. A. Fisher [3] gives the following data for the effect of longitude (X_1), latitude (X_2), and altitude (X_3) on yield Y.

$$\Sigma y^2 = 1786.6$$

$\Sigma(x_1y) = 1137.4$	$\Sigma(x_1)^2 = 1934.1$	$\Sigma(x_1x_2) = -772.2$
$\Sigma(x_2y) = 592.9$	$\Sigma(x_2^2) = 2889.5$	$\Sigma(x_1x_3) = 924.1$
$\Sigma(x_3y) = 891.8$	$\Sigma(x_3^2) = 1750.8$	$\Sigma(x_2x_3) = 119.6$
$b_{Y1\cdot 23} = 0.3962$	$b_{Y2\cdot 13} = -0.1120$	$b_{Y3\cdot 12} = 0.3079$

Calculate the partial regression coefficients for these data (*a*) by the direct method as in Example 8–1 and (*b*) by obtaining a matrix of multipliers as in Example 8–2.

2. Test the significance of the partial regression coefficients obtained in Exercise 1, applying formulas (10). Devise a method of determining the fiducial limits of b_3.

3. Test the significance of the difference between b_1 and b_2 in Example 8–2.

4. From the data of Exercise 1 obtain the correlation coefficients $r_{12}, r_{13}, r_{14}, r_{23}, r_{24}, r_{34}$, substituting X_1 for Y, X_2 for X_1, X_3 for X_2, and X_4 for X_3. Then solve for the partial correlation coefficients as in Example 8–4.

5. Calculate from Exercise 4 the multiple correlation coefficient $r_{1\cdot 234}$ and test its significance.

6. For $n' = 40$, determine the multiple correlation $r_{1\cdot 234}$ that is just significant.

7. Determine the significance of the gain in information through the calculation of multiple correlations in the examples given below. For each comparison, state your conclusion in words.

$$n' = 40 \qquad r_{12} = 0.7643 \qquad r_{1\cdot 234} = 0.8031$$

$$n' = 62 \qquad r_{12} = 0.8744 \qquad r_{1\cdot 2345} = 0.9664$$

$$n' = 20 \qquad r_{12} = 0.7621 \qquad r_{1\cdot 23} = 0.7635$$

$$n' = 20 \qquad r_{12} = 0.7316 \qquad r_{1\cdot 23456} = 0.7329$$

REFERENCES

1. Prescott D. Crout, *Trans. Am. Inst. Elec. Engrs.*, **60**, 1–7, 1941.
2. P. S. Dwyer, *Psychometrika*, **6**, 101–129, 1941.
3. R. A. Fisher, *Statistical Methods for Research Workers*, Oliver and Boyd, Edinburgh and London, 10th ed., 1948.
4. W. F. Geddes and C. H. Goulden, *Cereal Chem.*, **7**, 527–556, 1930.
5. W. F. Geddes, G. J. Malloch, and R. K. Larmour, *Can. J. Research*, **6**, 119–155, 1932.
6. H. A. Wallace and G. W. Snedecor, Correlation and Machine Calculation, *Iowa State Coll. Bull.*, **4**, 1931.
7. J. Wishart, Table of the Significant Values of the Multiple Correlation Coefficient, *Quart. J. Roy. Meteor. Soc.*, **54**, 258–259, 1928.

CHAPTER 9

The Analysis of Covariance

1. Principles of covariance analysis. In the analysis of variance for a single variable, the variation can be partitioned into different components. Having a two-way classification, we can sort out the variance components into rows, columns, and residual. In a randomized block experiment we can sort out the variance components attributable to blocks, treatments, and error. The same is true for the correlated variability or covariation of two variables, and the mechanism for sorting out the covariance effects is known as the *analysis of covariance*.

In order to think in terms of actual values, we can assume that the variables are yields of grain and straw from cereal plots. Assuming a test of n treatments conducted in r randomized blocks, we would have the following sets of values, where Y represents the yield and X the straw.

		Treatment 1	Treatment 2	· · ·	Treatment n	Block Mean
Block	1	$X_{11}\ Y_{11}$	$X_{12}\ Y_{12}$	· · ·	$X_{1n}\ Y_{1n}$	$\bar{X}_{b1}\ \bar{Y}_{b1}$
	2	$X_{21}\ Y_{21}$	$X_{22}\ Y_{22}$	· · ·	$X_{2n}\ Y_{2n}$	$\bar{X}_{b2}\ \bar{Y}_{b2}$
	⋮	⋮	⋮		⋮	⋮
	r	$X_{r1}\ Y_{r1}$	$X_{r2}\ Y_{r2}$	· · ·	$X_{rn}\ Y_{rn}$	$\bar{X}_{br}\ \bar{Y}_{br}$
Treatment Mean		$\bar{X}_{t1}\ \bar{Y}_{t1}$	$\bar{X}_{t2}\ \bar{Y}_{t2}$	· · ·	$\bar{X}_{tn}\ \bar{Y}_{tn}$	$\bar{X}\ \bar{Y}$ General Mean

Note that there are n treatment means of X and Y, and r block means of X and Y, and each of these sets of paired values can determine a coefficient for the regression of Y on X. Also there is a set of rn values representing individual deviations of X and Y from the general mean, less the effects due to block and treatment means.

Specifically, these are

$$(X_{11} - \bar{X}_{b1} - \bar{X}_{t1} + \bar{X})(Y_{11} - \bar{Y}_{b1} - \bar{Y}_{t1} + \bar{Y})$$
$$(X_{12} - \bar{X}_{b1} - \bar{X}_{t2} + \bar{X})(Y_{12} - \bar{Y}_{b1} - \bar{Y}_{t2} + \bar{Y})$$
$$\vdots \qquad\qquad \vdots$$
$$(X_{rn} - \bar{X}_{br} - \bar{X}_{tn} + \bar{X})(Y_{rn} - \bar{Y}_{br} - \bar{Y}_{tn} + \bar{Y})$$

This set will also yield a regression coefficient of Y on X.

In connection with the problem of sorting out regression effects the first question we ask is: What are the expected values of the regression coefficients, which we shall represent by b_b for block means, b_t for treatment means, and b_e for the residual or error term? Let us suppose that we have a large population to be sampled in which Y is normally distributed for each level of X and in which the regression coefficient of Y on X is β_{YX}. Then, if the pairs of values of X and Y are selected at random from this population and arranged in the two-way classification for blocks and treatments, it can be shown that the expected value of b_b, b_t, and b_e is β_{YX}. That is, if in an actual experiment b_t is considerably larger than b_e, which in any event has the expected value β_{YX}, we are led to the conclusion that the data are heterogeneous for regression effects, or, in other words, that the regression effects for the treatments did not arise merely from random sampling of the regression in the population represented by the error term.

The sorting out of regression and correlation effects is, therefore, an obvious application of the covariance analysis. A regression coefficient measuring a total effect is not capable of a definite interpretation, nor can it be submitted to valid tests of significance if heterogeneity is present. Suppose that we have a total regression of yield of barley on quantity of malt extract for 20 plots located at each of 6 stations. The sums of squares and degrees of freedom can be sorted out as follows

SS	DF
Regression	1
Deviations from regression	118
Total	119

and the regression may appear to be highly significant, but, if it is sorted out into its components, between and within stations, we have two analyses:

Between Stations	DF	Within Stations	DF
Regression	1	Regression	1
Deviations from regression	4	Deviations from regression	113
Total	5	Total	114

and, if the greater part of the total regression is caused by the station means, it is quite possible that there will be no significance in either case, as the between-station regression has to be tested against an error based on only 4 degrees of freedom.

A total covariance of the type mentioned above is sometimes referred to as containing a spurious effect. This is taken care of in the covariance analysis, and the so-called spurious effect is not only removed but evaluated as a distinct component of the total.

2. Applications of the covariance method to the control of error. One of the most important applications of the analysis of covariance is in the control of errors that arise at random throughout the experiment and cannot be taken care of by replication. For example, the number of plants per plot for such crops as mangels and sugar beets may occur at random throughout the experiment and, so far as they affect the yields of single plots, add to the experimental error. Correction of the yields on the basis that yield is directly proportional to the number of plants is a frequent practice, but it is not difficult to demonstrate that yield is rarely if ever proportional to the number of plants per plot and that such an adjustment is likely to exaggerate the yields of plots in which plants are missing. Correction on the basis of the exact relation between yield and number of plants as indicated by the data is, however, perfectly justifiable, and the method of making such a correction is a natural development of the covariance technique. Numerous applications of the same method will undoubtedly occur to workers in other fields.

In order to demonstrate the control of error by the covariance method we shall represent a covariance analysis algebraically as follows, in which the experiment is presumed to be a randomized block field plot test.

	DF	$\Sigma(x^2)$	$\Sigma(xy)$	$\Sigma(y^2)$	b_{yx}	$b_{yx}\Sigma(xy)$	$\Sigma(y_d^2)$	DF for $\Sigma(y_d^2)$
Blocks	p	A_0	B_0	C_0				
Treatments	q	A_1	B_1	C_1	$b_1 = B_1/A_1$	b_1B_1	$C_1 - b_1B_1$	$q - 1$
Error	n	A_2	B_2	C_2	$b_2 = B_2/A_2$	b_2B_2	$C_2 - b_2B_2$	$n - 1$
$T + E$	$n + q$	A_t	B_t	C_t	$b_t = B_t/A_t$	b_tB_t	$C_t - b_tB_t$	$n + q - 1$

In the column headings, $\Sigma(y_d^2)$ indicates a sum of squares for Y adjusted by the regression coefficient in the same line.

The calculations are complete in each line of the table. The regression coefficient is B/A, and the adjustment in the sum of squares for Y is bB or B^2/A. In the last line we are considering only treatments and error so that $A_t = A_1 + A_2$, $B_t = B_1 + B_2$, and $C_t = C_1 + C_2$.

The second step in the procedure is indicated as follows.

	DF	SS	MS
$T + E$	$n + q - 1$	$C_t - b_t B_t$	
E	$n - 1$	$C_2 - b_2 B_2$	v_2
T (difference)	q	$C_1 + b_2 B_2 - b_t B_t$	v_1
T	$q - 1$	$C_1 - b_1 B_1$	v_3
$(b_1 - b_2)$ (difference)	1	$b_1 B_1 + b_2 B_2 - b_t B_t$	v_4

The first sum of squares for treatments is obviously represented by q degrees of freedom, the expression for degrees of freedom corresponding to $C_1 + b_2 B_2 - b_t B_t$ being $q + 1 - 1$. The second treatment sum of squares is written down from the first table and is represented by $q - 1$ degrees of freedom, as it has been adjusted by the treatment coefficient. On subtracting the second treatment sum of squares from the first, we have a sum of squares given by $b_1 B_1 + b_2 B_2 - b_t B_t$, and it is not difficult to prove the following equality:

$$b_1 B_1 + b_2 B_2 - b_t B_t = b_1^2 A_1 + b_2^2 A_2 - b_t^2 A_t = \frac{A_1 A_2}{A_1 + A_2} (b_1 - b_2)^2$$

It follows that when $b_1 = b_2$ this sum of squares is zero, and that a test of significance of the corresponding variance v_4 is a test of the significance of the difference between the error and treatment regression coefficients.

The test of significance of the treatment differences involves a comparison of the variances v_2 and v_1. The fact that v_1 may contain a significant effect due to $b_1 - b_2$ does not vitiate the meaning of the test, as such an effect is obviously due to some factor characteristic of the treatments. In respect to yield and number of plants per plot, the treatment regression coefficient b_1 may be higher than b_2, and this will contribute to the significance of v_1; but b_2 represents the regression of yield on number of plants within treatments and may be taken as a true measure of the effect of number of plants on yield. If the treatment regression coefficient is higher than b_2, this probably reflects an additional genetic relationship and one that should contribute to the significance of the differences between the treatments. A further test may be applied, however, to v_3, and by a comparison of the significance of v_3 and v_4 a complete picture of the variety effects is obtained. The value of such an analysis, if, for example, number of roots has a significant effect on yield, is that the error variance will be reduced with a consequent increase in the significance of the treatment differences, if such differences exist. If the analysis of the unadjusted yields shows significant differences when the adjusted yields do not, this simply means that the original differences were due to number of roots and not to the effect of the treatments as measured by average yield per root.

R. A. Fisher [5] has pointed out that an appropriate scale for measuring the effectiveness of methods of reducing the error is the inverse of the variance. This is sometimes called the *invariance*, or the *quantity of information*, and is represented by $1/v$. In measuring the reduction of error by means of the covariance analysis, this scale is particularly valuable. If the original error variance is twice as large as the final error variance obtained by adjusting the sum of squares for the associated variable, in the original form about twice as many replicates would be necessary to give the same accuracy as for the adjusted results. One should not reason from this that the significance of the differences between the treatments will always be increased accordingly, as it must be remembered that at the same time differences between the treatments due to the associated variable are also being removed.

The test of significance having been applied as outlined, the next step is to make corrections to the variety means. Since the regression coefficient in the error line may be considered as representing the actual effect of number of roots on yield, this regression coefficient should enter into the formula for making corrections. The corrected means should then be the best possible estimates of what the means would have been if they had not been affected by variations in number of roots. The regression equation will be of the form

$$Y_1 = \bar{Y}_{t1} - b_{yx}(\bar{X}_{t1} - \bar{X}) \qquad 1$$

where $\bar{X}_{t1}$ is the mean of X for treatment 1, $\bar{Y}_{t1}$ is the mean of Y for the same treatment, b_{yx} is the regression of Y on X in the error line, and Y_1 is the estimated mean of the variety.

Formulas for the standard error of differences between corrected means have been given by Wishart [12]. To compare two corrected means such as Y_p and Y_q the standard error of the difference between two means is

$$\sqrt{s^2\left[\frac{2}{r} + \frac{(\bar{X}_p - \bar{X}_q)^2}{A_2}\right]} \qquad 2$$

where s^2 is the mean square in the error line of the analysis of covariance table (for example, in Table 9–2 it will be 19.56/8 = 2.445), A_2 is the sum of squares for X in the same line, r is the number of replications, and $(\bar{X}_p - \bar{X}_q)$ is the difference between the two means in the two expressions for calculating Y_p and Y_q from equation (1). Thus

$$Y_p = \bar{Y}_p - b_{yx}(\bar{X}_p - \bar{X}) \qquad \text{and} \qquad Y_q = \bar{Y}_q - b_{yx}(\bar{X}_q - \bar{X})$$

In comparing two means corrected for two variables X_1 and X_2, we calculate the standard error of a mean difference as follows.

$$\sqrt{s^2\left(\frac{2}{r} + \frac{u^2B - 2uvP + v^2A}{AB - P^2}\right)} \tag{3}$$

where A and B are the sums of squares in the error line for X_1 and X_2, P is the sum of products for X_1 and X_2 in the error line, $u = (\bar{X}_{1p} - \bar{X}_{1q})$, difference between X_1 means, and $v = (\bar{X}_{2p} - \bar{X}_{2q})$, difference between X_2 means.

Finney [4] has suggested a simple formula for the variance of the difference between two adjusted means. The exact formula given above is different for each comparison, and Finney's suggestion is to compromise by incorporating the average value of $(\bar{X}_p - \bar{X}_q)^2$, which can be equated to

$$\frac{2A_1}{r(t - 1)} \tag{4}$$

where A_1 is the treatment sum of squares for X, r is the number of replications, and t is the number of treatments. The general formula for the variance of a difference simplifies to

$$\frac{2s^2}{r}\left[1 + \frac{A_1}{A_2(t - 1)}\right] \tag{5}$$

where A_2 is the sum of squares for X in the error line.

3. Testing the heterogeneity of a series of regression coefficients. The analysis of covariance provides a unique method for testing the significance of the differences between two or more regression coefficients. Following the same symbolism as in the previous section, the procedure is as given on p. 159.

The last sum of squares may be shown to be

$$\sum_{1}(bB) - b_tB_t = \sum^{{}_pC_2}\left[\frac{A_jA_k(b_j - b_k)^2}{A + A + \cdots + Ap}\right] \tag{6}$$

where b_j and b_k represent all possible pairs of the regression coefficients, and A_j and A_k all possible pairs of the corresponding sums of squares of X.

The comparison of v_1 and v_2 by means of the F test furnishes, therefore, the required test of the heterogeneity of the regression coefficients.

Preliminary Calculations

Group	DF	$\Sigma(x^2)$	$\Sigma(xy)$	$\Sigma(y^2)$	b_{yx}	$b_{yx}\Sigma(xy)$	$\Sigma(y_d^2)$	DF for $\Sigma(y_d^2)$
1	q	A_1	B_1	C_1	$b_1 = B_1/A_1$	b_1B_1	$C_1 - b_1B_1$	$q - 1$
2	q	A_2	B_2	C_2	$b_2 = B_2/A_2$	b_2B_2	$C_2 - b_2B_2$	$q - 1$
.	.	.	.	.	.	.	.	.
.	.	.	.	.	.	.	.	.
.	.	.	.	.	.	.	.	.
p	q	A_p	B_p	C_p	$b_p = B_p/A_p$	b_pB_p	$C_p - b_pB_p$	$q - 1$
Total	pq	A_t	B_t	C_t	$b_t = B_t/A_t$	b_tB_t	$C_t - b_tB_t$	$pq - 1$

Test of Significance

	DF	$\Sigma(y_d^2)$	MS
Total	$pq - 1$	$C_t - b_tB_t$	
Within groups	$p(q - 1)$	$\sum_1^p(C - bB)$	v_1 (error mean square)
Difference	$(p - 1)$	$\sum_1^p(bB) - b_tB_t$	v_2 (due to differences between regression coefficients)

4. Selection of variable for error control. A certain amount of care is necessary in selecting variables that are to be used in the control of error. A simple rule is not to choose any variable that might itself be affected by the treatments because with such a variable the exercise of control results in the removal of part of the treatment effects we wish to measure. The yields from a uniformity trial carried out on a series of plots that are to be used the following year for an actual trial are obviously ideal for error control. In a fruit-tree experiment we might take the yield of fruit per tree before the treatments are laid down. The size of the trees might also be a convenient variable for error control, and possibly for more than one year, but this variable would not be suitable after the time when the treatments could affect the size. Similarly, with all error control variables, treatment effects must be excluded.

5. Calculation of sums of products. The sums of products for the various components in an analysis of covariance can be calculated by a procedure exactly analogous to that for calculating sums of squares. Assume a set of values for n treatments in r replicates, as in the following table.

		Treatment 1	2	$\cdots$	n	Replicate Total
Replicate	1	$X_{11}\ Y_{11}$	$X_{12}\ Y_{12}$	$\cdots$	$X_{1n}\ Y_{1n}$	$\Sigma X_{b1}\ \Sigma Y_{b1}$
	2	$X_{21}\ Y_{21}$	$X_{22}\ Y_{22}$	$\cdots$	$X_{2n}\ Y_{2n}$	$\Sigma X_{b2}\ \Sigma Y_{b2}$
	$\vdots$	$\vdots$	$\vdots$		$\vdots$	$\vdots$
	r	$X_{r1}\ Y_{r1}$	$X_{r2}\ Y_{r2}$	$\cdots$	$X_{rn}\ Y_{rn}$	$\Sigma X_{br}\ \Sigma Y_{br}$
Treatment Total		$\Sigma X_{t1}\ \Sigma Y_{t1}$	$\Sigma X_{t2}\ \Sigma Y_{t2}$	$\cdots$	$\Sigma X_{tn}\ \Sigma Y_{tn}$	$G_x\ \ G_y$ Grand Total

The sums of products are

Total $$\sum_1^{nr}(xy) = \sum_1^{nr}(XY) - \frac{G_xG_y}{nr}$$

Treatments $$r\sum_1^{n}(\bar{x}_t\bar{y}_t) = \sum_1^{n}\left(\frac{\Sigma X_t \Sigma Y_t}{r}\right) - \frac{G_xG_y}{nr}$$

Replicates $$n\sum_1^{r}(\bar{x}_b\bar{y}_b) = \sum_1^{r}\left(\frac{\Sigma X_b \Sigma Y_b}{n}\right) - \frac{G_xG_y}{nr}$$

$$\text{Error} = \text{Total} - \text{Treatments} - \text{Replicates}$$

where $\bar{x}_t = \bar{X}_t - \bar{X}$, $\bar{y}_t = \bar{Y}_t - \bar{Y}$, $\bar{x}_b = \bar{X}_b - \bar{X}$, $\bar{y}_b = \bar{Y}_b - \bar{Y}$.

6. Example 9–1. Analysis of covariance. This one example will demonstrate some of the important applications of the covariance analysis. Data are taken from Bartlett [1]. The data were presented originally in a demonstration of the application of the covariance technique to the estimation of a missing value. The results obtained are given in Table 9–1. In Bartlett's analysis it was shown that the results in replicate E for ration 3 were erratic, and estimated values were substituted. Here the analysis is performed on the original values.

In this experiment cows were tested during a control period in order to obtain their potential milk yield. The results for this control period provided a basis for error control through the analysis of covariance.

The analysis of covariance is set up in Table 9–2. It is recommended that sums of squares, products, and totals be obtained by treatments as they will be required in this form for a test of heterogeneity.

The calculation of sums of products is as follows.

Total

Ration 1	1937
Ration 2	1405
Ration 3	1861
Ration 4	2068
	7271

$$7271 - \frac{388 \times 293}{16} = 165.75$$

Replicates
$$\frac{(111 \times 81) + (93 \times 72) + \cdots}{4} - \frac{388 \times 293}{16} = 92.50$$

Rations
$$\frac{(97 \times 79) + (85 \times 66) + \cdots}{4} - \frac{388 \times 293}{16} = 24.00$$

Error
$$165.75 - 92.50 - 24.00 = 49.25$$

After also calculating the sums of squares, the analysis of covariance can be set up as in Table 9–2.

TABLE 9–1

MEAN YIELD OF MILK IN (POUNDS PER WEEK)/10 FOR CONTROL AND EXPERIMENTAL PERIODS, DAIRY COW FEEDING TRIAL—CONTROL PERIOD YIELD = X, EXPERIMENTAL PERIOD YIELD = Y

		Ration								Total	
		1		2		3		4			
		X	Y	X	Y	X	Y	X	Y	X	Y
Replicate	B	28	21	22	17	27	18	34	25	111	81
	C	24	21	22	16	26	20	21	15	93	72
	D	20	16	18	16	19	14	21	16	78	62
	E	25	21	23	17	31	19	27	21	106	78
Total		97	79	85	66	103	71	103	77	388	293

TABLE 9–2

ANALYSIS OF COVARIANCE, DATA OF TABLE 9–1

	DF	x^2	xy	y^2	b_{yx}	$b_{yx}\Sigma xy$	Σy_d^2	DF
Replicates	3	163.50	92.50	52.69				
Treatments	3	54.00	24.00	26.19	0.444 44	10.67	15.52	2
Error	9	73.50	49.25	52.56	0.670 07	33.00	19.56	8
Treatments + Error	12	127.50	73.25	78.75	0.574 51	42.08	36.67	11

Notice that the last line is obtained by adding the sums of squares and products for treatments and error. The column head Σy_d^2 is obtained by subtracting the previous column (sum of squares for regression) from the sum of squares for Y.

The next step in the analysis should be to determine the significance of the regression in the error line. This must be significant in order to make adjustments worth while. We have the simple analysis:

	SS	DF	MS	F
Regression	33.00	1	33.00	13.5
Error	19.56	8	2.445	

Since F is much greater than the 1% point, we are assured of the significance of the regression of experimental yield on control yield, and adjustments to the treatment means should be worth while.

We still have to test the significance of differences between treatment means. The test is carried out in Table 9–3.

TABLE 9–3

TEST OF SIGNIFICANCE OF TREATMENT EFFECTS

	DF	SS	MS	F	5% Point
Treatments + Error	11	36.67			
Error	8	19.56	2.445		
Difference = Treatments	3	17.11	5.703	2.33	4.07
Treatments (adjusted by treatment regression)	2	15.52			
$b_e - b_t$	1	1.59	1.59		

The reduced sum of squares for treatments + error is brought down from Table 9–2, together with the reduced sum of squares for error. The difference is a sum of squares for treatments that can be tested against the reduced error. The further step carried out in the last two lines is to obtain a test of the significance of the difference between the treatment and error regressions.

For testing the significance of differences between pairs of adjusted treatment means we can apply formula (5), suggested by Finney [4]. Here the variance of a difference between two means is taken as

$$\frac{2 \times 2.445}{4}\left(1 + \frac{54.00}{73.50 \times 3}\right) = 1.522$$

and the standard error of a mean difference $= \sqrt{1.522} = 1.23$.

The analysis of this experiment brings out some interesting points. In the first place, the reduction in the error from adjustment by the milk yields in the control period is quite marked. The relative precision of the results before and after adjustment is approximately

$$\frac{52.56}{9} \div \frac{19.56}{8} = 2.39$$

indicating a very decided gain in information.

The F test of the ration effects before adjustment yields an F value of 1.49 whereas after adjustment the F value is 2.33. Neither of these is equal to the 5% point, but there is sufficient improvement after adjustment to indicate that the method is sound. Owing to the large gain in precision one might expect a greater effect on the significance of the rations, but in this connection it must be remembered that a portion of the ration effects in the unadjusted data must correspond with true ration effects and this is removed by the adjustment.

7. Example 9–2. Testing for heterogeneity of regression. If the sums of squares and products are determined for each ration, an analysis such as that of Table 9–4 can be set up.

TABLE 9–4

TEST OF HETEROGENEITY OF REGRESSION BETWEEN TREATMENTS

Ration	DF	x^2	xy	y^2	b_{yx}	$b_{yx}\Sigma xy$	Σy_d^2		DF	
1	3	32.75	21.25	18.75	0.6488	13.79	4.96	13.36	2	8
2	3	14.75	2.50	1.00	0.1695	0.42	0.58		2	
3	3	74.75	32.75	20.75	0.4381	14.35	6.40		2	
4	3	114.75	85.25	64.75	0.7429	63.33	1.42		2	
Total	12	237.00	141.75	105.25	0.5981	84.78	20.47		11	

It will be noted that although the total reduced sum of squares accounts for 11 degrees of freedom, the reduced sums of squares for each ration account for only $4 \times 2 = 8$ degrees of freedom. The remaining 3 degrees of freedom represent differences between the 4 regression coefficients. This enables us to set up the following analysis.

	DF	SS	MS	F
Total	11	20.47		
Rations	8	13.36	1.670	
Difference	3	7.11	2.370	1.42

There is very little evidence of significant heterogeneity.

8. Exercises

1. The data in Table 9–5 are grain and straw yields given by Eden and Fisher [3] for 8 manurial treatments and 8 replicates of each. Take the straw weight as a concomitant variable in an analysis of covariance and test the significance of the adjusted grain yields. From the results obtained and from other characteristics of the data decide as to the suitability of straw yield for the adjustment of grain yields.

TABLE 9–5

THE MEAN GRAIN AND STRAW YIELDS FOR EACH OF 64 PLOTS, THERE BEING 8 DIFFERENT MANURIAL TREATMENTS AND 8 REPLICATES OF EACH

Treatments	Block 1		Block 2		Block 3		Block 4	
	Straw	Grain	Straw	Grain	Straw	Grain	Straw	Grain
A	242	620	321	646	261	681	317	644
B	267	644	382	745	201	542	316	711
C	215	523	330	713	298	686	381	688
D	212	601	292	693	265	685	255	714
E	322	664	370	693	284	666	323	516
F	200	514	261	637	259	697	361	710
G	260	550	318	708	266	663	340	673
H	203	521	275	661	207	594	331	730

Treatments	Block 5		Block 6		Block 7		Block 8	
	Straw	Grain	Straw	Grain	Straw	Grain	Straw	Grain
A	255	706	331	615	216	552	295	726
B	280	705	285	637	200	543	309	646
C	300	692	294	612	256	635	284	748
D	238	699	309	697	283	701	324	746
E	232	656	393	663	351	657	363	683
F	234	633	258	595	306	697	376	712
G	362	671	400	626	276	655	385	671
H	229	625	266	644	276	745	328	747

REFERENCES

1. M. S. Bartlett, *J. Roy. Stat. Soc. Suppl.*, **4**, 137–170, 1937.
2. W. G. Cochran, Long-Term Agricultural Experiments, *J. Roy. Stat. Soc. Suppl.*, **6**, 104–139, 1939.
3. T. Eden and R. A. Fisher, *J. Agr. Sci.*, **17**, 548–562, 1927.
4. D. J. Finney, *Biometrics Bull.*, **2**, 53–55, 1946.

5. R. A. Fisher, *The Design of Experiments*, Oliver and Boyd, Edinburgh and London, 4th ed., 1947.
6. R. A. Fisher, *Statistical Methods for Research Workers*, Oliver and Boyd, Edinburgh and London, 10th ed., 1948.
7. H. G. Sanders, *J. Agr. Sci.*, **20,** 63–73, 1930.
8. G. W. Snedecor, *Statistical Methods*, Iowa State College Press, Ames, Iowa, 4th ed., 1946.
9. R. Summerby, *Macdonald College Tech. Bull.*, **15,** 1934.
10. A. G. O. Whiteside, J. Edgar, and C. H. Goulden, *Cereal Chem.*, **11,** 615–625, 1934.
11. J. Wishart and H. G. Sanders, *Principles and Practices of Yield Trials*, Empire Cotton Growing Corp., London, 1935.
12. J. Wishart, *J. Roy. Stat. Soc. Suppl.*, **3,** 79–82, 1936.

CHAPTER 10

Non-Linear Regression

1. Analysis of linear and non-linear regression components. In Chapter 5, Section 12, it was pointed out that sums of squares representing a set of means could be broken up into sums of squares representing individual degrees of freedom. By following a simple rule it was shown that, having decided on a given comparison, other comparisons could be selected such that all comparisons would be orthogonal. A situation of particular interest arises when we require a comparison that represents what is known as the *linear* effect. Suppose, for example, that we have the following results, representing a response to four levels of treatment.

Levels (X)	1	2	3	4
Response (Y)	9.4	12.6	8.7	6.3

The results show that there is an increase in response up to the second level and then a gradual decrease. The linear response will be simply that portion of the total that can be represented by a straight-line regression equation of the form $Y = a + bX$. From our knowledge of regression methods it is clear that the equation to be fitted is expressed in the form

$$Y = (\bar{Y} - b\bar{X}) + bX$$

where b is the regression coefficient and is given by

$$b = \frac{\Sigma xy}{\Sigma x^2}$$

where $x = X - \bar{X}$ and $y = Y - \bar{Y}$. We shall make this calculation and show later how it may be done by a much easier method.

$$\Sigma(xy) = 85.9 - \frac{10.0 \times 37.0}{4} = -6.60$$

$$\Sigma x^2 = 30.0 - \frac{10.0^2}{4} = 5.00$$

Then the required sum of squares for linear regression is

$$\frac{(\Sigma xy)^2}{\Sigma x^2} = \frac{6.6^2}{5} = 8.71$$

The total sum of squares for Y is of course

$$9.4^2 + 12.6^2 + 8.7^2 + 6.3^2 - \frac{37.0^2}{4} = 20.25$$

An analysis can then be made as follows.

	SS	DF	MS
Linear regression	8.71	1	8.71
Deviations from regression	11.54	2	5 77
Total	20.25	3	

The sum of squares for linear regression does not take up a very large proportion of the total. This is to be expected, owing to the rise and fall in the response which is definitely not linear. This result emphasizes the need for fitting by means of a more complicated function such as $Y = a + bX + cX^2$, which is known as a quadratic and will give a parabola. This curve can be fitted by a procedure similar to that for the equation $Y = a + bX$, but the method is rather complicated and a much easier one is available by the application of tables given by Fisher and Yates [3]. Actually with these tables we calculate the sums of squares directly and do not go as far as determining the equation unless it is required for a particular purpose. Furthermore, by means of the tables, it is quite easy to determine the sums of squares for equations of higher degree such as the cubic $Y = a + bX + cX^2 + dX^3$.

The section from Fisher and Yates tables required for our problem is reproduced below together with the values of Y.

	Y		
9.4	12.6	8.7	6.3
− 3	− 1	+ 1	+ 3
+ 1	− 1	− 1	+ 1
− 1	+ 3	− 3	+ 1

The required sums of squares are then calculated as follows.

Linear response

$$\frac{(-3 \times 9.4 - 1 \times 12.6 + 1 \times 8.7 + 3 \times 6.3)^2}{20} = 8.71$$

Quadratic response

$$\frac{(1 \times 9.4 - 1 \times 12.6 - 1 \times 8.7 + 1 \times 6.3)^2}{4} = 7.84$$

Cubic response

$$\frac{(-1 \times 9.4 + 3 \times 12.6 - 3 \times 8.7 + 1 \times 6.3)^2}{20} = 3.70$$

where the divisor for each response is the sum of the squares of the coefficients from Fisher and Yates' tables. Thus the first divisor is $3^2 + 1^2 + 1^2 + 3^2 = 20$.

Adding the sums of squares gives a total of 20.25, showing that all the components have been calculated. It is important to note here that the quadratic response does not represent the sum of squares due to fitting a quadratic of the form $Y = a + bX + cX^2$. It represents merely the additional sum of squares obtained on fitting the quadratic over and above that for fitting the linear equation. Actually the total sum of squares that can be accounted for by the quadratic is $8.71 + 7.84 = 16.55$. Similarly the sum of squares 3.70 represents the additional sum of squares due to fitting the cubic. It follows, too, from this that each sum of squares represents 1 degree of freedom.

The complete analysis is:

	SS	DF	MS
Linear response	8.71	1	8.71
Quadratic response	7.84	1	7.84
Cubic response	3.70	1	3.70

If each determination had been made in duplicate, there would have been an additional sum of squares for 3 degrees of freedom that might be suitable as an error for testing the significance of the three effects.

It should also be noted that the effects determined are orthogonal. This is true because the sum of the coefficients in each line is zero and the sum of the products of the corresponding coefficients for any two lines is zero.

2. Analysis of regression components in an actual example. In an experiment on the effect of adding different levels of bromate in baking loaves from a series of flours from 17 varieties of wheat, Larmour [5] obtained the results given in Table 10–1. The data are loaf volumes in cubic centimeters coded by dividing by 100 and rounding off to one decimal place.

TABLE 10–1

LOAF VOLUMES FOR FLOUR OF 17 VARIETIES OF WHEAT, TESTED AT 4 LEVELS OF POTASSIUM BROMATE ADDED IN BAKING

Variety	Level of Bromate				Variety Total	Regression Component		
	1	2	3	4		Linear	Quadratic	Cubic
1	10.8	10.6	9.8	8.8	40.0	− 6.8	− 0.8	0.4
2	9.8	9.6	8.6	8.2	36.2	− 5.8	− 0.2	1.4
3	8.5	8.2	7.7	7.4	31.8	− 3.8	0	0.4
4	8.2	7.6	7.2	7.0	30.0	− 4.0	0.4	0
5	10.4	10.6	9.8	9.4	40.2	− 3.8	− 0.6	1.4
6	9.6	9.8	9.2	8.4	37.0	− 4.2	− 1.0	0.6
7	9.0	9.0	8.8	7.8	34.6	− 3.8	− 1.0	− 0.6
8	8.6	8.7	8.5	8.5	34.3	− 0.5	− 0.1	0.5
9	9.4	10.0	9.6	9.6	38.6	0.2	− 0.6	1.4
10	10.0	10.2	9.6	9.0	38.8	− 3.6	− 0.8	0.8
11	9.4	9.6	9.5	9.2	37.7	− 0.7	− 0.5	0.1
12	8.4	8.7	8.8	8.8	34.7	1.3	− 0.3	0.1
13	6.6	6.5	6.8	6.6	26.5	0.3	− 0.1	− 0.9
14	9.1	8.9	8.4	7.8	34.2	− 4.4	− 0.4	0.2
15	10.8	10.7	10.2	10.0	41.7	− 2.9	− 0.1	0.7
16	7.5	7.4	7.2	7.2	29.3	− 1.1	0.1	0.3
17	8.4	8.6	8.2	8.2	33.4	− 1.0	− 0.2	1.0
Total	154.5	154.7	147.9	141.9	599.0	− 44.6	− 6.2	7.8

TABLE 10–2

ANALYSIS OF VARIANCE, DATA OF TABLE 10–1

	SS	DF	MS	F	5% Point
Varieties	70.0097	16	4.376	40.1	1.86
Treatments	6.5947	3	2.198	20.2	2.80
Interaction	5.2303	48	0.1090		

The simple analysis of variance for these data is given in Table 10–2. The interaction is taken as an error, since there was only one sample of flour of each variety at each level. Note that the effect of bromate is quite significant, but on examining the treatment totals we find that there is a slight increase from the first to the second level and a decrease from the second to the third and from the third to the fourth. This suggests a quadratic effect, so it is of interest to determine the linear, quadratic, and cubic components of the regression of the mean loaf volumes on bromate levels. The calculations are:

Linear component

$$\frac{(-3 \times 154.5 - 1 \times 154.7 + 1 \times 147.9 + 3 \times 141.9)^2}{17 \times 20} = 5.8505$$

Quadratic component

$$\frac{(1 \times 154.5 - 1 \times 154.7 - 1 \times 147.9 + 1 \times 141.9)^2}{17 \times 4} = 0.5653$$

Cubic component

$$\frac{(-1 \times 154.5 + 3 \times 154.7 - 3 \times 147.9 + 1 \times 141.9)^2}{17 \times 20} = 0.1789$$

$$\text{Total} \quad = 6.5947$$

Notice that when totals enter into these calculations the divisor is multiplied by the number of observations in each total.

TABLE 10–3

ANALYSIS OF TREATMENT EFFECTS INTO LINEAR, QUADRATIC, AND CUBIC COMPONENTS

	SS	DF	MS	*F*	5% Point
Linear component	5.8505	1	5.850	53.7	4.04
Quadratic component	0.5653	1	0.5653	5.19	4.04
Cubic component	0.1789	1	0.1789	1.64	4.04
Interaction	5.2303	48	0.1090		

A more complete analysis can now be given as in Table 10–3. The linear and quadratic effects are significant, but the cubic effect is not.

Further information can be obtained from the data by an examination of the consistency of the linear and quadratic effects for the different varieties. In other words, we require for this study the interaction of the linear effect with varieties and of the quadratic effect with varieties. The interaction components are calculated from the figures given in columns 7 and 8 of Table 10–1. These figures are obtained by calculating linear, quadratic, and cubic components in each line. Thus,

$$-6.8 = -3 \times 10.8 - 1 \times 10.6 + 1 \times 9.8 + 3 \times 8.8$$

$$-0.8 = 1 \times 10.8 - 1 \times 10.6 - 1 \times 9.8 + 1 \times 8.8$$

$$0.4 = -1 \times 10.8 + 3 \times 10.6 - 3 \times 9.8 + 1 \times 8.8$$

etc.

Then the sums of squares are:

Linear effect × Varieties

$$\frac{(6.8^2 + 5.8^2 + \cdots + 1.0^2)}{20} - 5.8505 = 4.2665$$

Quadratic effect × Varieties

$$\frac{(0.8^2 + 0.2^2 + \cdots + 0.2^2)}{4} - 0.5655 = 0.6297$$

The complete partitioning of the sum of squares and degrees of freedom is now:

	SS	DF
Varieties	70.0097	16
Treatments		
Linear component	5.8505	1
Quadratic component	0.5653	1
Cubic component	0.1789	1
Interactions		
Linear × Varieties	4.2665	16
Quadratic × Varieties	0.6297	16
Cubic × Varieties	0.3341	16
Total	81.8347	67

Lacking an experimental error determined from variation within true replicates of the experiment, tests of significance of the interactions must be made against residual variation that would seem to be appropriate. For example, the linear × varieties component might be tested against an error made up from adding the sums of squares and degrees of freedom in the last two lines. The quadratic interaction effect could only be tested against the cubic interaction effect.

3. Basic factors in non-linear regression. In Sections 1 and 2 the student is introduced to non-linear regression as a simple extension of the methods of the analysis of variance applied to experimental data. The remainder of the chapter is devoted to the general problems and methods of fitting curves to data having non-linear characteristics. In Chapter 6 we studied methods of fitting a straight line to data representing pairs of values of X and Y, where Y was taken to be the dependent variable. The frequency with which essentially linear relations are encountered is the reason for the emphasis on the linear equation, but as our experience is broadened through a study of data of various kinds it is soon realized that in a great many examples a straight line is inadequate and that if a mathematical function is to be fitted it must be somewhat more complicated than the simple linear form. It should be realized, of course, that the variables studied show, in general, variation due to two sources. One source is in the actual measurement, and the other source is "organic," or, in other words, due to a multitude of influential factors varying in number and intensity. With such variables any tendency towards a *slightly* curvilinear relation would not be brought out except by the study of very large numbers. A second point to keep in mind is that usually we are dealing with the behavior of two variables over a *limited* range of variations. For example, in a study of the relation between temperature and crop yield, under conditions in nature we have actually a very limited range of temperature. Suppose that there is a positive regression of yield on temperature under these conditions, and then we decide to set up a similar type of experiment under artificial conditions. Obviously if the temperature is increased beyond a certain point the yield will be decreased, and the complete result will be represented by a curve that rises at first in a straight line and then begins to curve downward, falling finally to the zero axis. In fertilizer experiments it is a common experience to find that yield increases with the quantity of fertilizer applied, but such a relation has a very obvious limit. At a certain point there will be no further increases in yield, and eventually if enough fertilizer is applied the effect is toxic and yields decrease. There are also for biological variables certain relations that are essentially curved because of fundamental curvilinear relations in the background. The growth curve is a very familiar example. Consider the increase with time of the number of bacteria on a plate. Let the unit of time be the time required for a bacterium to divide and form 2 bacteria. Obviously the theoretical increase, starting with a single unit, is represented by 1, 2, 4, 8, 16, 32, · · ·, and so forth, until conditions become crowded and the rate is slowed down. The equation is $Y = 2^X$ where Y is the number of bacteria and X is the number of units of time. In general such curves are represented by equations of the type $Y = ab^X$ or $Y = ae^X$, where a and b are constants and e = approximately 2.718 28 and is the base of the Naperian system of natural logarithms. These are referred to as *exponential* functions.

In general the functions that can be used for fitting can be divided into two groups: (1) algebraic, such as $Y = a + bX + cX^2$, and (2) exponential such as $Y = ce^{X^2}$ where the variable X appears as an exponent.

4. Reasons for fitting curves. The type of data with which we are dealing, the object of the experiment, and other factors enter into the reasons for fitting curves. It is sometimes stated that the basic reason underlying all regression studies is the setting up of a prediction equation, but this is not always the important feature in the study of biological data and has perhaps been overemphasized. When faced with the analysis of a set of pairs of values of two variables, there is a definite necessity for the reduction of these data to statistics that summarize the results and to which tests of significance can be applied. This in itself is a sufficient reason for fitting a curve.

The need for statistical reduction and the making of tests of significance simplifies also the problem of selecting the type of equation to be fitted. All we require is something that is reasonable and gives a good fit. There may be several equations that will give a good fit, and of these we should select the simplest and the one that can be most easily fitted.

In this reasoning there is a fairly clear-cut distinction between the two types of problems that arise: in the first place, when there is a definite mathematical function in the background based on some fundamental law, and, in the second place, when the object is merely to reduce the data to a simpler form. The first problem arises frequently in experiments in physics or chemistry where the assumption frequently is that all variations from some mathematical law are due to errors of measurement. Success in such an experiment lies not so much in obtaining a curve that gives a good fit but in obtaining a good fit to an equation that expresses a fundamental law.

5. Selecting a regression equation where the trend is non-linear. This is not always a simple problem as there is a very large number of equations from which to choose, and for each we must take into consideration the work involved, the goodness of fit, and whether or not valid tests of significance can be made. These are of two general types: (1) polynomials and (2) exponentials. The exponentials are often referred to as logarithmic curves because they are best transformed to logarithms before fitting. Typical examples are:

Polynomials	Logarithmic
$Y = a + bX$ (linear)	$Y = a + b \log X$
$Y = a + bX + cX^2$ (quadratic)	$\log Y = a + bX$
$Y = a + bX + cX^2 + dX^3$ (cubic)	$\log Y = a + b \log X$
etc., with a number of variations	etc.

Reference to Figure 10–1 will give some idea as to the types of data to which polynomial curves will give the best fit. Note the general shape of polynomials of different degree. The curves of different degree are distinguished by the number of inflection points. The first inflection point comes with the cubic, and there is one additional point for each degree of fitting. Data requiring a curve with several twists must be fitted with a polynomial of high degree. One of the desirable features of the polynomial equations is that they lend themselves readily to tests of goodness of fit for each degree of fitting. This simplifies the problem of selecting the curve required.

Logarithmic curves are characterized by a flattening out at one end of the range. This can be observed quite simply by plotting the logarithms

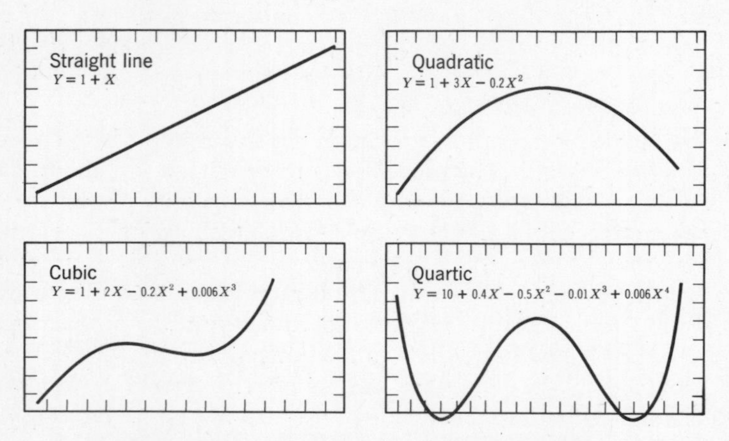

FIGURE 10–1. Graphs of 4 polynomial functions.

of the numbers 1, 2, 3, 4, 5, 6, · · ·. It will be noticed that the interval between the logarithms becomes less at each step and eventually is very small. The characteristics of the above three types should be observed by working out the values of Y for some imaginary equations and plotting on graph paper. Specially ruled paper for plotting logarithmic curves should also be studied to observe how logarithmic equations are transformed to linear equations by plotting on the appropriate type of log paper.

6. Fitting polynomial equations. If a polynomial of the form

$$Y_e = a + bX + cX^2 + dX^2 \qquad 1$$

is required, the problem resolves itself into one of determining the values of a, b, c, and d that will make the sum of squares of the errors of estimation a minimum. The expression to be minimized is

$$\sum_{1}^{n}(Y - a - bX - cX^2 - dX^3) \qquad 2$$

and this leads to a set of four simultaneous equations as follows.

$$\begin{aligned} an \quad &+ b\Sigma X + c\Sigma X^2 + d\Sigma X^3 = \Sigma Y \\ a\Sigma X &+ b\Sigma X^2 + c\Sigma X^3 + d\Sigma X^4 = \Sigma XY \\ a\Sigma X^2 &+ b\Sigma X^3 + c\Sigma X^4 + d\Sigma X^5 = \Sigma X^2 Y \\ a\Sigma X^3 &+ b\Sigma X^4 + c\Sigma X^5 + d\Sigma X^6 = \Sigma X^3 Y \end{aligned} \qquad 3$$

This set of equations can be expanded or contracted as desired, according to the degree of the polynomial required. If we let r represent the degree of fitting, there will be $r + 1$ equations and $r + 1$ terms on the left, one for each coefficient to be determined.

The simultaneous equations provide a general method of fitting polynomials of any degree. The procedure is to determine ΣY, ΣXY, $\Sigma X^2 Y$, etc., and the sums of the powers of X. The equations can be set up in tabular form and solved by the method with which one is most familiar. The Doolittle tabular method is given here, but some workers prefer a direct solution by elimination and substitution which is equivalent to the Doolittle method. Others prefer the solution by means of determinents as in the Crout method described in the Appendix.

Before studying the details of the solution it should be noted that certain simplifications are possible. In the first place it is almost essential in order to avoid large numbers to code the values of X and Y to make them as small as possible. Starting with a table such as 10–4, to which a polynomial is to be fitted, it is desirable first to make unit class intervals and then to set up arbitrary origins for X and Y that are close to the actual means.

With certain types of data there are other simplifications, and when possible there are definite advantages in fitting what are known as *orthogonal* polynomials, which are described briefly in the next section.

7. Orthogonal polynomials. If we fit a polynomial of the form $Y = a_1 + b_1 X + c_1 X^2$ to a given set of data and then fit another of the form $Y = a_2 + b_2 X + c_2 X^2 + d_2 X^3$, we shall find as indicated by the notation that $a_1 \neq a_2$, $b_1 \neq b_2$, etc. Another way of looking at this is to say that, after fitting to the second degree, the procedure of fitting to the third degree is not merely a matter of adding a term in X^3 to the original equation. In other words it is not possible to fit by successive stages, testing the goodness of fit as we proceed, unless we go through the whole procedure of solving the simultaneous equations at each stage.

With orthogonal polynomials the type of equation fitted is of the form

$$Y = A + B\xi_1 + C\xi_2 + D\xi_3 + \cdots \qquad 4$$

where the ξ's are themselves orthogonal functions of X. For example, we might have $\xi_1 = k_1 + X_1$, $\xi_2 = k_2 + k_3X + X^2$, etc., these functions being determined in such a way as to make

$$\Sigma\xi_1 = 0,\ \Sigma\xi_2 = 0, \cdots,\ \Sigma\xi_1\xi_2 = 0,\ \Sigma\xi_1\xi_3 = 0, \cdots \qquad 5$$

When X can be taken as a series of natural numbers and the Y's have equal weight, the algebraic derivation of the values of the ξ's is fairly simple. Taking x in place of X, it can be shown that

$$\xi_1 = x$$

$$\xi_2 = \left(x^2 - \frac{n}{12}\right) \qquad 6$$

etc.

The error to be minimized for an orthogonal polynomial of the second degree is

$$\Sigma(Y - A - B\xi_1 - C\xi_2)^2$$

leading to the simultaneous equations

$$\begin{aligned} nA + B\Sigma\xi_1 + C\Sigma\xi_2 &= \Sigma Y \\ \Sigma\xi_1 A + B\Sigma\xi_1^2 + C\Sigma\xi_1\xi_2 &= \Sigma\xi_1 Y \\ \Sigma\xi_2 A + B\Sigma\xi_1\xi_2 + C\Sigma\xi_2^2 &= \Sigma\xi_2 Y \end{aligned} \qquad 7$$

and, since by definition $\Sigma\xi_1 = 0$, $\Sigma\xi_2 = 0$, $\Sigma\xi_1\xi_2 = 0$, these simplify to

$$nA = \Sigma Y \qquad B\Sigma\xi_1^2 = \Sigma\xi_1 Y \qquad C\Sigma\xi_2^2 = \Sigma\xi_2 Y \qquad 8$$

or

$$A = \frac{\Sigma Y}{n} \qquad B = \frac{\Sigma\xi_1 Y}{\Sigma\xi_1^2} \qquad C = \frac{\Sigma\xi_2 Y}{\Sigma\xi_2^2} \qquad 9$$

It will be obvious that on minimizing an orthogonal polynomial of the third degree we get the same results as above for A, B, and C, and in addition we will have

$$D = \frac{\Sigma\xi_3 Y}{\Sigma\xi_3^2}$$

Since the sums of squares for regression are given by

Linear regression $\quad B\Sigma\xi_1 Y$

Quadratic regression $\quad B\Sigma\xi_1 Y + C\Sigma\xi_2 Y \qquad 10$

Cubic regression $\quad B\Sigma\xi_1 Y + C\Sigma\xi_2 Y + D\Sigma\xi_3 Y$

it follows that the sums of squares for regression for each degree of freedom can be obtained at each stage of fitting.

8. Example 10–1. Fitting a polynomial to data where the values of Y have unequal weight. In an example of this type it is not convenient to fit orthogonal polynomials, so we proceed directly by obtaining the

TABLE 10–4

DATA SET UP FOR CALCULATION OF A POLYNOMIAL REGRESSION EQUATION

Loaf volume (Y) \ Percent protein (X)	−4	−3	−2	−1	0	1	2	3	4	5	Total
	5	13	23	23	35	15	16	26	6	2	164
4								1			1
3							2	5			7
2					5	2	5	6	3	1	22
1				6	15	7	3	12	2		45
0			9	12	14	5	6	2	1	1	50
−1		1	7	3	1	1					13
−2		4	5	2							11
−3	4	6	2								12
−4		2									2
−5	1										1

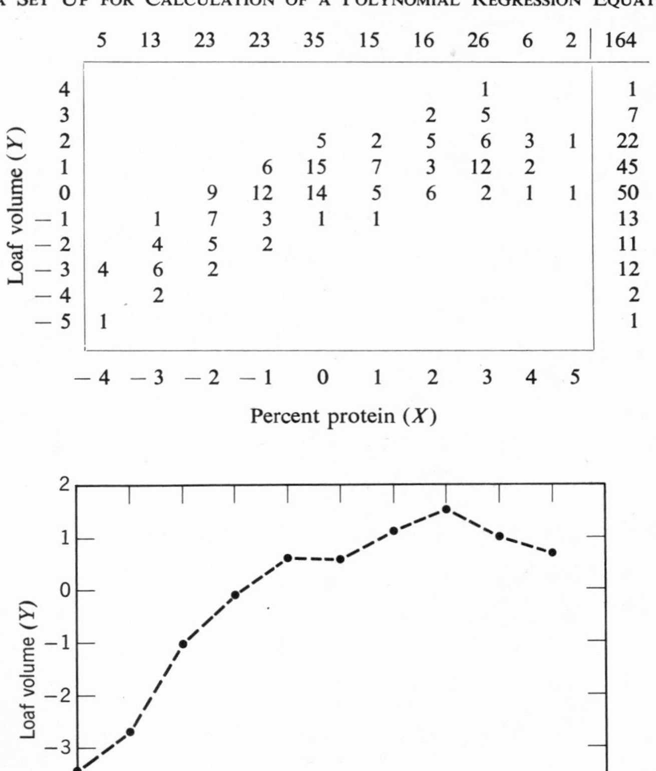

FIGURE 10–2. Graph of loaf volume means from Table 10–1.

values of ΣX, $\Sigma X^2, \cdots, \Sigma Y$, $\Sigma XY, \cdots$ and solving a system of normal equations as shown in (3).

Table 10–4 is the usual regression table, but, for the purpose of fitting, the actual intervals of Y and X have been changed to unit intervals and an arbitrary origin for Y has been taken at 6 and for X at 5. This is a simple method of coding that reduces the labor of calculation. The first step is to decide on the polynomial to be fitted, and accordingly a graph is made of the means of the Y arrays, Figure 10–2. It is obvious that a straight line will not give a good fit, but there is little indication that we shall need to go beyond the third degree. As a matter of fact a curve of the second degree should give a good fit, but we shall proceed to the fitting of a third-degree curve, and if the three degrees of fitting are not required it will be a simple matter to revert to the quadratic.

Table 10–5 must be set up next in order to obtain the values required for the solution of the normal equations, as written out below.

$$an \quad + b\Sigma x + c\Sigma x^2 = \Sigma y$$

$$a\Sigma x + b\Sigma x^2 + c\Sigma x^3 = \Sigma xy$$

$$a\Sigma x^2 + b\Sigma x^3 + c\Sigma x^4 = \Sigma x^2 y$$

where $x = X - 5$, and $y = Y - 6$.

TABLE 10–5

CALCULATION OF DATA REQUIRED FOR FITTING A POLYNOMIAL OF THE THIRD DEGREE

1	2	3	4	5	6	7	8	9	10	11	12
x	Totals y Arrays	xy	x^2y	x^3y	f_x	$f_x x$	$f_x x^2$	$f_x x^3$	$f_x x^4$	$f_x x^5$	$f_x x^6$
– 4	– 17	68	– 272	1,088	5	– 20	80	– 320	1,280	– 5,120	20,480
– 3	– 35	105	– 315	945	13	– 39	117	– 351	1,053	– 3,159	9,477
– 2	– 23	46	– 92	184	23	– 46	92	– 184	368	– 736	1,472
– 1	– 1	1	– 1	1	23	– 23	23	– 23	23	– 23	23
0	24				35						
1	10	10	10	10	15	15	15	15	15	15	15
2	19	38	76	152	16	32	64	128	256	512	1,024
3	43	129	387	1,161	26	78	234	702	2,106	6,318	18,954
4	8	32	128	512	6	24	96	384	1,536	6,144	24,576
5	2	10	50	250	2	10	50	250	1,250	6,250	31,250
	30	439	– 29	4,303	164	31	771	601	7,887	10,201	107,271
	Σy	Σxy	Σx^2y	Σx^3y	n	Σx	Σx^2	Σx^3	Σx^4	Σx^5	Σx^6

Note that columns 1, 2, and 6 are taken directly from the original regression table, 1 and 6 being copied and 2 worked out in the usual way. We can then work right across the table from left to right as follows.

$$-4 \times 17 = 68 \qquad -4 \times 68 = -272 \qquad -4 \times -272 = 1{,}088$$

$$-4 \times 5 = -20 \qquad -4 \times -20 = 80 \qquad -4 \times 80 = -320$$

etc.

The columns are summed to give the values indicated in the last line. The equations to be solved can now be set up in the following manner.

$$\begin{aligned}
164a + 31b + 771c + 601d &= 30 \\
31a + 771b + 601c + 7{,}887d &= 439 \\
771a + 601b + 7{,}887c + 10{,}201d &= -29 \\
601a + 7{,}887b + 10{,}201c + 107{,}271d &= 4{,}303
\end{aligned}$$

Table 10–6 is then set up for solving the equations by the Doolittle method. The abbreviated Doolittle method can be followed if desired, but the full solution is more convenient here. Note that the procedure followed in this table is the same as that described in Chapter 8, Section 5, for the abbreviated Doolittle solution, but all terms are written down. Check by inserting the determined values of a, b, c, d in *all* the equations.

The polynomial values can now be built up from the equation

$$y = 0.5728 + 0.5957x - 0.1096x^2 + 0.003\,533x^3$$

where $y = Y - 6$ and $x = X - 5$. Note that, for $X = 1$, $x = 1 - 5 = -4$. Therefore, substituting -4 in the above equation is equal to substituting $X = 1$. For $x = -4$, we get $y = -3.79$. Then $Y = 6 - 3.79 = 2.21$, etc. Thus it is not necessary to put $(Y - 6)$ for y and $(X - 5)$ for x and simplify before calculating polynomial values.

The most interesting part of the work is in testing the goodness of fit of the regression curve. Table 10–6 will provide the data for testing the goodness of fit not only of the third-degree curve but also of second- and first-degree curves. This enables us to decide the degree of fitting required. We first calculate the total sum of squares of Y from Table 10–4. This gives

$$434 - \frac{(30)^2}{164} = 428.51$$

Then from Table 10–6 the sum of squares for regression due to fitting the straight-line equation $y_0 = a_0 + b_0x$ is given by $(5, 2) \times (6, 5)^2$ where the numbers refer to row and column, respectively. The figures are

$$765.1402 \times (0.566\,339\,7)^2 = 245.41$$

TABLE 10–6

SOLUTION OF SIMULTANEOUS EQUATIONS FOR FITTING A POLYNOMIAL OF THE THIRD DEGREE

	1	2	3	4	5
1	164	31	771	601	30
2	1.0	0.189 024 4	4.701 220	3.664 634	0.182 926 8
3		771	601	7,887	439
4		– 5.859 756	– 145.737 8	– 113.603 7	– 5.670 732
5		765.140 2	455.262 2	7,773.396 3	433.329 3
6		1.0	0.595 004 9	10.159 44	0.566 339 7
7			7,887	10,201	– 29
8			– 3,624.640 6	– 2,825.433 2	– 141.036 6
9			– 270.883 2	– 4,625.208 9	– 257.833 1
10			3,991.476 2	2,750.375 9	– 427.869 7
11			1.0	0.689 062 3	– 0.107 195 8
12				107,271	4,303
13				– 2,202.445 0	– 109.939 0
14				– 78,973.353 3	– 4,402.383 0
15				– 1,895.180 3	294.828 9
16				24,200.021	85.506 9
17				1.0	0.003 533 339
18				$d =$ 0.003 533 34	0.003 533 34
19			$c = -$ 0.109 630 5	– 0.002 434 69	– 0.107 195 8
20		$b =$ 0.595 673 6	0.065 230 7	– 0.035 896 8	0.566 339 7
21	$a =$ 0.572 778 7	– 0.112 596 8	0.515 397 1	– 0.012 948 4	0.182 926 8

For fitting a quadratic of the form $y_1 = a_1 + b_1x + c_1x^2$, the sum of squares for regression is

$$245.41 + (10, 3) \times (11, 5)^2 = 245.41 + 3991.4762 \times (0.107\,195\,8)^2$$
$$= 291.27$$

Finally, for the cubic $y_2 = a_2 + b_2x + c_2x^2 + d_2x^3$, the sum of squares is

$$245.41 + 45.86 + (16, 4) \times (17, 5)^2$$
$$= 245.41 + 45.86 + 24{,}200.021 \times (0.003\,533\,34)^2 = 291.57$$

The next step is to set up an analysis of variance for testing the increase in the sum of squares for regression due to each degree of fitting. We have

	SS	DF	MS
Linear regression	245.41	1	245.41
Excess due to quadratic	45.86	1	45.86
Excess due to cubic	0.30	1	0.30
Residual	136.94	160	0.86
Total	428.51	163	

Obviously there is significant linear regression, but the fitting of the quadratic makes a very worth-while improvement. The fitting of the cubic is of no value whatever.

9. Fisher's summation method of fitting orthogonal polynomials. When the Y values are, or can be assumed to be, of equal weight and are given for equal intervals of X, the method of fitting orthogonal polynomials developed by R. A. Fisher [2] provides a decided short cut from the actual to the theoretical polynomial values. The arithmetical labor is likewise easy as it consists largely of a process of continuous summation that can be done on an adding machine. A more recent development arising from the same mathematical background is a method of fitting given by Fisher and Yates [3] which is still more rapid, but a calculating machine and certain tables supplied by them are required. This method, described in detail in Example 10–3, was used in Sections 1 and 2.

Fisher's summation method can be described most conveniently by means of an example.

10. Example 10–2. Fitting orthogonal polynomials—summation method. The data given in Table 10–7 are for loaf volumes in a baking experiment reported by Larmour [5] wherein the dough was subjected to mixing in a high-speed mixer for varying lengths of time from 1 to 4 minutes.

TABLE 10–7

RESULTS OF AN EXPERIMENT ON THE EFFECT OF TIME OF MIXING OF DOUGH ON LOAF VOLUME

Mixing Time in Minutes (X)	Loaf Volume in Cubic Centimetres less 550 (Y)
1.0	235
1.5	280
2.0	255
2.5	190
3.0	120
3.5	55
4.0	20

The procedure of fitting is divided into a series of steps as indicated below.

1. *Calculation of* S_0, S_1, S_2, $\cdots$, S_r, *where r represents the degree of fitting to be carried out.* The data are set up as in Table 10–8, after the actual values of X have been replaced by the natural numbers 1, 2, 3, $\cdots$, 7. The process of continuous summation is illustrated for obtaining S_0, S_1, S_2, S_3, it being assumed at this stage that a third-degree curve will be sufficient.

TABLE 10–8

CALCULATION OF S_0, S_1, S_2, S_3

X	Y			
1	235	235	235	235
2	280	515	750	985
3	255	770	1,520	2,505
4	190	960	2,480	4,985
5	120	1,080	3,560	8,545
6	55	1,135	4,695	13,240
7	20	1,155	5,850	19,090
	1,155	5,850	19,090	49,585
	S_0	S_1	S_2	S_3

In the third column

$235 + 280 = 515$

$515 + 255 = 770$

etc.

Similarly in the fourth and fifth columns

2. *Calculation of a, b, c, d, e, · · · and a′, b′, c′, d′, e′, · · ·, where there are r + 1 of these to be calculated for fitting to the rth degree.*

Degree of Fitting		
0	$a = \frac{1}{n} S_0$	$a' = a$
1	$b = \frac{2}{n(n+1)} S_1$	$b' = a - b$
2	$c = \frac{6}{n(n+1)(n+2)} S_2$	$c' = a - 3b + 2c$
3	$d = \frac{24}{n(n+1)(n+2)(n+3)} S_3$	$d' = a - 6b + 10c - 5d$
4	$e = \frac{120}{n(n+1)\cdots(n+4)} S_4$	$e' = a - 10b + 30c - 35d + 14e$
5	$f = \frac{720}{n(n+1)\cdots(n+5)} S_5$	$f' = 15b + 70c - 140d + 126e - 42a$
⋮	⋮	
r	$= \frac{(r+1)!}{n(n+1)\cdots(n+r)} S_r$	

11

Coefficients in the equations on the right above are formed by successive multiplication by $\frac{r(r+1)}{1 \times 2}$, $\frac{(r-1)(r+2)}{2 \times 3}$, $\frac{(r-2)(r+3)}{3 \times 4}$, etc., until series terminates. For example, in obtaining coefficients for calculating d', $r = 3$. Then $\frac{3 \times 4}{2} = 6$, $6 \times \frac{2 \times 5}{2 \times 3} = 10$, $10 \times \frac{1 \times 6}{3 \times 4} = 5$.

Here we have

$a = \frac{1}{7}(1155) = 165.000\,00$ $\qquad a' = 165.000\,00$

$b = \frac{1}{28}(5850) = 208.928\,57$ $\qquad b' = (165.000\,00 - 208.928\,57) = -43.928\,57$

$c = \frac{1}{84}(19{,}090) = 227.261\,90$ $\qquad c' = 165.000\,00 - (3 \times 208.928\,57) + (2 \times 227.261\,90) = -7.261\,91$

$d = \frac{1}{210}(49{,}585) = 236.119\,05$ $\qquad d' = 3.452\,33$

3. *Calculation of sums of squares for each degree of fitting and making tests of significance.* At this point, tests of significance can be made that will determine the degree of fitting required. The sums of squares for each degree of fitting are given by

Degree of Fitting	Formula for Sum of Squares	In Example
0	na'^2 (represents fitting of mean)	$7 \times (165.0)^2 = 190{,}575.00$
1	$3\dfrac{n(n+1)}{n-1}b'^2$	$28 \times (43.928\,57)^2 = 54{,}032.14$
2	$5\dfrac{n(n+1)(n+2)}{(n-1)(n-2)}c'^2$	$84 \times (7.261\,91)^2 = 4{,}429.77$
3	$7\dfrac{n(n+1)\cdots(n+3)}{(n-1)(n-2)(n-3)}d'^2$	$294 \times (3.452\,33)^2 = 3{,}504.06$
4	$9\dfrac{n(n+1)\cdots(n+4)}{(n-1)(n-2)\cdots(n-4)}e'^2$	
5	$11\dfrac{n(n+1)\cdots(n+5)}{(n-1)(n-2)\cdots(n-5)}f'^2$	
⋮		
r	$(2r+1)\dfrac{n(n+1)\cdots(n+r)}{(n-1)(n-2)\cdots(n-r)}(\text{constant})^2$	

Since $\Sigma Y^2 = 252{,}575$, $\Sigma y^2 = 252{,}575 - 190{,}575.00 = 62{,}000.00$, and we can set up an analysis of variance as follows.

	SS	DF	MS
Linear regression	54,032.14	1	54,032
Excess due to quadratic	4,429.77	1	4,430
Excess due to cubic	3,504.06	1	3,504
Residual	34.03	3	11.35
Total	62,000.00	6	

The regression sums of squares are all highly significant. The question as to whether or not we should proceed to further stages is answered reasonably well by the smallness of the residual sum of squares. It does not seem likely that additional fitting would reduce this appreciably.

4. *Calculation of polynomial values.* In order to make a graph of the fitted curve it is necessary to determine the values of the polynomial for each value of X. The procedure is first to obtain the quantities Y, ΔY_1, ΔY_2, ΔY_3, $\cdot\cdot\cdot$, ΔY_r given by the following general formulas for fitting to the fifth degree, which can be expanded or contracted as desired.

General Formula for Fitting to the Fifth Degree	In Example
$Y_1 = a' + 3b' + 5c' + 7d' + 9e' + 11f'$	$Y_1 = 165.0 + (3 \times -43.928\,57) + (5 \times -7.261\,91) + (7 \times 3.452\,33) = 21.071\,05$
$\Delta Y_1 = (-1)^1 \dfrac{6}{n-1}(b' + 5c' + 14d' + 30e' + 55f')$	$\Delta Y_1 = -\left(\dfrac{6}{6}\right)[(-43.928\,57) + (5 \times -7.261\,91) + (14 \times 3.452\,33)] = 31.905\,50$
$\Delta Y_2 = (-1)^2 \dfrac{60}{(n-1)(n-2)}(c' + 7d' + 27e' + 77f')$	$\Delta Y_2 = \dfrac{60}{30} \times (-7.261\,91) + (7 \times 3.452\,33) = 33.808\,80$
$\Delta Y_3 = (-1)^3 \dfrac{840}{(n-1)(n-2)(n-3)}(d' + 9e' + 44f')$	$\Delta Y_3 = -\dfrac{840}{120} \times 3.452\,33 = -24.166\,31$
$\Delta Y_4 = (-1)^4 \dfrac{15{,}120}{(n-1)(n-2)\cdots(n-4)}(e' + 11f')$	
$\Delta Y_5 = (-1)^5 \dfrac{332{,}640}{(n-1)(n-2)\cdots(n-5)}(f')$	

13

The polynomials are finally built up by a process of continuous summation originating with the values of Y_1, ΔY_1, ΔY_2, $\cdot\cdot\cdot$, ΔY_r. This process is illustrated with the data of the example:

X	Y_e			
1	236.31			
2	277.02	− 40.714		
3	254.88	22.143	− 62.8564	
4	194.05	60.833	− 38.6901	
5	118.69	75.357	− 14.5238	
6	52.98	65.714	9.6425	
7	21.071	31.9055	33.80880	− 24.16631

The starting point of the summation is at the lower right-hand corner. Thus $33.808\,80 - 24.166\,31 = 9.6425$, $9.6425 - 24.166\,31 = -14.5238$, etc., where all decimal places are carried but only four are written down.

In the next column, $31.9055 + 33.8088 = 65.714$, $65.714 + 9.6425 = 75.357$, etc., again carrying on the machine one more place than is required.

11. Fitting orthogonal polynomials using Fisher and Yates' table of ξ. When available, the Fisher and Yates [3] tables provide the most rapid method for fitting orthogonal polynomials. It is required that the values of Y be of equal weight and at equal intervals of X.

The equation to be fitted is of the form

$$Y_e = A + B\xi_1 + C\xi_2 + D\xi_3 + \cdots \qquad 14$$

where the ξ's are themselves polynomials in X (see Section 7). For simplicity in fitting, the actual equation is

$$Y_e = A + B'\xi'_1 + C'\xi'_2 + D'\xi'_3 + \cdots \qquad 15$$

where $\xi' = \lambda\xi$ and the values of λ are given in the tables.

A small section of the tables of ξ' is reproduced here for fitting a fifth-degree polynomial to 7 points.

X	Y	ξ'_1	ξ'_2	ξ'_3	ξ'_4	ξ'_5
1	Y_1	−3	5	−1	3	−1
2	Y_2	−2	0	1	−7	4
3	Y_3	−1	−3	1	1	−5
4	Y_4	0	−4	0	6	0
5	Y_5	1	−3	−1	1	5
6	Y_6	2	0	−1	−7	−4
7	Y_7	3	5	1	3	1
	$\Sigma(\xi')^2$	28	84	6	154	84
	λ	1	1	1/6	7/12	7/20

To fit a straight line we require the values of ξ'_1 only; for the quadratic we require ξ'_1 and ξ'_2, and so forth.

The first step is to determine the sums of squares for each degree of fitting and, by setting up an analysis of variance, to decide on the polynomial required. The sums of squares are given by

$$\text{First degree} \quad \frac{(\Sigma Y\xi'_1)^2}{\Sigma\xi'^2_1}$$

$$\text{Second degree} \quad \frac{(\Sigma Y\xi'_2)^2}{\Sigma\xi'^2_2} \qquad 16$$

etc.

Having decided on the degree of the polynomial that is required, we determine

$$A' = \frac{\Sigma Y\xi'_1}{\Sigma(\xi'_1)^2}$$

$$B' = \frac{\Sigma Y\xi'_2}{\Sigma(\xi'_2)^2} \qquad 17$$

etc.

Then, by substituting the tabulated values of ξ'_1, ξ'_2, etc., in the equation, the polynomial values can be determined. For example, in fitting a fourth-degree curve to data for 7 points, we would have

$$Y_1 = A' + B'(-3) + C'(5) + D'(-1) + E'(3)$$

$$Y_2 = A' + B'(-2) + C'(0) + D'(1) \quad + E'(-7)$$

etc.

If necessary, equation (15) can be transformed into an equation giving Y in terms of X. It is best to do this in two stages, transforming first to x and then to X. This is done by means of the identities given below for equations up to the fifth degree.

$$\xi'_1 = \lambda\xi_1 = \lambda x$$

$$\xi'_2 = \lambda\xi_2 = \lambda\left(x^2 - \frac{n^2-1}{12}\right)$$

$$\xi'_3 = \lambda\xi_3 = \lambda\left(x^3 - \frac{3n^2-7}{20}x\right) \qquad 18$$

$$\xi'_4 = \lambda\xi_4 = \lambda\left[x^4 - \frac{3n^2-13}{14}x^2 + \frac{3(n^2-1)(n^2-9)}{560}\right]$$

$$\xi'_5 = \lambda\xi_5 = \lambda\left[x^5 - \frac{5(n^2-7)}{18}x^3 + \frac{15n^4-230n^2+407}{1008}x\right]$$

where the values of λ are different in each line and are given in the tables of Fisher and Yates.

After finding the numerical values of the expressions containing n in the above formulas, these are substituted in (15) and simplified. If the equation is required in terms of X instead of x, it is necessary to substitute $(X - \bar{X})$, in which $\bar{X}$ is the actual numerical value of $\bar{X}$, and simplify further.

12. Example 10–3. Fitting polynomials with Fisher and Yates' table of ξ. This process of fitting polynomials by successive stages using Fisher and Yates' table of ξ' is illustrated with the data of Table 10–9, for the relation between pH and activity of the enzyme asparaginase, Geddes and Hunter [4]. The table also gives the values of ξ' which have been taken from Fisher and Yates' table.

TABLE 10–9

DATA FOR pH(X) AND ACTIVITY OF THE ENZYME ASPARAGINASE (Y), WITH VALUES OF ξ' REQUIRED FOR FITTING A FIFTH-DEGREE ORTHOGONAL POLYNOMIAL

	X	Y		ξ'_1	ξ'_2	ξ'_3	ξ'_4	ξ'_5	Y for Fourth-Degree Equation
	1	0.2		− 13	13	− 143	143	− 143	0.27
	2	0.4		− 11	7	− 11	− 77	187	0.17
	3	1.4		− 9	2	66	− 132	132	1.69
	4	4.1		− 7	− 2	98	− 92	− 28	4.02
	5	6.6		− 5	− 5	95	− 13	− 139	6.48
	6	8.7		− 3	− 7	67	63	− 145	8.55
	7	9.8		− 1	− 8	24	108	− 60	9.89
	8	9.9		1	− 8	− 24	108	60	10.26
	9	9.5		3	− 7	− 67	63	145	9.62
	10	8.2		5	− 5	− 95	− 13	139	8.05
	11	6.4		7	− 2	− 98	− 92	28	5.81
	12	3.3		9	2	− 66	− 132	− 132	3.29
	13	0.3		11	7	11	− 77	− 187	1.04
	14	0.1		13	13	143	143	143	− 0.24
Sum	105	68.9	$\Sigma(\xi')^2$	910	728	97,240	136,136	235,144	68.90
Mean	7.5	4.9214	λ	2	1/2	5/3	7/12	7/30	

The calculations for A, B', C', D', E', and F' are given below, together with the sums of squares representing each additional degree of fitting.

$$\Sigma y^2 = 541.7100 - 339.0864 = 202.6236$$

$$\Sigma(\xi'_1 Y) = 41.3 \qquad B' = 0.045\,385 \qquad SS = \frac{(41.3)^2}{910} = 1.8744$$

$$\Sigma(\xi'_2 Y) = -361.8 \qquad C' = -0.496\,98 \qquad SS = \frac{(361.8)^2}{728} = 179.8066$$

$$\Sigma(\xi'_3 Y) = -574.2 \qquad D' = -0.005\,905\,0 \qquad SS = \frac{(574.2)^2}{97{,}240} = 3.3906$$

$$\Sigma(\xi'_4 Y) = 1484.4 \qquad E' = 0.010\,904 \qquad SS = \frac{(1484.4)^2}{136.136} = 16.1856$$

$$\Sigma(\xi'_5 Y) = 162.4 \qquad F' = 0.000\,690\,64 \quad SS = \frac{(162.4)^2}{235{,}144} = 0.1122$$

$$\text{Residual} = 1.2542$$

The analysis of variance takes the form given in Table 10–10.

TABLE 10–10

ANALYSIS OF VARIANCE FOR INDIVIDUAL DEGREES OF FITTING

	SS	DF	MS	F	5% Point
First degree	1.8744	1	1.8744	12.0	5.32
Second degree	179.8066	1	179.8066	1147	5.32
Third degree	3.3906	1	3.3906	21.6	5.32
Fourth degree	16.1856	1	16.1856	103	5.32
Fifth degree	0.1122	1	0.1122		
Residual	1.2542	8	0.1568		

It is clear from this analysis that a polynomial of the fourth degree should be fitted. The simplest possible equation that will give the polynomial values is

$$Y = A + B'\xi'_1 + C'\xi'_2 + D'\xi'_3 + E'\xi'_4 \qquad 19$$

Therefore

$$Y_1 = 4.921 + 0.045\,38\,(-13) - 0.4970\,(13) - 0.005\,905\,(-143) + 0.010\,90\,(143) = 0.273$$

and, by substituting further values of ξ'_1, ξ'_2, ξ'_3, and ξ'_4, the complete set of polynomial values are obtained as given in the last column.

The equation of the polynomial can be expressed in terms of powers of X, but a little more labor is required. In the first place ξ'_1, ξ'_2, ξ'_3, and ξ'_4 must be expressed in powers of x, where x, as usual, represents $(X - \bar{X})$. The equations for conversion are given in (18). In using these it must be noted that $\xi'_1 = \xi_1$, and as follows for the other values of ξ'.

$$\xi'_1 = 2\xi_1 = 2x$$

$$\xi'_2 = \tfrac{1}{2}\xi_2 = \tfrac{1}{2}(x^2 - 16.25) = \tfrac{1}{2}x^2 - 8.125$$

$$\xi'_3 = \tfrac{5}{3}\xi_3 = \tfrac{5}{3}(x^3 - 29.05) = \tfrac{5}{3}x^3 - 48.4167x$$

$$\xi'_4 = \tfrac{7}{12}\xi_4 = \tfrac{7}{12}(x^4 - 41.0714x^2 + 195.3482)$$

$$= \tfrac{7}{12}x^4 - 23.9583x^2 + 113.9531$$

Substituting in (19) gives

$$Y = 4.9214 + 0.045\,38(2x) - 0.4970\left(\frac{x^2}{2} - 8.125\right) -$$

$$0.005\,905\,(\tfrac{5}{3}x^3 - 48.4167x) + 0.010\,90\,(\tfrac{7}{12}x^4 - 23.9583x^2 + 113.9531)$$

$$= 10.2016 + 0.3767x - 0.5096x^2 - 0.009\,842x^3 + 0.006\,358x^4$$

This equation gives estimates of the values of Y by substituting deviations from the mean of X. Thus

$$Y_1 = 10.2016 + 0.3767(-6.5) - 0.5096(42.25) - 0.009\,842(-274.625) + 0.006\,358\,(1785.0625) = 0.27$$

If necessary we can substitute $(X - 7.5)$ in place of x and simplify arriving at an equation in which X can be substituted directly.

13. Exercises.

TABLE 10–11

DIFFERENCE IN RATE OF GROWTH OF LARVAE OF *Choristoneura fumiferanae* (Clem), THE SPRUCE BUD WORM, FED ON 2 TYPES OF FOOD*

Instar	2	3	4	5	6	7
Difference	6	20	63	75	64	39

TABLE 10–12

AGE OF ONSET OF MUSCULAR DYSTROPHY IN PAIRS OF FIRST COUSINS (Bell)

		10	68	28	13	7	4	4	134
Age of Y	60–69				2	1	1		4
	50–59		1	1	1			1	4
	40–49			3	3			1	7
	30–39			3	4	3	1	2	13
	20–29		9	12	3	3	1		28
	10–19	2	56	9			1		68
	0–9	8	2						10
	Age of X	0–9	10–19	20–29	30–39	40–49	50–59	60–69	

Mean Squares: *Quadratic* = *13.653*
Cubic = *0.203*
Residual = *0.930*

* Data courtesy of R. Lejeune, Forest Insects Laboratory, Winnipeg, Manitoba.

1. Fit an orthogonal polynomial by the method of Example 10–3 for the data of Table 10–11, determining the best fitting curve by testing at each stage of fitting. Calculate the polynomial values and graph with actual values on the same chart.

2. Table 10–12 was obtained in a study by Julia Bell [1] on hereditary muscular dystrophy. This is a symmetrical table, familiar in heredity studies, owing to 2 entries being made for each pair. Take Y and X as shown and calculate and graph the means of the Y arrays. Carry the fitting of a third-degree polynomial, as in Example 10–1, to the stage of testing the linear, quadratic, and cubic components of regression.

REFERENCES

1. Julia Bell, *Ann. of Eugen.*, **2**, 272–289, 1942.
2. R. A. Fisher, *Statistical Methods for Research Workers*, Oliver and Boyd, Edinburgh and London, 10th ed., 1948.
3. R. A. Fisher and F. Yates, *Statistical Tables*, Oliver and Boyd, Edinburgh and London, 3rd ed., 1949.
4. W. F. Geddes and A. Hunter, *J. Biol. Chem.*, **77**, 197–229, 1928.
5. R. K. Larmour, *Cereal Chem.*, **18**, 778–789, 1941.

CHAPTER 11

Basic Experimental Designs

1. Principles of experimental design. The logical procedure of drawing conclusions from experiments is analogous to the everyday procedure of learning by experience. The main difference is that in experimental work our experience is planned in advance, whereas in merely learning by experience we are exposed to events in a more or less haphazard fashion. In theory, therefore, we should be able to learn rapidly and efficiently by performing experiments, but, although there is a distinct advantage from being able to plan in advance, there is also a danger in that our planning may be faulty, and the experience from which we had anticipated learning turns out to be a waste of time and energy. There is a great need, therefore, for careful thought with respect to experimental design. There is need for searching investigations into principles of design in order that these may stand out clearly and supply a framework on which sound designs may be built.

Although certain principles of experimentation were developed gradually along with increasing research work in all lines of endeavor, it is now generally accepted that the fundamental principles of experimental design were for the first time brought clearly into focus with the writings of Professor R. A. Fisher and especially with the first edition of *Statistical Methods for Research Workers* in 1925, and *The Design of Experiments* in 1935. Previous to 1925, Professor Fisher had developed the technique of the analysis of variance and discovered the distribution that furnished appropriate tests of significance in conjunction with the analysis procedure. It is possible, however, that the greatest contribution made by Professor Fisher was his attitude toward the logic of experimentation. Research workers generally draw their conclusions by inductive inference. They reason from the particular to the general. This they are forced to do because there is no alternative, but mathematical methods are usually deductive, and there existed a great gulf between the experimentalist and the mathematician, which very few had been able to bridge. Great contributions such as those made by Professor Karl Pearson were largely ineffective in experimental work because of a general belief that they were useless unless we could deal with large samples. A start was made by

"Student" in 1908 with the development of the distribution that evolved finally into the distribution of t. Then with the appearance of Professor Fisher's *Statistical Methods for Research Workers* the experimentalist found for the first time a type of statistical reasoning that was essentially similar to his own. There was complete recognition of inductive logic and at the same time a presentation of statistical tools that could be applied without breaking faith with mathematical principles of probability. Only history will give the complete picture, but a personal opinion can be ventured that this point of view, presented by Professor Fisher and since developed by many others, was the primary cause of a change of attitude on the part of experimentalists towards statistical methods, and the rapid increase in the application of statistical methods in practically all research laboratories. We shall find it profitable, therefore, to summarize a few of the basic principles of experimental design at this point. Others will emerge as we proceed, but the most essential can be stated now.

1. The experiment must be free from bias. An experiment must be planned so that it gives unbiased estimates of the values we wish to measure. This is not simply a matter of the experimenter claiming that there is no bias in his experiments. It is a matter of the design being such that no bias on the part of the experimenter can possibly enter into the results. This is accomplished mainly by randomization. We do not say, merely, "These two greenhouse benches are as nearly alike as possible with respect to conditions, so I will put treatment A on the plants on this bench and treatment B on the other one." As a *routine* procedure we allow a table of random numbers to decide the issue. In administering two treatments to a series of pairs of animals we do not select the animals to receive the alternate treatments "without bias." We make *sure* that there is no bias by referring again to a table of random numbers.

It should not be inferred that the absence of a conscious bias on the part of the experimenter is sufficient. In classifying wheat plants at the Dominion Laboratory of Cereal Breeding into two classes, resistant and susceptible, there was no anxiety on the part of the plant breeders to obtain any specific ratios, but it was found that if one pile of plants was quite small there was a tendency to place borderline plants in this pile rather than in a larger one. For some illuminating accounts of unconscious personal bias the student is referred to an excellent article by Yates [14] cited at the end of this chapter.

2. There must be a measure of error. This principle is related in part to the necessity for freedom from bias. The treatments being compared may appear to be producing decidedly different results. But this is merely a matter of opinion on the part of the investigator. It is a purely subjective conclusion. The true experiment is one that is strictly objective. It should itself furnish a measure of error and this error alone should be the measuring stick of significance. To argue against this is merely to argue for a type of experiment that is not really a scientific experiment because its significance depends on the judgment of some individual.

Are we to discard all experimental results where there is no measure of error? This would seem to be the alternative in view of what has been said above. Actually, the technique does not need to be quite so drastic, because when we look more closely at almost any experiment we find usually that there is some measure of error, and if this error is chosen objectively the experiment may be salvaged. A series of unreplicated plot treatments can be carried on over a period of years, and the years will then constitute replications and an error can be obtained. Even in a single series of unreplicated plots certain comparisons can be made by making an orthogonal division of sums of squares and degrees of freedom. Finally, there are cases where the results are definitely significant and there is no measure of error, as in a pair of plots to which we apply a method of weed control and get a 100% kill in the treated plot and no kill whatsoever in the control plot. Basically, however, our thinking in such instances is dependent on the existence of an experimental error that we can gauge by experience. Our knowledge of plots and weeds tells us that such a result cannot have happened by chance. If this is true, it is admittedly desirable to have a real measure of error furnished by the experiment itself.

We should also keep in mind the possibility of errors of the second kind (see Chapter 4, Section 1). If we have no measure of error and will accept only those results that are obviously significant, we must be prepared to allow a great many real effects to go unnoticed. In these days of accurate and well-controlled experiments, the latter may be a greater "sin" than pronouncing an effect to be real when it actually is not.

3. There must be a clearly defined objective. From experience in giving advice to experimenters and discussing their plans with them, one soon learns that experiments are very frequently designed without a perfectly clear objective. We frequently hear "I want to compare this series of treatments." This is not enough. We must have a good reason for selecting these treatments. Do they represent the combinations and levels that will give the required information? To which areas are the results to apply, and under what conditions? Are we seeking merely empirical results or do we want to know the reason why? What measures are to form the basis of comparison? On looking over these questions it must be realized that unless we know the answers we cannot set up a null hypothesis, and if we cannot set up a hypothesis we cannot make a test of significance. If there is no hypothesis, there is no experiment.

The logic of the methods of statistics is an essential in designing an experiment correctly, because it teaches us the importance of clear thinking with respect to the hypothesis that we wish to test. Possibly, we can regard the hypothesis as the core of the experiment or the foundation on which it is built. Without this foundation we do not know how to plan the experiment, nor do we know how to make tests of significance.

4. The experiment should have sufficient accuracy to accomplish its purpose. Increased accuracy in experimentation is brought about, first, by the elimination of technical errors, and second, by increased replication. Generally speaking we think chiefly in terms of replication as our principle method for improving accuracy, and this is true with respect to uncontrolled errors or to errors that are inherent in and characteristic of the experimental material, but it should not be assumed that replication will overcome errors in technique. Although replication will *tend* to overcome such errors, it is a very uneconomical way to accomplish the desired end.

Assuming that technical errors are reduced to a minimum, we have to decide on the number of replications required to produce a given degree of accuracy. The actual method will be elaborated later, but we can emphasize at this point that it is poor economy to cut down on replications to such an extent that the results of the experiment may be lost. Usually, there is previous experience that can be applied in order to arrive at a rough measure of the number of replications required, but in any new field of research where the extent of the errors is uncertain some preliminary investigation may be necessary.

5. The experiment should have sufficient scope. To illustrate the meaning of *scope* in the design of an experiment we can consider the two extremes. Suppose that an experiment is planned in which we wish to estimate the effect of milk as compared to no milk in the diet of young pigs. We ask ourselves immediately: To what actual ages do we refer when we say "young pigs"? In other words, we are asking what is to be the scope of the experiment. If it is limited in scope, it will apply to one particular stage of growth. If it is broad in scope, it will apply over the whole range of growth during which milk is likely to be fed. There is, of course, no objection to confining such an experiment to one stage of growth only. This experiment would have adequate scope for deciding on the value of milk in the particular stage studied, but it would be decidedly limited in scope if we wished to know the effect of milk throughout the whole period. Here again we have the principle of a clear objective. Knowing the objective, we can decide on the scope required.

The value of having adequate scope in an experiment was at one time thought to be taken care of by repeating the experiment several times, in each experiment holding all but one of the factors constant. This procedure is now outmoded and has been replaced largely by what is known as factorial experimentation. In a factorial experiment, we vary all the factors simultaneously that are required to be varied in order to obtain sufficient scope. For example, suppose that two kinds of fertilizers are to be tested at different levels. We do not set up one experiment to compare them at the first level, another at the second level, and so forth. We make up all the required combinations of fertilizer and levels and test them all in one experiment. This adds further to the scope of the experiment by enabling us to test the interaction effects of the fertilizer and levels.

2. Ungrouped randomized experiments. This is the simplest of the basic designs. Suppose that 2 treatments A and B are to be tested on a series of 100 field plots. The ungrouped experiment would involve selecting 50 plots at random to receive A and 50 to receive B. The analysis of variance of the yields* would be as follows:

	DF
Treatments	1
Error	98
Total	99

If the yields of treatment A are X_a and those of B are X_b, the sums of squares are calculated from

$$\text{Error (SS)} = \sum_{1}^{50} X_a^2 - \frac{(\Sigma X_a)^2}{50} + \sum_{1}^{50} X_b^2 - \frac{(\Sigma X_b)^2}{50} \qquad 1$$

$$\text{Treatments (SS)} = \frac{(\Sigma X_a - \Sigma X_b)^2}{100} \qquad 2$$

* Yield is used here and throughout the remainder of this book in a general sense. It may represent real yields in pounds, bushels, or tons per acre, or it may be strength of straw, the gain in weight of an animal, or some other characteristic that has been measured and is appropriate for comparing the treatments. The term treatment may also be interpreted in a broad sense.

We are not so much concerned here with how to carry out such an experiment as we are in assessing its value as a design. It has certain advantages, such as simplicity and ease of calculation, and if one or more plots are missing there is no loss of orthogonality. Its chief disadvantage is that there is no attempt in the structure of the design to reduce the error to a minimum by the exercise of error control. The simplest design in which there is exercise of error control is the next one to be discussed.

3. The randomized block experiment. This name was first applied to field experiments by R. A. Fisher. It had been a common practice among field plot investigators to have 2 or more replicates, each replicate containing a complete set of the treatments, but the usual practice was to arrange the treatments in systematic order in the replicate. Fisher [8] pointed out that the systematic arrangement was likely to cause a bias and introduced the principle of arranging the treatments within each replicate strictly at random. In terms of the analysis of variance and the making of tests of significance, the systematic arrangement annuls the assumption that the errors be uncorrelated. Plots that are adjacent tend to yield alike, and hence they will have similar deviations from the replicate mean, the treatment mean, and the general mean. Randomization does not render the yields of adjacent or nearby plots uncorrelated, but it distributes the correlation effect over the whole set of plots in such a way that the F distribution is realized.

Assuming that there are c treatments and r replicates in a randomized block experiment, each replicate contains c plots, one of each treatment. For 6 treatments A, B, C, D, E, F in 3 replicates the design might be as follows, where the treatments have been arranged entirely at random.

Replicate 1	*D*	*B*	*A*	*F*	*C*	*E*
Replicate 2	*E*	*C*	*B*	*F*	*D*	*A*
Replicate 3	*C*	*F*	*B*	*D*	*A*	*E*

This is the design as we set it down on paper. In the field the treatments would occupy plots in positions corresponding to those in the diagram. The data from the experiment would be set up in an $r \times c$ table, and the method of analysis would follow that of Example 5–2.

The outline of the analysis for a randomized block experiment will be

	DF	MS
Replicates	$r - 1$	
Treatments	$c - 1$	E_t
Error	$(r - 1)(c - 1)$	E_e
Total	$rc - 1$	

The error mean square will provide the standard errors.

$$\text{SE (single plot)} = \sqrt{E_e} \qquad 3$$

$$\text{SE (mean of 1 treatment)} = \sqrt{\frac{E_e}{r}} \qquad 4$$

$$\text{SE (difference of 2 treatment means)} = \sqrt{\frac{2E_e}{r}} \qquad 5$$

and a significant difference between 2 treatment means selected at random will be*

$$t_{0.05}\sqrt{\frac{2E_e}{r}} \qquad 6$$

---

* After having conducted an experiment and found a significant F, it is a common practice to select 2 means and make the t test given in (6) above. Actually this procedure is correct only if the 2 means are selected at random, and then of course it has very little practical value. The difficulty arises from the fact that, if the means are arranged in order from the lowest to the highest and we select, say, the 2 extreme values, a significant t will nearly always be obtained even if F indicates that no significant differences are present. Snedecor [10, page 409] points out that such a test is not really a test of a random difference but the *range* of the random means included. It is possible to make a t test of the significance of a range based on the distribution of the range divided by its standard deviation, but on making a series of such comparisons these are complications arising from their not being independent. This whole problem has been considered by Tukey [11], and a method given for dividing up the ranked means into groups. D. B. Duncan (1. A Significance Test for Differences between Ranked Treatments in an Analysis of Variance, 1951, to be published. 2. On the Properties of the Multiple Comparisons Test, 1951, to be published.) has also presented a logical procedure. The student of this problem is advised to examine the methods presented by Tukey and Duncan.

For a fairly large number of means (say 25) and with an absence of noticeable gaps we can take the general mean $\bar{X}$ and calculate $\bar{X} \pm 2.8s_m$ where s_m is the standard deviation of a mean determined from the error mean square of the analysis. All those means exceeding $\bar{X} + 2.8s_m$ will constitute a small group that are significantly higher than the remainder. In plant breeding work where the test forms the basis for the selection of high yielding types, this procedure is reasonably satisfactory.

As a general rule in the interpretation of differences among means it is impossible and quite impractical to discard entirely the information that can be obtained from a t test. It is necessary, however, to observe three points quite closely.

1. Do not apply the t test to any differences between means unless the F test indicates that real differences are present. This does not mean that an F exceeding the 5% point must necessarily be obtained, but it must certainly exceed the 10% point.

2. Do not apply the t test simply because a difference looks big and you think it should be significant. There must be some logical reason for wishing to make the comparison, quite independent of the results obtained.

3. It is valid to make any t test provided that the test is preconceived at the time the experiment is designed.

The chief advantage of the randomized block experiment over the ungrouped design as outlined in Section 2 is that it makes an attempt to control the error by identifying a portion of the total variation with the replicate means. Any variation due to the replicates which, by virtue of the design, is orthogonal with the treatments is therefore independent of the treatment variation. Assuming that in a certain experimental area there is given total variation, any portion that is represented by the replicates is therefore virtually removed from the experiment with a consequent increase in precision.

The effect of the blocks in increasing the precision of an experiment can be demonstrated very neatly by breaking down each mean square into the variance components being estimated. For the ungrouped and randomized block experiments, the variance components are as follows.

Ungrouped Experiment				Randomized Blocks			
	MS	Variance Components Estimated	DF		MS	Variance Components Estimated	DF
Error	E_1	σ_1^2	$c(r-1)$	Error	E_2	σ_2^2	$(r-1)(c-1)$
Treatments	E_{t1}	$\sigma_1^2 + r\sigma_t^2$	$c-1$	Treatments	E_{t2}	$\sigma_2^2 + r\sigma_t^2$	$c-1$
				Replicates	E_b	$\sigma_2^2 + c\sigma_b^2$	$r-1$

Assuming that the total sum of squares is the same for the two experiments, we have estimates of the sums of squares in each line by multiplying the variance components by the degrees of freedom, giving, with some simplification,

$$(rc-1)\sigma_1^2 = (rc-1)\sigma_2^2 + c(r-1)\sigma_b^2$$

or

$$\sigma_2^2 = \sigma_1^2 - \frac{c(r-1)}{rc-1}\sigma_b^2 \qquad 7$$

showing that σ_2^2 must be less than σ_1^2 in the population sampled unless $\sigma_b^2 = 0$. Since E_1 is an estimate of σ_1^2, and E_2 is an estimate of σ_2^2, it follows that, on the average, $E_2 < E_1$. Similarly, for the F values we have

Ungrouped experiment $\quad F \sim \dfrac{\sigma_1^2 + r\sigma_t^2}{\sigma_1^2} = 1 + \dfrac{r\sigma_t^2}{\sigma_1^2}$ *

Randomized blocks $\quad F \sim \dfrac{\sigma_2^2 + r\sigma_t^2}{\sigma_2^2} = 1 + \dfrac{r\sigma_t^2}{\sigma_2^2}$

* The symbol $\sim$ is to be read "is an estimate of."

and it follows that, on the average, F for the randomized block experiment will be larger than F for the ungrouped experiment, unless $\sigma_b^2 = 0$. Equation (7) can be used after a randomized block experiment has been conducted to obtain an estimate of what the error would have been for an ungrouped experiment. For the randomized block design, E_2 is an estimate of σ_2^2, and E_b is an estimate of $\sigma_2^2 + c\sigma_b^2$, or, in a different form, $(E_b - E_2)/c$ is an estimate of σ_b^2. Substituting in (7) gives

$$\frac{(r-1)E_b + c(r-1)E_2}{cr-1} \qquad 8$$

The success of the randomized block experiment depends to a considerable extent on the skill of the operator in setting up the design so that the replicates will coincide with some major source of variability. In a field plot experiment this can sometimes be accomplished by making the replicates agree with topographical features of the land or known fertility trends. In general, it will be found desirable to make the blocks as compact as possible, especially when there is no previous knowledge of the nature of fertility trends. The ideal randomized block field experiment on the average is one in which the replicates are square and the plots are strips running the full length of one side of the square. In other types of experiments the replicates can be identified usually with sources of variability corresponding with time, position, classification of the experimental units, and so forth. In a feeding experiment the animals may be divided into replicates according to weight, age, or some other factor. In laboratory determinations time trends are frequently important, and it is then customary to make one determination for each combination being tested during a given period of time. Each period then becomes a replication, and major time trend effects are removed. It is impossible to list the various ways in which treatments can be grouped in order to obtain error control. The experience of the experimenter must be relied upon to furnish the necessary information. In any event it is very unusual to find a condition for which grouping of the treatments will not bring about some measure of error control. It should be borne in mind when planning an experiment that the advantages gained by correct design, with particular reference to the exercise of error control, means that the additional labor and costs are practically negligible. The gain in precision is a function of the design itself and is not necessarily related to the expenditure of effort. Frequently, the best design is the easiest design to carry out and there is an actual economy involved over and above obtaining a higher degree of precision.

The randomized block experiment has certain advantages over more complex designs. In the first place, it can be adapted to a varied number of treatments and replications without any restrictions. In the second place, it is always possible to separate the sum of squares for error into components corresponding to particular treatment effects. This feature is of distinct advantage when the error is not homogeneous and it is not strictly correct to use a pooled error for a comparison of all treatment combinations. This problem is dealt with in detail by Cochran [3]. The example given by Cochran, and originally by Bartlett [1] is reproduced in Example 11–1, except that one of the treatments has been omitted in order to illustrate the change that this requires in the calculations.

The effect of grouping the treatments into replicates can be indicated very neatly by formula (8) which is repeated below in the form given by Cochran and Cox [4]. The formula is

$$E_{\text{c.r.}} = \frac{n_b E_b + (n_t + n_e)E_e}{n_b + n_t + n_e} \qquad 9$$

where n_b, n_t, and n_e are the degrees of freedom for blocks, treatments, and error, and E_b and E_e are the mean squares for blocks and error. $E_{\text{c.r.}}$ is an estimate of what the error mean square would have been in an ungrouped experiment using the same set of experimental units.

One characteristic of the randomized block experiment, especially with reference to field plot experiments, is that with increasing numbers of treatments per block the efficiency of error control decreases. As will be noted in later chapters, when the number of treatments is large (approximately 20 or more) there are other designs that are more efficient than randomized blocks.

4. Example 11–1. Analysis of a randomized block experiment in which the error sum of squares is split into components corresponding to specific treatment effects. The data are for numbers of poppies in plots of oats subjected to different treatments (Bartlett [1]).

TABLE 11–1

NUMBERS OF POPPIES IN OATS

		Treatment					
		1	2	3	4	5	Total
Replicate	*A*	538	438	77	115	17	1185
	B	422	442	61	57	31	1013
	C	377	319	157	100	87	1040
	D	315	380	52	45	16	808
Total		1652	1579	347	317	151	4046
Mean		413.0	394.8	86.8	79.2	37.8	

The data show that (1) and (2) are much higher than the remaining three treatments, and also that (5) is lower than (3) and (4). On making a simple analysis we have:

	SS	DF	MS
Replicates	14,465.8	3	
Treatments	548,005.2	4	137,001
Error	35,851.2	12	2,987.6
Total	598,322.2		

The standard error of a single plot is $\sqrt{2987.6} = 54.66$; therefore, since t at the 5% point for 12 degrees of freedom is 2.179, a significant difference between the 2 means must be as large as $(54.66/\sqrt{4}) \times \sqrt{2} \times 2.179 = 84.2$. It rather surprises us to find that the mean difference between treatments (3) and (5) does not approach significance according to this test; however, a casual examination of the data indicates that the errors are not homogeneous and emphasizes that the error sum of squares should be broken down into components appropriate for different comparisons.

The most logical procedure is to break down the error into components corresponding to the comparisons:

(*a*) (1) − (2)	1 DF
(*b*) Between (3), (4), (5)	2 DF
(*c*) 3[(1) + (2)] − 2[(3) + (4) + (5)]	1 DF
Total	4 DF

using the methods described in Chapter 5, Section 12. In order to do this we must list the first and third comparisons for each replicate. The second can be worked out by treating the data containing (3), (4), and (5) as a separate experiment.

(*a*)	(*c*)
(1) − (2)	3[(1) + (2)] − 2[(3) + (4) + (5)]
100	2510
− 20	2294
58	1400
− 65	1859
73	8063

The figures listed under (*a*) will give us the sum of squares for the treatment comparison (1) -- (2) and also the corresponding error term. We have

$$\text{Error term} = \frac{100^2 + 20^2 + 58^2 + 65^2}{2} - \frac{73^2}{8} = 8994.5 - 666.1 = 8328.4$$

$$(1) - (2) = 666.1$$

where the divisor of the first term is $1^2 + 1^2 = 2$, and that of the second term is $4(1^2 + 1^2) = 8$.

For (*c*) the sums of squares required are

$$\text{Error term} = \frac{2510^2 + 2294^2 + 1400^2 + 1859^2}{30} - \frac{8063^2}{120}$$

$$= 565{,}947.2 - 541{,}766.4 = 24{,}180.8$$

$$3[(1) + (2)] - 2[(3) + (4) + (5)] = 541{,}766.4$$

Here, the divisor of the first term is $(3^2 + 3^2 + 2^2 + 2^2 + 2^2) = 30$, and that of the second term is $4 \times 30 = 120$. Treating (3), (4), and (5) as a separate experiment, we have

	SS	DF
(3), (4), (5)	5,572.7	2
Replicates	10,310.2	3
Error	3,342.0	6
Total	19,224.9	11

The complete analysis is:

	SS	DF	MS	SE of a Single Plot
(1) – (2)	666.1	1	666.1	
Error	8,328.4	3	2,776.1	52.6
(3), (4), (5)	5,572.7	2	2,786.4	
Error	3,342.0	6	557.0	23.6
3[(1) + (2)] – 2[(3) + (4) + (5)]	541,766.4	1	541,766.4	
Error	24,180.8	3	8,060.3	89.8

The errors for (1) – (2) and for 3[(1) + (2)] – 2[(3) + (4) + (5)] are significantly greater than for (3), (4), and (5). This is verified by calculating F values as follows.

$$F_1 = \frac{2776.1}{557.0} = 4.98 \qquad 5\% \text{ point} = 4.76$$

$$F_2 = \frac{8060.3}{557.0} = 14.5 \qquad 5\% \text{ point} = 4.76$$

This example demonstrates a fundamental principle of the analysis of variance with respect to tests of significance. The treatment comparisons must be such that they can reasonably be expected to have the same variance. In a randomized block experiment where there is evidence of heterogeneity of the errors it is frequently possible by means of the method illustrated to break up the treatment comparisons into groups that can be measured with a fair degree of accuracy.

5. Missing values in a randomized block experiment. The data from a randomized block experiment can be set up in the form of an $r \times c$ table, where r corresponds to the number of replicates and c to the number of treatments. The estimation of missing values and the corresponding analysis is that for an $r \times c$ table as outlined in detail in Chapter 14, Sections 7 and 8.

6. Latin squares. The Latin square differs from the randomized block design in that the treatments are arranged in complete groups in two directions, the two classifications being orthogonal to each other and to the treatments. Thus, if we have 4 treatments they can be arranged in rows and columns as follows:

$$\begin{matrix} A & B & C & D \\ D & A & B & C \\ C & D & A & B \\ B & C & D & A \end{matrix}$$

where each row and each column contains a complete set of the treatments. In order to take advantage of this arrangement for the control of error the groups in the rows and columns must be made to correspond with major sources of variation to which the experimental units are subject. In field plot experiments, the Latin square is usually laid out in the conventional square with the rows and columns corresponding to possible fertility trends in two directions across the field. When there is a major fertility trend in one direction, it may be more effective to lay out the Latin square as illustrated below for a 4×4 square.

Row	1				2				3				4			
Column	1	2	3	4	1	2	3	4	1	2	3	4	1	2	3	4
Treatment	*A*	*B*	*C*	*D*	*D*	*A*	*B*	*C*	*C*	*D*	*A*	*B*	*B*	*C*	*D*	*A*

It will be seen that with this arrangement the row groups will eliminate the major fertility trend and the column groups will eliminate fertility trends within row groups that are alike.

In other types of experiments the rows and columns may be made to correspond to different sources of error as in an animal feeding experiment where the column groups may correspond with initial weight and the row groups with age.

It should be emphasized at this point that the Latin square is not suitable when the number of treatments is large. In the first place, there must be as many replicates as there are treatments, and if we do not wish to go beyond 10 replications it is obvious that we cannot compare more than 10 treatments. Furthermore, when we have as many as 10 treatments it may be difficult to allocate the rows and columns to sources of variability in an efficient manner. When the number of treatments is small, the Latin square does not provide a sufficient number of replicates or sufficient degrees of freedom to give a reliable error, but this can be overcome by repeating the square as many times as desired.

If we let r represent the number of treatments, rows, and columns in a Latin square, the form of the analysis is:

	SS	DF	
Rows	$\sum_1^r \frac{(R_i^2)}{r} - \frac{G^2}{r^2}$	$r-1$	10
Columns	$\sum_1^r \frac{(C_i^2)}{r} - \frac{G^2}{r^2}$	$r-1$	11
Treatments	$\sum_1^r \frac{(T_i^2)}{r} - \frac{G^2}{r^2}$	$r-1$	12
Error	By difference	$(r-1)(r-2)$	13
Total		r^2-1	

where R_i, C_i, and T_i represent row, column, and treatment totals, and G the grand total.

For Latin squares it is frequently of interest to study the efficiency in comparison with the corresponding randomized block design in which either columns or rows are omitted. The approximate formula for estimating the mean square for error is given by Cochran and Cox [4] as follows.

$$E' = \frac{n_r E_r + (n_t + n_e)E_e}{n_r + n_t + n_e} \tag{14}$$

where E_r is the mean square for rows, E_e is the mean square for error, and n_r, n_t, and n_e are the degrees of freedom for rows, treatments, and error. This formula gives an estimate of the error expected if rows are removed. It is obvious that the effect of removing columns could be obtained by substituting E_c for E_r.

7. Randomization of a Latin square. The need for randomization applies in a Latin square as in all experimental designs. This involves placing the treatments at random in position in the square, subject to the restriction that a treatment can occur only once in a row or column. The basic principle as stated by Fisher [7] is that "each plot has an equal probability of receiving any of the possible treatments, and each pair of plots not in the same row or column has the same probability of being treated alike." Yates [13] discusses in detail the procedures necessary for the randomization of Latin squares from the 3×3 to 12×12. In general, if we have all the possible arrangements for a Latin square of given dimensions, the process of randomization involves drawing one of these at random. For example, for the 3×3 square:

$$\begin{array}{ccc} A & B & C \\ B & C & A \\ C & A & B \end{array}$$

there are only 12 possible arrangements as given below.

(1)	(2)	(3)	(4)	(5)	(6)
A B C	*A C B*	*B A C*	*C A B*	*B C A*	*C B A*
B C A	*B A C*	*C B A*	*A B C*	*C A B*	*A C B*
C A B	*C B A*	*A C B*	*B C A*	*A B C*	*B A C*

(7)	(8)	(9)	(10)	(11)	(12)
A B C	*A C B*	*B A C*	*C A B*	*B C A*	*C B A*
C A B	*C B A*	*A C B*	*B C A*	*A B C*	*B A C*
B C A	*B A C*	*C B A*	*A B C*	*C A B*	*A C B*

and if we require a square for actual use it is necessary only to select one of these at random.

With larger squares the problem is more complex. For the 4×4 square Yates [13] gives the following "reduced squares" in that the first row and column contains *A*, *B*, *C*, *D* always in the same order, and shows that randomization is obtained by selecting a reduced square at random and a random permutation of all the columns, and all the rows except the first.

(1)	(2)	(3)	(4)
A B C D	*A B C D*	*A B C D*	*A B C D*
B A D C	*B C D A*	*B D A C*	*B A D C*
C D B A	*C D A B*	*C A D B*	*C D A B*
D C A B	*D A B C*	*D C B A*	*D C B A*

Since we usually represent treatments by numbers, the squares are reproduced, replacing *A*, *B*, *C*, *D* by 1, 2, 3, 4.

(1)	(2)	(3)	(4)
1 2 3 4	1 2 3 4	1 2 3 4	1 2 3 4
2 1 4 3	2 3 4 1	2 4 1 3	2 1 4 3
3 4 2 1	3 4 1 2	3 1 4 2	3 4 1 2
4 3 1 2	4 1 2 3	4 3 2 1	4 3 2 1

and we shall illustrate the procedure of selecting a square at random. Opening a table of random numbers, Table A–7, we decide arbitrarily before looking at the table to take the first 2-digit number in, say, the sixth column and twentieth row. Suppose that this is 86, and dividing by 4 gives a remainder of 2. This indicates that our design is to be made up from the second square. The next step is to draw a random permutation of the numbers 1, 2, 3, 4. Starting at random in the table and proceeding systematically, we put down the numbers 1, 2, 3, 4 as they occur. Suppose we get 4, 3, 1, 2; then square (2) is written down with the columns in that order.

4 3 1 2
1 4 2 3
2 1 3 4
3 2 4 1

For the next step a random permutation of the numbers 1, 2, 3 is required. We get 2, 3, 1, and these decide the arrangement of the last 3 rows. The final square is

4 3 1 2
2 1 3 4
3 2 4 1
1 4 2 3

For the 5 × 5 squares Yates gives 2 reduced squares as follows.

1 2 3 4 5	1 2 3 4 5
2 1 4 5 3	2 3 4 5 1
3 5 1 2 4	3 4 5 1 2
4 3 5 1 2	4 5 1 2 3
5 4 2 3 1	5 1 2 3 4
(1–50)	(51–56)

Note the numbers below the squares. In order to select a square at random we take a number at random from 1 to 56. If the number is between 1 and 50, inclusive, we use the first square. If the number is between 51 to 56 inclusive, we use the second square.

After selecting a square, randomization is completed by permuting all columns, all rows, and all numbers. Suppose that the first square is selected, then from a table of random numbers we select 3 random permutations of the numbers 1, 2, 3, 4, 5. Let these be (1, 5, 4, 2, 3), (4, 5, 2, 1, 3) (3, 1, 5, 4, 2). Permuting the columns gives

```
1 5 4 2 3
2 3 5 1 4
3 4 2 5 1
4 2 1 3 5
5 1 3 4 2
```

and permuting the rows gives

```
4 2 1 3 5
5 1 3 4 2
2 3 5 1 4
1 5 4 2 3
3 4 2 5 1
```

To permute the numbers it is convenient to write down

```
1 2 3 4 5
3 1 5 4 2
```

the second row being our random permutation. This shows that 1 is changed to 3, 2 to 1, etc. Our final square is

```
4 1 3 5 2
2 3 5 4 1
1 5 2 3 4
3 2 4 1 5
5 4 1 2 3
```

The 6×6 squares have been dealt with in the same manner, and the appropriate squares can be found in Yates [13] and Fisher and Yates [9]. The higher squares have not been treated in detail, but Yates points out that, if the following squares are randomized by selecting a random permutation of the rows, columns, and numbers, a sufficient number of the possible squares are represented for all practical purposes.

1	2	3	4	5	6	7
2	4	5	6	1	7	3
3	7	6	5	2	1	4
4	5	1	2	7	3	6
5	3	2	7	6	4	1
6	1	7	3	4	5	2
7	6	4	1	3	2	5

(7 × 7)

1	2	3	4	5	6	7	8
2	3	1	5	6	4	8	7
3	1	4	7	8	5	6	2
4	6	7	3	1	8	2	5
5	8	2	6	7	3	1	4
6	4	8	1	2	7	5	3
7	5	6	8	3	2	4	1
8	7	5	2	4	1	3	6

(8 × 8)

1	2	3	4	5	6	7	8	9
2	3	5	7	4	9	6	1	8
3	4	6	1	8	7	9	5	2
4	8	1	2	6	5	3	9	7
5	7	2	9	3	8	4	6	1
6	9	8	5	2	4	1	7	3
7	6	9	3	1	2	8	4	5
8	5	7	6	9	1	2	3	4
9	1	4	8	7	3	5	2	6

(9 × 9)

1	2	3	4	5	6	7	8	9	0
2	7	1	5	8	3	6	9	0	4
3	8	0	7	6	2	5	1	4	9
4	1	7	9	0	5	3	2	6	8
5	6	8	0	9	7	1	4	2	3
6	5	2	3	4	9	0	7	8	1
7	9	6	2	1	4	8	0	3	5
8	3	9	6	7	0	4	5	1	2
9	0	4	1	3	8	2	6	5	7
0	4	5	8	2	1	9	3	7	6

(10 × 10)

The 11 × 11 and 12 × 12 squares are also given by Fisher and Yates [9].

It is well to keep in mind that, regardless of the availability of squares for which we can take random permutations of the rows, columns, and numbers, we can always select a square at random by trial and error. This involves trying out various random permutations and selecting those that will fit. For example, if we need a 6 × 6 square, we can take any random permutation for the first row. Suppose that we get

3 2 6 4 5 1

Then in selecting the second permutation only those numbers are taken that do not occur in the same column. While setting up the fourth and fifth rows it may be found that only certain combinations of numbers will fit, and these are filled in without reference to the table of random numbers. The sixth row is of course fixed when the fifth is complete. Occasionally, combinations are obtained that will not work, and it is then necessary to eliminate one or more rows and start again.

8. Missing values in a Latin square. The formula for the estimation of a missing value as developed in Chapter 14, Section 10, is

$$\frac{r(R + C + T) - 2G}{(r - 1)(r - 2)} \qquad 15$$

where R, C, T, and G are the row total, column total, treatment total, and grand total containing the missing value. For comparing a mean containing an estimated value with a mean for a treatment for which the results are complete, the approximate standard error is—

$$\sqrt{s^2 \left[\frac{2}{r} + \frac{1}{(r - 1)(r - 2)}\right]} \qquad 16$$

where s^2 is the error mean square.

Corrections to the treatment mean square for an exact test of significance can be worked out by the methods described in Chapter 14, Section 10.

For testing the significance of mean differences between treatments containing missing plots, apply the rule given by Yates [12] that the effective replication is as follows, assuming that the treatments are A and B.

For each value of A determine

B present in row and column, replications $= 1$
B present in a row or column, replications $= \frac{2}{3}$
B missing, replications $= \frac{1}{3}$
A missing, replications $= 0$

Similarly calculate the effective replication for B based on the presence or absence of A in corresponding rows and columns. For example, in Table 11–6, comparing rations 1.9 and 6.4 and beginning with the first row, we have

1.9 $\quad 0 + 1 + 0 + 1 + 1 + 1 = 4$
6.4 $\quad \frac{1}{3} + \frac{2}{3} + \frac{2}{3} + 1 + 1 + 1 = 4\frac{2}{3}$

Then the standard error of a mean difference between these two rations is

$$\sqrt{s^2 \left(\frac{1}{4} + \frac{1}{4\frac{2}{3}}\right)}$$

Yates [15] and Yates and Hale [16] have developed methods of analysis for the situations where one or more entire rows, columns, or treatments are missing.

9. The Graeco-Latin square. This design is of interest chiefly from the theoretical standpoint, although Dunlop [6] has pointed out how it could be applied in an actual experiment. Fisher [7] states: "The principal use of Graeco-Latin and higher squares consists in clarifying complex combinatorial situations · · ·." This is particularly true of the designs referred to later under the heading of Incomplete Block Experiments.

In Latin squares it is possible to attach Greek letters to the Latin letters in such a way that both Greek letters and Latin letters are orthogonal to each other and to the rows and columns. Fisher [7] gives the following 3×3 Graeco-Latin square.

$$\begin{matrix} A\alpha & B\beta & C\gamma \\ B\gamma & C\alpha & A\beta \\ C\beta & A\gamma & B\alpha \end{matrix}$$

and it will be noted that A has attached to it the three Greek letters, α, β, γ. The same is true for B and C. Thus, if α, β, and γ represent some effect in the experiment, this effect will be orthogonal to the treatments represented by A, B, and C. Similarly, we note that the Greek letters, like the Latin letters, occur once in each row and once in each column.

In a 3×3 Latin square the degrees of freedom can be apportioned as follows.

Rows	2
Columns	2
Treatments	2
Error	2

and obviously the 2 degrees of freedom for error can be identified with the 2 for Greek letters in a Graeco-Latin square. Therefore, a 3×3 Graeco-Latin square would not be a possible design for an actual experiment in that there would be no degrees of freedom for estimating the error, unless we use 2 or more squares. In a 4×4 Latin square the degrees of freedom may be partitioned as follows.

Rows	3
Columns	3
Treatments	3
Error	6

and for a Graeco-Latin square the outline is

Rows	3
Columns	3
Treatments	3
Greek letters	3
Error	3

This opens up the possibility of a continuation of the process, for example, by using numbers as subscripts to the Greek letters, giving finally

Rows	3
Columns	3
Latin letters	3
Greek letters	3
Numbers	3

Fisher [7] gives the following square as an example.

$A_1\alpha$	$B_2\beta$	$C_3\gamma$	$D_4\delta$
$B_4\gamma$	$A_3\delta$	$D_2\alpha$	$C_1\beta$
$C_2\delta$	$D_1\gamma$	$A_4\beta$	$B_3\alpha$
$D_3\beta$	$C_4\alpha$	$B_1\delta$	$A_2\gamma$

The principle is suggested by these squares that a square of r dimensions can be divided into $r + 1$ mutually orthogonal sets of $r - 1$ degrees of freedom, but unfortunately this is not true as exemplified particularly by the 6×6 square for which even a Graeco-Latin square does not exist. If the side of the square is a prime number or any power of a prime number, however, the $r^2 - 1$ degrees of freedom for the $r \times r$ square can be divided into $r + 1$ orthogonal sets of $r - 1$ degrees of freedom. This is a particularly important proposition in connection with the principles underlying incomplete block experiments. Further, for r^2 objects arranged in an $r \times r$ square, where r is a prime number, the division can be made by a simple mechanical procedure. Thus in a 3×3 square the 9 objects can be represented by the numbers

11	12	13
21	22	23
31	32	33

The rows and columns give the first two divisions into orthogonal sets. The third can be taken from the diagonals, thus:

11	22	33
21	32	13
31	12	23

and the fourth from the diagonals of the last square as follows.

11	32	23
21	12	33
31	22	13

If we write a fifth set, the original square is regenerated, showing that all possible sets have been written.

If the square is not that of a prime number or a power of a prime number, there is considerable difficulty in writing out the orthogonal sets, except for the 4 × 4, which can be done simply by trial and error. However, Fisher and Yates [9] have given completely orthogonalized 8 × 8 and 9 × 9 squares. These squares can also be found in Cochran and Cox [4]. The higher squares have not been investigated.

10. The cross-over design. This design may be regarded as a variant of the Latin square. If there are 2 treatments *A* and *B* in 10 replicates, the layout may be as follows.

	Column									
Row	1	2	3	4	5	6	7	8	9	10
1	*A*	*B*	*B*	*A*	*B*	*B*	*B*	*A*	*A*	*A*
2	*B*	*A*	*A*	*B*	*A*	*A*	*A*	*B*	*B*	*B*

The pairs of treatments are at random subject to the restriction that *A* and *B* must occur an equal number of times in each row. The correspondence with the Latin square is seen by comparison of the above with five 2 × 2 Latin squares.

Row	1		2		3		4		5	
1	*A*	*B*	*A*	*B*	*B*	*A*	*A*	*B*	*B*	*A*
2	*B*	*A*	*B*	*A*	*A*	*B*	*B*	*A*	*A*	*B*

Comparing the analyses of these two designs, we have:

Cross-Over Design		Latin Squares	
	DF		DF
Treatments	1	Treatments	1
Rows	1	Squares	4
Columns	9	Rows	5
Error	8	Columns	5
		Error	4
Total	19	Total	19

and it is clear that the cross-over design may have an advantage in that more degrees of freedom are available for the estimation of error. Its particular value, however, would seem to be under conditions in which a consistent difference is known to exist between the rows throughout all the pairs. In biological assay work the rows may be 2 animals that are treated consecutively as indicated by the columns, the latter representing, therefore, the time element in the experiment. For further details on this design, see Cochran and Cox [4].

11. Efficiency in experimental design. In order to compare 2 experimental designs or even to think in terms of the comparison of designs we require some sort of basis of comparison. Fisher [7] has discussed this from the standpoint of the relative amount of information furnished by a given experiment and suggests that the inverse of the error variance be taken as a general measure. Thus, if one design gives an error variance of 2 and another design a variance of 1, the relative amounts of information given by the 2 designs are 1/2 and 1. Although there are other ways of setting up such standards this is a very practical method because it can be interpreted directly in terms of the amount of replication required in order to obtain a given degree of accuracy. Since the variance of a mean is estimated by E/r, where E is the error mean square and r the number of replications, it follows that for the 2 designs referred to above the former would require twice as many replications as the latter to give equal precision.

If we have 2 designs, one giving an error mean square of E_1 and the other E_2, a measure of the relative efficiency of the first design as compared to the second is given by the ratio E_1/E_2. Suppose that this equals 2, and the second experiment has 6 replications. The first experiment would require 12 replications to obtain the same degree of accuracy. In general

$$\left(\frac{E_1}{E_2}\right) r_2 \qquad 17$$

where r_2 is the number of replications in experiment 2, gives the number of replications required for experiment 1 in order to attain equal precision.

In comparing 2 designs for the same experiment it is usual to have to take into consideration a difference in the degrees of freedom available for the estimation of error. It will have been noted that error control by means of blocks, rows, columns, etc., involves corresponding reductions in the degrees of freedom for error. Thus, in a completely randomized experiment for 8 treatments with each treatment tested in 3 experimental units, there are 16 degrees of freedom for error. The same experiment set up in randomized blocks would have 14 degrees of freedom for error. On looking up the table of t at the 5% point, we find that the corresponding values of $t_{0.05}$ are 2.12 and 2.14; therefore, the randomized block error will have to be proportionately smaller in order to make up for this difference. This whole question is not quite so simple as it may appear at first, because in comparing t values at the 5% point we are considering only one level of significance. At the 1% level we have $t_{0.01} = 2.92$ for $n = 16$, and $t_{0.01} = 2.98$ for $n = 14$, and the ratio of these t values is not quite the same as at the 5% point. Cochran and Cox [4] discuss this point in some detail, giving a table showing the effect of the levels of significance on the relative efficiencies of experiments with different numbers of degrees of freedom for error. Fisher [7] has developed a formula that enables us to make a comparison of the efficiency of 2 experiments and to take into account the effect of the degrees of freedom throughout the full range of t. For 2 experiments with error mean squares E_1 and E_2 and degrees of freedom n_1 and n_2 we can take

$$\frac{(n_2 + 1)(n_1 + 3)E_1}{(n_1 + 1)(n_2 + 3)E_2} \qquad 18$$

as an expression for the relative efficiency of the second experiment as compared to the first. The first part of the formula makes a correction for the difference in degrees of freedom. This formula is applied in Examples 11–2 and 11–3.

12. Example 11–2. A randomized block experiment. Table 11–2 gives the yields of 6 wheat varieties in an experiment in 4 randomized blocks.

TABLE 11–2

YIELDS OF WHEAT VARIETIES

		Variety						Block
		A	*B*	*C*	*D*	*E*	*F*	Total
Block	1	27.8	30.6	27.7	16.2	16.2	24.9	143.4
	2	27.3	28.8	22.7	15.0	17.0	22.5	133.3
	3	28.5	31.0	34.9	14.1	17.7	22.7	148.9
	4	38.5	39.5	36.8	19.6	15.4	26.3	176.1
Variety total		122.1	129.9	122.1	64.9	66.3	96.4	601.7

The nature of the yields in this experiment gives some indication of heterogeneity with respect to the errors. For example, the ranges in yield for the 6 varieties in order are 11.2, 10.7, 14.1, 5.5, 2.3, 3.8; therefore, it is possible that error components should be isolated. However, this is left to be done by the student and is given as one of the exercises at the end of this chapter.

Calculating the sums of squares we get:

Total	= 16,460.05 – 15,085.12		= 1374.93
Blocks	= 15,252.48 – 15,085.12		= 167.36
Varieties	= 16,147.87 – 15,085.12		= 1062.75
Error	= 1,374.93 – 167.36 – 1,062.75		= 144.82

We then have the analysis of variance:

	SS	DF	MS	F	5% Point
Blocks	167.36	3	55.79	5.78	3.29
Varieties	1062.75	5	212.55	22.0	2.90
Error	144.82	15	9.655		
Total	1374.93	23			

It is of interest to test the significance of the block effect in order to note the extent to which error control has been realized.

In order to test the significance of the differences between randomly selected pairs of variety means, we can determine the minimum significant difference as follows:

Since $t_{0.05} = 2.13$ for 15 degrees of freedom, we have

$$2.13 \times \sqrt{\frac{2 \times 9.655}{4}} = 4.68$$

Or we may use the t test in the conventional manner, calculating first the standard error of a mean difference from

$$\sqrt{\frac{2 \times 9.655}{4}} = 2.20$$

Then if we wish to compare varieties D and F for which the means are 16.2 and 24.1, we have

$$t = \frac{24.1 - 16.2}{2.20} = 3.59$$

and this difference is significant since the 5% point of t for 15 degrees of freedom is 2.13.

The relative efficiency of this randomized block experiment as compared to an ungrouped experiment can be determined by first applying the formula given by Cochran and Cox [4] in order to obtain an estimate of the error of the ungrouped experiment. Here we have

$$E_{\text{c.r.}} = \frac{3 \times 55.79 + 20 \times 9.655}{23} = 15.67$$

The relative efficiency is given approximately by

$$\frac{15.67}{9.655} = 1.62$$

This is reduced slightly due to the fact that in the completely randomized experiment there are 18 degrees of freedom for error as compared to 15 for the randomized blocks, but this effect is small. We can estimate this effect by using formula (18) described in Section 11. It is

$$\frac{(15 + 1)(18 + 3)}{(18 + 1)(15 + 3)} = \frac{336}{342} = 0.982$$

The corrected relative efficiency is then

$$1.62 \times 0.982 = 1.59$$

13. Example 11–3. Analysis of a Latin square experiment. The plan below is for a Latin square experiment to test the efficiency of methods of dusting with sulphur in order to control stem rust of wheat. The key to the treatments is given with the plan.

		1	2	3	4	5
	1	*B*	*D*	*E*	*A*	*C*
	2	*C*	*A*	*B*	*E*	*D*
Row	3	*D*	*C*	*A*	*B*	*E*
	4	*E*	*B*	*C*	*D*	*A*
	5	*A*	*E*	*D*	*C*	*B*

Key to Treatments

A = Dusted before rains
B = Dusted after rains
C = Dusted once each week
D = Drifting, once each week
E = Not dusted

All applications were 30 pounds to the acre at each treatment. Drifting means that the dust was allowed to settle over the plants from above, as in airplane dusting. The plot yields in bushels per acre are given in Table 11–3, where the figures in the table correspond to the position of the plots and treatments in the plan.

TABLE 11–3

YIELDS IN A LATIN SQUARE EXPERIMENT

		Column 1	2	3	4	5	Row Total		Treatment Total	Treatment Mean
	1	4.9	6.4	3.3	9.5	11.8	35.9	*A*	34.2	6.84
	2	9.3	4.0	6.2	5.1	5.4	30.0	*B*	32.3	6.46
Row	3	7.6	15.4	6.5	6.0	4.6	40.1	*C*	65.6	13.12
	4	5.3	7.6	13.2	8.6	4.9	39.6	*D*	39.8	7.96
	5	9.3	6.3	11.8	15.9	7.6	50.9	*E*	24.6	4.92
Column Total		36.4	39.7	41.0	45.1	34.3	196.5		196.5	

The calculation of the sums of squares is given below.

$$\text{Total} = 1829.83 - 1544.49 = 285.34$$

$$\text{Rows} = 1591.16 - 1544.49 = 46.67$$

$$\text{Columns} = 1558.51 - 1544.49 = 14.02$$

$$\text{Treatments} = 1741.10 - 1544.49 = 196.61$$

$$\text{Error} = 285.34 - 46.67 - 14.02 - 196.61 = 28.04$$

Then the analysis of variance is:

	SS	DF	MS	F	5% Point
Rows	46.67	4	11.67	4.99	3.26
Columns	14.02	4	3.505	1.50	3.26
Treatments	196.61	4	49.15	21.0	3.26
Error	28.04	12	2.337		
Total	285.34	24			

The column mean square is not significant. This is probably due to the shape of the plots. They were long and narrow; hence the columns are narrow strips running the length of the rectangular area. Under these conditions the Latin square may have little advantage on the average over a randomized block plan.

To compare means of pairs of treatments we look up $t_{0.05}$ for 12 degrees of freedom = 2.18; then a significant difference between 2 means must be equal to

$$2.18\sqrt{\frac{2 \times 2.337}{5}} = 2.11$$

and on examining the means we see that the significance of the treatment mean square is due chiefly to treatment C which is much more effective than any of the others.

Since the columns in this experiment contribute less to the control of error than the rows, it is of interest to apply the formula given by Cochran and Cox [4] to estimate the error mean square that would have been obtained if this had been a randomized block experiment with the rows as replicates.

$$E' = \frac{4 \times 3.505 + 16 \times 2.337}{20} = 2.571$$

The relative efficiency is measured by 2.571/2.337 = 1.10. The effect of the reduction in degrees of freedom can be estimated from Fisher's formula as given in Section 11. We have

$$\frac{(12 + 1)(16 + 3)}{(16 + 1)(12 + 3)} = 0.9686$$

and 0.9686 × 1.10 = 1.07, or the gain is actually only 7%.

14. Exercises.

1. Make up designs showing the complete randomized layout for the following types of experiments.

a. Randomized blocks, 10 treatments in 4 replications.

b. Latin square (7 × 7).

c. Cross-over design, 3 treatments and 9 columns. Compare the outline of the analysis obtained for this experiment with that of three 3 × 3 Latin squares.

2. Analyze the randomized block experiment data given in Table 11–4 for a feeding trial conducted by Crampton and Hopkins [5]. Determine the standard error of a difference between 2 randomly selected means, and make a t test of the difference between the means of any 2 treatments. *Error mean square = 243.6.*

TABLE 11–4

GAINS IN WEIGHT FOR FEEDING TRIAL (POUNDS — 100)

		Lot 1	2	3	4	5
Replicate	1	65	68	64	85	101
	2	56	80	56	95	89
	3	59	80	89	86	73
	4	67	66	38	101	93
	5	70	70	53	65	64
	6	46	61	90	75	60
	7	30	71	60	87	100
	8	51	69	72	77	42
	9	64	79	42	66	84
	10	58	91	55	65	49

3. Make an analysis of variance for the 5 × 5 Latin square experiment given in Table 11–5. Use formula (14) to test the error control effect due to rows and columns separately. *Error mean square = 399.35.*

4. Take the data of Table 11–2 for a randomized block experiment and divide the error sum of squares into components representing:

a	A, B, C	2 DF
b	D, E	1 DF
c	$D + E - 2F$	1 DF
d	$(A + B + C) - (D + E + F)$	1 DF

and test each component against the corresponding error.

Error mean squares: a = 6.670; b = 5.687; c = 0.990; d = 28.26.

TABLE 11-5

YIELD OF POTATOES (POUNDS — 250) FOR LATIN SQUARE FERTILITY EXPERIMENT, ROTHAMSTED REPORT, 1927–1928

130	120	118	43	137
70	81	104	84	72
120	109	18	82	71
42	97	72	97	48
48	32	72	71	45

2C	1S	1C	0	2S
1S	1C	2C	2S	0
2S	2C	0	1C	1S
0	2S	1S	2C	1C
1C	0	2S	1S	2C

Treatments: 0 = Control

1C = Cyanamide = 1 cwt sulphate of ammonia

2C = Cyanamide (double dressing)

1S = Sulphate of ammonia (1 cwt)

2S = Sulphate of ammonia (double dressing)

REFERENCES

1. M. S. Bartlett, *J. Roy. Stat. Soc. Suppl.*, **3**, 68–78, 1936.
2. M. S. Bartlett, *J. Roy. Stat. Soc.*, **4**, 137–170, 1937.
3. W. G. Cochran, *Empire J. Exptl. Agr.*, **6**, 157–175, 1938.
4. W. G. Cochran and Gertrude M. Cox, *Experimental Designs*, John Wiley and Sons, New York, 1950.
5. E. W. Crampton and J. W. Hopkins, *J. Nutrition*, **8**, 329–339, 1934.
6. G. Dunlop, *J. Agr. Sci.*, **25**, 445–459, 1935.
7. R. A. Fisher, *The Design of Experiments*, Oliver and Boyd, Edinburgh and London, 4th ed., 1947.
8. R. A. Fisher, *Statistical Methods for Research Workers*, Oliver and Boyd, Edinburgh and London, 10th ed., 1948.
9. R. A. Fisher and F. Yates, *Statistical Tables*, Oliver and Boyd, Edinburgh and London, 3rd ed., 1949.
10. G. W. Snedecor, *Statistical Methods*, Iowa State College Press, Ames, Iowa, 4th ed., 1946.
11. J. W. Tukey, *Biometrics*, **5**, 99–114, 1949.
12. F. Yates, *Empire J. Exptl. Agr.*, **1**, 129–142, 1933.
13. F. Yates, *Empire J. Exptl. Agr.*, **1**, 235–244, 1933.
14. F. Yates, *Applications of Sampling Technique to Crop Estimation and Forecasting*, Manchester Statistical Society, December, 1936.
15. F. Yates, Incomplete Latin Squares, *J. Agr. Sci.*, **26**, 301–315, 1936.
16. F. Yates and R. W. Hale, *J. Roy. Stat. Soc. Suppl.*, **6**, 67–79, 1939.

CHAPTER 12

Factorial Experiments

1. Principle of factorial experimentation. As pointed out in Chapter 11, Section 1, it is necessary for an experiment to have sufficient scope in order to obtain reliable information on the questions asked. Suppose that we are planning an experiment to test varieties of oats for an area where oats are grown on summer fallow as well as a second crop in the rotation. Under dry conditions the second crop growth may be less favorable than on fallow, and varieties may behave differently. An obvious procedure to overcome this difficulty is to have one-half the plots on fallow and one-half on stubble land. A further possibility is that the optimum rates of seeding will be different for the two conditions, and this may be different for the varieties. This calls for a variation in the rate of seeding. We have, then, 3 factors: (*a*) variety, (*b*) cultural practice, and (*c*) rate of seeding; and at this point our problem is to decide on the detailed design of the experiment. One might try to test each of the factors separately, holding all other factors constant in a given experiment, but with a little thought it will be clear that such an experiment may not give the information required. For example, it may be that only one variety is to be recommended; therefore we want to know which variety will give the best results under all conditions. The logical procedure is to vary all factors simultaneously, that is, within the framework of the same experiment. When we do so, we have what is now widely known as a factorial experiment.

One of the advantages of the factorial experiment therefore is that it increases the scope of the experiment and its inductive value, and it does so mainly by giving information not only on the main factors but on their interactions. A further advantage is that the various levels of 1 factor constitute replications of other factors and increases the amount of information obtained on all factors. For example, if we have 6 varieties in a test, each at 3 rates of seeding, in 1 replication there will be 3 plots of each variety, 1 for each rate, and in 4 replications there will be a total of 12 plots. Similarly for any 1 rate of seeding there are 6 plots in a replicate and a total of 24 plots in all. It is for this reason that replication can be kept to the minimum, and with a sufficient number of factors and levels it is possible to design a quite satisfactory experiment with one replicate.

The introduction of factors and levels in an experiment is of course limited by space and cost. If we study all possible combinations in an experiment with 4 factors, each at 3 levels, we have $3^4 = 81$ combinations. The addition of another factor at 3 levels brings the total to 243, at which point the experiment becomes bulky, and since the blocks would be quite large they would not operate efficiently in error control. However, the device known as *confounding* can be utilized to increase the efficiency of error control, and this will be discussed in following sections. Furthermore it is always possible by a wise selection of factors and levels to keep the experiment within reasonable limits. In extreme cases where a large number of combinations seem to be called for, the device known as *fractional replication* can be utilized and this also will be discussed briefly.

2. Design and analysis of a simple factorial experiment. A simple example of a factorial experiment would be one with 6 varieties, each at 3 rates of seeding, making a total of 18 treatment combinations. It will make the general principle somewhat clearer to imagine the factors and levels outlined in a 6×3 table as follows, where the rates refer to pounds per acre.

		Varieties (B)					
	30	a_1b_1	a_1b_2	a_1b_3	a_1b_4	a_1b_5	a_1b_6
Rates of seeding (A)	60	a_2b_1	a_2b_2	a_2b_3	a_2b_4	a_2b_5	a_2b_6
	90	a_3b_1	a_3b_2	a_3b_3	a_3b_4	a_3b_5	a_3b_6

In this table the letters and subscripts are in accord with the conventional notation for factorial experimentation in which the main factors are referred to as A, B, C, etc., and the small letters indicate the actual combinations, or the yield results. The subscripts indicate the various levels. Since the main effects are represented by A and B, the interaction will be AB.

The table indicates immediately that the 17 degrees of freedom for treatments can be divided into

A	2 DF
B	5 DF
AB	10 DF

and from our knowledge of the methods of analysis of two-way tables there is no difficulty in dividing up the sums of squares similarly.

The procedure in setting up this experiment, if we regard both factors of equal importance, will be to select a randomized block design and consider the 18 combinations as individual treatments. In other words each set of 18 will be randomized over an entire block.

The analysis of the results will be according to the following outline, assuming 3 replications.

		DF
Replicates		2
Treatments, 17 DF	A	2
	B	5
	AB	10
Error		34

A variant of the analysis that can be introduced here if necessary is to split up the degrees of freedom and sums of squares for A into linear and quadratic components (see Chapter 10, Section 1). This would ordinarily be done when the increase in yield with rate of seeding appears to be linear, the object being to make an actual estimate of the linear increase in yield for each additional 30 pounds in the rate of seeding.

3. Split-plot experiments. There are two conditions under which it is not satisfactory to randomize all combinations over an entire block. The first is when one of the factors is such that it cannot conveniently be applied to individual units. In plant disease work, for example, it may be necessary to establish different soil organisms that are to be tested for their effect on crops. These organisms cannot be established and kept separate on individual plots, and the best that can be done is to put them on reasonably convenient strips or blocks, which, however, are much too large for single plots. Assuming, therefore, an experiment with 4 soil organisms and 4 varieties, the plan would have to be set up somewhat as follows, where the organisms are indicated as levels of A and the varieties as levels of B. The plan shows 1 replicate only.

Plan of Split-Plot Experiment

a_1b_1	a_1b_2	a_1b_3	a_1b_4	a_2b_1	a_2b_2	a_2b_3	a_2b_4
a_3b_1	a_3b_2	a_3b_3	a_3b_4	a_4b_1	a_4b_2	a_4b_3	a_4b_4

In the actual plan the levels of B would of course be randomized within the 4 plot blocks, and the levels of A among the 4 plot blocks.

An experiment of this sort is referred to as a *split-plot* experiment. Note that there are 2 plot sizes: those that contain levels of A, referred to as the main plots, and those within the main plots containing the levels of B, referred to as the sub-plots. Any difficulties in arriving at the correct form of the analysis of split-plot experiments are due usually to a failure to grasp the principle of the presence of distinct plot sizes.

To arrive at the method of analysis let r = number of replicates, p = number of main plots per replicate, and q = number of sub-plots per main plot. Here we have $p = 4$, $q = 4$, and we shall take $r = 3$. The A levels are being tested in a simple randomized block in which $r = 3$; therefore the analysis for A will take the form

	DF
Replicates	2
A	3
Error (a)	6

We note next that all B comparisons are *within* main plots; therefore we are concerned only with degrees of freedom within the main plots, making a total of $3 \times 12 = 36$ in all. Out of the 36 we have 3 for the levels of B and 9 for the interaction AB. It should be clear that this is the correct place for the interaction as it arises from differences between levels of B for given levels of A. The analysis for sub-plots is therefore

	DF
B	3
AB	9
Error (b)	24

Note that the degrees of freedom for error (b) can be obtained by subtraction, or from $(3 + 9) \times 2$, where $3 + 9$ comes from the treatment degrees of freedom for B and AB, and 2 from the degrees of freedom for replicates. In general, therefore, the complete analysis is

	DF
Replicates	$r - 1$
A	$p - 1$
Error (a)	$(r - 1)(p - 1)$
B	$q - 1$
AB	$(p - 1)(q - 1)$
Error (b)	$p(q - 1)(r - 1)$

To obtain sums of squares a straightforward procedure can be followed. The one exception is that it is usual to put all sums of squares on a sub-plot basis. Thus, if R_i represents a replicate total, the replicate sum of squares is given by

$$\frac{\sum_1^r (R_i^2)}{pq} - \frac{G^2}{rpq}$$

Also, if A_j represents a main-plot treatment total, the sum of squares for A is

$$\frac{\sum_1^p (A_j^2)}{rp} - \frac{G^2}{rpq}$$

Further details of the analytical procedure can be obtained from Example 12–1.

The second condition wherein the split-plot experiment is the most satisfactory is when one or more factors are included merely to increase the scope of the experiment and where results on the main effects of this factor are not required. In plant disease work, when a series of seed treatments are to be tested, it is customary to include more than one variety in the test or perhaps more than one cultural practice. The object is not to obtain information on the mean yields of the varieties but to observe if the treatments behave alike on all varieties. The logical procedure is to sacrifice accuracy on the variety comparisons by putting them in the main plots, as thereby an increase in accuracy is obtained for the seed treatments and for the interaction of these treatments with the varieties.

A general picture with respect to the efficiency of split-plot experiments can be obtained by noting that the design does not result in an average increase in accuracy over randomized blocks. The randomized block error would in fact be given by summing the sums of squares and degrees of freedom for error (*a*) and error (*b*). The effect is to split the randomized block error into two parts, error (*a*), which is larger than the randomized block error on the average, and error (*b*), which is smaller. It is simply a question of sacrificing precision on one set of comparisons in order to obtain increased precision on another set.

4. Standard errors in split-plot experiments. There is a slight complication in the comparison of means from a split-plot experiment which is interesting not only from the practical but the theoretical standpoint. In the type of experiment we have outlined in Section 3 there are four different types of comparisons that one might wish to make. These are as follows, together with formulas given by Cochran and Cox [2] for the standard errors of a mean difference. E_a refers to the mean square for error (a) and E_b to the mean square for error (b).

1. Between 2 means of A over all levels of B, such as $\bar{a}_1 - \bar{a}_2$:

$$\sqrt{\frac{2E_a}{rq}}$$

2. Between 2 means of B over all levels of A, such as $\bar{b}_1 - \bar{b}_2$:

$$\sqrt{\frac{2E_b}{rp}}$$

3. Between 2 means of B for 1 level of A, such as $\overline{a_1b_1} - \overline{a_1b_2}$:

$$\sqrt{\frac{2E_b}{r}}$$

4. Between 2 means of A for 1 level of B, such as $\overline{a_1b_1} - \overline{a_3b_1}$:

$$\sqrt{\frac{2[(q-1)E_b + E_a]}{rq}}$$

The first three comparisons are straightforward and are merely variations of the usual formula with all results expressed on a single-plot basis. The fourth comparison involves the 2 errors of the split-plot experiment and is a weighted mean of E_a and E_b. These 2 errors are admittedly different, and we are faced with the problem of making a test of significance of a difference between 2 means drawn from populations having a different variance. This problem has been dealt with by Behrens [1] and Fisher [5], and tables at the 5% level have been prepared by Sukhatme [8]. For our purpose an approximation to the exact test suggested by Cochran and Cox [2] is sufficient.

Since E_a and E_b are based usually on different degrees of freedom, $t_{0.05}$ for each case will be different. The approximation involves calculating a t as follows.

$$t = \frac{(q-1)E_b t_b + E_a t_a}{(q-1)E_b + E_a}$$

where $t_b = t_{0.05}$ for E_b, and $t_a = t_{0.05}$ for E_a.

5. Example 12–1. A simple split-plot experiment. Table 12–1 gives the yields obtained in an experiment with barley on the control of disease by dusting the seed before planting with mercury dust. Six classes of seed, based on the degree of infection were included, the infection classes being arbitrarily designated 1, 2, 3, · · ·, 6. Each plot was divided, one half receiving dusted seed and another half receiving undusted seed. The yields are reported in bushels per acre.

TABLE 12–1

YIELDS OF BARLEY IN A SPLIT-PLOT EXPERIMENT

Infection	Treatment	Replicate 1	2	3	4	5	6	7	8	Treatment Total	Infection Total
1	*D*	52.6	53.8	54.4	57.6	63.6	57.6	53.5	44.2	437.3	
	U	53.4	64.8	63.2	55.8	50.1	59.7	49.4	56.4	452.8	890.1
2	*D*	57.0	64.8	55.4	55.4	54.0	61.4	54.0	53.0	455.0	
	U	54.2	56.2	54.0	58.8	58.0	43.8	50.1	53.8	428.9	883.9
3	*D*	58.9	58.8	58.2	56.2	54.2	56.1	56.4	54.0	452.8	
	U	54.2	49.8	54.0	45.6	57.6	63.9	59.4	63.2	447.7	900.5
4	*D*	50.4	63.4	58.2	63.0	63.6	60.0	55.2	50.1	463.9	
	U	48.0	57.4	54.0	57.4	50.4	45.6	48.0	50.1	410.9	874.8
5	*D*	49.0	64.8	62.2	57.0	68.4	65.4	64.8	57.0	488.6	
	U	39.2	40.2	51.0	49.8	48.2	64.8	53.4	52.8	399.4	888.0
6	*D*	55.4	52.8	51.4	63.0	60.2	45.6	61.2	58.8	448.4	
	U	33.4	38.2	40.2	57.0	49.0	55.4	44.6	47.0	364.8	813.2
Replicate Total		605.7	665.0	656.2	676.6	677.3	679.3	650.0	640.4		5250.5

The first step is to outline the analysis. This is given below.

	DF
Replicates	7
Infection classes	5
Error (*a*)	35
Dusting	1
Dusting × Infections	5
Error (*b*)	42
Total	95

To complete the first set of calculations based on the main plots we require the main-plot totals, and, for the remainder, the differences for the dusted and undusted pairs making up each main plot. These are given in Table 12–2. Either one of these sets of values can be omitted and the required sum of squares obtained by subtraction, but the method illustrated provides a complete check on the calculations.

TABLE 12–2

MAIN-PLOT TOTALS AND CORRESPONDING DIFFERENCES BETWEEN DUSTED AND UNDUSTED PLOTS

		Replicate								
		1	2	3	4	5	6	7	8	Total
Infection class	1	106.0	118.6	117.6	113.4	113.7	117.3	102.9	100.6	890.1
		– 0.8	– 11.0	– 8.8	1.8	13.5	– 2.1	4.1	– 12.2	– 15.5
	2	111.2	121.0	109.4	114.2	112.0	105.2	104.1	106.8	883.9
		2.8	8.6	1.4	– 3.4	– 4.0	17.6	3.9	– 0.8	26.1
	3	113.1	108.6	112.2	101.8	111.8	120.0	115.8	117.2	900.5
		4.7	9.0	4.2	10.6	– 3.4	– 7.8	– 3.0	– 9.2	5.1
	4	98.4	120.8	112.2	120.4	114.0	105.6	103.2	100.2	874.8
		2.4	6.0	4.2	5.6	13.2	14.4	7.2	0.0	53.0
	5	88.2	105.0	113.2	106.8	116.6	130.2	118.2	109.8	888.0
		9.8	24.6	11.2	7.2	20.2	0.6	11.4	4.2	89.2
	6	88.8	91.0	91.6	120.0	109.2	101.0	105.8	105.8	813.2
		22.0	14.6	11.2	6.0	11.2	– 9.8	16.6	11.8	83.6
								Grand total		5250.5
								Difference total		241.5

It is a good plan to determine the total sum of squares and divide this into between and within main plots by direct calculation. Thus,

$$\text{Total} = 291{,}475.77 - \frac{5250.5^2}{96} = 291{,}475.77 - 287{,}164.07$$
$$= 4311.70$$

$$\text{Main plots} = \frac{578{,}107.29}{2} - 287{,}164.07 = 1889.57$$

$$\text{Within main plots} = \frac{4844.25}{2} = 2422.12$$

Then 1889.57 + 2422.12 = 4311.69, giving a check on the calculations.

The next step is to divide up the main-plot sum of squares according to replicates, infection classes, and error. We have

$$\text{Replicates} = \frac{3{,}450{,}279.43}{12} - 287{,}164.07 = 359.22$$

$$\text{Infection classes} = \frac{4{,}599{,}570.75}{16} - 287{,}164.07 = 309.10$$

Then the main-plot error = 1889.57 − 359.22 − 309.10 = 1221.25.

In order to divide up the sum of squares for within main plots we calculate

$$\text{Interaction} = \frac{15.5^2 + 26.1^2 + \cdots + 83.6^2}{16} - \frac{241.5^2}{96}$$

$$= 1168.88 - 607.52 = 561.36$$

$$D \text{ vs } U = \frac{241.5^2}{96} = 607.52$$

$$\text{Error} = 2422.12 - 561.36 - 607.52 = 1253.24$$

The complete analysis can now be set up.

	SS	DF	MS	F	5% Point
Replicates	359.22	7	51.32		
Infection classes	309.10	5	61.82	1.77	2.49
Error (*a*)	1221.25	35	34.89		
D vs *U*	607.52	1	607.52	20.36	4.07
Interaction	561.36	5	112.27	3.76	2.44
Error (*b*)	1253.24	42	29.84		
Total	4311.69				

The means for the infection classes are not significantly different, but this does not mean that the experiment has not supplied the information required. The objective of the experiment was to compare the treated and untreated plots and to find out if the effect of treating was dependent on the extent of the infection on the seed. The latter point is brought out by the significance of the interaction. It is indicated in the data by the trend of the differences shown in the last column of Table 12–2.

Standard errors of mean differences can be worked out according to the formulas of Section 4. They are illustrated below for the 4 types of comparisons that may be needed.

1. Infection class 4 with 6. Mean difference = 54.68 – 50.82 = 3.86.

$$\text{SE (mean difference)} = \sqrt{\frac{2 \times 34.89}{16}} = 2.09$$

$$t = \frac{3.86}{2.09} = 1.85, \ 5\% \text{ point for 35 degrees of freedom} = 2.03$$

2. Dusted and undusted. Mean difference = 57.21 – 52.18 = 5.03.

$$\text{SE (mean difference)} = \sqrt{\frac{2 \times 29.84}{48}} = 1.12$$

$$t = \frac{5.03}{1.12} = 4.49, \ 5\% \text{ point for 42 degrees of freedom} = 2.02$$

3. Dusted and undusted for infection class 4. Mean difference = 6.62.

$$\text{SE (mean difference)} = \sqrt{\frac{2 \times 29.84}{8}} = 2.73$$

$$t = \frac{6.62}{2.73} = 2.42, \ 5\% \text{ point for 42 degrees of freedom} = 2.02$$

4. Infection class 2 with infection class 6 for the undusted plots. Mean difference = 53.61 – 45.60 = 8.01.

$$\text{SE (mean difference)} = \sqrt{\frac{2(34.89 + 29.84)}{16}} = 2.84$$

$$t = \frac{8.01}{2.84} = 2.82$$

Since $t_{0.05}$ for 35 degrees of freedom = 2.03 and for 42 degrees of freedom is 2.02, any difficulty due to the standard error being a weighted mean is of not much importance here. However, the method of finding an approximate t at the 5% level recommended by Cochran and Cox [2] is given as an illustration.

$$t = \frac{29.84 \times 2.02 + 34.89 \times 2.03}{29.84 + 34.89} = 2.03$$

6. Confounding in factorial experiments. It has already been pointed out in Chapter 11, Section 3, that if a large number of treatments are tested in a randomized block experiment the design is not likely to be efficient. In field plot experiments this is a reflection of the fact that plots that are close together tend to yield alike. Thus the maximum control over the error would in most cases be obtained by having only 2 long narrow plots placed side-by-side in each replicate. As the size of the block increases, variations between plots at some distance from each other are not only uncorrelated but major changes such as definite fertility trends occur within the block. A point is reached in increasing the number of plots in the replicate, where error control is practically non-existent.

In factorial experiments the device known as *confounding* is introduced in order to reduce the size of the blocks and obtain greater error control. Confounding involves the selection of certain comparisons deemed relatively unimportant and arranging the treatment combinations in such a way that these unimportant comparisons cannot be separated from the block effects, the blocks being subdivisions of a complete replicate. All other comparisons are made within blocks, and consequently the error to which they are subject is less than if they were distributed at random over the entire replicate. The comparisons entangled with block effects are said to be confounded with blocks. Although this would appear at first to involve a definite loss of information on certain comparisons, we shall find that by a process known as partial confounding it is frequently possible to increase the over-all accuracy to such an extent that even the partially confounded comparisons are determined more accurately than in a non-confounded design.

There are now a great many designs for confounding factorial experiments, and it is therefore impossible to describe them here.* We are concerned chiefly with making clear the principles on which such experiments are based, and this can best be done by explaining the simpler designs in some detail. Detailed descriptions and layouts of the various types of confounded designs can be found in Fisher [6], Yates [11], and Cochran and Cox [2].

7. Complete confounding in a 2^3 experiment. A 2^3 experiment is one in which there are 3 factors, each at 2 levels. Following the conventional notation of Section 2, the factors can be represented by A, B, and C, and if the first level of each factor is zero the combinations are (1) a, b, c, ab,

* The split-plot design discussed above actually involves confounding in that the main-plot treatments may be thought of as being confounded with main plots.

ac, *bc*, and *abc*, where the symbol (1) represents the zero level of all 3 factors at once. Thus in detail

$$(1) = a_0 b_0 c_0$$

$$b = a_0 b_1 c_0$$

$$ab = a_1 b_1 c_0$$

etc.

It will be realized that this symbolism will apply equally well even if the first level of any of the factors is not a zero level. Comparable to the treatment combinations there are the effects of the combinations, represented by *A*, *B*, *C* for the main effects, *AB*, *AC*, *BC* for the 2-factor interactions, and *ABC* for the 3-factor interaction. The 7 degrees of freedom for the $2^3 = 8$ treatment effects are

	DF
A	1
B	1
C	1
AB	1
AC	1
BC	1
ABC	1

If the treatment combinations were randomized within each replicate of 8 plots, with 4 complete replications, the analysis of variance would be of the form

	DF
Replicates	3
Main effects	3
2-factor interactions	3
3-factor interaction	1
Error	21

As a basis for introducing confounding into this experiment it is necessary to decide on the treatment combinations that enter into the different comparisons. The main effects are obviously

$$A = [a + ab + ac + abc] - [(1) + b + c + bc]$$

$$B = [b + ab + bc + abc] - [(1) + a + c + ac]$$

$$C = [c + ac + bc + abc] - [(1) + a + b + ab]$$

these equations being purely formal and not representing actual totals or means wherein summations and divisors would be given. For interactions, as well as for main effects, a rule can be given for writing down the combinations directly, but it is preferable at first to see how this can be done from first principles. Thus the interaction AB will come from the difference between the diagonal totals of the 2×2 table.

	B	
A	$(1) + c$	$b + bc$
	$a + ac$	$ab + abc$

Therefore the required contrast AB is

$$AB = [(1) + c + ab + abc] - [a + ac + b + bc]$$

and in a similar manner

$$AC = [(1) + ac + b + abc] - [a + c + ab + bc]$$

$$BC = [(1) + bc + a + abc] - [b + c + ab + ac]$$

The 3-factor interaction can be derived from the two 2×2 tables:

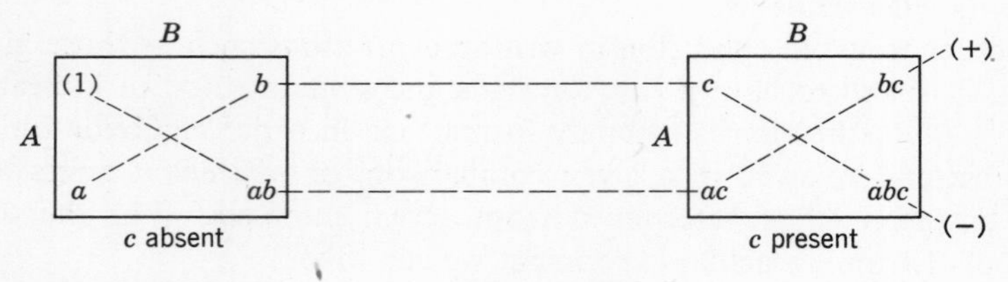

which show that

$$ABC = [a + b + c + abc] - [(1) + ab + ac + bc]$$

The simplest method for practical purposes is to follow the rule given by Finney [3] which enables us to write down the components of the required comparisons directly. First we define the block or group of combinations containing the treatment (1) as the *principal block*. Then for a 3-factor interaction such as ABC, referred to as the *defining contrast*, we write down for the principal block, (1), plus all combinations containing 2 of the letters in ABC. This gives directly (1), ab, ac, bc. The remaining group can be obtained by writing all combinations not in the principal block or by a process of multiplication involving a slight modification of the rules of algebra. We say $(1) \times a = a$, $a \times c = ac$, in the conventional manner, but $a \times ab = b$, $ac \times c = a$, etc., and the rule is that if a letter occurs as a square it is struck out. Now if we take the principal block and multiply by any combination not in the block, the second block is generated thus

$$[(1) + ab + ac + bc]\,a = a + b + c + abc$$

or

$$[(1) + ab + ac + bc]\,b = b + a + abc + c$$

To obtain the combinations for a 2-factor interaction such as AB, where a third factor C is involved, it is simply necessary to write the principal block with C absent and C present. It is convenient to write $AB(C)$ for such an interaction, giving

$$AB(C) = (1) + ab + [(1) + ab]\,c = (1) + ab + c + abc$$

As a check on the method we can apply it in writing the combinations for a main effect. For example, the principal block for $A(BC)$ is

$$(1) + (1)[b + c + bc] = (1) + b + c + bc$$

and the remaining block is $a + ab + ac + abc$. In the bracket in the expression on the left, the letters b, c, bc are simply all combinations of the letters bc, one and two at a time. It will be shown later how this rule can be generalized for the design and analysis of 2^n experiments where its chief value lies.

In order to avoid confusion in writing expressions such as those given above, it is well to have a rule for signs and some method of indicating whether the expression is a purely formal one in order to decide on the combinations involved in a given comparison, or whether it refers to a total or mean effect determined from actual numbers. For the total effect of A from an actual experiment we can take

$$A_t = \{[(1) + b + c + bc] - [a + ab + ac + abc]\}(-1)^1$$

where the exponent of (-1) represents a main effect and ensures that the sign will be correct. In this formula it is assumed that the values within the brackets are summed over all replicates. To abbreviate we can put

$$A_p = (1) + b + c + bc$$

$$A_q = a + ab + ac + abc$$

Therefore A_p will represent summation over all replicates for the combinations in which a is absent, or from a different standpoint over all combinations falling in the principal block if A were confounded. Finally

$$A_t = (A_p - A_q)(-1)^1$$

and the mean effect of A is

$$\bar{A} = \frac{1}{4r}(A_p - A_q)(-1)^1$$

where the 4 in the divisor arises from the fact that there are 3 factors; i.e., for n factors the divisor will be $2^{n-1}r$. Following the same notation

$$\overline{AB} = \frac{1}{4r}(AB_p - AB_q)(-1)^2$$

$$\overline{ABC} = \frac{1}{4r}(ABC_p - ABC_q)(-1)^3$$

Returning now to the procedure of confounding, the least important comparison is the 3-factor interaction ABC, and, if one comparison is to be completely confounded with blocks, this is the logical selection.* In each replicate therefore we will have 2 blocks as follows:

	Block 1	Block 2
Replicate	(1) *ab ac bc*	*a b c abc*

and it is clear that with this layout the 3-factor interaction will be completely confounded with blocks. In other words from such an experiment $\overline{ABC}$ will be in part due to the interaction and in part to the blocks.

If we have 4 similar replicates, the outline of the analysis will be

	DF
Blocks	7
Main effects	3
2-factor interactions	3
Error	18
Total	31

As compared to a randomized block plan there are 4 more degrees of freedom for error control, one of which represents the interaction ABC; therefore the error degrees of freedom is reduced by 3. It is important

* Obviously the objective of the experiment must be considered in selecting the comparison to be confounded. The 3-factor interaction could have the most important interaction effect and in that case should not be confounded.

to note that the 3-factor interaction has not been completely sacrificed in that the 7 degrees of freedom for blocks can be divided up into

	DF
Replicates	3
ABC	1
Error (between blocks)	3

and hence a very rough test is available. However, it is unlikely that the test will be made as the effect of the interaction would ordinarily have to be very large to reach significance.

Since the procedure adopted here is open to some criticism in that we have completely sacrificed one effect, it is of interest to inquire into another confounding procedure which enables us to distribute the confounding over more than one effect by confounding a different degree of freedom in each replicate. This is known as *partial confounding*.

8. Partial confounding in a 2^3 experiment. Partial confounding in a 2^3 experiment can be obtained by confounding *AB* in the first replicate, *AC* in the second, *BC* in the third, and *ABC* in the fourth. The blocks will be:

	Block 1	Block 2	Comparison Confounded
Replicate 1	(1) *ab* *c* *abc*	*a* *b* *ac* *bc*	*AB*
Replicate 2	(1) *ac* *b* *abc*	*a* *c* *ab* *bc*	*AC*
Replicate 3	(1) *bc* *a* *abc*	*b* *c* *ab* *ac*	*BC*
Replicate 4	(1) *ab* *ac* *bc*	*a* *b* *c* *abc*	*ABC*

We can now speak of an interaction such as *AB* being partially confounded because it is confounded in only 1 replicate out of 4. The analysis of this experiment can be outlined as follows.

	DF	
Blocks	7	
A	1	
B	1	
C	1	
AB	1	Precision factor = $\frac{3}{4}$
AC	1	
BC	1	
ABC	1	
Error	17	

The precision of the interactions is $^3/_4$ because they are tested in only $^3/_4$ of the replicates. The method of analysis is to determine the sums of squares for the blocks and the main effects in the usual way, and the interaction sums of squares from those blocks in which they are not confounded. The details are illustrated in Example 12–3.

9. Adjustments to means in confounded 2^3 experiments. In order to see why adjustments should sometimes be required in means taken from confounded experiments, suppose that we have 2 blocks in which the yields are represented as follows. On the left we have the various treatment combinations. In the center these are represented by algebraic symbols; and on the right by figures.

	I_p	I_q	I_p	I_q	I_p	I_q
	(1)	a	$x + \alpha_1$	$y + \beta_1$	$4 + 2$	$6 + 3$
	ab	b	$x + \alpha_2$	$y + \beta_2$	$4 + 6$	$6 + 2$
	ac	c	$x + \alpha_3$	$y + \beta_3$	$4 + 3$	$6 + 8$
	bc	abc	$x + \alpha_4$	$y + \beta_4$	$4 + 5$	$6 + 7$
Mean			$x + \bar{\alpha}$	$y + \bar{\beta}$	$4 + 4$	$6 + 5$

The block effect is represented by x in block p and y in block q. Then α_1 corresponds with the response to treatment (1), β_1 to the response to treatment a, and so forth. If we wish to compare ab with b, it is clear that the comparison we require is $\alpha_2 - \beta_2$, but what we have is $(x + \alpha_2) - (y + \beta_2)$ or $(x - y) + (\alpha_2 - \beta_2)$ which contains the block effect. Suppose then that we have some means of estimating $\bar{\alpha} - \bar{\beta}$, which for the particular blocks we have set up is the interaction effect $\overline{ABC}$ as this is the comparison that is confounded. This gives us

$$D_m \text{ (difference of block means)} = (x - y) + (\bar{\alpha} - \bar{\beta}) = (x - y) + \overline{ABC}$$

Then $x - y = D_m - \overline{ABC}$. The difference between the 2 means we wish to compare is

$$d_2 = (x - y) + (\alpha_2 - \beta_2)$$

$$\therefore\ (\alpha_2 - \beta_2) = d_2 - (x - y) = d_2 - (D_m - \overline{ABC})$$

and the term on the right is the required correction. To apply a correction to an individual mean we can put $(x - y) = D_m - \overline{ABC}$ in the form

$$x - \tfrac{1}{2}(D_m - \overline{ABC}) = y + \tfrac{1}{2}(D_m - ABC)$$

Therefore the correction to means in block p is $-\tfrac{1}{2}(D_m - \overline{ABC})$ and in block q it is $+\tfrac{1}{2}(D_m - \overline{ABC})$.

Applying this to the numerical example, we have $\bar{\alpha} - \bar{\beta} = 4 - 5 = -1$, which in this case is known but normally estimated from other data. Then

$$-\tfrac{1}{2}[D_m - (\bar{\alpha} - \bar{\beta})] = -\tfrac{1}{2}[(8 - 11) - (-1)] = +1$$

and

$$+\tfrac{1}{2}[D_m - (\bar{\alpha} - \bar{\beta})] = -1$$

The corrections applied to the means of *ab* and *a* give $10 + 1 = 11$, and $(8 - 1) = 7$. The difference is $11 - 7 = 4$, and this corresponds as it should to $\alpha_2 - \beta_2 = 6 - 2 = 4$. In applying this principle to actual data, it is only necessary to make sure that all calculations are on a single-plot basis. The procedure is illustrated in Examples 12–2 and 12–3.

10. Example 12–2. Complete confounding in a 2^3 experiment. The factors are *A*, *B*, *C*, and the experiment is conducted in 4 replicates. In each replicate the interaction *ABC* is confounded. The results are as shown in Table 12–3. An actual experiment of this type not being available, the data are taken from uniformity trials by Sayer et al. [7].

TABLE 12–3

YIELD RESULTS FROM A 2^3 EXPERIMENT

	I_p		I_q		II_p		II_q	
	(1)	19.1	*a*	18.6	(1)	20.7	*a*	25.9
	ab	19.2	*b*	18.2	*ab*	22.1	*b*	23.0
	ac	18.8	*c*	19.0	*ac*	21.2	*c*	24.9
	bc	19.4	*abc*	20.4	*bc*	20.1	*abc*	23.4
Block Total		76.5		76.2		84.1		97.2

	III_p		III_q		IV_p		IV_q	
	(1)	23.4	*a*	22.2	(1)	19.1	*a*	23.6
	ab	20.4	*b*	21.0	*ab*	21.9	*b*	23.7
	ac	23.2	*c*	23.6	*ac*	18.6	*c*	21.0
	bc	20.3	*abc*	21.6	*bc*	21.5	*abc*	22.8
Block Total		87.3		88.4		81.1		91.1
								$G = 681.9$

	(1)	*a*	*b*	*c*	*ab*	*ac*	*bc*	*abc*
Treatment Total	82.3	90.3	85.9	88.5	83.6	81.8	81.3	88.2
Treatment Mean	20.58	22.58	21.48	22.12	20.90	20.45	20.32	22.05

The calculation of sums of squares proceeds as follows.

Total $14{,}658.870 - \dfrac{681.9^2}{32} = 14{,}658.870 - 14{,}530.863 = 128.007$

Blocks $\dfrac{58{,}491.6}{4} - 14{,}530.863 = 14{,}622.902 - 14{,}530.863 = 92.039$

$A \quad (343.9 - 338.0)^2/32 = 5.9^2/32 = 1.088$

$B \quad (339.0 - 342.9)^2/32 = -3.9^2/32 = 0.475$

$C \quad (339.8 - 342.1)^2/32 = -2.3^2/32 = 0.165$

$AB \quad \{[(1) + ab + c + abc] - [a + b + ac + bc]\}^2/32$
$= (342.6 - 339.3)^2/32 = 3.3^2/32 = 0.340$

$AC \quad \{[(1) + ac + b + abc] - [a + c + ab + bc]\}^2/32$
$= (338.2 - 343.7)^2/32 = -5.5^2/32 = 0.945$

$BC \quad \{[(1) + bc + a + abc] - [b + c + ab + ac]\}^2/32$
$= (342.1 - 339.8)^2/32 = 2.3^2/32 = 0.165$

The complete analysis can now be set up.

	SS	DF	MS	*F*	5% Point
Blocks	92.039	7	13.15	7.22	2.58
A	1.088	1	1.088	0.60	4.41
B	0.475	1	0.475	0.26	4.41
C	0.165	1	0.165	0.09	4.41
AB	0.340	1	0.340	0.19	4.41
AC	0.945	1	0.945	0.52	4.41
BC	0.165	1	0.165	0.09	4.41
Error	32.790	18	1.822		
Total	128.007	31			

Note that the interaction *ABC* is not calculated since it is completely confounded with blocks. In this example none of the treatment effects is significant as would be expected for data taken from a uniformity trial. The dummy treatment effects appear actually to be abnormally low, an effect that seems to be due to some systematic characteristic of the data.

Corrections to means for block effects cannot be made effectively in an experiment of this sort unless we are prepared to assume that the interaction *ABC* is negligible as it cannot be eliminated from the block effect.

Assuming that *ABC* is negligible, the means can be set up in 2 groups as follows, corresponding to the arrangement in blocks for confounding *ABC*.

	(1)	20.58	*a*	22.58
	ab	20.90	*b*	21.48
	ac	20.45	*c*	22.12
	bc	20.32	*abc*	22.05
Group means		20.56		22.06
Difference			+ 1.50	
Correction		+ 0.75		− 0.75

The correction is simply $^1/_2$ the difference between the 2 group means, and the sign is taken such as to eliminate the block difference in a comparison of any 2 means in different groups. Thus *ab* becomes 20.90 + 0.75 = 21.65, and *b* becomes 21.48 − 0.75 = 20.73.

It should be clear that, if there is a real *ABC* effect, this correction which assumes all the difference to be block effect would not be justified. Its application must be governed by judgment of a particular case. If the 3-factor interaction is likely to be small, as evidenced for example by a low value of the 2-factor interaction, and the block effect is appreciable, the correction should be made. It should also be clear that two-way tables showing 2-factor interaction effects do not require correction. The following table is an example.

	B	
A	(1), *c* } 21.35	*b*, *bc* } 20.90
	a, *ac* } 21.52	*ab*, *abc* } 21.48

Corrections are not required here because the main effects *A* and *B* and the interaction *AB* are not confounded.

Single expressions representing the mean responses for the main effects and interactions are often useful. These are defined algebraically in Section 7. Here we have

$$\bar{A} = \frac{(343.9 - 338.0)}{16} = +0.37$$

$$\bar{B} = \frac{-3.9}{16} = -0.24$$

$$\bar{C} = \frac{-2.3}{16} = -0.14$$

$$\overline{AB} = \frac{3.3}{16} = +0.21$$

$$\overline{AC} = \frac{-5.5}{16} = -0.34$$

$$\overline{BC} = \frac{2.3}{16} = +0.14$$

11. Example 12–3. Partial confounding in a 2^3 experiment. In this experiment the factors are *A*, *B*, *C*, and the data are given in Table 12–4. Since an actual example was not available, Table 12–4 was set up from uniformity data from Sayer et al. [7].

TABLE 12–4

DATA BY BLOCKS AND TREATMENTS FOR A PARTIALLY CONFOUNDED 2^3 EXPERIMENT

Effect confounded	*AB*				*AC*			
Block	I_p		I_q		II_p		II_q	
	(1)	25.7	*a*	23.2	(1)	27.6	*a*	25.6
	ab	21.1	*b*	21.0	*ac*	26.7	*c*	27.9
	c	17.6	*ac*	18.6	*b*	26.2	*ab*	28.5
	abc	17.5	*bc*	18.3	*abc*	22.0	*bc*	27.2
Block Total		81.9		81.1		102.5		109.2
	BC				*ABC*			
	III_p		III_q		IV_p		IV_q	
	(1)	21.4	*b*	18.8	(1)	23.9	*a*	25.4
	bc	18.6	*c*	16.0	*ab*	21.4	*b*	26.9
	a	18.8	*ab*	16.4	*ac*	20.6	*c*	25.2
	abc	18.2	*ac*	16.6	*bc*	22.4	*abc*	30.1
Block Total		77.0		67.8		88.3		107.6
								$G = 715.4$

	(1)	*a*	*b*	*c*	*ab*	*ac*	*bc*	*abc*
Treatment Total	98.6	93.0	92.9	86.7	87.4	82.5	86.5	87.8
Treatment Mean (uncorrected)	24.65	23.25	23.22	21.68	21.85	20.62	21.62	21.95

The sums of squares for the total and for blocks are calculated as in Example 12–2. For the treatment main effects the sum of squares can be calculated directly from the treatment totals in Table 12–5, but for a particular interaction we calculate the interaction sum of squares only from those replicates in which the interaction is unconfounded. It is convenient to prepare the totals as in Table 12–5.

TABLE 12–5

TREATMENT TOTALS FOR CALCULATION OF INTERACTIONS

For Calculation of		*AB*	*AC*	*BC*	*ABC*	
Treatment	All Replicates	Less I	Less II	Less III	Less IV	Check Sum
(1)	98.6	72.9	71.0	77.2	74.7	295.8
a	93.0	69.8	67.4	74.2	67.6	279.0
b	92.9	71.9	66.7	74.1	66.0	278.7
c	86.7	69.1	58.8	70.7	61.5	260.1
ab	87.4	66.3	58.9	71.0	66.0	262.2
ac	82.5	63.9	55.8	65.9	61.9	247.5
bc	86.5	68.2	59.3	67.9	64.1	259.5
abc	87.8	70.3	65.8	69.6	57.7	263.4
Grand Total	715.4	552.4	503.7	570.6	519.5	
Block Total		163.0	211.7	144.8	195.9	
Sum		715.4	715.4	715.4	715.4	

In the preparation of Table 12–5, a double check can be obtained. In the first row the total $295.8 = 98.6 \times 3$. Then the total of each column plus the corresponding block total gives the grand total for the experiment.

We now calculate the sums of squares for treatment effects, keeping in mind that the interactions are based on only 24 plots. At the same time it is convenient to calculate the mean effects.

$$A \quad -14.0^2/32 = 6.125 \qquad \overline{A} = -14.0/16 = -0.875$$

$$B \quad -6.2^2/32 = 1.201 \qquad \overline{B} = -6.2/16 = -0.388$$

$$C \quad -28.4^2/32 = 25.205 \qquad \overline{C} = -28.4/16 = -1.775$$

$$AB \quad 4.8^2/24 = 0.960 \qquad \overline{AB} = 4.8/12 = 0.400$$

$$AC \quad -14.9^2/24 = 9.250 \qquad \overline{AC} = -14.9/12 = -1.242$$

$$BC \quad 7.2^2/24 = 2.160 \qquad \overline{BC} = 7.2/12 = 0.600$$

$$ABC \quad -13.9^2/24 = 8.050 \qquad \overline{ABC} = -13.9/12 = -1.158$$

The complete analysis is given below.

	SS	DF	MS
Blocks	410.389	7	58.63
A	6.125	1	6.125
B	1.201	1	1.201
C	25.205	1	25.205
AB	0.960	1	0.960
AC	9.250	1	9.250
BC	2.160	1	2.160
ABC	8.050	1	8.050
Error	63.419	17	3.731
Total	526.759	31	

If a table of individual treatment means is to be presented, it is necessary to make corrections for block effects. The procedure shown below demonstrates how this can be done systematically, the first step being to calculate the appropriate corrections. We list the block totals in pairs, showing the effects confounded in a particular pair. The subscript p indicates the principal block, and q the remaining block. The plus and minus signs show how the difference between the block totals is to be taken. These arise from the conventional expressions for main effects and interactions such as

$$AB = \tfrac{1}{4}(a-1)(b-1)(c+1)$$

$$ABC = \tfrac{1}{4}(a-1)(b-1)(c-1)$$

Note that the principal block always contains the treatment combination (1); therefore the sign can be determined by inspection. The formulas show that for a 2-factor interaction the results for the treatments in the principal block are added, and for a 3-factor interaction they are subtracted. The blocks can be indicated as plus or minus, and the procedure given leads to the correction for the minus block. The correction for the plus block is the same value of opposite sign.

Comparison confounded	AB		AC		BC		ABC	
Block	I_p	I_q	II_p	II_q	III_p	III_q	IV_p	IV_q
Block total	81.9	81.1	102.5	109.2	77.0	67.8	88.3	107.6
Sign	+	−	+	−	+	−	−	+
Difference		0.80		− 6.70		9.20	19.30	
Difference/8		0.10		− 0.84		1.15	2.41	
½ mean effect (calculated above)		0.20		− 0.62		0.30	− 0.58	
Difference = Correction to minus block		− 0.10		− 0.22		0.85	2.99	
Correction to plus block	+ 0.10		+ 0.22		− 0.85			− 2.99

These corrections are on a single-plot basis; therefore a corrected total will be given by adding the corrections, one for each plot in the original total. Thus the corrected totals for some of the treatments are

$$\begin{array}{ll} (1) & 98.6 + 0.10 + 0.22 - 0.85 + 2.99 = 101.1 \\ a & 93.0 - 0.10 - 0.22 - 0.85 - 2.99 = 88.8 \\ b & 92.9 - 0.10 + 0.22 + 0.85 - 2.99 = 90.9 \end{array}$$

etc.

In comparing means it is important to keep in mind that the interactions are determined on only $^3/_4$ of the replications; thus the standard error of a mean interaction response is

$$\sqrt{\frac{2 \times 3.731}{12}} = 0.788$$

The error is the mean square from the analysis of variance. It is multiplied by 2 because such a response is a difference between 2 means. It is divided by 12 because it represents a difference between means of 12 plots. Similarly the standard error of a main effect will be

$$\sqrt{\frac{2 \times 3.731}{16}} = 0.683$$

Since only 1 degree of freedom is involved in each comparison, the analysis of variance table may be dispensed with and the t test applied to all effects. There is no reduction in the work, however, through this procedure.

12. Confounding in 2^n experiments. For a 2^5 experiment with the factors A, B, C, D, E, it is obvious that we will have 32 treatment combinations. Confounding of one comparison such as the interaction $ABCDE$ will enable us to divide the replicates into 2 blocks of 16 plots each, but these may not be small enough to bring about sufficient error control. In order to divide the replicate into 4 blocks of 8 plots, it is necessary to confound 3 degrees of freedom. The selection of the contrasts for confounding is simplified by the rule given by Yates [11] and described further by Finney [3]: If two contrasts such as ABC and DE are confounded, their product as defined by the algebraic rule given in Section 7 is also confounded. In this example the third contrast would be $ABC \times DE = ABCDE$. If we selected $ABCD$ and $BCDE$, their product AE would also be confounded. The reason for this is seen by examining the 2^3

experiment again and deciding to confound AB and AC. The principal blocks for confounding AB and AC separately are

$$AB \mid (1) \quad ab \quad c \quad abc \mid$$
$$AC \mid (1) \quad ac \quad b \quad abc \mid$$

The combinations that are common to both make up the principal block for confounding AB and AC. This is $\mid (1)\ abc \mid$, and by multiplication the remaining blocks are generated, giving the four 2-plot blocks

$$\mid (1) \quad abc \mid \qquad \mid a \quad bc \mid \qquad \mid b \quad ac \mid \qquad \mid c \quad ab \mid$$

Now, on writing out the principal block for confounding BC, which is $\mid (1)\ bc\ a\ abc \mid$, it is noted that this contains the first 2 of the blocks given above, and it is clear that BC is confounded.

By means of this rule it is possible to make a wise selection of the effects to be confounded and to write out the blocks without difficulty. For a 2^5 experiment the following are some of the sets of contrasts that can be confounded.

ABCDE	*ABCD*	*E*
ABCDE	*BCD*	*AE*
ABE	*ACD*	*BCDE*

The third set is obviously the best set to confound as it does not involve the confounding of a main effect or a 2-factor interaction. The procedure is illustrated below for writing out the blocks for confounding this set. The simplest method is to write out the principal block for confounding ABE and ACD separately. We have

ABE	(1)	*ab*	*ae*	*be*	*c*	*abc*	*ace*	*bce*
	d	*abd*	*ade*	*bde*	*cd*	*abcd*	*acde*	*bcde*
ACD	(1)	*ac*	*ad*	*cd*	*b*	*abc*	*abd*	*bcd*
	e	*ace*	*ade*	*cde*	*be*	*abce*	*abde*	*bcde*

Those that are common to both are underlined. Putting these down and multiplying successively by a, b, and c, the whole set is generated.

$ABE \cdot ACD$	(1)	*be*	*cd*	*abc*	*ace*	*abd*	*ade*	*bcde*	Block 1
$\times a$	*a*	*abe*	*acd*	*bc*	*ce*	*bd*	*de*	*abcde*	Block 2
$\times b$	*b*	*e*	*bcd*	*ac*	*abce*	*ad*	*abde*	*cde*	Block 3
$\times c$	*c*	*bce*	*d*	*ab*	*ae*	*abcd*	*acde*	*bde*	Block 4

As a check we can write the principal block for confounding $BCDE$. This is

(1)	*bc*	*bd*	*be*	*cd*	*ce*	*de*	*bcde*
a	*abc*	*abd*	*abe*	*acd*	*ace*	*ade*	*abcde*

and it will be found that the treatments are identical with the treatments of blocks 1 and 2. This proves that all 3 interactions are confounded.

It is of course unnecessary to confound in the same manner in each replicate. There are 5 sets of 3 interactions of the type confounded here. These are:

ABC	*ADE*	*BCDE*
ABD	*BCE*	*ACDE*
ACE	*BCD*	*ABDE*
ACD	*BDE*	*ABCE*
ABE	*CDE*	*ABCD*

The above comprise a balanced set, as in 5 replications each of the interactions is confounded once only. All interactions are tested on $^4/_5$ of the replications.

It is obvious that the confounding procedure can be continued indefinitely as the number of factors is increased. Each additional factor doubles the number of treatments per replicate, and more degrees of freedom must be confounded in order to retain error control. For example, with 6 factors we have $2^6 = 64$ treatment combinations, and we have to confound 7 degrees of freedom in order to have 8-plot blocks. A logical selection of interactions to be confounded would be

ABCD *ABEF* *CDEF* *AED* *BCE* *BDF* *ACF*

For further information on designs of this type, the reader is referred to Yates [11] and Cochran and Cox [2].

13. Factorial designs for 2^n experiments in one replication. In a consideration of factorial experiments generally and especially with respect to 2^n experiments it is of interest to write down the disposition of degrees of freedom among the main factors and interactions as follows.

	Factors					
	2	3	4	5	6	7
Main effects	2	3	4	5	6	7
2-factor interactions	1	3	6	10	15	21
3-factor interactions		1	4	10	20	35
4-factor interactions			1	5	15	35
5-factor interactions				1	6	21
6-factor interactions					1	7
7-factor interactions						1
Percentage in interactions having 3 or more factors	0	14.3	33.3	51.6	66.7	80.0

Since we do not as a general rule expect to get important results from 3-factor and higher interactions, in unconfounded experiments with 4 or more factors, it is remarkable that so much of the experimentation effort is put into the determination of comparisons that are of no practical value. It follows that in such experiments confounding is practically a necessity if a reasonably high efficiency is to be expected.

Another important point arises from a consideration of the analysis of variance procedure as a method of estimating variances, as outlined in Chapter 11. Each of the interactions provides an estimate of its own variance plus an estimate of the error variance, the latter being a measure of the extent to which all treatment differences vary from replicate to replicate. For any given mean square such as s_5^2, the mean square for a 5-factor interaction, we can put $s_5^2 \sim \sigma_e^2 + \sigma_5^2$ where σ_e^2 is the error variance. The error mean square s_e^2 furnishes an estimate of σ_e^2 directly. Now s_5^2 is not altered by the number of replicates except with respect to the accuracy with which the variances are estimated. In other words its mean value in a large series of trials will be the same regardless of the number of replicates in each trial. Consequently, even if we have only 1 replicate, s_5^2 gives a valid estimate of $\sigma_e^2 + \sigma_5^2$. Assuming then that σ_5^2 is negligible, it follows that s_5^2 is a valid estimate of σ_e^2. The practical value of such an estimate will depend on the number of degrees of freedom available. In a 6-factor experiment, pooling the 3-, 4-, 5-, and 6-factor interactions gives a total of 42 degrees of freedom for an estimate of the error. Even with 5 factors there are 16 degrees of freedom for the estimation of error. The general conclusion is that, with a reasonable degree of assurance that the high-order interactions are not important, it is feasible to conduct such experiments in one replicate and to use the interaction mean squares as error. This is particularly important in exploratory experiments where it is important to include as many factors as possible. In other words it is more important to include these factors than it is to have replication. As a simple example we can compare an experiment involving 4 factors in 4 replications, making a total of 64 plots, with an experiment involving 6 factors in 1 replicate, again with a total of 64 plots. For a preliminary experiment, where very little is known about the effect of the factors, the 6-factor experiment in one replicate would be much more likely to provide the information required than the 4-factor experiment in 4 replicates.

14. Fractional replication. With 7 or more factors even a single replicate requires more plots than are usually available for a field plot experiment. Finney [3] has examined the problem of the replication of factors without replication of all combinations of their levels, so as to permit the drawing of conclusions from experiments having less than a single replicate.

The basic principle of fractional replication can be illustrated with reference to a simple 2-factor experiment. If the factors are A, B, the treatment combinations are (1), a, b, ab, and testing only 2 of the treatments, (1) and ab, what kind of conclusions can be drawn? The only measure of the A or the B responses is $ab - (1)$; therefore the 2 responses cannot be distinguished and this is expressed in symbols by

$$A = B$$

or, in other words, B is an *alias* of A. On this basis and noting that the 2 treatment combinations tested are from the principal block for confounding AB, *the defining contrast*, Finney develops the following rule.

> If instead of a complete replicate of an experiment, only the treatment combinations forming the principal block of a certain confounding arrangement are used, there is no measure of the contrasts which would be confounded in that arrangement; these will be termed the defining contrasts. The product of any other contrast with a defining contrast is an alias of the former.

Suppose that we have a 2^4 experiment with factors A, B, C, D, and we take the principal block arising from confounding ABC. The block is

$$| \; (1) \quad bc \quad d \quad bcd \quad ab \quad ac \quad abd \quad acd \; |$$

The only measure of the response to A comes from a comparison of the first 4 treatments with the remainder. On writing out the treatments to be compared for an estimate of BC, however, we have

$$\begin{array}{cccccccc} \underline{(1)} & \underline{bc} & \underline{d} & \underline{bcd} & a & abc & ad & abcd \\ \underline{ab} & \underline{ac} & \underline{abd} & \underline{acd} & b & c & bd & cd \end{array}$$

and those underlined are the only treatment combinations available for an estimate of A. In other words BC is an alias of A. This is given by the rule quoted above; for

$$ABC \times A = BC$$

ABC is the defining contrast, and, multiplying this by A, the product obtained is an alias of A. Similarly

$$ABC \times ABCD = D$$

and D is an alias of $ABCD$.

The conclusion from these considerations is that all effects will have a corresponding alias, and if an arrangement can be worked out such that the aliases of the important effects can be considered negligible the whole of the observed effect can be assumed to be due to the former. Thus if *ABCD* is an alias of *D* it would be logical to assume that the result for this particular contrast is due to *D*. This can be done with a reasonable degree of assurance when there are several factors in the experiment.

A 2^6 experiment can be designed in a $^1/_2$ replicate taking *ABCDEF* as the defining contrast. Then we will have such alias sets as

$$A = BCDEF$$

$$B = ACDEF$$

$$AB = CDEF$$

$$AC = BDEF$$

$$ABC = DEF$$

etc.

There will obviously be no difficulty in such an experiment in assessing the main effects and 2-factor interactions. Three-factor interactions will be indistinguishable, but in any event they will be required for an estimate of error. The outline of the analysis will be

	DF
Main effects (type $A = BCDEF$)	6
2-factor interactions (type $AB = CDEF$)	15
Error	10
Total	31

If we wish to reduce the size of the blocks, it is necessary to introduce confounding. Blocks of 16 can be used if it is satisfactory to confound two 3-factor interactions such as $ABC = DEF$. Blocks of 8 require the confounding of one 2-factor interaction. For example, we can confound *CD*, *ABC*, and *ABD* as well as their corresponding aliases *ABEF*, *DEF*, and *CEF*. The constitution of the blocks for such a confounding arrangement are determined by another rule given by Finney [3], which is as follows.

The principal block for a fractional replicate design is the same as the principal block of the complete replicate for a design which confounds the same contrasts (including all aliases) together with the defining contrast.

Suppose that we wish to write the principal block for a 2^6 experiment confounding *ABC*, *ABD*, *CD*, and their aliases, as well as the defining contrast *ABCDEF*. We put these down as follows,

Primary Contrasts			Aliases			Defining Contrast
ABC	*ABD*	*CD*	*DEF*	*CEF*	*ABEF*	*ABCDEF*

and proceed to set up the principal block. Since it would be tedious to write out the principal blocks for all contrasts and find those that are common, we can adopt a shorter method which is assisted by another rule given by Finney [3]. This rule states that "the product of any 2 treatment combinations occurring in a principal block also belong to that block." Thus if we find 2 of the combinations, their product will give a third and the next one that we find will generate others. Writing down some of the combinations arising from the principal block of *ABC*, we find that, for example, *ab* and *ef* are common to all interactions. Their product is *abef*. The next combination found to be common is *acde*. Multiplying this by those found previously, the complete principal block is obtained, which is

| (1) *ab* *ef* *abef* *acde* *bcde* *acdf* *bcdf* |

The remaining blocks are obtained by multiplication with the one restriction that, since all the combinations produced must belong to the principal block for confounding *ABCDEF*, they must contain an even number of letters. Choosing *ac*, *ad*, *ae*, we have, finally

ac	*bc*	*acef*	*bcef*	*de*	*abde*	*df*	*abdf*
ad	*bd*	*adef*	*bdef*	*ce*	*abce*	*cf*	*abcf*
ae	*be*	*af*	*bf*	*cd*	*abcd*	*cdef*	*abcdef*

The analysis of variance will be of the form:

	DF
Blocks	3
Main effects	6
2-factor interactions	14
Error	8
Total	31

The method of analysis of fractional replicate experiments is a straightforward application of the methods outlined for the analysis of 2^3 experiments and should present no difficulty.

15. A 3^2 factorial experiment. The 2 factors A, B in an experiment of this type are each at 3 levels. The 9 treatment combinations can therefore be designated as follows:

		B	
	00	01	02
A	10	11	12
	20	21	22

where 01, for example, represents a_0b_1 in the conventional notation. Note that the level of A is always written first.

Assuming that there is no confounding, the outline of the analysis of a 3^2 experiment in 4 replicates would be

	DF
Replicates	3
A	2
B	2
AB	4
Error	24
Total	35

An interesting and important fact in connection with 3^2 experiments follows from the properties of a 3×3 Graeco-Latin square as described in Chapter 11, Section 9. We noted there that the 8 degrees of freedom could be divided into 4 pairs that are mutually orthogonal. In the 3×3 experiment this would involve the partitioning of the 4 degrees of freedom for AB into 2 orthogonal pairs. This is accomplished as follows by a procedure which is the same as assigning Latin letters and subscripts in a Graeco-Latin square. Let the treatment symbols represent yields in a 3×3 square.

		B	
	00	01	02
A	10	11	12
	20	21	22

The row totals can be represented by A_0, A_1, A_2, and the column totals by B_0, B_1, B_2. Then let the diagonal totals be

$$I_0 = 00 + 11 + 22 \qquad J_0 = 00 + 21 + 12$$

$$I_1 = 10 + 21 + 02 \qquad J_1 = 10 + 01 + 22$$

$$I_2 = 20 + 01 + 12 \qquad J_2 = 20 + 11 + 02$$

Since in each of these totals one yield is taken from each row and each column, it is obvious that they are orthogonal with rows and columns. They are also orthogonal with each other. This is seen by noting that any total, such as I_1, contains one yield from each of the J totals.

The I and J totals obviously represent the 4 degrees of freedom for AB, but the separation into I and J components is purely formal. Regardless of any effects in the experiment, the sums of squares for I and J would tend to be of the same magnitude. These facts can be utilized to make a direct calculation of the interaction sum of squares. For example, if there are r replications and G is the grand total, we have

$$I = \frac{\Sigma(I^2)}{3r} - \frac{G^2}{9r}$$

$$J = \frac{\Sigma(J^2)}{3r} - \frac{G^2}{9r}$$

and $AB = I + J$. If the interaction sum of squares has been calculated by subtraction, the above method furnishes a complete check on all the work.

Although it is unlikely that we would want to do any confounding in an experiment with only 9 treatments, it is of interest to inquire how this would be done with a view to extending the principle to 3^3 experiments. The only possible division of the replicate is into 3 blocks of 3 plots each; therefore only 2 degrees of freedom can be confounded. The logical procedure is to select I or J. If we select I, the treatments placed in the blocks will correspond to those given above for the I totals. Assuming I to be completely confounded in 4 replicates, the form of the analysis will be

	DF
Blocks	11
A	2
B	2
AB (estimated from J totals)	2
Error	18
Total	35

It is important to observe here that, although a portion of the 3-factor interaction is confounded, we still have a portion remaining which will enable us to obtain a test of significance of the triple interaction effect.

The design outlined is such as to make it impossible to present a 3×3 table of means because of the partial confounding of these totals with blocks. It is therefore more satisfactory to confound I in one replicate and J in the remaining replicates. It is then possible to make appropriate corrections to the means for single-treatment combinations. To see how these corrections are made we can assume a set of yields for a 3^2 experiment in 2 replicates. I is confounded in the first replicate and J in the second.

					Block mean						Block mean
I_0	Treatment	00	11	22		J_0	Treatment	00	21	12	
	Yield	18	16	14	16.00		Yield	19	16	15	16.67
I_1	Treatment	10	21	02		J_1	Treatment	10	01	22	
	Yield	16	14	13	14.33		Yield	18	13	18	16.33
I_2	Treatment	20	01	12		J_2	Treatment	20	11	02	
	Yield	12	18	17	15.67		Yield	13	17	19	16.33
Replicate mean		15.33						16.44			

The treatments 00, 11, and 22 in block I_0 occur in different blocks in the second replicate. Thus the mean of I_0 contains treatment plus block effect, but the mean of the 3 treatments 00, 11, 22 in the second replicate is free from block effect. The difference of these means less the portion due to the replicate means is the required measure of block effect per plot. We have, therefore, for block I_0

$$\left[\frac{(19 + 17 + 18)}{3} - 16.00\right] - (16.44 - 15.33) = 0.89$$

Similarly for block J_0

$$\left[\frac{(18 + 14 + 17)}{3} - 16.67\right] - (15.33 - 16.44) = 0.77$$

The full set of corrections are finally

I_0	0.89	J_0	0.77
I_1	2.23	J_1	0.78
I_2	− 3.11	J_2	− 1.55

Since these are corrections per plot, they can be added in with the treatment totals. Thus for treatment 00 the corrected total is

$$18.00 + 0.89 + 19.00 + 0.77 = 38.7$$

16. A 3^3 factorial experiment. Since there are 27 treatment combinations in this type of experiment, there should be considerable gain in precision due to confounding. If the factors are A, B, C, the treatment degrees of freedom can be sorted out as follows.

	DF
Main effects	6
2-factor interactions	12
3-factor interactions	8
Total	26

We look naturally for a method of confounding a portion of the degrees of freedom of the 3-factor interaction. Since the replicates contain 27 plots, a logical procedure is to attempt to confound 2 degrees of freedom of this interaction, enabling us to divide each replicate into 3 blocks of 9 plots each. The clue to the confounding method is given by the principle applied in Section 15 for dividing a 2-factor interaction for 4 degrees of freedom into 2 orthogonal pairs. A continuation of the method enables us to divide the 8 degrees of freedom for a 3-factor interaction into 4 orthogonal pairs. The first step is to write out the treatment combinations.

000	010	020	001	011	021	002	012	022
100	110	120	101	111	121	102	112	122
200	210	220	201	211	221	202	212	222

The I diagonals of each square will give a new 3×3 square of I totals as follows.

$X_1 = (000 + 110 + 220)$ $\quad Y_1 = (001 + 111 + 221)$ $\quad Z_1 = (002 + 112 + 222)$

$X_2 = (100 + 210 + 020)$ $\quad Y_2 = (101 + 211 + 021)$ $\quad Z_2 = (102 + 212 + 022)$

$X_3 = (200 + 010 + 120)$ $\quad Y_3 = (201 + 011 + 121)$ $\quad Z_3 = (202 + 012 + 122)$

Taking both I and J diagonals from this square, we have:

II	IJ
$X_1 + Y_2 + Z_3$	$X_1 + Y_3 + Z_2$
$X_2 + Y_3 + Z_1$	$X_2 + Y_1 + Z_3$
$X_3 + Y_1 + Z_2$	$X_3 + Y_2 + Z_1$

The whole procedure can be repeated starting with J diagonals. Thus,

$X'_1 = (000 + 210 + 120)$ $Y'_1 = (001 + 211 + 121)$ $Z'_1 = (002 + 212 + 122)$

$X'_2 = (100 + 010 + 220)$ $Y'_2 = (101 + 011 + 221)$ $Z'_2 = (102 + 012 + 222)$

$X'_3 = (200 + 110 + 020)$ $Y'_3 = (201 + 111 + 021)$ $Z'_3 = (202 + 112 + 022)$

These yield

JI	JJ
$X'_1 + Y'_2 + Z'_3$	$X'_1 + Y'_3 + Z'_2$
$X'_2 + Y'_3 + Z'_1$	$X'_2 + Y'_1 + Z'_3$
$X'_3 + Y'_1 + Z'_2$	$X'_3 + Y'_2 + Z'_1$

Each set of 3 totals represents 2 degrees of freedom of the 3-factor interaction ABC. It follows that in order to confound 2 degrees of freedom among 3 blocks of a replicate it is simply a matter of placing the combinations occurring in one of the above sets of 3 totals in different blocks. For example, to confound IJ the blocks would be as follows.

Block 1	000	110	220	201	011	121	102	212	022
Block 2	100	210	020	001	111	221	202	012	122
Block 3	200	010	120	101	211	021	002	112	222

If this plan is followed in all replications, there is complete confounding of the 2 degrees of freedom for IJ and the outline of the analysis of variance for 4 replicates would be

	DF
Main effects	6
2-factor interactions	12
3-factor interactions	6
Blocks	11
Error	72
Total	107

The 3-factor interaction sum of squares comes from pooling the sums of squares for each pair of degrees of freedom. Having confounded IJ in all replicates, the effects formally represented by II, JI, and JJ would be unconfounded and the totals would be taken over all replicates. The interaction mean square for ABC represented by 6 degrees of freedom provides a perfectly satisfactory test of the interaction effect, and it would seem at first that from the standpoint of simplicity it would be best to confound the same pair of degrees of freedom in each replicate. However, if we do this, the IJ effect is completely sacrificed and it is then impossible to isolate certain components of the interaction for special study. For example, we might wish to study the 3-factor interaction resulting from the linear responses of all factors, which in the notation of Fisher [6] would be A, B, C, and with complete confounding this effect could not be sorted out.

The method of partial confounding in a 3^3 experiment would obviously be to confound a different pair of degrees of freedom of the 3-factor interaction in each replicate. Four replicates provide what is known as a balanced set as each pair is confounded once. For the reasons given in the preceding paragraph partial is preferred to complete confounding even if it is not possible to have a balanced set. A complete set of blocks which can be used for an actual partially confounded experiment is given in Table 12–6.

TABLE 12–6

BALANCED SET OF BLOCKS FOR A PARTIALLY CONFOUNDED 3^3 EXPERIMENT

	Block									
	1	000	110	220	101	211	021	202	012	122
II	2	100	210	020	201	011	121	002	112	222
	3	200	010	120	001	111	221	102	212	022
	1	000	110	220	201	011	121	102	212	022
IJ	2	100	210	020	001	111	221	202	012	122
	3	200	010	120	101	211	021	002	112	222
	1	000	210	120	101	011	221	202	112	022
JI	2	100	010	220	201	111	021	002	212	122
	3	200	110	020	001	211	121	102	012	222
	1	000	210	120	201	111	021	102	012	222
JJ	2	100	010	220	001	211	121	202	112	022
	3	200	110	020	101	011	221	002	212	122

17. Exercises.

1. Table 12–7 gives data taken from a uniformity experiment with mangels, conducted by Summerby [9]. The yields are in pounds of dry matter per plot. A partially confounded 2^3 has been assumed on 32 plots as shown in the table.

Make an analysis of the results and obtain treatment means corrected for block effect.

Error (SS) $= 56.867$. $\overline{AB} = -1.233$. *ac (corrected)* $= 30.4$.

2. Design complete layouts for the following experiments:

a. To compare treated and untreated seed of 12 varieties of wheat. The variety comparison is not important.

b. To compare 2 fertilizers each at 4 levels.

c. To test 3 fertilizers at 3 levels, each with 3 cultural treatments.

d. A preliminary experiment involving 6 factors, each at 2 levels.

3. Assume that the experiment designed in 2*c* above is superimposed on a section of the yields of Table 2–3; then make an analysis of the results.

TABLE 12–7

YIELDS IN A 2^3 EXPERIMENT WITH PARTIAL CONFOUNDING

	I_p		I_q		II_p		II_q	
	ab	24.0	*b*	26.2	(1)	27.5	*ab*	27.0
	abc	29.6	*a*	28.2	*abc*	25.9	*c*	30.8
	(1)	30.0	*bc*	29.1	*ac*	27.4	*bc*	32.8
	c	30.5	*ac*	25.2	*b*	29.6	*a*	33.2
Block total		114.1		108.7		110.4		123.8

	III_p		III_q		IV_p		IV_q	
	abc	30.2	*b*	31.0	(1)	31.7	*a*	33.5
	a	32.4	*ab*	34.4	*bc*	29.8	*abc*	33.2
	bc	31.9	*c*	35.2	*ac*	32.5	*b*	35.6
	(1)	31.6	*ac*	34.2	*ab*	29.2	*c*	32.4
Block total		126.1		134.8		123.2		134.7

$G = 975.8$

REFERENCES

1. W. V. Behrens, *Landw. Jb.*, **68**, 807–837, 1929.
2. W. G. Cochran and Gertrude M. Cox, *Experimental Designs*, John Wiley and Sons, New York, 1950.
3. D. J. Finney, *Ann. Eugen.*, **12**, 291–301, 1945.
4. D. J. Finney, *Empire J. Exptl. Agr.*, **15**, 107–112, 1947.
5. R. A. Fisher, *Ann. Eugen.*, **2**, 141–172, 1941.
6. R. A. Fisher, *The Design of Experiments*, Oliver and Boyd, Edinburgh and London, 4th ed., 1947.
7. W. Sayer, M. Vaidyanatham, and S. S. Iyer, *Indian J. Agr. Sci.*, **6**, 684–714, 1936.
8. P. V. Sukhatme, *Sankhyā*, **4**, 39–48, 1938.
9. R. Summerby, *Macdonald College Tech. Bull.*, **15**, 1934.
10. F. Yates, *J. Roy. Stat. Soc. Suppl.*, **2**, 181–223, 1935.
11. F. Yates, The Design and Analysis of Factorial Experiments, *Imp. Bur. Soil Sci. Tech. Commun.*, **35**, 1937.

CHAPTER 13

Incomplete Block Experiments

1. Meaning of incomplete blocks. An incomplete block is one that does not contain all the treatments that go to make up a complete replication. It is not a new concept at this stage of our study of experimental design because we have met with it twice previously, once in split-block experiments and again in factorial experiments in which interaction effects were confounded with blocks. In order not to have any confusion of ideas, the incomplete block experiments now to be described must be thought of as a group in which there is no basis for discrimination between comparisons with respect to accuracy. In split-plot experiments we are satisfied to sacrifice the accuracy of the comparisons for one main effect in order to increase accuracy for another. In a factorial experiment with confounding we are satisfied to lose accuracy on a high-order interaction or even to completely confound it in order to gain accuracy for comparisons involving the main effects and interactions of a lower order. A typical incomplete block experiment would be one designed to test a number of varieties. It is obvious in such an experiment that ordinarily there is no basis for deciding that certain comparisons are more valuable than others.

With the above general concept in mind it is not difficult to see the intimate relation between all incomplete block experiments in a broad sense and those to which the term is specifically applied wherein all comparisons are to be made with at least approximately equal accuracy.

2. An elementary type of incomplete block experiment. When the number of treatments to be tested is quite large, we have already noted (Chapter 12, Section 6) that randomized blocks do not exercise sufficient control over the error. In an attempt to overcome this, experiments were devised in which the varieties were divided into groups. The groups remained the same in each replicate so that the effect is similar to that obtained in a split-plot experiment. The analysis would follow the same general plan, there being one error for intra-block comparisons and another for inter-block comparisons. Suppose that we have 20 varieties in 4 groups of 5, and there are 6 replications. The analysis would be as follows.

	DF	MS
Replicates	5	
Groups	3	
Error (*a*)	15	E_a
Within groups	16	
Error (*b*)	80	E_b
Total	119	

For the comparison of varieties within a group the variance of a mean difference would be

$$\tfrac{2}{6}E_b \qquad 1$$

and for the comparison of means of group we would have the variance

$$\frac{2}{6}\left(\frac{E_a}{5}\right) \qquad 2$$

The difficulty with such an experiment arises from the need for comparing varieties in different groups. The error variance for the difference between 2 means is a weighted mean of E_a and E_b,

$$\tfrac{2}{6}(\tfrac{4}{5}E_b + \tfrac{1}{5}E_a) \qquad 3$$

To see what this really means we should examine the situation over the entire range of the ratio E_a/E_b that it would be reasonable to expect in many experiments. This would of course be quite difficult, but individual cases can be studied. Experience shows that the ratio $E_a/E_b = 3$ is a definite possibility. Taking this value and comparing formulas (1) and (3) on this basis, we have

Within groups $\tfrac{2}{6}E_b$

Between groups $\tfrac{2}{6}(\tfrac{4}{5}E_b + \tfrac{1}{5}E_a) = \tfrac{7}{15}E_b$

The ratio of the second of these variances to the first $= 7/5 = 1.4$, which is a measure of the relative efficiency of the two kinds of comparisons. This result can be interpreted by saying that 40% more replication would be required in order to increase the accuracy of the comparison of varieties in different groups to the point of accuracy obtained in 6 replicates for comparing varieties within groups. This is too great a discrepancy on the assumption that our actual requirement is to make all comparisons with approximately equal accuracy.

3. Lattice experiments. In discussing the type of experiment described in Section 2, Cochran [2] states:

> · · · the design · · · is at fault in keeping the same groups of varieties together in all replications, a pair of varieties either appearing *always* in the same group or *never* in the same group. It is clearly better to make the opposite rule, that a pair of varieties which are in the same group in the first replication shall not appear in the same group in a subsequent replication. This rule leads to the construction of lattice designs.

Lattice designs are incomplete block designs for which the number of varieties or treatments can be set up in the form of a square lattice* with

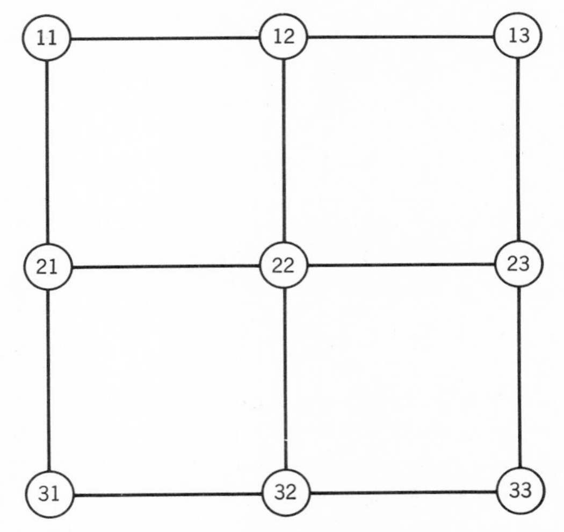

FIGURE 13–1. Diagram of a 3 × 3 lattice.

variety numbers at the intersection of the lines. A 3 × 3 lattice is shown in Figure 13–1 where the varieties are represented by 2-digit numbers, the first representing the rows and the second the columns.

Lattice designs were first described by Yates [17] and were known in the first place as pseudo-factorial designs, later as quasi-factorial designs, and finally as lattice designs. There has been considerable development since the first description in 1936, and much the greater part of this has also been due to Yates.

---

* A design made up from a rectangular lattice is possible, but the analysis is somewhat more complex. See Yates [17], Harshbarger [12, 13, 14], and Cochran and Cox [4].

The procedure of allocating the varieties to groups so that a pair of varieties appearing together in the same block shall not appear together in the same block in subsequent replicates may be illustrated for the simplest case with the 9 varieties shown in a 3 × 3 lattice in Figure 13–1. In one replicate the blocks may consist of the varieties in the rows of the lattice, giving the replicate

| 11 12 13 | 21 22 23 | 31 32 33 |

Then in the second replicate the blocks can be made up from the columns, giving

| 11 21 31 | 12 22 32 | 13 23 33 |

This gives us 2 replicates, and if we wish these can be repeated in an experiment containing 4, 6, 8, 10, or more replicates. There are other possibilities, however, and these should be studied before going into further details with respect to methods of analysis.

4. The simple lattice. The simple lattice is frequently known as a *square* lattice. There are only 2 types of blocks, those made up from the rows of the square and those from the columns. We shall refer to these as group *A* and group *B*. It requires a minimum of 2 replicates, and if more replicates are required the groups are repeated as many times as desired.

5. The triple lattice. A third group in addition to those required for a simple lattice, is added by making up blocks from the diagonals of the square. Referring to Figure 13–1 of a 3 × 3 lattice, the third group, group *C*, would be

| 11 22 33 | 21 32 13 | 31 12 23 |

The minimum number of replications is 3, but repetition of these gives 6, 9, or any multiple of 3.

6. The quadruple and other partially balanced lattice designs. Suppose that we have 25 varieties with the corresponding numbers arranged in a 5 × 5 lattice. Table 13–1 (*a*) shows the original square from which groups *A* and *B* from the rows and columns can be derived. If we write out a new square putting those numbers in the rows that occur in the diagonals of the original, we have (*b*), which gives us group *C*. Continuing by writing another square from the diagonals of the square for group *C*, we have (*c*), which provides group *D*. The 4 groups would give us a *quadruple* lattice just as the 3 groups give a triple lattice.

It will be obvious with a little study that the groups formed by these methods are orthogonal to each other. For example, on examining any block such as 31, 52, 23, 44, 15 in group *D*, we note that in group *C* each of the varieties comes from a different block. Similarly they come from different rows and different columns of the original square. The question then arises as to how many orthogonal squares can be formed. This problem has resulted in an interesting series of studies by well-known statisticians. For all squares where p is a prime number or a power of a prime number it is possible to write out $p + 1$ orthogonal groups. If p is a prime number, the groups can be written consecutively following the simple mechanical method outlined above for the 5×5 square. For the squares where $p = 4, 8, 9$ the orthogonal groups can also be written by rule,* but completely orthogonalized squares are given by Fisher and Yates [10]. The 6×6 square cannot be carried beyond the third group which is of course possible for all squares. The 10×10 has not yet been carried beyond 3 groups, and the 12×12 beyond 4 groups. These are given by Cochran and Cox [4]. When the completely orthogonalized square can be written, experiments in which all groups are used, one in each replicate, possess special properties and are referred to as *balanced* lattice designs.

TABLE 13–1

Original					Group *C*					Group *D*				
11	12	13	14	15	11	22	33	44	55	11	32	53	24	45
21	22	23	24	25	21	32	43	54	15	21	42	13	34	55
31	32	33	34	35	31	42	53	14	25	31	52	23	44	15
41	42	43	44	45	41	52	13	24	35	41	12	33	54	25
51	52	53	54	55	51	12	23	34	45	51	22	43	14	35
(*a*)					(*b*)					(*c*)				

7. The balanced lattice. The method of laying out a balanced lattice design will be clear from the discussion in Section 6. It will also be obvious that except for the 6×6 and 10×10 squares a partially balanced lattice can be designed with any number of replicates between 2 and 11, inclusive, but for complete balance the minimum number of replicates is $p + 1$. Thus for 64 varieties we require 9 replications. The advantage of the balanced lattice is that all comparisons are made with equal accuracy and the method of analysis is somewhat simpler than for partially balanced designs. Its chief disadvantage is the number of replicates required. It is ideal for 25 varieties since ordinarily in variety tests we require about 6 replications. It is also satisfactory for 49 varieties if the conditions are sufficiently variable to warrant 8 replications. In partially

* See H. B. Mann, *Analysis and Design of Experiments*, Dover Publishing Co., New York, 1949.

balanced designs certain pairs of varieties do not occur together in the same block and are therefore compared with somewhat less accuracy than those that do occur in the same block. This difference is greatest in the simple lattice and decreases with the number of groups used. Even for the simple lattice, however, the difference in the accuracy of the comparison of varieties occurring in the same and in different blocks is not great enough to be of much concern. The appropriate standard errors for the two kinds of comparisons can be worked out, but in general it is satisfactory to apply a mean standard error to all comparisons.

8. Theory of lattice designs. The principles upon which lattice designs are based are most easily explained with the simple or square lattice as an example. Suppose that we have a 9-variety experiment with the varieties designated as in the square below.*

11	12	13
21	22	23
31	32	33

In a 2-replicate experiment these would be arranged in blocks and replicates as follows, and then the position of the blocks within replicates and varieties within blocks would be randomized.

Replicate 1	11	12	13	21	22	23	31	32	33
Replicate 2	11	21	31	12	22	32	13	23	33

The yields from replicate 1 can be represented by the symbol x, those from the second replicate by y, and the varietal totals by t. These can be assumed set up in 3 squares as shown in Table 13–2 with marginal totals represented by the capital letters. The dotted lines group the varieties into the blocks in which they occur in the field.

TABLE 13–2

x_{11}	x_{12}	x_{13}	$X_{1\cdot}$	y_{11}	y_{12}	y_{13}	$Y_{1\cdot}$	t_{11}	t_{12}	t_{13}	$T_{1\cdot}$
x_{21}	x_{22}	x_{23}	$X_{2\cdot}$	y_{21}	y_{22}	y_{23}	$Y_{2\cdot}$	t_{21}	t_{22}	t_{23}	$T_{2\cdot}$
x_{31}	x_{32}	x_{33}	$X_{3\cdot}$	y_{31}	y_{32}	y_{33}	$Y_{3\cdot}$	t_{31}	t_{32}	t_{33}	$T_{3\cdot}$
$X_{\cdot 1}$	$X_{\cdot 2}$	$X_{\cdot 3}$	$X_{\cdot\cdot}$	$Y_{\cdot 1}$	$Y_{\cdot 2}$	$Y_{\cdot 3}$	$Y_{\cdot\cdot}$	$T_{\cdot 1}$	$T_{\cdot 2}$	$T_{\cdot 3}$	$T_{\cdot\cdot}$

* This experiment would not usually have sufficient varieties to warrant using an incomplete block design, but an example of this size is sufficient for explanatory purposes.

From the square on the right it can be seen that the 8 degrees of freedom for the variety totals can be divided into

	DF
Rows	2
Columns	2
Interactions	4
Total	8

which corresponds with a 2-factor experiment in which the rows represent 1 factor and columns the other. Thus if the factors are A and B we would have

	DF
A	2
B	2
AB	4
Total	8

With such an arrangement, in replicate 1 the factor A would be confounded with blocks, and in replicate 2 the factor B. This is merely partial confounding as it was outlined in Chapter 12, but here we have confounded the main effects and left the interaction unconfounded. Of course this makes no difference here as the classification of the variety effects into two main effects and their interaction is purely formal and for the purpose only of developing a method of analysis.

If there is a real block effect, the result of confounding is to make those components of the varieties represented by A and B too large. Thus the A effect is obtained from the totals $T_{1\cdot}$, $T_{2\cdot}$, and $T_{3\cdot}$, and these are made up as follows.

$$T_{1\cdot} = X_{1\cdot} + Y_{1\cdot}$$

$$T_{2\cdot} = X_{2\cdot} + Y_{2\cdot}$$

$$T_{3\cdot} = X_{3\cdot} + Y_{3\cdot}$$

Since $X_{1\cdot}$, $X_{2\cdot}$, and $X_{3\cdot}$ come from different blocks, they will contain block effects. Similarly the totals $T_{\cdot 1}$, $T_{\cdot 2}$, and $T_{\cdot 3}$, representing B, contain block effects from the second replicate. The interaction component is made up of variation among totals such as

$$t_{11} + t_{22} + t_{33} = (x_{11} + x_{22} + x_{33}) + (y_{11} + y_{22} + y_{33})$$

$$t_{21} + t_{32} + t_{13} = (x_{21} + x_{32} + x_{13}) + (y_{21} + y_{32} + y_{13})$$

$$t_{31} + t_{12} + t_{23} = (x_{31} + x_{12} + x_{23}) + (y_{31} + y_{12} + y_{23})$$

these representing 2 out of the total of 4 degrees of freedom. Each total contains 1 yield from each of the 6 blocks in the experiment; therefore these totals do not contain block effects.

The next step is to derive estimates of A and B from which the block effect has been removed. Thus the mean $T_{1\cdot}/6 = \bar{t}_{1\cdot}$ is the unadjusted mean for the first level of A, and $\bar{t}_{\cdot 1}$ for the first level of B, both of which require correction for block effect. If we can obtain estimates of these from which the block effect has been removed, the adjusted varietal means can be constructed. This follows from the fact that an unadjusted mean for variety 12, as an example, can be expressed as follows, where $\bar{t}_{1\cdot}$ and $\bar{t}_{\cdot 2}$ are the corresponding row and column means, and m is the general mean.

$$v_{12} - m = (\bar{t}_{1\cdot} - m) + (\bar{t}_{\cdot 2} - m) + (v_{12} - \bar{t}_{1\cdot} - \bar{t}_{\cdot 2} + m) \qquad 4$$

In other words the deviation of a mean of a variety from the general mean can be expressed in terms of the deviations of the row and column means plus an interaction term. The origin of the latter is more obvious if it is expressed as

$$(v_{12} - m) - (\bar{t}_{1\cdot} - m) - (\bar{t}_{\cdot 2} - m)$$

which shows that it is the total deviation of the variety mean less the deviations due to corresponding row and column means.

For further analysis of the situation it is simpler to adopt symbols similar to those employed by Cochran [1], whose explanation is followed very closely in this discussion. An estimate A_i or B_i, where i stands for intra-blocks, can be made which is free from block effect. Thus for the first level of A, $A_i = Y_{1\cdot}/3$, and for the first level of B, $B_i = X_{\cdot 1}/3$. Similarly we have estimates A_b and B_b that are confounded with blocks. Again, at the first level we have $A_b = X_{1\cdot}/3$ and $B_b = Y_{\cdot 1}/3$. The combined unadjusted effects are represented by A_0 and B_0. That is,

$$A_0 = \frac{A_i + A_b}{2} \qquad B_0 = \frac{B_i + B_b}{2} \qquad 5$$

and for the first level these would correspond with $\bar{t}_{1\cdot}$ and $\bar{t}_{\cdot 1}$.

What we require are adjusted values of A and B. These can be obtained if suitable error variances for the intra-block and inter-block effects can be found. Assuming that these error variances on a single-plot basis are σ^2 and σ'^2, then good estimates of A and B arise from the simple procedure of using σ^2 and σ'^2 as weights. Thus, if $w = 1/\sigma^2$ and $w' = 1/\sigma'^2$, the weighted estimates of A and B are

$$A = \frac{wA_i + w'A_b}{w + w'} \qquad B = \frac{wB_i + w'B_b}{w + w'} \qquad 6$$

This gives us a basis for estimating A and B from all the information available. Historically this point is very interesting, because when the lattice designs were first presented by Yates [17] he was not certain that a sufficiently reliable estimate of σ'^2 could be obtained, and he discarded A_b and B_b entirely, taking A_i and B_i only for the estimates of A and B. Now when σ'^2 is equal to σ^2, A_i and A_b are equally important and therefore A_b cannot be discarded without loss of information. This condition is obtained when the blocks are of no value in error control, that is, when the variation between blocks is no larger than within blocks. To discard A_b and B_b under these conditions is to make the experiment less efficient than if it had been laid out in randomized blocks. Yates [19, 20] then developed the method outlined above wherein due weight is given to the two components of A and B. The result is completely satisfying because, if $\sigma'^2 = \sigma^2$, then there is no weighting and A becomes the simple arithmetic mean of A_i and A_b, and there are no corrections to be applied to the variety means. Yates [19] also showed that a lattice experiment could be analyzed as if it had been laid out in randomized blocks and there would be no bias in the tests of significance. This means that, when the results of the lattice experiment indicate that error control by means of the blocks is not effective, the logical procedure is to discontinue the analysis as a lattice design and continue as for randomized blocks. Thus the lowest efficiency that can be reached in a lattice design is that of randomized blocks.*

Having obtained estimates of A and B, we can follow equation (4), writing it first in terms of the symbols just described. This gives us

$$v_0 - m = (A_0 - m) + (B_0 - m) + (v_0 - A_0 - B_0 + m) \qquad 7$$

where v_0 is an unadjusted variety mean. From the adjusted values of A and B we will have

$$v - m = (A - m) + (B - m) + (v - A - B + m) \qquad 8$$

and, on subtracting the first from the second,

$$v - v_0 = (A - A_0) + (B - B_0)$$

or

$$v = v_0 + (A - A_0) + (B - B_0) \qquad 9$$

* There is no bias in the F test when results from a lattice experiment are analyzed as if coming from a randomized block experiment. This does not apply strictly to t tests because the accuracy of all comparisons is not the same, but the variation in accuracy is small. Also the lowest efficiency of a lattice design may actually be slightly lower than for randomized blocks if we take into consideration the error in estimating the weights that are used in deciding between the lattice analysis and the randomized block analysis.

and this can be applied in making corrections to variety means. However, it is more convenient in practice to put it into a different form. In the first place, with some manipulation, we can show that

$$A - A_0 = \frac{w - w'}{w + w'}(A_0 - A_b)$$

$$B - B_0 = \frac{w - w'}{w + w'}(B_0 - B_b)$$

For convenience we put $\lambda = (w - w')/(w + w')$; then equation (9) is

$$v = v_0 + \lambda(A_0 - A_b) + \lambda(B_0 - B_b) \qquad 10$$

In order to work out the actual correction to a variety mean, say to variety 11, we have to obtain A_0, A_b, B_0, and B_b, for the first level of A and B. Thus

$$A_{i1} = \frac{Y_{1\cdot}}{3} \qquad A_{b1} = \frac{X_{1\cdot}}{3}$$

Then

$$A_{01} = \frac{A_{i1} + A_{b1}}{2} = \frac{Y_{1\cdot} + X_{1\cdot}}{6}$$

Similarly

$$B_{01} = \frac{X_{\cdot1} + Y_{\cdot1}}{6}$$

Therefore

$$A_{01} - A_{b1} = \frac{Y_{1\cdot} + X_{1\cdot}}{6} - \frac{X_{1\cdot}}{3} = \frac{Y_{1\cdot} - X_{1\cdot}}{6}$$

and

$$B_{01} - B_{b1} = \frac{X_{\cdot1} + Y_{\cdot1}}{6} - \frac{Y_{\cdot1}}{3} = \frac{X_{\cdot1} - Y_{\cdot1}}{6}$$

Representing these as c'_a and c'_b, respectively, the complete expression for a corrected variety mean is

$$v_{ef} = v_0 + \lambda c'_a + \lambda c'_b \qquad 11$$

where ef is the 2-digit number representing a variety.

In general when the simple lattice design is for p^2 varieties and there are 2 repetitions of each group, making a total of 4 replications, we have

$$c'_a = \frac{Y_{e\cdot} - X_{e\cdot}}{2p} \qquad c'_b = \frac{X_{\cdot f} - Y_{\cdot f}}{2p} \qquad 12$$

There will be a value of c'_a for each row of the table of variety means and of c'_b for each column. These and the values of $c_a = \lambda c'_a$ and $c_b = \lambda c'_b$ can be worked out first and entered in the margins of the table, and then applied to the unadjusted variety means by addition.

Our explanation up to this point depends on being able to make reliable estimates of σ^2 and σ'^2 in order to obtain the required weights, $w = 1/\sigma^2$ and $w' = 1/\sigma'^2$. The former will present no difficulty. It is comparable to intra-block error in a confounded factorial experiment and is therefore the mean square E_i for intra-block error in the analysis of variance. It can be obtained in the analysis by methods similar to those employed in Chapter 10 dealing with the analysis of non-orthogonal data. Thus either of the analyses given for the 9-variety experiment with 2 replications yield the intra-block error mean square. The second method is the one that we shall apply because it yields values of E_i and E_b from which an estimate of σ'^2 can be obtained. The first method would obviously fail in this respect because E'_b contains variety effects.

		DF	MS
Method 1	Replicates	1	
	Blocks (ignoring varieties)	4	E'_b
	Varieties (eliminating blocks)	8	
	Intra-block error	4	E_i
	Total	17	

		DF	MS
Method 2	Replicates	1	
	Blocks (eliminating varieties)	4	E_b
	Varieties (ignoring blocks)	8	
	Intra-block error	4	E_i
	Total	17	

In accordance with the principles of the analysis of variance, for an experiment with p^2 varieties with p units in each block the estimate of block effect that we require is $\sigma^2 = \sigma_i^2 + p\sigma_b^2$, where σ_b^2 represents the effect of blocks alone. That is, if the variation due to blocks arises only from plot variation, σ_b^2 will be equal to zero. If the blocks containing the same sets of varieties are repeated as in a 4- or 6-replicate experiment, a direct estimate of σ_b^2 can be made from the differences between such blocks. In the 9-variety experiment such blocks as | 11 12 13 | will occur twice and differences between them freed of replicate effect will be due entirely to blocks. This component of block effect commonly referred to as component (*a*) would correspond to only 4 out of the 8 degrees of freedom for blocks in a 4-replicate experiment. The other 4 represent what is commonly referred to as component (*b*), the value of which arises from the fact that it can be estimated without repeating the blocks. Thus for the 9-variety experiment with only 2 replicates we have differences between such totals as $X_{1\cdot}$ and $Y_{\cdot 1}$ which contain the same set of varieties. When freed of replicate effects they must represent blocks.

The best way to understand clearly how components (*a*) and (*b*) are obtained and what they represent is to visualize a 4-replicate simple lattice experiment for which the data are set up as in Table 13–3.

TABLE 13–3

DIAGRAMMATIC REPRESENTATION OF DATA FROM A SIMPLE LATTICE EXPERIMENT

Group A								Group B							
Replicate 1				Replicate 2				Replicate 3				Replicate 4			
11	12	13	g_{11}	11	12	13	g_{12}	11	12	13		11	12	13	
21	22	23	g_{21}	21	22	23	g_{22}	21	22	23		21	22	23	
31	32	33	g_{31}	31	32	33	g_{32}	31	32	33		31	32	33	
			G_1				G_2	g_{13}	g_{23}	g_{33}	G_3	g_{14}	g_{24}	g_{34}	G_4

a_{11}	a_{12}	a_{13}	$X_{1\cdot}$
a_{21}	a_{22}	a_{23}	$X_{2\cdot}$
a_{31}	a_{32}	a_{33}	$X_{3\cdot}$
$X_{\cdot 1}$	$X_{\cdot 2}$	$X_{\cdot 3}$	$X_{\cdot\cdot}$

b_{11}	b_{12}	b_{13}	$Y_{1\cdot}$
b_{21}	b_{22}	b_{23}	$Y_{2\cdot}$
b_{31}	b_{32}	b_{33}	$Y_{3\cdot}$
$Y_{\cdot 1}$	$Y_{\cdot 2}$	$Y_{\cdot 3}$	$Y_{\cdot\cdot}$

t_{11}	t_{12}	t_{13}	$T_{1\cdot}$
t_{21}	t_{22}	t_{23}	$T_{2\cdot}$
t_{31}	t_{32}	t_{33}	$T_{3\cdot}$
$T_{\cdot 1}$	$T_{\cdot 2}$	$T_{\cdot 3}$	$T_{\cdot\cdot}$

Component (*a*) can be calculated in 2 parts as follows.

$$\frac{(g_{11}-g_{12})^2+(g_{21}-g_{22})^2+(g_{31}-g_{32})^2}{2\times 3}-\frac{(G_1-G_2)^2}{2\times 9}$$
$$\frac{(g_{13}-g_{14})^2+(g_{23}-g_{24})^2+(g_{33}-g_{34})^2}{2\times 3}-\frac{(G_3-G_4)^2}{2\times 9} \qquad 13$$

Component (*b*) can also be obtained in 2 parts.

$$\frac{(X_{1\cdot}-Y_{1\cdot})^2+(X_{2\cdot}-Y_{2\cdot})^2+(X_{3\cdot}-Y_{3\cdot})^2}{4\times 3}-\frac{(X_{\cdot\cdot}-Y_{\cdot\cdot})^2}{4\times 9}$$
$$\frac{(X_{\cdot 1}-Y_{\cdot 1})^2+(X_{\cdot 2}-Y_{\cdot 2})^2+(X_{\cdot 3}-Y_{\cdot 3})^2}{4\times 3}-\frac{(X_{\cdot\cdot}-Y_{\cdot\cdot})^2}{4\times 9} \qquad 14$$

A formula for component (*b*) that is generally more convenient arises from such equalities as

$$T_{1\cdot} - 2X_{1\cdot} = (X_{1\cdot} + Y_{1\cdot} - 2X_{1\cdot}) = Y_{1\cdot} - X_{1\cdot}$$

The complete expression is then

$$\frac{(T_{1\cdot}-2X_{1\cdot})^2+(T_{2\cdot}-2X_{2\cdot})^2+(T_{3\cdot}-2X_{3\cdot})^2+(T_{\cdot1}-2Y_{\cdot1})^2+(T_{\cdot2}-2Y_{\cdot2})^2+(T_{\cdot3}-2Y_{\cdot3})^2}{4\times 3} - \frac{2(X_{\cdot\cdot}-Y_{\cdot\cdot})^2}{4\times 9} \qquad 15$$

An interesting and important fact with respect to components (*a*) and (*b*) is explained in detail by Yates [17, 18] and Cochran [1]. The expectation of the mean square for component (*a*) is $\sigma_i^2 + p\sigma_b^2$, but that of component (*b*) is $\sigma_i^2 + {}^1/_2 p\sigma_b^2$. The sense of this arises from the fact that the 2 parts of component (*b*) come from the same data arranged in 2 different ways and are therefore not completely independent. It means that, if an estimate of $\sigma'^2 + p\sigma_b^2$ is obtained from component (*b*), some allowance must be made for the different expectation. Thus if E_b, the mean square for component (*b*), can be equated as follows, where E_i is the mean square for intra-block error,

$$E_b = E_i + \tfrac{1}{2}p\sigma_b^2$$

$$2E_b = 2E_i + p\sigma_b^2$$

$$2E_b - E_i = E_i + p\sigma_b^2$$

Therefore

$$w' = \frac{1}{2E_b - E_i} \qquad 16$$

The combined mean square for components (*a*) and (*b*) has an expectation of $\sigma_i^2 + {}^3/_4 p\sigma_b^2$; therefore

$$E_b = E_i + \tfrac{3}{4}p\sigma_b^2$$

$$\tfrac{4}{3}E_b = \tfrac{4}{3}E_i + p\sigma_b^2$$

$$\frac{4E_b - E_i}{3} = E_i + p\sigma_b^2$$

and

$$w' = \frac{3}{4E_b - E_i} \qquad 17$$

It should be pointed out in this connection that the method of weighting employed here is approximate and not exact, and consequently there is a slight loss of efficiency. The exact method is rather complex and makes so little difference that it is therefore not worth while.

Finally we must have appropriate variances for the differences between variety means. These are given by Cochran [1] in the following form.

V_s (varieties occurring together in the same block)

$$= \frac{2}{rwp}\left[(p-1) + \frac{2w}{w+w'}\right] \qquad 18$$

V_d (varieties that do not occur in the same block)

$$= \frac{2}{rwp}\left[(p-2) + \frac{4w}{w+w'}\right] \qquad 19$$

V_m (mean variance for all pairs of varieties)

$$= \frac{2}{rw(p+1)}\left[(p-1) + \frac{4w}{w+w'}\right] \qquad 20$$

If we take $\lambda = (w - w')/(w + w')$, the above formulas can be expressed in the simpler and more fundamental form,

$$V_s = \frac{2E_i}{r}\left(1 + \frac{\lambda}{p}\right) \qquad 21$$

$$V_d = \frac{2E_i}{r}\left[1 + 2\left(\frac{\lambda}{p}\right)\right] \qquad 22$$

$$V_m = \frac{2E_i}{r}\left[1 + 2\left(\frac{\lambda}{p+1}\right)\right] \qquad 23$$

These formulas are very instructive with respect to the effect of the block variance. Assuming for simplicity that w' is estimated from component (*a*) only, we have $w' = 1/E_b$. Then $\lambda = (E_b - E_i)/(E_b + E_i)$. When $E_b \leq E_i$, $\lambda = 0$ and all the formulas reduce to $2E_i/r$, which is the same as for randomized blocks. As E_b increases without limit, it is easy to show that λ approaches 1. The three formulas then become

$$V_s = \frac{2E_i}{r}\left(\frac{p+1}{p}\right) \qquad 24$$

$$V_d = \frac{2E_i}{r}\left(\frac{p+2}{p}\right) \qquad 25$$

$$V_m = \frac{2E_i}{r}\left(\frac{p+3}{p+1}\right) \qquad 26$$

which are the formulas appropriate for the type of analysis where the A and B effects are estimated from A_i and B_i only, or in other words when no information is recovered, with respect to A and B, from A_b and B_b.

If we require an F test of the significance of the variety variance, it should be clear that an adjustment must be made in the variety variance calculated directly from the variety totals, as this will contain block effect. For the simple lattice Cochran [1] gives this adjustment as

$$-\lambda\left[\left(1+\frac{w'}{w}\right)S_u - S_b\right] \tag{27}$$

where S_u and S_b are, respectively, the unadjusted and adjusted sums of squares for component (b). S_b is calculated as explained above for component (b). Referring to Table 13–3, S_u will be

$$\frac{X_{1\cdot}^2 + X_{2\cdot}^2 + X_{3\cdot}^2}{6} - \frac{X_{\cdot\cdot}^2}{18} + \frac{Y_{\cdot 1}^2 + Y_{\cdot 2}^2 + Y_{\cdot 3}^2}{6} - \frac{Y_{\cdot\cdot}^2}{18} \tag{28}$$

The adjustment is shown with a negative sign, indicating that it must always be subtracted from the unadjusted variety sum of squares. After this adjustment the F test can be made in the usual manner.

9. Lattice designs with from 2 to p groups. As pointed out in Section 6, triple, quadruple, and other partially balanced lattice designs can be made up by writing out additional orthogonal groups. The only restriction on designs of practical significance (those for $p = 3$ to 11) is that for $p = 6$ and 10; we cannot go higher than the triple lattice. If we write $p + 1$ groups, the design becomes a *balanced lattice* and has special properties that justify our placing it in a separate class.

There is little difficulty in the analysis of designs of higher order than the simple lattice. Let $k =$ the number of groups, and the formulas given above can be restated for the general case. These are given below and a convenient analytical procedure outlined.

A valuable preliminary step is to perform an analysis of variance as if the experiment had been laid out in randomized blocks, as all the sums of squares determined will be required in the complete analysis. An F test of the significance of the variety mean square can be made, and if the F is significant further tests will not be necessary as in the complete analysis the significance may be increased but cannot be decreased. The outline of the analysis will be as follows.

	DF
Replications	$r - 1$
Varieties	$p^2 - 1$
Error	$(p^2 - 1)(r - 1)$
Total	$rp^2 - 1$

Assuming that the variety differences are significant, we proceed to the detailed analysis wherein the first major objective is to obtain block sums of squares from which the effect of varieties has been eliminated. There will be 2 forms of the analysis, depending on whether the groups are or are not repeated. These are given in outline form below.

Groups Not Repeated ($r = k$)	DF	Groups Repeated ($r = 2k$)	DF	
Replicates	$r - 1$	Replicates	$r - 1$	
Component (b)	$r(p - 1)$	Component (a)	$k(p - 1)$	$r(p - 1)$
		Component (b)	$k(p - 1)$	
Varieties	$p^2 - 1$	Varieties	$p^2 - 1$	
Intra-block error	$(p - 1)(rp - p - 1)$	Intra-block error	$(p - 1)(rp - p - 1)$	
Total	$rp^2 - 1$	Total	$rp^2 - 1$	

Note that we could have $r = 3k$, $r = 4k$, etc., but such designs are not of much practical importance since the main objective will be to increase the number of replications by increasing the number of groups rather than the number of repetitions. Thus for a 6-replicate experiment we have the choice $6 = 3 \times 2$, or $6 = 2 \times 3$, where the last figure is k. The latter design is to be preferred, so it is hardly necessary to consider the other.

For any variety such as 12, let b_{12} represent the total of the block in which it occurs, or, when $k \geq 2$, the total of all similar blocks. Referring to Table 13–3 it is noted that there are 2 values of b_{12}, $X_{1\cdot}$ in group A and $Y_{\cdot 2}$ in group B. Then let u_{12} represent a total of all varieties occurring in the same block with 12. Again from Table 13–3, one value of u_{12} is $T_{1\cdot}$, and the other one is $T_{\cdot 2}$. Then for variety 12 the quantity W_{12} is

$$W_{12} = (T_{1\cdot} - 2X_{1\cdot}) + (T_{\cdot 2} - 2Y_{\cdot 2})$$

or in general, where ef represents the variety number,

$$W_{ef} = \sum_{1}^{k} (u_{ef} - kb_{ef}) \qquad 29$$

and the p^2 quantities so determined yield the sum of squares for component (b) and the corrections to the variety means. Component (b) sum of squares is simply

$$\frac{\sum_{1}^{p^2} (W_{ef}^2)}{r(k - 1)p^2} \qquad 30$$

Component (a) will be calculated by obtaining the sum of squares for differences between similar blocks. We can then set up the analysis and determine the mean squares E_b and E_i.

The next step is to determine the values of w and w'. The value of w is always given by $1/E_i$, but the method of calculating w' depends on the number of degrees of freedom available for estimating component (a). If n represents the number of repetitions of the groups, a table can be set up as follows, giving the degrees of freedom available for estimating component (a). Each quantity in the table is to be multiplied by $(p - 1)$.

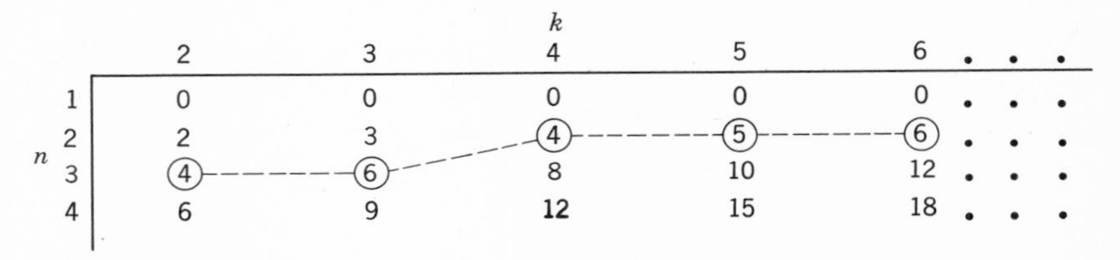

				k			
		2	3	4	5	6	. . .
	1	0	0	0	0	0	. . .
n	2	2	3	(4)	(5)	(6)	. . .
	3	(4)	(6)	8	10	12	. . .
	4	6	9	12	15	18	. . .

The general formula is $k(n - 1)(p - 1)$. Since a lattice experiment will rarely if ever be used for p^2 less than 25, the numbers circled and connected by a dotted line indicate those for which there are sufficient degrees of freedom to give a fairly reliable estimate of the block mean square from component (a) alone. The same will apply of course to those cases below the circled ones. In the first row we have component (b) only, so that there are actually only 2 situations in which components (a) and (b) are both required in order to obtain an estimate of the mean square for blocks. For these we have

$$w' = \frac{r - 1}{rE_b - E_i} \qquad 31$$

This is actually a general formula because when we have component (b) alone it is also correct for the calculation of w'. When component (a) alone is sufficient, we have

$$w' = \frac{1}{E_b} \qquad 32$$

The general formula for λ is

$$\lambda = (k - 1)\left[\frac{w - w'}{(k - 1)w + w'}\right] \qquad 33$$

Then a corrected variety total is given by

$$rv_{ef} = t_{ef} + \left[\frac{\lambda}{(k - 1)p}\right] W_{ef} \qquad 34$$

and the variances for differences between variety means are

$$V_s = \frac{2E_i}{r}\left(1 + \frac{\lambda}{p}\right) \qquad 35$$

$$V_d = \frac{2E_i}{r}\left[1 + \left(\frac{k}{k-1}\right)\left(\frac{\lambda}{p}\right)\right] \qquad 36$$

$$V_m = \frac{2E_i}{r}\left[1 + \left(\frac{k}{k-1}\right)\left(\frac{\lambda}{p+1}\right)\right] \qquad 37$$

Finally, the adjustment to the variety sum of squares in order to make an F test is

$$-\lambda\left\{\left[1 + \frac{w'}{(k-1)w}\right] S_u - S_b\right\} \qquad 38$$

10. Analysis of a balanced lattice. As already noted, a balanced lattice arises from the use of $p + 1$ orthogonal groups. The method of analysis is essentially the same as for the partially balanced lattice but with certain simplifications.

In the first place it is easier to calculate the values of W_{ef}. The reason for this can be seen from examining the plan for a balanced lattice with 9 varieties as given below.

11	12	13	11	21	31	11	22	33	11	32	23
21	22	23	12	22	32	21	32	13	21	12	33
31	32	33	13	23	33	31	12	23	31	22	13

For any one variety such as 11 we can write the value of the u_{11} for each block as follows.

$$(t_{11} + t_{12} + t_{13}) + (t_{11} + t_{21} + t_{31}) + (t_{11} + t_{22} + t_{33}) + (t_{11} + t_{32} + t_{23})$$

which is obviously equal to $3t_{11} + G$, where G is the grand total for the whole experiment. We have then

$$W_{11} = 3t_{11} + G - 4\Sigma b_{11}$$

or in general

$$W_{ef} = pt_{ef} + G - r\Sigma(b_{ef}) \qquad 39$$

The formula for the sum of squares for component (b) is

$$\frac{\Sigma(W_{ef}^2)}{r(k-1)p^2} \qquad 40$$

as in the case of the partially balanced lattice. Also a corrected variety total is

$$rv_{ef} = t_{ef} + \left[\frac{\lambda}{(k-1)p}\right] W_{ef}$$

where

$$\lambda = (k-1)\left[\frac{w - w'}{(k-1)w + w'}\right] \qquad 41$$

and

$$w = \frac{1}{E_i} \qquad w' = \frac{r-1}{rE_b - E_i}$$

There is only one variance for differences between means as all comparisons are made with equal precision. This, as would be expected, is

$$\frac{2E_i}{r}\left(1 + \frac{\lambda}{p}\right) \qquad 42$$

showing that in the balanced lattice all comparisons are of the same precision as the most precise comparison in a partially balanced lattice.

Finally the sum of squares for varieties, adjusted so that it can be compared with the intra-block error, comes from the sum of squares of the corrected variety totals, divided by the factor $(1 + \lambda/p)$. It may be expressed therefore as

$$\frac{\dfrac{\sum_1^{p^2} (rv_{ef})^2}{r} - \dfrac{G^2}{rp^2}}{1 + \dfrac{\lambda}{p}} \qquad 43$$

11. Example 13–1. Partially balanced lattice. Table 13–4 gives the yields in bushels per acre for a 4-replicate quadruple lattice experiment with 25 varieties of wheat. Variety totals are given in Table 13–5. The preliminary analysis of variance is given in Table 13–6.

The next step to obtain the complete analysis is to find the sum of squares for blocks from which variety effect has been eliminated. To do this we require the quantities W_{ef} calculated from formula (29), from the values of u_{ef} and b_{ef} as given in Table 13–4. For example we have

$$W_{23} = -173.9 - 153.2 + 262.4 + 63.0 = -1.7$$

These have been calculated and set up in Table 13–7. From formula (30) the sum of squares for blocks is

$$\frac{282{,}806.58}{300} = 942.689$$

TABLE 13–4

PLOT YIELDS, BLOCK TOTALS AND VALUES OF u AND $u - kb$, FOR 4-REPLICATE QUADRUPLE LATTICE

	Replicate 1		Replicate 2		Replicate 3		Replicate 4	
Block	Variety	Group *A*	Variety	Group *B*	Variety	Group *C*	Variety	Group *D*
	11	27.4	11	37.2	11	23.4	11	20.0
	12	38.6	21	37.5	22	19.0	32	20.8
1	13	29.1	31	18.0	33	11.8	53	27.6
	14	21.3	41	42.2	44	13.3	24	23.9
	15	34.1	51	43.3	55	18.9	45	25.5
b		150.5		178.2		86.4		117.8
u		575.5		578.8		584.4		576.8
$u - kb$		− 26.5		− 134.0		238.8		105.6
	21	36.6	12	40.9	21	22.5	21	23.8
	22	46.1	22	44.2	32	22.7	42	38.5
2	23	44.7	32	36.7	43	25.0	13	25.4
	24	40.6	42	34.8	54	22.3	34	30.1
	25	37.3	52	35.8	15	34.0	55	29.8
b		205.3		192.4		126.5		147.6
u		647.3		616.3		628.5		597.6
$u - kb$		− 173.9		− 153.3		122.5		7.2
	31	16.7	13	31.6	31	18.0	31	21.0
	32	30.0	23	45.0	42	19.3	52	21.5
3	33	28.0	33	37.8	53	25.0	23	34.5
	34	33.3	43	40.8	14	19.9	44	21.0
	35	26.2	53	36.4	25	28.3	15	32.5
b		134.2		191.6		110.5		130.5
u		516.6		613.2		536.4		585.0
$u - kb$		− 20.2		− 153.2		94.4		63.0
	41	40.1	14	24.4	41	22.7	41	39.2
	42	25.6	24	28.0	52	25.0	12	39.9
4	43	39.7	34	38.6	13	22.4	33	28.4
	44	36.4	44	38.8	24	25.4	54	28.2
	45	37.3	54	36.0	35	24.4	25	32.7

TABLE 13–4—(*continued*)

	Replicate 1		Replicate 2		Replicate 3		Replicate 4	
Block	Variety	Group *A*	Variety	Group *B*	Variety	Group *C*	Variety	Group *D*
b		179.1		165.8		119.9		168.4
u		622.5		562.0		594.5		640.7
$u - kb$		− 93.9		− 101.2		114.9		− 32.9
	51	33.4	15	39.3	51	27.8	51	28.0
	52	38.8	25	35.6	12	13.1	22	25.0
5	53	35.0	35	31.2	23	16.6	43	28.4
	54	37.6	45	37.3	34	21.9	14	21.0
	55	38.4	55	39.5	45	16.6	35	21.0
b		183.2		182.9		96.0		123.4
u		628.3		619.9		646.4		590.1
$u - kb$		− 104.5		− 111.7		262.4		96.5
Replicate Total		852.3		910.9		539.3		687.7

TABLE 13–5

VARIETY TOTALS, 4-REPLICATE QUADRUPLE LATTICE

						Row Total
	11	12	13	14	15	
	108.0	132.5	108.5	86.6	139.9	575.5
	21	22	23	24	25	
	120.4	134.3	140.8	117.9	133.9	647.3
	31	32	33	34	35	
	73.7	110.2	106.0	123.9	102.8	516.6
	41	42	43	44	45	
	144.2	118.2	133.9	109.5	116.7	622.5
	51	52	53	54	55	
	132.5	121.1	124.0	124.1	126.6	628.3
Column Total	578.8	616.3	613.2	562.0	619.9	2990.2 = G

TABLE 13–6

PRELIMINARY ANALYSIS OF VARIANCE FOR QUADRUPLE LATTICE

	SS	DF	MS	F	5% Point
Replicates	3384.235	3			
Varieties	1664.745	24	69.3644	2.59	1.67
Error	1927.960	72	26.7772		
Total	6976.940	99			

TABLE 13–7

VALUES OF W_{ef}, CORRECTED VARIETY TOTALS (rv_{ef}) AND CORRECTED VARIETY MEANS (v_{ef}). QUADRUPLE LATTICE IN 4 REPLICATIONS

Variety	W_{ef}	rv_{ef}	v_{ef}
11	183.9	116.60	29.2
12	49.7	134.82	33.7
13	− 57.6	105.81	26.5
14	63.2	89.56	22.4
15	47.3	142.11	35.5
21	− 178.2	112.07	28.0
22	8.1	134.68	33.7
23	− 1.7	140.72	35.2
24	− 54.6	115.35	28.8
25	− 224.1	123.42	30.9
31	3.2	73.85	18.5
32	54.6	112.75	28.2
33	32.5	107.52	26.9
34	148.2	130.83	32.7
35	79.5	106.52	26.6
41	− 145.9	137.38	34.3
42	− 145.6	111.39	27.8
43	− 28.1	132.59	33.1
44	106.7	114.49	28.6
45	162.4	124.29	31.1
51	120.4	138.13	34.5
52	− 79.9	117.36	29.3
53	− 57.7	121.30	30.3
54	− 116.1	118.67	29.7
55	29.8	127.99	32.0
Total	0	2990.2	

This sum of squares is all that is required in order to set up the more complete analysis given in Table 13–8.

TABLE 13–8

COMPLETE ANALYSIS OF QUADRUPLE LATTICE WITH 25 VARIETIES

	SS	DF	MS
Replicates	3384.235	3	
Blocks (eliminating varieties)	942.689	16	$58.9181 = E_b$
Varieties (ignoring blocks)	1664.745	24	
Intra-block error	985.271	56	$17.5941 = E_i$
Total	6976.940	99	

Since E_b is considerably larger than E_i, the analysis indicates that the variety means should be corrected. We find

$$w = \frac{1}{E_i} = \frac{1}{17.5941} = 0.056\,837\,24$$

$$w' = \frac{r-1}{rE_b - E_i} = \frac{3}{4 \times 58.9181 - 17.5941} = \frac{3}{218.0783} = 0.013\,756\,53$$

$$\lambda = (k-1)\left[\frac{w - w'}{(k-1)w + w'}\right] = 3\left(\frac{0.043\,080\,71}{0.184\,268\,25}\right) = 0.701\,380$$

For the partially balanced lattice that is not repeated, a short cut is available here which arises from the fact that the formula for λ can be expressed

$$\lambda = \frac{E_b - E_i}{E_b} = \frac{58.9181 - 17.5941}{58.9181} = 0.701\,380 \qquad 44$$

Next we require

$$\frac{\lambda}{(k-1)p} = \frac{0.701\,380}{15} = 0.046\,759$$

The corrected variety totals are then calculated from (34). Thus

$$rv_{23} = 140.8 + 0.046\,759 \times (-\,1.7) = 140.72$$

These totals are calculated and set up as in Table 13–7, and finally the variety means are set up in the same table. The sum of the corrected totals if carried to 2 decimals should check closely with the grand total of the experiment.

It remains to calculate V_m and the corresponding standard error. From (37) we have

$$V_m = \frac{2 \times 17.5941}{4}\left(1 + \frac{4}{3} \times \frac{0.701\,380}{6}\right)$$

$$= 8.797\,05(1.155\,862) = 10.1682$$

and

$$SE_m = \sqrt{10.1682} = 3.19$$

In order to make an F test that is more accurate than in the randomized block analysis of the significance of the variety differences, we apply formula (38), for which we require first the value of S_u, the unadjusted sum of squares for blocks. Calculating this from the block totals of Table 13–4, we have

$$S_u = \frac{470{,}421.08}{5} - \frac{2{,}319{,}929.88}{25} = 1287.021$$

where the correction term is the uncorrected sum of squares for replicates. We then have

$$-\lambda\left\{\left[1 + \frac{w'}{(k-1)w}\right] S_u - S_b\right\}$$

$$= -0.701\,380\left[\left(1 + \frac{0.013\,756\,53}{3 \times 0.056\,837\,24}\right) 1287.021 - 942.689\right] = -314.335$$

The corrected sum of squares is 1664.745 − 314.335 = 1350.410, and the corrected variance is 1350.410/24 = 56.27. The F value is then 56.27/17.59 = 3.20. As would be expected, this is larger than the F value of Table 13–6.

12. Example 13–2. Partially balanced lattice with groups repeated. In this experiment 16 varieties are arranged in a simple lattice with 4 replicates. Table 13–9 gives the plot yields and the basic quantities d, b, u, and $u - kb$ that must be calculated first. Table 13–10 gives the variety totals in the form of a square. Note that the row and column totals are the values of u for Table 13–9.

The preliminary analysis, assuming the experiment to be laid out in randomized blocks, is performed first, but it is not necessary to reproduce the calculations here.

TABLE 13–9

PLOT YIELDS, BLOCK TOTALS, AND VALUES OF u AND $u - kb$ FOR A SIMPLE LATTICE IN 4 REPLICATIONS

Block	Variety	Replicate 1	Replicate 3	Group A	Variety	Replicate 2	Replicate 4	Group B
1	11	93.6	105.0	198.6	11	76.0	85.0	161.0
	12	99.5	97.0	196.5	21	113.5	115.6	229.1
	13	113.3	115.2	228.5	31	84.4	101.5	185.9
	14	100.8	95.8	196.6	41	87.5	98.6	186.1
Total		407.2 $d = -5.8$	413.0	820.2 b 1558.8 u -81.6 $u - kb$		361.4 $d = -39.3$	400.7	762.1 b 1529.2 u 5.0 $u - kb$
2	21	109.0	102.7	211.7	12	98.1	78.2	176.3
	22	90.6	95.3	185.9	22	78.2	83.1	161.3
	23	79.4	106.6	186.0	32	93.0	93.6	186.6
	24	73.0	72.3	145.3	42	48.8	73.7	122.5
Total		352.0 $d = -24.9$	376.9	728.9 b 1471.8 u 14.0 $u - kb$		318.1 $d = -10.5$	328.6	646.7 b 1359.3 u 65.9 $u - kb$
3	31	76.1	105.0	181.1	13	113.1	102.5	215.6
	32	61.6	101.5	163.1	23	75.9	91.7	167.6
	33	80.6	93.0	173.6	33	104.5	78.2	182.7
	34	88.5	103.3	191.8	43	129.7	110.9	240.6
Total		306.8 $d = -96.0$	402.8	709.6 b 1495.6 u 76.4 $u - kb$		423.2 $d = 39.9$	383.3	806.5 b 1606.1 u -6.9 $u - kb$
4	41	89.6	86.1	175.7	14	71.6	114.1	185.7
	42	76.4	90.7	167.1	24	92.5	92.4	184.9
	43	100.6	110.9	211.5	34	117.8	113.0	230.8
	44	80.2	91.8	172.0	44	92.6	96.4	189.0
Total		346.8 $d = -32.7$	379.5	726.3 b 1464.5 u 11.9 $u - kb$		374.5 $d = -41.4$	415.9	790.4 b 1496.1 u -84.7 $u - kb$
Replicate and Group Total		1412.8 $D = -159.4$	1572.2	2985.0 $5990.7 = G$ $20.7 = \Sigma(u - kb)_A$		1477.2 $D = -51.3$	1528.5	3005.7 $5990.7 = G$ $-20.7 = \Sigma(u - kb)_B$

TABLE 13–10

VARIETY TOTALS FOR SIMPLE LATTICE IN 4 REPLICATIONS

					Row Total
	11	12	13	14	
	359.6	372.8	444.1	382.3	1558.8
	21	22	23	24	
	440.8	347.2	353.6	330.2	1471.8
	31	32	33	34	
	367.0	349.7	356.3	422.6	1495.6
	41	42	43	44	
	361.8	289.6	452.1	361.0	1464.5
Column Total	1529.2	1359.3	1606.1	1496.1	5990.7

TABLE 13–11

VALUES BY VARIETIES OF W_{ef}, rv_{ef}, AND v_{ef}. SIMPLE LATTICE IN 4 REPLICATIONS

Variety	W_{ef}	rv_{ef}	v_{ef}
11	− 76.6	351.88	88.0
12	− 15.7	371.22	92.8
13	− 88.5	435.18	108.8
14	− 166.3	365.54	91.4
21	19.0	442.71	110.7
22	79.9	355.25	88.8
23	7.1	354.32	88.6
24	− 70.7	323.07	80.8
31	81.4	375.20	93.8
32	142.3	364.04	91.0
33	69.5	363.30	90.8
34	− 8.3	421.76	105.4
41	16.9	363.50	90.9
42	77.8	297.44	74.4
43	5.0	452.60	113.2
44	− 72.8	353.66	88.4
Total	0	5990.7	

With the preliminary analysis made and the data set up as in Tables 13–9 and 13–10, the following steps are required to perform the complete analysis.

1. Calculate values of W_{ef} from formula (29). For example

$$W_{32} = 76.4 + 65.9 = 142.3$$

2. Calculate sum of squares for blocks. This is obtained in two parts.

$$\text{Component } (a) = \frac{\Sigma(d^2)}{2p} - \frac{\Sigma(D^2)}{2p^2} \qquad 45$$

$$= \frac{15{,}899.65}{8} - \frac{28{,}040.05}{32} = 1111.204$$

Component (b) formula (30)

$$= \frac{96{,}833.58}{64} = 1513.025$$

Combining components (a) and (b) gives $1111.204 + 1513.025 = 2624.229$.

3. The total sum of squares and the sums of squares for varieties and replicates are obtained in the usual manner, and the complete analysis can then be set up as in Table 13–12.

TABLE 13–12

Complete Analysis of Variance for Partially Balanced Lattice with Groups Repeated

	SS	DF	MS
Replicates	882.947	3	
Blocks (eliminating varieties)	2,624.229	12	$218.686 = E_b$
Varieties (ignoring blocks)	7,389.881	15	
Intrablock error	3,584.612	33	$108.625 = E_i$
Total	14,481.669	63	

4. Compute λ and $\lambda/(k-1)p$. We require w and w', where

$$w = \frac{1}{E_i} = 0.009\,205\,984$$

and, according to formula (31),

$$w' = \frac{3}{766.119} = 0.003\,915\,841$$

Then λ from (33) is

$$\lambda = \frac{0.005\ 290\ 143}{0.013\ 121\ 825} = 0.403\ 156$$

There is also a short cut here in that λ can be computed directly from

$$(k-1)\left[\frac{2(E_b - E_i)}{2(k-1)E_b + E_i}\right] = \frac{2(E_b - E_i)}{2E_b + E_i} \qquad \text{when } k = 2 \qquad 46$$

It is assumed in this formula that there are not more than 2 repetitions of each group. For this example

$$\lambda = \frac{2(218.686 - 108.625)}{2 \times 218.686 + 108.625} = 0.403\ 156$$

Finally

$$\frac{\lambda}{(k-1)p} = \frac{0.403\ 156}{4} = 0.100\ 789$$

5. Calculate corrected variety totals from (34). For example,

$$rv_{42} = 289.6 + 0.100\ 789 \times 77.8 = 297.44$$

These, together with the variety means, are given in Table 13–11.

6. Determine the standard error for comparing variety means. From (37)

$$v_m = \frac{2 \times 108.625}{4}\left[1 + 2\left(\frac{0.403\ 156}{5}\right)\right]$$

$$= 54.3125(1 + 0.161\ 262) = 63.071\ 04$$

and

$$\text{SE}_m = \sqrt{63.071\ 04} = 7.94$$

7. Make an F test of the variety variance if this seems to be necessary. From (38) the correction to the variety variance is

$$-\ 0.403\ 156\left[\left(1 + \frac{0.003\ 915\ 841}{0.009\ 205\ 984}\right) S_u - 1513.025\right]$$

where S_u is the unadjusted sum of squares for component b, and S_b is the adjusted sum of squares for component b. S_u is calculated as follows.

$$\frac{820.2^2 + 728.9^2 + \cdots + 790.4^2}{8} - \frac{2985.0^2 + 3005.7^2}{32} = 2893.055$$

Substituting in the expression above, we have

$$-\ 0.403\ 156[(1.425\ 358 \times 2893.055) - 1513.025] = -\ 1052.485$$

Then the corrected sum of squares is 7389.881 − 1052.485 = 6337.397, and the corrected variance is 6337.397/15 = 422.493. Finally the F value is 422.493/108.625 = 3.89.

13. Example 13–3. Balanced lattice, with 25 varieties in 6 replications. Table 13–13 gives the plot yields and block totals with replicate totals.

TABLE 13–13

PLOT YIELDS FROM BALANCED LATTICE EXPERIMENT WITH 25 VARIETIES IN 6 REPLICATES

	Replicate 1		Replicate 2		Replicate 3		Replicate 4		Replicate 5		Replicate 6	
	Variety	Group 1	Variety	Group 2	Variety	Group 3	Variety	Group 4	Variety	Group 5	Variety	Group 6
	11	34.5	11	39.1	11	42.3	11	42.2	11	37.2	11	40.0
	12	48.6	21	41.5	22	41.1	32	44.8	42	33.9	52	46.3
	13	45.9	31	35.9	33	36.0	53	34.7	23	32.0	43	40.2
	14	45.1	41	44.6	44	44.2	24	43.7	54	42.7	34	46.0
	15	44.6	51	43.2	55	44.1	45	40.0	35	40.6	25	36.6
b		218.7		204.3		207.7		205.4		186.4		209.1
	21	51.1	12	43.2	21	34.6	21	43.7	21	50.8	21	48.8
	22	46.9	22	46.5	32	44.3	42	23.9	52	47.4	12	46.2
	23	31.0	32	49.6	43	44.7	13	39.1	33	37.0	53	44.3
	24	42.4	42	45.1	54	38.3	34	38.5	14	46.7	44	47.3
	25	34.3	52	48.8	15	36.7	55	38.5	45	47.2	35	49.2
b_v		205.7		233.2		198.6		183.7		229.1		235.8
	31	32.7	13	49.8	31	30.9	31	34.9	31	26.5	31	31.4
	32	36.6	23	33.4	42	46.1	52	42.0	12	45.8	22	40.8
	33	43.3	33	41.4	53	42.6	23	30.6	43	39.5	13	40.8
	34	49.2	43	44.0	14	46.6	44	41.5	24	40.2	54	35.3
	35	35.1	53	41.5	25	31.0	15	44.6	55	42.3	45	32.3
b_v		196.9		210.1		197.2		193.6		194.3		180.6
	41	50.5	14	46.6	41	50.1	41	50.9	41	23.6	41	41.4
	42	40.2	24	40.8	52	46.4	12	46.7	22	53.2	32	39.3
	43	46.9	34	40.0	13	52.8	33	41.4	53	38.2	23	29.8
	44	48.3	44	37.6	24	51.4	54	43.1	34	44.6	14	36.0
	45	55.0	54	47.4	35	51.7	25	35.6	15	43.1	55	35.8
b_v		240.9		212.4		252.4		217.7		202.7		182.3
	51	44.6	15	44.8	51	46.9	51	40.1	51	31.6	51	42.4
	52	48.8	25	37.0	12	50.8	22	48.8	32	35.5	42	38.2
	53	48.8	35	44.6	23	34.4	43	40.0	13	39.5	33	34.9
	54	41.2	45	44.4	34	46.8	14	48.3	44	35.7	24	38.8
	55	41.1	55	44.0	45	46.3	35	44.2	25	29.1	15	34.8
b_v		224.5		214.8		225.2		221.4		171.4		189.1
Replicate Totals		1086.7		1074.8		1081.1		1021.8		983.9		996.9

After the preliminary analysis on the basis of the experiment's having been laid out in randomized blocks, the following are the steps in the calculations.

1. Calculate W_{ef} for each variety, using formula (39). For example,

$$W_{11} = 5 \times 235.3 + 6245.2 - 6(218.7 + 204.3 + 207.7 + 205.4 + 186.4 + 209.1) = 32.1$$

2. Obtain from formula (30) the sum of squares for blocks from which the variety effect has been eliminated. This is

$$\frac{921{,}964.14}{750} = 1229.286$$

The values of W_{ef} in this example are given in Table 13–14.

TABLE 13–14

VARIETY TOTALS, VALUES OF W_v, rv_v, AND v_v FOR BALANCED LATTICE EXPERIMENT

Variety	T_v	W_v	rv_v	v_v
11	235.3	32.1	236.16	39.4
12	281.3	− 297.7	273.27	45.5
13	267.9	283.3	275.54	45.9
14	269.3	25.1	269.98	45.0
15	248.6	183.2	253.54	42.3
21	270.5	54.5	271.97	45.3
22	277.3	123.9	280.64	46.8
23	191.2	− 18.6	190.70	31.8
24	257.3	− 24.1	256.65	42.8
25	203.6	− 32.2	202.73	33.8
31	192.3	205.3	197.84	33.0
32	250.1	368.9	260.05	43.3
33	234.0	− 88.4	231.62	38.6
34	265.1	190.7	270.24	45.0
35	265.4	− 274.0	258.01	43.0
41	261.1	− 251.1	254.33	42.4
42	227.4	− 0.8	227.38	37.9
43	255.3	− 124.7	251.94	42.0
44	254.6	− 52.6	253.18	42.2
45	265.2	− 204.8	259.68	43.3
51	248.8	73.8	250.79	41.8
52	279.7	− 407.7	268.70	44.8
53	250.1	− 158.5	245.82	41.0
54	248.0	164.0	252.42	42.1
55	245.8	230.4	252.01	42.0
Total	6245.2	0	6245.2	

3. Set up complete analysis and calculate E_b and E_i. This is given in Table 13–15.

TABLE 13–15

COMPLETE ANALYSIS FOR BALANCED LATTICE WITH 25 VARIETIES IN 6 REPLICATES

	SS	DF	MS
Replicates	416.508	5	
Blocks (eliminating varieties)	1229.286	24	$51.2202 = E_b$
Varieties (ignoring blocks)	2431.477	24	
Error	1601.469	96	$16.6820 = E_i$
Total	5678.740	149	

4. Calculate λ and obtain corrected variety totals. The formulas are (44) and (34).

$$\lambda = \frac{51.2202 - 16.6820}{51.2202} = 0.674\,308$$

For formula (44) we require

$$\frac{\lambda}{(k-1)p} = \frac{0.674\,308}{25} = 0.026\,972\,3$$

Then a corrected variety total such as that for variety 24 is

$$rv_{24} = 257.3 - 0.026\,972 \times 24.1 = 256.65$$

The corrected totals for this example will be found in Table 13–14.

5. The variance of a difference between variety means from (35) is

$$v_s = \frac{2 \times 16.682}{6}\left(1 + \frac{0.674\,308}{5}\right) = 6.3106$$

and the SE of a mean difference is $\sqrt{6.3106} = 2.51$.

6. Obtain the corrected variety sum of squares from (43). Here we have

$$\frac{(1{,}573{,}757.703/6) - (6245.2^2/150)}{1.134\,86} = 2005.65$$

Then the mean square is $2005.65/24 = 83.569$, and $F = 83.569/16.682 = 5.01$.

14. Lattice squares. The lattice square design, originally known as a quasi-Latin square, was first described by Yates [18] in 1937. In the basic design each replicate containing p^2 varieties is laid out so that there are p plots along each side, or in other words there are p plots in each row and column. These rows and columns are then the error control units similar to the incomplete blocks in square lattice designs. In this way variations in soil fertility in two directions across the field can be eliminated from the experimental error.

The lattice squares described by Yates may be classified as *balanced* types in that any one variety appears once either in a row or a column with every other variety. Actually the balanced types may be divided into class (1) in which $r = {}^1/_2(p + 1)$ and each variety occurs in either a row or a column with every other variety, and class (2) in which $r = (p + 1)$ and each variety occurs in both a row and a column with every other variety.

In 1943, Cochran [3] described lattice squares designs that may be designated as *partially balanced* in that each variety does not occur either in a row or a column with every other variety. This extended the application of lattice square designs in that the experimenter was given a greater choice with respect to number of replications. The types described by Yates and Cochran are possible only if the completely orthogonalized square exists. Kempthorne and Federer [15] in 1949 and Federer [7] in 1950 described what they term *unbalanced* lattice squares which are possible for any value of p where the Latin square exists, with replications in multiples of 3. Complete instructions for the analysis of these squares are given in the paper by Federer [7]. The possible lattice squares are summarized in Table 13–16.

TABLE 13–16

USEFUL RANGE OF LATTICE SQUARE DESIGNS FOR DIFFERENT VALUES OF p AND p^2, ACCORDING TO NUMBER OF REPLICATIONS

$p =$	4	5	6	7	8	9	10	11	12	13
$v = p^2 =$	16	25	36	49	64	81	100	121	144	169
Partially balanced				3	3, 4	3, 4		3, 4, 5		3, 4, 5, 6
Balanced										
$r = \frac{1}{2}(p + 1)$		3		4		5		6		7
$r = (p + 1)$	5	6		8	9	10		12		14
Unbalanced	3, 6	3, 6	3, 6	3, 6	3, 6	3, 6	3, 6	3, 6	3, 6	3, 6

15. Lattice squares—Partially balanced, and balanced of type $r = {}^1/_2(p + 1)$. Since there are only slight differences in method in the design and analysis of these two types, they can be considered together.

For the type $r = {}^1/_2(p + 1)$ the design of the squares is based on the method described in Section 6 for square lattices. We shall illustrate the method here for the 5×5 square, but for general application squares already made up can be obtained from the tables by Fisher and Yates [10] and from Cochran and Cox [4]. We first write out the 6 orthogonal squares for the 5×5 square as follows.

I

11	12	13	14	15
21	22	23	24	25
31	32	33	34	35
41	42	43	44	45
51	52	53	54	55

II

11	21	31	41	51
12	22	32	42	52
13	23	33	43	53
14	24	34	44	54
15	25	35	45	55

III

11	22	33	44	55
21	32	43	54	15
31	42	53	14	25
41	52	13	24	35
51	12	23	34	45

IV

11	32	53	24	45
21	42	13	34	55
31	52	23	44	15
41	12	33	54	25
51	22	43	14	35

V

11	42	23	54	35
21	52	33	14	45
31	12	43	24	55
41	22	53	34	15
51	32	13	44	25

VI

11	52	43	34	25
21	12	53	44	35
31	22	13	54	45
41	32	23	14	55
51	42	33	24	15

Then from any 2 of the above squares a new square can be formed such that the rows will come from the rows of the first square and the columns from the rows of the second square. Taking squares I and II, III and IV, and V and VI in pairs we get the following.

I and II

11	12	13	14	15
21	22	23	24	25
31	32	33	34	35
41	42	43	44	45
51	52	53	54	55

III and IV

11	22	33	44	55
32	43	54	15	21
53	14	25	31	42
24	35	41	52	13
45	51	12	23	34

V and VI

11	42	23	54	35
52	33	14	45	21
43	24	55	31	12
34	15	41	22	53
25	51	32	13	44

Note that in these 3 squares any one variety occurs either in a row or a column with every other variety.

Assuming that all 3 squares are included in the design, we have a balanced lattice square with $3 = {}^1/_2(5 + 1)$ replications. If only 2 of the squares are included, the design will be of the partially balanced type.

After the squares have been selected, the rows and columns of each are arranged at random and the actual varieties assigned at random to the numbers.

The analysis of the results follows a logical procedure as outlined below, after the data are set up in the form of squares as shown diagrammatically in Table 13–17. The yields are arranged to correspond with

TABLE 13–17

DIAGRAMMATIC REPRESENTATION OF RESULTS FROM A LATTICE SQUARE EXPERIMENT

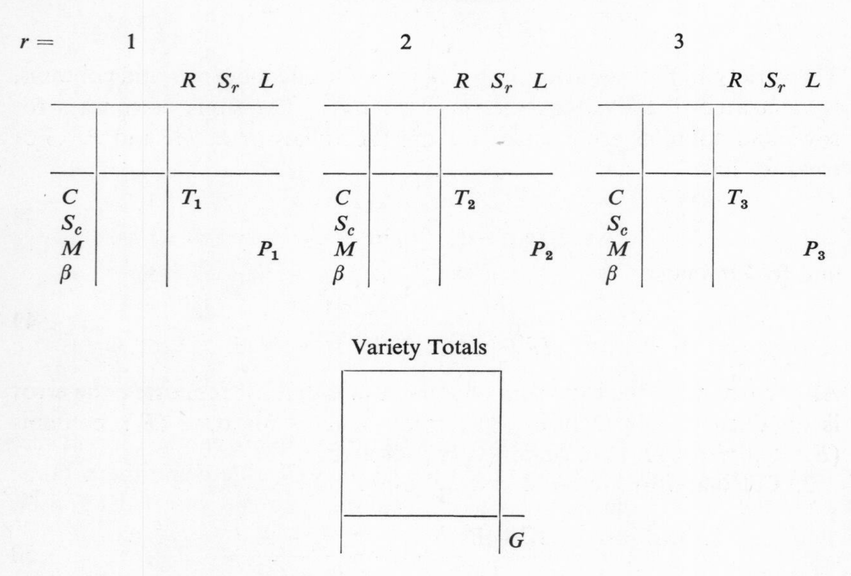

variety numbers as in the original squares before randomization. The row totals are represented by R, and the column totals by C. For each row S_r is the sum of the totals of the varieties in that row, and for each column S_c is the sum of the totals of the varieties in that column. The values of L and M are calculated as follows.

$$L = S_r - rR \qquad M = S_c - rC \tag{47}$$

P_r is the sum of the values of L and M in the corresponding replicate.

The various steps in the analysis are enumerated and described below.

1. Calculate L for each row and M for each column, and total to obtain the value of P. Also, for each replicate, if G is the grand total of the experiment, $P_r = G - rT_r$, where T_r is the replicate total, furnishing a check on the calculations.

2. Set up the outline of the analysis of variance as given below and calculate the sums of squares.

	DF	MS
Replicates	$r - 1$	
Varieties (ignoring rows and columns)	$p^2 - 1$	
Rows (eliminating varieties)	$r(p - 1)$	E_r
Columns (eliminating varieties)	$r(p - 1)$	E_c
Error	$(p - 1)(pr - p - r - 1)$	E_i
Total	$rp^2 - 1$	

The variety sum of squares, since it ignores the effect of rows and columns, is calculated directly from the variety totals. The sums of squares for rows and columns are calculated from the values of L, M, and P. For rows we have

$$\frac{\Sigma(L^2)}{rp(r-1)} - \frac{\Sigma(P^2)}{rp^2(r-1)} \qquad 48$$

and for columns

$$\frac{\Sigma(M^2)}{rp(r-1)} - \frac{\Sigma(P^2)}{rp^2(r-1)} \qquad 49$$

After calculating the total sum of squares and that for replicates, the error is obtained by subtraction. The mean squares for rows (E_r), columns (E_c), and error (E_i) are obtained as indicated.

3. Calculate the factors λ and μ from

$$\lambda = \frac{E_r - E_i}{(r-1)E_r} \qquad \mu = \frac{E_c - E_i}{(r-1)E_c} \qquad 50$$

noting that, if $E_r < E_i$, λ is taken as zero, and, if $E_c < E_i$, μ is taken as zero. From these factors we obtain λ/p and μ/p, which are used in converting the values of L into α and values of M into β by multiplication. Thus

$$\alpha = L\left(\frac{\lambda}{p}\right) \qquad \beta = M\left(\frac{\mu}{p}\right) \qquad 51$$

Corrections to variety totals are made by adding the quantities and α and β for each row and column in which the variety appears.

4. Calculate the mean standard error for comparing variety means from

$$\sqrt{\frac{2E_i}{r}\left[1 + \frac{r}{p+1}(\lambda + \mu)\right]} \qquad 52$$

Note that when $r = {}^1/_2(p + 1)$ this formula reduces to

$$\sqrt{\frac{2E_i}{r}\left[1 + \frac{1}{2}(\lambda + \mu)\right]} \qquad 53$$

The essential difference between partially balanced and balanced lattice squares is that in the former there are certain pairs of varieties that do not appear together in the same row or column. Further, in balanced lattice squares where $r = {}^1/_2(p + 1)$ there may be differences in the comparison of varieties, depending on whether they occur together in a column or in a row. These facts indicate that for the partially balanced lattice square there are three kinds of comparisons. Cochran [3] gives the formulas for the average experimental error per plot for these comparisons, which are converted here to standard errors of differences between means. These are:

Two varieties occurring in the same row:

$$\sqrt{\frac{2E_i}{r}\left[1 + (r - 1)\frac{\lambda}{p} + r\left(\frac{\mu}{p}\right)\right]} \qquad 54$$

Two varieties occurring in the same column:

$$\sqrt{\frac{2E_i}{r}\left[1 + r\left(\frac{\lambda}{p}\right) + (r - 1)\frac{\mu}{p}\right]} \qquad 55$$

Two varieties not occurring together in the same row or column:

$$\sqrt{\frac{2E_i}{r}\left[1 + r\left(\frac{\lambda}{p}\right) + r\left(\frac{\mu}{p}\right)\right]} \qquad 56$$

For the balanced lattice square the third formula is not applicable. For both the balanced type with $r = {}^1/_2(p + 1)$ and the partially balanced type formula (52) given above is general.

16. Example 13–4. The analysis of a 5 × 5 lattice square experiment in 3 replications.

Table 13–18 gives the plot yields in a lattice square experiment described by Yates [21] together with the values of L, M, α, and β. The experiment concerned the effect of 25 manurial combinations on sugar beets, and since the interactions were of particular interest it was decided that a lattice square experiment giving equal accuracy to all comparisons was preferable to a factorial experiment in which some of the interactions were confounded. Table 13–19 gives the required treatment totals collected from Table 13–18.

TABLE 13–18

Yields of a 5 × 5 Lattice Square Experiment with Sugar Beets

						Row Total	L	α
	sy 61.2	*ny* 67.7	*n* 68.1	*sz* 65.2	*s* 59.9	322.1	17.1	1.4
	mz 69.4	*nx* 67.4	*mx* 64.9	*nw* 77.6	*nz* 67.7	347.0	25.6	2.1
	w 46.3	*x* 59.7	*c* 76.2	*cy* 80.3	*m* 71.2	333.7	− 93.7	− 7.5
	o 55.2	*cx* 77.0	*my* 82.4	*cw* 80.4	*mw* 77.7	372.7	− 120.8	− 9.7
	sw 73.9	*sx* 79.0	*z* 51.6	*y* 44.8	*cz* 78.4	327.7	− 79.9	− 6.4
Column Total	306.0	350.8	343.2	348.3	354.9	1703.2		− 20.1
M	− 39.2	− 53.1	− 40.3	− 82.3	− 36.8		− 251.7	
β	− 1.4	− 1.9	− 1.4	− 2.9	− 1.3	− 8.9		
	mz 69.1	*y* 49.6	*c* 72.6	*s* 68.7	*cx* 74.0	334.0	− 38.1	− 3.1
	cw 62.7	*n* 74.0	*nx* 78.1	*w* 40.0	*cz* 66.3	321.1	3.8	0.3
	ny 68.9	*nz* 78.1	*sw* 69.6	*my* 68.1	*cy* 68.5	353.2	20.1	1.6
	m 64.7	*o* 38.6	*sz* 57.4	*sx* 65.5	*mx* 67.1	293.3	60.5	4.8
	z 48.0	*x* 39.0	*mw* 64.9	*nw* 72.2	*sy* 58.7	282.8	58.4	4.7
Column Total	313.4	279.3	342.6	314.5	334.6	1584.4		8.3
M	23.9	11.0	10.2	22.7	36.9		104.7	
β	0.9	0.4	0.4	0.8	1.3	3.8		
	sy 57.6	*my* 69.2	*nx* 64.0	*y* 31.8	*m* 58.4	281.0	84.2	6.7
	nz 72.2	*sz* 73.3	*z* 46.2	*w* 45.9	*cx* 73.4	311.0	− 16.7	− 1.3
	sx 61.4	*mz* 77.9	*cy* 73.1	*mw* 70.4	*n* 70.5	353.3	9.9	0.8
	c 58.6	*cz* 68.4	*o* 46.7	*ny* 71.3	*nw* 69.1	314.1	45.5	3.6
	cw 56.6	*x* 52.9	*s* 60.9	*mx* 71.8	*sw* 68.7	310.9	24.1	1.9
Column Total	306.4	341.7	290.9	291.2	340.1	1570.3		11.7
M	89.3	− 28.4	34.5	9.5	42.1		147.0	
β	3.2	− 1.0	1.2	0.3	1.5	5.2		

After the row and column totals are obtained, the following are the steps in the calculations.

1. Calculations of L and M. See Table 13–17 and formula (47). For example, the second value of L in the first square is

$$216.4 + 209.5 + 203.8 + 218.9 + 218.0 - 3 \times 347.0 = 25.6$$

The first value of M in the first square is

$$177.5 + 216.4 + 132.2 + 140.5 + 212.2 - 3 \times 306.0 = -39.2$$

2. Obtain sums of squares and set up analysis of variance as in Table 13–20. Note that the sums of squares for rows and columns eliminating treatments are obtained from the quantities L and M as indicated in formulas (48) and (49). Thus for rows eliminating treatments we have

$$\tfrac{1}{30}(17.1^2 + 25.6^2 + \cdots + 24.1^2) - \tfrac{1}{150}(251.7^2 + 104.7^2 + 147.0^2) = 1019.26$$

For columns

$$\tfrac{1}{30}(39.2^2 + 53.1^2 + \cdots + 42.1^2) - \tfrac{1}{150}(251.7^2 + 104.7^2 + 147.0^2) = 314.34$$

TABLE 13–19

Treatment Totals, Uncorrected and Corrected for Experiment of Table 13–18

Uncorrected

	o	*n*	*c*	*s*	*m*
o	140.5	212.6	207.4	189.5	194.3
w	132.2	218.9	199.7	212.2	213.0
x	151.6	209.5	224.4	205.9	203.8
y	126.2	207.9	221.9	177.5	219.7
z	145.8	218.0	213.1	195.9	216.4

$4857.9 = G$

Corrected

	o	*n*	*c*	*s*	*m*
o	139.4	215.6	202.6	190.4	199.4
w	123.4	228.7	193.4	209.8	208.2
x	148.2	218.3	211.2	207.2	212.8
y	121.2	213.8	216.4	193.4	216.7
z	143.5	222.7	209.6	197.3	214.7

$4857.9 = G$

The analysis of variance is given in Table 13–20.

TABLE 13–20

ANALYSIS OF VARIANCE OF 5 × 5 LATTICE SQUARE

	SS	DF	MS
Squares	426.33	3	
Rows (eliminating treatments)	1019.26	12	$84.94 = E_r$
Columns (eliminating treatments)	314.34	12	$26.20 = E_c$
Treatments	7346.68	24	
Error	405.04	24	$16.88 = E_i$
Total	9511.65		

3. Determine λ and μ and correct treatment totals. From (50)

$$\lambda = \frac{84.94 - 16.88}{2 \times 84.94} = 0.4006$$

$$\mu = \frac{26.20 - 16.88}{2 \times 26.20} = 0.1779$$

For the correction of treatment totals we require

$$\frac{\lambda}{p} = \frac{0.4006}{5} = 0.0801 \qquad \frac{\mu}{p} = \frac{0.1779}{5} = 0.0356$$

To obtain the quantities α and β set up in the margins of Table 13–18 we use formula (51). Thus the first value of α in square 1 is $17.1 \times 0.0801 = 1.4$, and the first value of β in square 1 is $-39.2 \times 0.0356 = -1.4$.

The corrections are then added to the corresponding treatment totals. Thus for *sy* the corrected total is

$$177.5 + 1.4 - 1.4 + 4.7 + 1.3 + 6.7 + 3.2 = 193.4$$

4. Variances of differences between treatment means are obtained from (52).

$$V_m = \frac{2 \times 16.88}{3}\left[1 + \frac{1}{2}(0.4006 + 0.1779)\right] = 11.253 \times 1.2892 = 14.507$$

and

$$\text{SE}_m = \sqrt{14.507} = 3.81$$

For this experiment it is of interest to compare the results with those that would have been obtained if the design had been randomized blocks. As pointed out by Yates [19] lattice square experiments, like lattice experiments, can be analyzed as if they were laid out in randomized blocks. This gives the analysis shown in Table 13–21.

TABLE 13–21

ANALYSIS OF LATTICE SQUARE AS A RANDOMIZED BLOCK EXPERIMENT

	SS	SD	MS
Replicates	426.33	2	
Treatments	7346.88	24	
Error	1738.44	48	36.22
Total	9511.65	74	

The variance of a mean difference between treatments is then

$$\frac{2 \times 36.22}{3} = 24.15$$

Comparing this with the variance of 14.51 obtained for the lattice square, we have $24.15/14.51 = 1.66$, showing that the gain in efficiency is 66%. The number of replicates of a randomized block experiment required to give the same accuracy as the lattice square is $1.66 \times 3 = 5$ approximately.

17. Balanced lattice squares with $r = p + 1$ when p is a prime number. The procedure for setting up a design of this type is very simple. We write out the $^1/_2(p + 1)$ squares as described in Section 15 and a second set formed from the first by turning them at right angles. In other words the rows of a square in the first set become the columns of a square in the second set. Complete randomization then gives the actual field layout. For $p = 4$, 8, and 9 it is best to consult the tables cited above for actual designs.

The analysis of the results can be followed from Table 13–22 which gives the results from a field test in diagrammatic form for 9 varieties in 4 replications and shows the basic quantities that must be calculated.

The outline of the analysis on which the calculation of the corrected variety yields is based is as follows.

		DF	MS
1	Squares	p	
2	Rows (eliminating varieties)	$p^2 - 1$	
3	Rows (eliminating varieties and columns)	$p^2 - 1$	E_r
4	Columns (eliminating varieties)	$p^2 - 1$	
5	Columns (eliminating varieties and rows)	$p^2 - 1$	E_c
6	Varieties (ignoring rows and columns)	$p^2 - 1$	
7	Error	$(p - 2)(p^2 - 1)$	E_i
8	Total	$p^2(p + 1) - 1$	

TABLE 13–22

DIAGRAMMATIC REPRESENTATION OF DATA FROM A BALANCED LATTICE SQUARE EXPERIMENT WITH $p + 1$ REPLICATIONS. RESULTS ARE ASSUMED TO BE ENTERED IN POSITIONS OCCUPIED BY VARIETY NUMBERS

			R
11	12	13	
21	22	23	
31	32	33	
C			

			R
11	21	31	
12	22	32	
13	23	33	
C			

			R
11	22	33	
32	13	21	
23	31	12	
C			

			R
11	32	23	
22	13	31	
33	21	12	
C			

$S(y_v)$ Variety Totals	$S(R_v)$	$S(C_v)$	$D_v = S(R_v) - S(C_v)$

L'_v	J_v	K_v	M'_v

$S(y_v)$ = variety totals

$S(R_v)$ = sum of all row totals containing variety v

$S(C_v)$ = sum of all column totals containing variety v

$D_v = S(R_v) - S(C_v)$

$L'_v = pS(y_v) - (p + 1)S(R_v) + G$

$J_v = L'_v + D_v$

$K_v = J_v + (p - 1)D_v$

$M'_v = K_v + D_v$

57

In order to obtain the error sum of squares by subtraction we require only the sums of squares 1, 2, 5, 6, and 8, or alternatively only 1, 3, 4, 6, and 8, but 3 and 5 are required in order to obtain E_r and E_c, so the logical procedure is to calculate all the sums of squares shown, following the alternative procedure to check the calculations. The following are the formulas required to obtain the sums of squares for rows and columns.

$$\begin{array}{ll} 2 & \dfrac{\Sigma(L')^2}{p^3(p+1)} \\[2ex] 3 & \dfrac{\Sigma(J^2)}{p^3(p+1)} \\[2ex] 4 & \dfrac{\Sigma(M)^2}{p^3(p+1)} \\[2ex] 5 & \dfrac{\Sigma(K^2)}{p^3(p-1)} \end{array} \tag{58}$$

The remaining sums of squares are calculated in the usual manner.

After obtaining E_r, E_c, and E_i, we find

$$w_r = \frac{p-1}{pE_r - E_i}, \quad w_c = \frac{p-1}{pE_c - E_i}, \quad w_i = \frac{1}{E_i} \tag{59}$$

Then

$$\lambda = \frac{w_i - w_r}{w_r + w_c + (p-1)w_i}, \quad \mu = \frac{w_i - w_c}{w_r + w_c + (p-1)w_i} \tag{60}$$

If $E_r \leq E_i$ we take $w_r = w_i$, and if $E_c \leq E_i$ we take $w_c = w_i$. The adjusted variety totals are calculated from

$$rv_v = S(y_v) + \left(\frac{\lambda}{p}\right) L_v + \left(\frac{\mu}{p}\right) M_v \tag{61}$$

The variance of a mean difference between 2 varieties is

$$V_m = \frac{2E_i(1 + \lambda + \mu)}{p + 1} \tag{62}$$

18. Loss of information due to inaccuracies of weighting. In all the lattice designs we have calculated the values of the weighting factors (w) from the data of the experiment. In the discussions of these designs by Yates [20] and Cochran [1] it is pointed out that the weighting factors are, strictly speaking, population parameters. In other words, if their true value were known and could be applied in the analyses, there would be no loss of information. Actually they are statistics calculated from samples, and consequently they are subject to variations due to random sampling. This variation introduces an additional element of variability into the corrected variety means, with a consequent loss of information. Yates [20] has presented data to show, however, that the loss of information is quite small and does not introduce sufficient error to reduce materially the efficiency of the lattice designs. Cochran [3] presents similar data for the partially balanced lattice squares.

19. Other incomplete block designs. The lattice designs that are dealt with above can be employed only when the number of varieties or treatments to be tested is a perfect square. Other designs involving the principle of error control by means of incomplete blocks are possible; some of them are extremely useful, but for lack of space it is impossible to describe them in detail here. There is, for example, the balanced incomplete block design based on a number of varieties equal to $p^2 - p + 1$ and $r = p$. Thus for $p = 5$ we can make up a test for 21 varieties in 5 replicates, or for $p = 6$ we can design a test for 31 varieties in 6 replicates. In this design the varieties cannot be arranged in groups in the field corresponding to complete replicates. This condition is undesirable because the investigator frequently wishes to check over all the varieties for some characteristic in 1 or 2 replicates and does not wish to cover the whole experiment. If the design is of the type where the number of varieties $= p^2 - p + 1$, such a check is practically impossible. Not having distinct replicates it is also impossible to revert to the randomized block method of analysis when the block variance proves to be equal to or less than the error variance.

Other incomplete block designs similar to the one described above are possible for various combinations of variety numbers and replicates. Descriptions of these will be found in the references at the end of this chapter and particularly in Cochran and Cox [4].

The cubic lattice is a particularly useful design for experiments in which the number of varieties exceeds 121. It is based on the fact that p^3

numbers can be set up in the form of a cube with p numbers along each side. The p^3 varieties may then be divided into p^2 groups of p each and arranged to occur correspondingly in blocks of p plots each in the field. For a complete description of this design and method of analysis, see Yates [19], Phipps et al. [16], and Cochran and Cox [4].

Other incomplete block designs can be made up from sets of numbers that can be arranged in a rectangle of $p \times q$ dimensions. These were first described by Yates [17] in 1936 but were not employed extensively on account of the somewhat complex analytical procedure. More recently another version of this design has been described by Harshbarger [12, 13, 14]. These designs are extremely valuable because they allow for experiments with variety numbers other than those possible for the square lattices and lattice squares. It is possible, for example, to employ Harshbarger's designs for $v = p(p + 1)$. Thus we can have $4 \times 5 = 20$, $5 \times 6 = 30$, $6 \times 7 = 42$, and so forth.

20. Missing values in incomplete block experiments. Methods of estimating missing values and making corresponding corrections in the analysis have been described by Cornish [5]. If one is satisfied with an approximate value, it is sufficient to treat the experiment as if it had been laid out in randomized blocks and apply the formula given in Chapter 11, Section 5. In many cases this will be adequate, but if the missing value occurs in a low-yielding block it will be slightly overestimated, and conversely it will be underestimated if it occurs in a high-yielding block.

21. Exercises.

1. Table 13–23 gives the yields of oats in bushels per acre in a simple lattice experiment. Carry the analysis through to step 3 of Example 13–2, and come to a conclusion as to how the analysis should proceed from that point. If in doubt work through steps 4 and 5 and note the size of the correction to the variety totals.

2. The yields for a 5×5 lattice square experiment are given in Table 13–24. This experiment is made up from uniformity data; therefore it is not expected that the variety variance will be significant. The yields are given in the table in the same position as the plots in the field. In order to reduce the work in this exercise, row, column, and replicate totals are given and the total sum of squares before taking away the correction term is 480,392.00. The following values for variety 1 will be of assistance in checking the methods.

$S(y_1) = 328$. $S(R_1) = 1670$. $S(C_1) = 1717$. $D_1 = -47$. $L'_1 = -2$. $J_1 = -49$. $M'_1 = -284$. $K_1 = -237$. $\alpha_1 = -0.08$. $\beta_1 = -12.95$. $rv_1 = 315.0$.

3. Design square lattice or lattice square experiments for the following numbers of varieties, giving reasons for the particular designs selected: $v = 25, 36, 49, 64, 81, 100$.

TABLE 13–23

YIELDS IN A SIMPLE LATTICE EXPERIMENT WITH 25 VARIETIES AND 4 REPLICATIONS

Variety*	Yield	Variety	Yield	Variety	Yield	Variety	Yield
11	50.8	11	55.4	41	88.6	54	62.0
12	88.2	21	88.4	44	61.3	44	53.8
13	50.3	31	75.4	45	71.1	24	58.4
14	73.9	41	94.8	43	48.1	34	52.4
15	49.2	51	52.1	42	52.7	14	70.6
21	66.5	12	67.7	14	81.6	43	67.1
22	41.6	22	50.6	12	76.2	53	49.5
23	76.6	32	68.1	15	72.3	33	61.4
24	45.3	42	48.5	13	59.6	23	94.1
25	83.8	52	70.5	11	48.8	13	80.3
31	69.4	13	60.9	54	52.9	31	68.3
32	71.0	23	66.8	52	72.6	21	60.1
33	59.1	33	59.5	51	50.3	41	65.1
34	39.7	43	54.3	55	88.6	11	61.8
35	64.2	53	73.3	53	76.6	51	52.7
41	82.8	14	58.1	24	78.3	32	44.9
42	50.6	24	60.0	22	40.7	22	53.6
43	67.3	34	49.4	25	89.9	42	59.1
44	51.3	44	79.0	21	85.7	52	52.3
45	82.1	54	46.3	23	85.5	12	60.9
51	68.1	15	49.6	31	67.5	45	68.6
52	72.3	25	62.7	34	40.0	35	61.8
53	65.7	35	72.2	32	64.8	55	65.4
54	46.7	45	52.7	35	58.9	25	97.6
55	69.7	55	69.7	33	57.9	15	58.0
Group X Replicate 1		Group Y Replicate 2		Group X Replicate 3		Group Y Replicate 4	

* Varieties shown in systematic order in replicates 1 and 2 but in the actual experiment blocks and varieties were fully randomized. This was a test of oat varieties conducted at Ottawa, Ontario, in 1942.

TABLE 13–24

YIELDS IN A 5 × 5 LATTICE SQUARE EXPERIMENT WITH 6 REPLICATIONS

Replicate 1

						Total
	*18**	*19*	*17*	*20*	*16*	
	62	60	53	44	45	264
	3	*4*	*2*	*5*	*1*	
	61	52	61	51	39	264
	23	*24*	*22*	*25*	*21*	
	59	62	60	44	43	268
	8	*9*	*7*	*10*	*6*	
	64	58	63	48	48	281
	13	*14*	*12*	*15*	*11*	
	69	65	69	55	51	309
Total	315	297	306	242	226	1386

Replicate 2

						Total
	19	*16*	*17*	*20*	*18*	
	63	61	54	46	46	270
	24	*21*	*22*	*25*	*23*	
	59	55	58	50	46	268
	4	*1*	*2*	*5*	*3*	
	64	63	66	55	52	300
	9	*6*	*7*	*10*	*8*	
	70	66	59	49	46	290
	14	*11*	*12*	*15*	*13*	
	57	53	60	46	41	257
Total	313	298	297	246	231	1385

Replicate 3

						Total
	2	*21*	*20*	*8*	*14*	
	53	55	57	45	42	252
	24	*18*	*12*	*5*	*6*	
	71	68	68	50	53	310
	10	*4*	*23*	*11*	*17*	
	79	71	74	59	58	341
	16	*15*	*9*	*22*	*3*	
	66	63	62	49	51	291
	13	*7*	*1*	*19*	*25*	
	61	58	50	49	50	268
Total	330	315	311	252	254	1462

Replicate 4

						Total
	9	*4*	*19*	*24*	*14*	
	64	65	49	43	48	269
	8	*3*	*18*	*23*	*13*	
	62	63	49	44	45	263
	6	*1*	*16*	*21*	*11*	
	75	63	55	45	51	289
	10	*5*	*20*	*25*	*15*	
	76	67	61	54	53	311
	7	*2*	*17*	*22*	*12*	
	63	64	49	44	44	264
Total	340	322	263	230	241	1396

Replicate 5

						Total
	15	*2*	*6*	*23*	*19*	
	62	54	49	41	44	250
	17	*9*	*13*	*5*	*21*	
	67	67	56	48	44	282
	1	*18*	*22*	*14*	*10*	
	65	63	54	46	46	274
	8	*25*	*4*	*16*	*12*	
	57	53	52	45	41	248
	24	*11*	*20*	*7*	*3*	
	57	49	54	48	39	247
Total	308	286	265	228	214	1301

Replicate 6

						Total
	21	*18*	*4*	*7*	*15*	
	69	64	59	51	47	290
	8	*5*	*11*	*19*	*22*	
	73	73	71	56	46	319
	20	*12*	*23*	*1*	*9*	
	62	63	59	48	43	275
	14	*6*	*17*	*25*	*3*	
	62	60	53	45	42	262
	2	*24*	*10*	*13*	*16*	
	66	68	68	52	48	302
Total	332	328	310	252	226	1448

* Italics are variety numbers.

REFERENCES

1. W. G. Cochran, The Analysis of Lattice and Triple Lattice Experiments in Corn Varietal Trials. II, Mathematical Theory, *Iowa Agr. Expt. Sta. Research Bull.*, **281,** 1940.
2. W. G. Cochran, *J. Am. Soc. Agron.*, **33,** 351–360, 1941.
3. W. G. Cochran, *Iowa Agr. Expt. Sta. Research Bull.*, **318,** 1943.
4. W. G. Cochran and Gertrude M. Cox, *Experimental Designs*, John Wiley and Sons, New York, 1950.
5. E. A. Cornish, *Australia Council Sci. Ind. Research Bull.*, **158,** 1943.
6. Gertrude M. Cox, R. C. Eckhardt, and W. G. Cochran, *Iowa Agr. Expt. Sta. Research Bull.*, **281,** 1940.
7. W. T. Federer, *Biometrics*, **6,** 34–58, 1950.
8. R. A. Fisher, *Ann. Eugen.*, **10,** 52–75, 1940.
9. R. A. Fisher, *Ann. Eugen.*, **11,** 290–299, 1942.
10. R. A. Fisher and F. Yates, *Statistical Tables*, Oliver and Boyd, Edinburgh and London, 3rd ed., 1949.
11. C. H. Goulden, *Sci. Agr.*, **25,** 115–136, 1944.
12. Boyd Harshbarger, *Biometrics*, **5,** 1–13, 1949.
13. Boyd Harshbarger, *Ann. Math. Stat.*, **16,** No. 4, 1945.
14. Boyd Harshbarger, *Ann. Math. Stat.*, **15,** No. 3, 1944.
15. Oscar Kempthorne and W. T. Federer, *Biometrics*, **4,** 109–121, 1948.
16. I. F. Phipps, *Australia Council Sci. Ind. Research Bull.*, **176,** 1944.
17. F. Yates, *J. Agr. Sci.*, **26,** 424–455, 1936.
18. F. Yates, *Ann. Eugen.*, **7,** 319–332, 1937.
19. F. Yates, *Ann. Eugen.*, **9,** 136–156, 1939.
20. F. Yates, *Ann. Eugen.*, **10,** 317–325, 1940.
21. F. Yates, *J. Agr. Sci.*, **30,** 672–687, 1940.

CHAPTER 14

The Treatment of Non-Orthogonal Data

1. The meaning of non-orthogonality. Ordinarily an experiment is so designed that the various effects to be measured are mutually orthogonal. This means that they are not entangled in any way and the means are direct estimates of the effects required. The data from a simple randomized block experiment may be represented as follows where there are 6 treatments and 4 replicates.

		Treatment						Replicate
		A	*B*	*C*	*D*	*E*	*F*	Total
Replicate	I							R_1
	II							R_2
	III							R_3
	IV							R_4
Treatment Total		C_1	C_2	C_3	C_4	C_5	C_6	G

It follows that, if the data are complete, any differences in the yields of the replicates will not affect the differences between means of the treatments. Similarly the differences between replicates will not be affected by treatments. In this instance the replicate and treatment effects are correctly referred to as orthogonal. Conversely, if there is any variation from the conditions as laid down, the treatment and replicate effects will be non-orthogonal. For example, if one or more of the plots are missing, treatment means will then not be independent of replicate means, and vice versa. If a plot of treatment *D*, for example, is missing in a high-yielding replicate, the mean of the remaining plots of *D* will be lower than it should be in comparison with the other treatments. It is obvious therefore that variation in the replicate means will be reflected by variation in the treatment means. In other words, a variance calculated for the treatments will be due partly to treatment effects and partly to variation in the replicates. Thus the two effects are entangled, and special methods must be adopted in order to obtain a variance for the treatments that is corrected for replicate effects, before tests of significance can be applied.

2. The effect of missing values. The effect of missing values on orthogonality can be demonstrated very simply in a 2×2 table. In a table such as the one given below we can take $-a$ and a to represent the response to A and, $-b$ and b for the response to B. Error terms are neglected because they do not make any difference to the general conclusion.

		B 0	B 1	A Total	A Mean
A	0	$-(a+b)$	$-(a-b)$	$-2a$	$-a$
	1	$(a-b)$	$(a+b)$	$2a$	a
B Total		$-2b$	$2b$	0	
B Mean		$-b$	b		

From the marginal totals and means of this table it is clear that the responses of A and B are independent. Suppose, however, that the value representing the combination A_0B_1 is missing. We then have the situation illustrated in the next 2×2 table. The differences between the unweighted means are $2a + b$ for A and $a + 2b$ for B, showing very clearly that the two responses are not independent.

		B 0	B 1	A Total	A Mean
A	0	$-(a+b)$		$-(a+b)$	$-(a+b)$
	1	$(a-b)$	$(a+b)$	$2a$	a
B Total		$-2b$	$a+b$	$a-b$	
B Mean		$-b$	$a+b$		

Another very striking feature of the non-orthogonal table is the failure of the addition theorem for sums of squares and degrees of freedom. In the first table it is easy to show that the sums of squares and degrees of freedom for A, B, and AB are

	SS	DF
A	$4a^2$	1
B	$4b^2$	1
AB	0	1
Total	$4(a^2 + b^2)$	3

If the total sum of squares is determined directly, we find it to be $4(a^2 + b^2)$, proving that the addition theorem holds. In the second square we have

	SS	DF
A	$\frac{2}{3}(2a + b)^2$	1
B	$\frac{2}{3}(a + 2b)$	1
AB	$\frac{2}{3}(a - b)^2$	1
Total	$4(a^2 + ab + b^2)$	3

where each of the component sums of squares is calculated directly, and these are added to obtain the total. Then on determining the sum of squares for the total directly it is found to be $^8/_3(a^2 + ab + b^2)$. This is less than that obtained by summation for the 3 effects by an amount equal to $^4/_3(a^2 + ab + b^2)$. Note also that there are only 3 determinations in the table so that it represents only 2 degrees of freedom, whereas on assuming 1 degree of freedom for each effect the total should be 3. This result for degrees of freedom agrees with that obtained for the sums of squares.

3. Treatment of a non-orthogonal 2 × 2 table. Having noted that the ordinary methods of analysis will not apply to non-orthogonal data, it remains to decide if anything can be done to obtain the maximum amount of information from the results. It is obviously unreasonable to discard the data as they may contain valuable information.

The 2 × 2 table is examined first because it is essentially the simplest case. Suppose that we have a 2 × 2 table as follows:

	B		Total
A	X		X
	Y	Z	$Y+Z$
	$X+Y$	Z	$X+Y+Z$

or if we prefer to think in terms of figures we can take

	B		Total
A	4		4
	8	7	15
	12	7	19

The first step is to decide how to insert an estimate of the missing value that will make the means comparable, i.e., without entanglement with the other factor. This can be done very simply by making the missing value $(X + Z - Y)$ or $11 - 8 = 3$, in the numerical table. The basis for this is that we have selected a value that will make the interaction zero. We then have a set of *completed values* as distinguished from the *original values*. The two tables are

	B		Total
A	X	$X + Z - Y$	$2X + Z - Y$
	Y	Z	$Y + Z$
	$X + Y$	$X + 2Z - Y$	$2(X + Z)$

	B		Total
A	4	3	7
	8	7	15
	12	10	22

The means for A are $(2X + Z - Y)/2$ and $(Y + Z)/2$, and the difference is

$$\frac{Y + Z}{2} - \frac{2X + Z - Y}{2} = Y - X$$

Similarly the means for B are $(X + 2Z - Y)/2$ and $(X + Y)/2$ and the difference is

$$\frac{X + 2Z - Y}{2} - \frac{X + Y}{2} = Z - Y$$

These differences are obviously free from any effect of one factor on the other. On examining the table it is clear that the method is logical. For example, the response to A can be measured only for the first level of B. The second level of B does not give a comparison, and consequently the observation represented by Z must be discarded.

The second step is to decide what tests of significance, if any, can be made. This is slightly more difficult as it involves the underlying theory of the analysis of variance. We note that since there are only 3 determinations there are only 2 degrees of freedom, and if 1 is used for an estimate of the variance for A, and 1 for B, there are no degrees of freedom left for an estimate of error. Since there is no estimate of error, this problem does not fall into the class for which a general solution can be found to the analytical procedure.

4. Missing values in a 2 × c table. In referring to tables of various dimensions we shall adopt a standard notation $r \times c$, where r refers to the number of rows and c the columns. Let us assume that the table is as follows, representing the data by means of both algebraic and numerical symbols.

		B 0	1	2	3	
A	0	X_{00}	X_{01}	X_{02}		R_1
	1	X_{10}	X_{11}	X_{12}	X_{13}	R_2
		C_0	C_1	C_2	C_3	G

		B 0	1	2	3	
A	0	4	6	8		18
	1	8	10	6	6	30
		12	16	14	6	48

The missing value is the one representing the result for the treatment combination A_0B_3, but the methods of analysis described below are quite general and can be applied without difficulty when any value is missing. In the first place it is instructive to apply methods that may be described as intuitive. This is important in that the application of these methods gives a clear idea of what happens when other methods are applied that otherwise may seem to be merely the manipulation of formulas and rules.

In the first place a decision must be made on what tests of significance can be applied, and this involves the calculation of mean squares for A and B that are free of entanglement, and a suitable error. The response to A can be obtained from the values that are present in both rows. Therefore, we take

$$T_1 = X_{00} + X_{01} + X_{02} \qquad T_2 = X_{10} + X_{11} + X_{12}$$

and the sum of squares for $A = (T_1 - T_2)^2/6 = (18 - 24)^2/6 = 6.0$. The sum of squares for B is slightly more difficult to calculate, but the method follows easily when we note that the 3 degrees of freedom for the B effect can be split up into 1 for the comparison $(X_{10} + X_{11} + X_{12} - 3X_{13}) = T_2 - 3X_{13}$, and 2 degrees of freedom for variation among the 3 totals C_0, C_1, and C_2. The sums of squares are therefore

1 DF $$\frac{(T_2 - 3X_{13})^2}{1 \times 3 + 3^2} = \frac{(24 - 18)^2}{12} = 3.0$$

2 DF $$\frac{C_0^2 + C_1^2 + C_2^2}{2} - \frac{(C_0 + C_1 + C_2)^2}{6}$$

$$= \frac{12^2 + 16^2 + 14^2}{2} - \frac{42^2}{6} = 4.0$$

$$\text{Total for } B \text{ (3 DF)} = 3.0 + 4.0 = 7.0$$

The next step is to obtain a sum of squares for error. An obvious procedure is to determine the sum of squares within levels of A and to subtract the portion that can be attributed to B. This gives

Within A_0	$4^2 + 6^2 + 8^2 - \frac{18^2}{3}$	$= 8.0$
Within A_1	$8^2 + 10^2 + 6^2 + 6^2 - \frac{30^2}{4}$	$= 11.0$
Total within A		$= 19.0$
B		$= 7.0$
Error		$= 12.0$

It is now possible to set up the analysis of variance.

	SS	DF	MS	F
B	7.0	3	2.3	
A	6.0	1	6.0	1.0
Error	12.0	2	6.0	
Total	25.0	6		

The failure of the additive property for non-orthogonal data is again demonstrated by this example. The total sum of squares determined directly from the 7 variate values is 22.86, which does not agree with that obtained by totaling the sums of squares obtained for A, B, and the error. The sums of squares for A and B may be regarded as adjusted sums of squares. There is an agreement with the total sum of squares calculated directly if the components are set up in either of the following ways.

	SS
B (unadjusted)	4.86
A (adjusted)	6.00
Error	12.00
Total	22.86

	SS
B (adjusted)	7.00
A (unadjusted)	3.86
Error	12.00
Total	22.86

This fact will be made use of in further developments. If, for example, the error sum of squares can be calculated directly, the adjusted sums of squares can be obtained by subtraction.

It now remains to obtain means for the rows and columns of the table that are directly comparable. The neatest method is to calculate a value for the missing variate which, if inserted in the table, will accomplish the desired result. This is done by reverting to the method illustrated for a 2×2 table except that now the table is made up from

$$\bar{X}_0 = \frac{X_{00} + X_{01} + X_{02}}{3} \qquad \bar{X}_1 = \frac{X_{10} + X_{11} + X_{12}}{3}$$

and X_{13} from column 3 of the original table. This provides a 2×2 table with one missing value.

$\bar{X}_0$	
$\bar{X}_1$	X_{13}

and the estimate of the missing value that will make the interaction zero is $\bar{X}_0 + X_{13} - \bar{X}_1$. Using figures, we have the 2×2 table

6	4
8	6

where 4 is the calculated value of the missing variate. The completed table is now

		B 0	1	2	3	
A	0	X_{00}	X_{01}	X_{02}	X_{03}	$T_1 + X_{03}$
	1	X_{10}	X_{11}	X_{12}	X_{13}	$T_2 + X_{13}$
		C_0	C_1	C_2	$C_3 + X_{03}$	$G + X_{03}$

		B 0	1	2	3	
A	0	4	6	8	4	22
	1	8	10	6	6	30
		12	16	14	10	52

The A means are $(T_1 + X_{03})/4$ and $(T_2 + X_{13})/4$, and their difference is

$$\frac{T_2 - T_1}{4} + \frac{X_{13} - X_{03}}{4} = \frac{24 - 18}{4} + \frac{6 - 4}{4} = \frac{6 + 2}{4} = 2$$

This is equal to $(T_2 - T_1)/3$, because X_{03} has been selected so that $X_{13} - X_{03} = (T_2 - T_1)/3$. It can be shown similarly that changes in the A response will not affect the means for B.

5. Treatment of non-orthogonal data by the method of fitting constants. The procedure outlined in Section 4 for a $2 \times c$ table with 1 missing value would be rather difficult to apply with more than 2 rows in the table and especially with more than 1 missing value. It is therefore desirable to have a general method that can be adapted to the analysis of any non-orthogonal example. Yates [6, 7] has presented for this purpose the method of fitting constants, and it is applied here to the simple 2 × 4 table discussed in Section 4.

Yates has pointed out that the whole procedure of the analysis of variance can be regarded as a process of fitting constants for the various effects. Thus, for a 2 × 4 table, as follows.

		B 0	1	2	3	Total	Mean
A	0	X_{00}	X_{01}	X_{02}	X_{03}	R_0	$\bar{r}_0$
	1	X_{10}	X_{11}	X_{12}	X_{13}	R_1	$\bar{r}_1$
Total		C_0	C_1	C_2	C_3	G	
Mean		$\bar{c}_0$	$\bar{c}_1$	$\bar{c}_2$	$\bar{c}_3$		$\bar{X}$

Each variate X can be regarded as made up of four parts:

$$a + b + m + z$$

where a represents the effect of the level of A, b the effect of the level of B, m the mean of the table, and z the random variation to be sorted out as experimental error. For a there will be 2 values a_0 and a_1, and for b there will be 4 values, b_0, b_1, b_2, and b_3. The obvious method of finding the values of a and b is by the method of least squares, i.e., by setting up an equation

$$Y = a + b + m \qquad 1$$

and minimizing the sum of squares $\Sigma(Y - a - b - m)^2$. This leads to a set of simultaneous equations that can be written down by rule. This rule can be observed from the equations for the above 2 × 4 table, which are written below.

$$\begin{aligned}
G &= 4a_0 + 4a_1 + 2b_0 + 2b_1 + 2b_2 + 2b_3 + 8m \\
R_0 &= 4a_0 + b_0 + b_1 + b_2 + b_3 + 4m \\
R_1 &= 4a_1 + b_0 + b_1 + b_2 + b_3 + 4m \\
C_0 &= a_0 + a_1 + 2b_0 + 2m \\
C_1 &= a_0 + a_1 + 2b_1 + 2m \\
C_2 &= a_0 + a_1 + 2b_2 + 2m \\
C_3 &= a_0 + a_1 + 2b_3 + 2m
\end{aligned} \qquad 2$$

The rule arises from writing down for any total such as C_0 the a, b, and m components involved.

Since the constant m has been included, it is permissible to define $\Sigma(a) = 0$ and $\Sigma(b) = 0$, and the quantities a and b will then represent plus and minus deviations from m. The above equations then solve as follows.

$$G = 8m \qquad m = \frac{G}{8} = \bar{X}$$

$$R_0 = 4a_0 + 4m \qquad a_0 + m = \frac{R_0}{4} \qquad a_0 = \frac{R_0}{4} - m = \bar{r}_0 - m$$

Similarly

$$a_1 = \bar{r}_1 - m$$

Also

$$C_0 = 2b_0 + 2m \qquad b_0 + m = \frac{C_0}{2} \qquad b_0 = \frac{C_0}{2} - m = \bar{c}_0 - m$$

Similarly

$$b_1 = \bar{c}_1 - m \qquad b_2 = \bar{c}_2 - m \qquad b_3 = \bar{c}_3 - m$$

It will be remembered from Chapter 8, Section 5, that the sum of squares representing the fitting of the partial regression coefficients was given by

$$\text{SS} = b_1\Sigma(x_1y) + b_2\Sigma(x_2y) + b_3\Sigma(x_3y) + \cdots \qquad 3$$

Similarly the sum of squares for the fitting of the above constants is given by

$$\text{SS} = b_0C_0 + b_1C_1 + b_2C_2 + b_3C_3 + a_0R_0 + a_1R_1 + mG \qquad 4$$

$$= \bar{c}_0C_0 + \bar{c}_1C_1 + \bar{c}_2C_2 + \bar{c}_3C_3 + \bar{r}_0R_0 + \bar{r}_1R_1 + \bar{X}G \qquad 5$$

$$= \frac{C_0^2 + C_1^2 + C_2^2 + C_3^2}{2} + \frac{R_0^2 + R_1^2}{4} + \frac{G^2}{8} \qquad 6$$

Now in the analysis of variance

$$\frac{C_0^2 + C_1^2 + C_2^2 + C_3^2}{2} - \frac{G^2}{8}$$

is the sum of squares for columns and

$$\frac{R_0^2 + R_1^2}{4} - \frac{G^2}{8}$$

is the sum of squares for rows. Therefore the total sum of squares less the sum of squares in (6) gives the sum of squares for error. Thus the sum of squares in (6) is the reduction in the total due to fitting the constants.

The essential difference between orthogonal and non-orthogonal data lies in the fact that for orthogonal data the fitted constants are equal to the means of the rows and columns and the general mean, whereas for non-orthogonal data the constants and the means do not necessarily correspond. Basically the fitting of constants is a procedure enabling us to set up a set of adjusted values, Y, corresponding to the original values such that in the adjusted values the interaction is zero. This applies to both orthogonal and non-orthogonal data. For the above example

$$Y_{00} = m + \bar{c}_0 + \bar{r}_0 \qquad Y_{01} = m + \bar{c}_1 + r_0 \qquad \text{etc.}$$

and it can be seen that for such a set of values the additive property is artificially imposed and therefore that the interaction will be nil. It is for this reason that in actual data the sum of squares of the differences $\Sigma(Y - X)^2$ will be the sum of squares representing interaction because it measures the extent of the discrepancy with the additive property. In the case where the rows are replicates and the columns treatments it is clear that $\Sigma(Y - X)^2$ will be the error sum of squares.

The above procedure will now be applied to a $2 \times c$ table in which there is a missing value. If the variate X_{03} is missing we will have the table:

		B 0	1	2	3	Total
A	0	X_{00}	X_{01}	X_{02}		R_0
	1	X_{10}	X_{11}	X_{12}	X_{13}	R_1
Total		C_0	C_1	C_2	C_3	G

and the simultaneous equations are

$$\begin{aligned}
G &= 3a_0 + 4a_1 + 2b_0 + 2b_1 + 2b_2 + b_3 + 7m \\
R_0 &= 3a_0 + b_0 + b_1 + b_2 + 3m \\
R_1 &= + 4a_1 + b_0 + b_1 + b_2 + b_3 + 4m \\
C_0 &= a_0 + a_1 + 2b_0 + 2m \\
C_1 &= a_0 + a_1 + 2b_1 + 2m \\
C_2 &= a_0 + a_1 + 2b_2 + 2m \\
C_3 &= a_1 + b_3 + m
\end{aligned} \qquad 7$$

and, from $\Sigma(a) = 0$ and $\Sigma(b) = 0$, these simplify to the following, and the first equation can be omitted because it is not independent of the others and therefore not required in the solution.

$$\begin{aligned} R_0 &= 3a_0 + b_0 + b_1 + b_2 + 3m \\ R_1 &= 4a_1 + 4m \\ C_0 &= 2b_0 + 2m \\ C_1 &= 2b_1 + 2m \\ C_2 &= 2b_2 + 2m \\ C_3 &= a_1 + b_3 + m \end{aligned} \qquad 8$$

By simplification and substitution in the above equations we have finally

$$m = \frac{2R_0 + R_1 + 2C_3}{12} \qquad 9$$

$$a_0 = \frac{R_0}{3} - \frac{C_0 + C_1 + C_2}{6} \qquad a_1 = -a_0 \qquad 10$$

$$b_0 = \frac{C_0}{2} - m \qquad b_1 = \frac{C_1}{2} - m \qquad b_2 = \frac{C_2}{2} - m \qquad b_3 = C_3 - \frac{R_1}{4} \qquad 11$$

These formulas are easily applied to the numerical example of Section 4, thus:

$$m = \frac{36 + 30 + 12}{12} = 6.5$$

$$a_0 = \frac{18}{3} - \frac{42}{6} = -1.0 \qquad a_1 = +1.0$$

$$b_0 = \frac{12}{2} - 6.5 = -0.5$$

$$b_1 = \frac{16}{2} - 6.5 = 1.5$$

$$b_2 = \frac{14}{2} - 6.5 = 0.5$$

$$b_3 = 6 - \frac{30}{4} = -1.5$$

As a check we note that $\Sigma(a) = 0$, and $\Sigma(b) = 0$.

The adjusted values for the table can now be obtained. For example, $Y_{00} = -1.0 - 0.5 + 6.5 = 5.0$. The completed table of adjusted values is as follows, with the fitted constants and the *original* totals in the margins.

					a	R
	5.0	7.0	6.0	4.0	− 1.0	18
	7.0	9.0	8.0	6.0	+ 1.0	30
b	− 0.5	1.5	0.5	− 1.5	$6.5 = m$	
C	12	16	14	6		$48 = G$

It should be noted at this point that the adjusted value for the missing variate is the same as that obtained in Section 4.

The next step is to calculate the sum of squares for the fitted constants. This is given most easily by equation 4. Here we have

$$\text{SS (constants)} = -0.5 \times 12 + 1.5 \times 16 + 0.5 \times 14 - 1.5 \times 6$$
$$-1.0 \times 18 + 1.0 \times 30 + 6.5 \times 48 = 340.00$$

This includes the correction for the mean which is $48^2/7 = 329.14$. Therefore the total for the constants is $340.00 - 329.14 = 10.86$. The meaning of this sum of squares is perhaps made more obvious by calculating it directly from the adjusted values, omitting the one substituted for the missing variate. Thus

$$5^2 + 7^2 + \cdots + 6^2 - \frac{48^2}{7} = 10.86$$

We are now in a position to determine the error sum of squares, or if A and B are two factors in an experiment it will be the sum of squares for their interaction. This is the total sum of squares for the original values less the sum for the fitted constants. This is

$$22.86 - 10.86 = 12.00$$

which agrees exactly with that obtained in the previous section. The meaning of this sum of squares can be illustrated by calculating it directly from the differences between the original and the adjusted values. These differences are

$X - Y$

− 1	− 1	2	
1	1	− 2	0

and $\Sigma(X - Y)^2 = 12.00$.

The adjusted sums of squares are now very easily obtained from the identities given below together with the actual figures.

$$\text{Total (original values)} - A \text{ (unadjusted)} - \text{Error} = B \text{ (adjusted)}$$

$$22.86 \quad - \quad 3.86 \quad - 12.00 = \quad 7.00$$

$$\text{Total (original values)} - B \text{ (unadjusted)} - \text{Error} = A \text{ (adjusted)}$$

$$22.86 \quad - \quad 4.86 \quad - 12.00 = \quad 6.00$$

It is even simpler to take

$$\text{Total (constants)} - A \text{ (unadjusted)} = B \text{ (adjusted)}$$

$$10.86 \quad - \quad 3.86 \quad = \quad 7.00$$

$$\text{Total (constants)} - B \text{ (unadjusted)} = A \text{ (adjusted)}$$

$$10.86 \quad - \quad 4.86 \quad = \quad 6.00$$

The results obtained by this method agree exactly with those of the previous section, and the analysis of variance will of course be the same.

For general application the formulas can be simplified considerably and the fitting of constants need not actually be carried out. The whole procedure can be developed from a knowledge of the estimate for the missing value. For a $2 \times c$ table we will have

$$X_{ij} = \frac{2R_j + cC_i - G}{c - 1} \qquad 12$$

where R_j is the total of the row containing the missing value and C_i is the total of the column containing the missing value. This is given directly in our example by

$$X_{03} = \frac{2R_0 + 4C_3 - G}{3} = \frac{36 + 24 - 48}{3} = 4.0$$

We then have two sets of data referred to as the *original* values and the *completed* values.

Original Values

		B 0	1	2	3	Total
A	0	4	6	8		18
	1	8	10	6	6	30
Total		12	16	14	6	48

Completed Values

	B 0	1	2	3	Total	Mean
0	4	6	8	4	22	5.5
1	8	10	6	6	30	7.5
Total	12	16	14	10	52	
Mean	6	8	7	5		

An analysis of variance of the completed values can be set up as follows, and this serves to obtain the error sum of squares.

	SS	DF
A	8.0	1
B	10.0	3
Error	12.00	2
Total	30.00	6

In order to make tests of significance, adjustments must be made to the sums of squares for A and B. General formulas for these adjustments have been given by Yates [6, 9] and Anderson [2], and these will be referred to in Section 6. For the $2 \times c$ table these are

$$\text{Adjustment to } A = \tfrac{1}{2}(X_{ij} - X_a)^2$$
$$\text{Adjustment to } B = \tfrac{1}{2}(X_{ij} - X_b)^2 \qquad 13$$

where X_{ij} is the estimate for the missing value, $X_a = C_3$, $X_b = R_0/3$, and the coefficients $^1/_2$ and $^3/_4$ arise from the dimensions of the table. For a $2 \times c$ table the coefficient of $(X_{ij} - X_a)^2$ is always $^1/_2$, and the coefficient of $(X_{ij} - X_b)^2$ is $(c - 1)/c$. The divisor of R_0 in calculating X_b is $c - 1$. In general, therefore, for a $2 \times c$ table

$$X_a = C_i \qquad 14$$

$$X_b = \frac{R_j}{c - 1} \qquad 15$$

Then

$$\text{Adjustment to } A \text{ (rows of table)} = \tfrac{1}{2}(X_{ij} - X_a)^2 \qquad 16$$

and

$$\text{Adjustment to } B \text{ (columns of table)} = \frac{c - 1}{c}(X_{ij} - X_b)^2 \qquad 17$$

Applying the adjustments to our example, we have

$$\text{Adjustment to } A = \tfrac{1}{2}(4 - 6)^2 = 2$$
$$\text{Adjustment to } B = \tfrac{3}{4}(4 - 6)^2 = 3$$

Then the adjusted sums of squares are

$$A = 8.0 - 2.0 = 6.0$$
$$B = 10.0 - 3.0 = 7.0$$

and we have the same results as with previous methods.

6. The 2 × c table with more than one missing value. The methods of analysis for this situation are described in the following section on $r \times c$ tables and can be applied without difficulty to the $2 \times c$ table.

7. Missing values in an $r \times c$ table. It should be apparent from a study of the previous sections in this chapter that the method of fitting constants is a general method that can be applied to any example provided that one can find a solution to the simultaneous equations. Fortunately, as pointed out by Yates [7], the problem of missing values can be solved merely by obtaining estimates for these values by methods that are based on the fitting of constants. The estimation of the missing values may be approached from three different standpoints although they all lead to the same results. These approaches are briefly:

1. The substitution of a value that will make the error sum of squares a minimum. Allan and Wishart [1] and Yates [6, 7, 9] have developed this method, Yates having generalized the method and shown that it agrees with fitting constants.

2. The fitting of constants, Yates [7]. The procedure gives an estimate of the missing value and furnishes a basic method for making tests of significance.

3. The covariance technique. This was first suggested and applied by Bartlett [3]. Anderson [2] gives a generalization of the method, showing in detail how it can be applied to split-plot experiments. The principle is based on substituting another variable X, (the original values are Y), and making $X = 0$ for all pairs where Y is present and -1 for the pair in which Y is missing.* The regression coefficient in the error line of the covariance analysis is the estimate of the missing value. This method also furnishes an easy derivation of the formula for the bias in a sum of squares to which a test of significance is to be applied.

The methods that are most easily applied are demonstrated in the following examples.

8. Example 14–1. One missing value in an $r \times c$ table. Table 14–1 gives the yields of 6 varieties in a 4-replicate experiment for which 1 value is missing. This is referred to as the table of *original* values.

The estimate of the missing value is given by

$$X_{ij} = \frac{cC_i + rR_j - G}{(c-1)(r-1)} \qquad 18$$

---

* Note that in previous sections the symbol X represented original values. The change to Y is made here because in the covariance method of estimating missing values the original values are presumed to be adjusted by a new variable X, and the symbolism adopted corresponds therefore with the symbolism of regression analysis.

where c represents the number of treatments and r the number of replicates. Here

$$X_{22} = \frac{6 \times 50.9 + 4 \times 68.4 - 365.3}{5 \times 3} = 14.25$$

TABLE 14–1

Block	Treatment 1	2	3	4	5	6	Block Total
1	18.5	15.7	16.2	14.1	13.0	13.6	91.1
2	11.7		12.9	14.4	16.9	12.5	68.4 $= R_j$
3	15.4	16.6	15.5	20.3	18.4	21.6	107.8
4	16.5	18.6	12.7	15.7	16.5	18.0	98.0
Treatment Total	62.1	50.9 $= C_i$	57.3	64.5	64.8	65.7	365.3 $= G$

We can now form a table of *completed* values, but only those figures need be entered where changes are made. This gives us Table 14–2.

TABLE 14–2

Block	Treatment 1	2	3	4	5	6	Block Total
1							
2		14.25					82.65
3							
4							
Treatment Total		65.15					379.55

We now set up an analysis of variance for the completed values. At the same time it is convenient to record the sum of squares and correction term for the original values.

$$\text{Total SS (original values)} = 5948.89 - 5801.92 = 146.97$$

$$\text{Total SS (completed values)} = 6151.95 - 6002.42 = 149.53$$

The analysis of variance is given below.

	SS	DF
Blocks	56.76	3
Treatments	12.58	5
Error	80.19	14
Total	149.53	22

Accurate tests of significance cannot be made at this point because of the bias in the sums of squares for blocks and treatments. A general formula is available for the calculation of the bias, which for the treatment sum of squares is

$$\frac{(R_j + cC_i - G)^2}{c(c-1)(r-1)^2} = \frac{(68.4 + 6 \times 50.9 - 365.3)^2}{270} = 0.27 \qquad 19$$

but we shall also give the general method applicable to the case where more than 1 value is missing. The procedure is outlined below.

	DF	SS	MS
Total (original values)	22	146.97	
− Error (completed values)	14	80.19	5.728
= Blocks + Treatments	8	66.78	
− Blocks (unadjusted)	3	54.47	
= Treatments (adjusted)	5	12.31	2.462

The unadjusted sum of squares for blocks is of course calculated from the original block totals.

$$\frac{91.1^2 + 107.8^2 + 98.0^2}{6} + \frac{68.4^2}{5} - \frac{365.3^2}{23} = 54.47$$

The only remaining problem is to make the correct adjustment to the standard error of a difference between 2 means where 1 of the means contains a missing value. For comparing 2 treatments, one of which contains a missing value, we have the formula given by Yates for the standard error of a mean difference,

$$\sqrt{\frac{s^2}{r}\left[2 + \frac{c}{(c-1)(r-1)}\right]} \qquad 20$$

giving in the example

$$\sqrt{\frac{5.728}{4}\left(2 + \frac{6}{5 \times 3}\right)} = 1.85$$

9. Example 14–2. More than 1 missing value in an $r \times c$ table. The data of Example 14–1 are repeated in Table 14–3 with 3 values missing.

TABLE 14–3

Block	Treatment 1	2	3	4	5	6	Block Total
1	18.5	15.7	16.2	14.1	13.0	13.6	91.1
2	11.7	Y_{22}	12.9	Y_{24}	16.9	12.5	54.0
3	15.4	16.6	15.5	20.3	18.4	21.6	107.8
4	Y_{41}	18.6	12.7	15.7	16.5	18.0	81.5
Treatment Total	45.6	50.9	57.3	50.1	64.8	65.7	334.4

Mean = 15.9

The estimation of the missing values is accomplished by repeated applications of the formula for estimating single values. We start by estimating Y_{41}, using an approximate value for Y_{22} and Y_{24}. A convenient approximate value to begin with is the mean of the experiment. The method is illustrated below.

First approximation

$R_j = 81.5 \qquad C_i = 45.6 \quad G = 334.4 + 2 \times 15.9 = 366.2$

$$X_{41} = \frac{6 \times 45.6 + 4 \times 81.5 - 366.2}{15} = 15.6$$

$R_j = 54.0 + 15.9 = 69.9 \quad C_i = 50.9 \quad G = 334.4 + 15.6 + 15.9 = 365.9$

$$X_{22} = \frac{6 \times 50.9 + 4 \times 69.9 - 365.9}{15} = 14.6$$

$R_j = 54.0 + 14.6 = 68.6 \quad C_i = 50.1 \quad G = 334.4 + 15.6 + 14.6 = 364.6$

$$X_{24} = \frac{6 \times 50.1 + 4 \times 68.6 - 364.6}{15} = 14.0$$

Second approximation

$R_j = 81.5 \qquad C_i = 45.6 \quad G = 334.4 + 14.6 + 14.0 = 363.0$

$$X_{41} = \frac{6 \times 45.6 + 4 \times 81.5 - 363.0}{15} = 15.8$$

$R_j = 54.0 + 14.0 = 68.0 \quad C_i = 50.9 \quad G = 334.4 + 15.8 + 14.0 = 364.2$

$$X_{22} = \frac{6 \times 50.9 + 4 \times 68.0 - 364.2}{15} = 14.2$$

$R_j = 54.0 + 14.2 = 68.2 \quad C_i = 50.1 \quad G = 334.4 + 15.8 + 14.2 = 364.4$

$$X_{24} = \frac{6 \times 50.1 + 4 \times 68.2 - 364.4}{15} = 13.9$$

Third approximation

$R_j = 81.5 \qquad C_i = 45.6 \quad G = 334.4 + 14.2 + 13.9 = 362.5$

$$X_{41} = 15.8$$

$R_j = 54.0 + 13.9 = 67.9 \quad C_i = 50.9 \quad G = 334.4 + 15.8 + 13.9 = 364.1$

$$X_{22} = 14.2$$

$R_j = 54.0 + 14.2 = 68.2 \quad C_i = 50.1 \quad G = 334.4 + 15.8 + 14.2 = 364.4$

$$X_{24} = 13.9$$

Since the second and third approximations give the same values, it is obvious that further calculations are unnecessary.

A table of completed values is then set up and an analysis of variance made, keeping a record of the sum of squares of the original values for future work. We have

$$\text{Total SS (original values)} = 5469.28 - 5324.92 = 144.36$$

$$\text{Total SS (completed values)} = 6113.77 - 5962.95 = 150.82$$

Completed Values

Block	Treatment 1	2	3	4	5	6	Block Total
1							
2		14.2		13.9			82.1
3							
4	15.8						97.3
Treatment Total	61.4	65.1		64.0			378.3

The analysis is

	SS	DF
Blocks	58.34	3
Treatments	12.75	5
Error	79.73	12
Total	150.82	20

The next step is to obtain the adjusted sum of squares for treatments as given below.

	SS	DF	MS
Total (original values)	144.36	20	
− Error (completed values)	79.73	12	6.644
= Blocks + Treatments	64.63	8	
− Blocks (unadjusted)	52.54	3	
Treatments (adjusted)	12.09	5	2.418

The unadjusted block sum of squares is obtained from the original values by calculating

$$\frac{91.1^2}{6} + \frac{54.0^2}{4} + \frac{107.8^2}{6} + \frac{81.5^2}{5} - \frac{334.4^2}{21} = 52.54$$

To obtain the standard error of a mean difference between 2 treatments we must note how the missing values, if any, occur. The various possibilities are:

1. No missing values.

$$s_{\bar{d}} = \sqrt{\frac{2s^2}{r}} \qquad 21$$

2. One treatment contains a missing value. We apply the formula given by Yates.

$$s_{\bar{d}} = \sqrt{\frac{s^2}{r}\left[2 + \frac{c}{(c-1)(r-1)}\right]} \qquad 22$$

3. Both treatments contain missing values. Count the effective replication for a given treatment as 1 in each replication where the other treatment is present, $^1/_2$ when the other treatment is missing, and 0 when the value is missing. Thus, for comparing treatment 1 with 2, we have

		Replicate 1	2	3	4	
Treatment	1	1	$\frac{1}{2}$	1	0	$= 2\frac{1}{2}$
	2	1	0	1	$\frac{1}{2}$	$= 2\frac{1}{2}$

Then

$$s_{\bar{d}} = \sqrt{s^2 \left(\frac{1}{2\frac{1}{2}} + \frac{1}{2\frac{1}{2}} \right)} \qquad 23$$

10. Application of the covariance technique to the estimation of missing values. As pointed out briefly in Section 7 it is possible to obtain an estimate of a missing value by a procedure that arises out of the methods of the covariance analysis. This method is described in detail by Anderson [2] with special reference to its application to split-plot experiments. The general principles of the method can be demonstrated for a simple experiment, and once it is clearly understood it can be applied quite readily to more complex layouts.

Assume a randomized block experiment with 2 replicates and 3 treatments from which the result for 1 plot is missing. We can set up the data as follows, where the yields are represented by Y and the concomitant variable by X which takes the value of -1 for the missing plot and 0 for all others. The treatments are A_1, A_2, and A_3, and the plot for A_1 in replicate 1 is missing.

		A_1	A_2	A_3	Total
Replicate 1	X	-1	0	0	-1
	Y	$Y_{11} = 0$	Y_{12}	Y_{13}	R_1
Replicate 2	X	0	0	0	0
	Y	Y_{21}	Y_{22}	Y_{23}	R_2
Total	X	-1	0	0	-1
	Y	T_1	T_2	T_3	G

In detail the total sum of products is seen to be

$$(-1) \times 0 + (0 \times Y_{12}) + \cdots + (0 \times Y_{23}) - \frac{(-1)G}{6} = \frac{G}{6}$$

Then for A we have

$$\frac{(-1) \times T_1 + 0 \times T_2 + 0 \times T_3}{2} - \frac{(-1)G}{6} = \frac{-T_1}{2} + \frac{G}{6}$$

Similarly for replicates we have $-R/3 + G/6$. The error term is

$$\frac{G}{6} + \frac{T_1}{2} - \frac{G}{6} + \frac{R_1}{3} - \frac{G}{6} = \frac{T_1}{2} + \frac{R_1}{3} - \frac{G}{6} = \frac{3T_1 + 2R_1 - G}{6}$$

To obtain regression coefficients we require the sums of squares of X. It is easily seen that these are

$$\text{Total } (-1)^2 - \frac{(-1)^2}{6} = 1 - \frac{1}{6} = \frac{5}{6}$$

$$A \qquad = \frac{2}{6}$$

$$B \qquad = \frac{1}{6}$$

$$\text{Error} \qquad = \frac{2}{6}$$

and the rule is that in any line of the covariance analysis the sum of squares of X is equal to the degrees of freedom divided by the total number of observations.

The regression coefficient in the error line is

$$Y_e = \frac{3T_1 + 2R_1 - G}{6} \times \frac{6}{2} = \frac{3T_1 + 2R_1 - G}{2}$$

which is the well-known formula (see Section 8) for estimating the value of a missing plot for a randomized block experiment.

A feature of this method is that it provides an easy solution to the bias in the sum of squares for treatments when this is computed from the completed values. We obtain a new estimate of the missing value that we shall represent as Y_1, which comes from combining the sums of products, and the sums of squares of X, for treatments and error. Thus

$$\Sigma(X_1 Y) \text{ (sum of products)} = -\frac{T_1}{2} + \frac{G}{6} + \frac{3T_1 + 2R_1 - G}{6} = \frac{R_1}{3}$$

$$\Sigma(X_1^2) \text{ (sum of squares)} = \frac{2}{6} + \frac{2}{6} = \frac{2}{3}$$

Then

$$Y_1 = \frac{R_1}{3} \times \frac{3}{2} = \frac{R_1}{2}$$

and the bias in the sum of squares for treatments is

$$(Y_e - Y_1)^2 \Sigma(X_1^2) = \frac{2}{3}\left(Y_e - \frac{R_1}{2}\right)^2$$

In general, for a randomized block experiment we have

$$Y_e = \frac{rR + pT - G}{(p-1)(r-1)} \tag{24}$$

$$\left.\begin{aligned} \Sigma(X_1 Y) &= \frac{R}{p} \\ \Sigma(X_1^2) &= \frac{p-1}{p} \end{aligned}\right\} \text{giving } Y_1 = \frac{R}{p-1} \tag{25}$$

$$\text{Bias} = (Y_e - Y_1)^2 \frac{p-1}{p} = \frac{(R + pT - G)^2}{p(p-1)(r-1)^2} \tag{26}$$

where R = yield of replicate, T = yield of treatment containing the missing plot, G = total of all existing values, r = number of replicates, and p = number of treatments.

Applying the same procedure to a Latin square, we get

$$Y_e = \frac{r(R + C + T) - 2G}{(r-1)(r-2)} \tag{27}$$

$$\Sigma(X_1 Y) = \frac{r(R + C) - G}{r^2} \tag{28}$$

$$\Sigma(X_1^2) = \left(\frac{r-1}{r}\right)^2 \tag{29}$$

$$Y_1 = \frac{r(R + C) - G}{(r-1)^2} \tag{30}$$

$$\text{Bias} = (Y_e - Y_1)^2 \left(\frac{r-1}{r}\right)^2 = \frac{[R + C + (r-1)T - G]^2}{(r-1)(r-2)} \tag{31}$$

11. Disproportionate sub-class numbers. We have seen that non-orthogonality arises when values are missing, and methods were discussed that enable us to make appropriate tests of significance and extract the maximum amount of information from the data. Actually there is no clear line of distinction between data from which values are missing and data in which the numbers of determinations on which the various effects are based are unequal. Where the numbers are unequal, the examples can be divided into three general classes as follows.

1. *Single classification.* For example, a series of lots of wheat have been taken from different areas and a determination of weight per bushel

made on each lot. There are different numbers of lots in the areas so that the data can be represented as:

					Grand Total
Area	A	B	C	$D \cdots$	
Number	N_a	N_b	N_c	$N_d \cdots$	N
Total	T_a	T_b	T_c	$T_d \cdots$	G

It is of course a simple matter to make a test of the significance of the variation among the means for areas. The sum of squares for error is obtained by pooling the sums of squares for each area arising from deviations from the area mean. The sum of squares for the means is

$$\frac{T_a^2}{N_a} + \frac{T_b^2}{N_b} + \frac{T_c^2}{N_c} + \frac{T_d^2}{N_d} + \cdots - \frac{G^2}{N} \qquad 32$$

With single classification, therefore, we have no problem.

2. *Multiple classification.* (*a*) Proportionate sub-class numbers. For an illustration of this condition we can again think of samples of wheat taken from different areas, but in this case there are 2 varieties and it has not been possible to obtain the same number of samples from each area and for each variety. The numbers, however, are proportional. The following is a typical example showing numbers on the left and totals on the right.

		Area				
		A	B	C	D	
Variety	1	12	24	18	14	68
	2	6	12	9	7	34
		18	36	27	21	102

		Area				
		A	B	C	D	
Variety	1	S_{1a}	S_{1b}	S_{1c}	S_{1d}	T_1
	2	S_{2a}	S_{2b}	S_{2c}	S_{2d}	T_2
		T_a	T_b	T_c	T_d	G

This example does not create any difficulties. The sum of squares for error comes from within *sub-classes*, a single sub-class, for example, being the 12 determinations of variety 1 in area A. The sum of squares for areas would be obtained as for a single classification with unequal numbers. That is

$$\frac{T_a^2}{18} + \frac{T_b^2}{36} + \frac{T_c^2}{27} + \frac{T_d^2}{21} - \frac{G^2}{102}$$

The variety sum of squares would be

$$\frac{(68T_2 - 34T_1)^2}{34 \times 68 \times 102}$$

The interaction sum of squares could be determined by subtraction from the total for sub-classes given by

$$\frac{S_{1a}{}^2}{12} + \frac{S_{1b}{}^2}{24} + \cdots + \frac{S_{2d}{}^2}{7} - \frac{G^2}{102} \qquad 33$$

or it could be calculated directly from

$$\frac{(12S_{2a} - 6S_{1a})^2}{6 \times 12 \times 18} + \frac{(24S_{2b} - 12S_{1b})^2}{12 \times 24 \times 36} + \cdots - \frac{(68T_2 - 34T_1)^2}{34 \times 68 \times 102}$$

The form of the analysis would be

	DF
Areas	3
Varieties	1
Interaction	3
Error	94

and tests of significance made in the usual way.

(*b*) Disproportionate sub-class numbers. With a similar example the numbers might be

A	*B*	*C*	*D*	
12	18	7	8	45
6	15	13	14	48
18	33	20	22	93

and it is clear that there is no proportionality in either direction in the table. It is this lack of proportionality that introduces non-orthogonality, requiring methods of analysis somewhat different from those we are accustomed to apply to orthogonal data.

12. Considerations arising out of unequal and disproportionate sub-class numbers. Since we are concerned here mainly with understanding the principles of the methods of analysis we employ rather than with the mere elaboration of appropriate techniques, it is important to examine the effect of unequal and disproportionate numbers on our method of deduction from experimental data. It may not be clear, for example, that it is necessary to make certain assumptions regarding the population we are sampling before we can decide how we are going to handle the data. A simple example will make it obvious that such assumptions must be made. Suppose that we have 2 samples of weights. One consists of a sample of 200 men with a mean weight of 160 pounds, and the other is a sample of 120 women with a mean weight of 120 pounds. What is the best estimate we can make of the mean weight of the population from which these samples were drawn? This will depend on how the sexes are distributed. If we know that there are approximately equal numbers of the 2 sexes, the obvious conclusion is that the samples were not drawn in such a way that there was equal opportunity for both sexes to be included, and the best estimate is the unweighted mean, or

$$\frac{160 + 120}{2} = 140$$

However, suppose that we have no good reason to think that the 2 sexes are equally represented in the population (for example, the weights might be taken from a certain occupational group where there is a predominance of men), and it is the mean weight of this group for which we wish to obtain an estimate. The obvious course is to assume that the numbers in the samples represent the approximate numbers in the population, and the best estimate is the weighted mean or

$$\frac{(160 \times 200) + (120 \times 120)}{320} = 145$$

This example makes it clear that it may be necessary to make assumptions regarding the population before conclusions can be drawn. Actually this is always the case, regardless of unequal numbers. Strictly speaking, the mean of a sample is a good estimate of the mean of the population from which the sample was drawn only if the population is normally distributed. If the population is *J*-shaped, bimodal, decidedly skewed, or shows any definite abnormality, some statistic other than the mean may give a better estimate of the central tendency of the population.

With disproportionate sub-class numbers there is always the problem of non-orthogonality, and, in addition, assumptions made regarding the population sampled have an important bearing on the method to be chosen for making tests of significance and obtaining estimates of the main effects and interactions.

13. Effect of the presence or absence of interaction. Regardless of disproportionate numbers it should be obvious that the sub-class means are in themselves efficient estimates of the hypothetical sub-class means of the population sampled. This is so because the sub-classes may be regarded as a series of individual samples and each sample is capable of giving an estimate of the mean or the variance of the population. In the estimates of the variance, division of the sums of squares by the degrees of freedom in each sample ensures that the estimates are unbiased. Furthermore the sub-class means are capable of providing an estimate of the variance of the population. It is only necessary in calculating the sum of squares to make due allowance for unequal numbers. It is therefore only in connection with the multiple classification of the data that difficulties arise, in other words, in obtaining estimates of the effects represented by the marginal means and the interaction. In order to illustrate this point it is desirable to set up a hypothetical example.

Suppose that we have a 2×2 table in which the numbers are represented by n, the sub-class means by $\bar{Y}$, and the sub-class totals by S. Subscripts can be added to define the sub-classes and the marginal values. A table of numbers, means, and totals can be set up as follows

Numbers

	B		
A	n_{11}	n_{12}	$N_{1\cdot}$
	n_{21}	n_{22}	$N_{2\cdot}$
	$N_{\cdot 1}$	$N_{\cdot 2}$	N

Means

	B		
A	$\bar{Y}_{11}$	$\bar{Y}_{12}$	$\bar{Y}_{1\cdot}$
	$\bar{Y}_{21}$	$\bar{Y}_{22}$	$\bar{Y}_{2\cdot}$
	$\bar{Y}_{\cdot 1}$	$\bar{Y}_{\cdot 2}$	$\bar{Y}_{\cdot\cdot}$

Totals

	B		
A	S_{11}	S_{12}	$S_{1\cdot}$
	S_{21}	S_{22}	$S_{2\cdot}$
	$S_{\cdot 1}$	$S_{\cdot 2}$	$S_{\cdot\cdot}$

where the marginal means here are the weighted means of the rows and columns. Thus $\bar{Y}_{1\cdot} = (n_{11}\bar{Y}_{11} + n_{12}\bar{Y}_{12})/N_{1\cdot}$. If there is *no interaction* in the population, the individual variates can be represented by an equation of the form

$$Y = a + b + m$$

where a represents the effect of the level of A, b the effect of B, and m the general mean. There will be an error term for each variate so that strictly speaking we should have

$$Y = a + b + m + x$$

where x is the error term but can be omitted here without affecting the conclusions. Summing the various components over the Y's in each cell and in the margin for the A totals, we have

$$n_{11}(a_1 + b_1 + m) \quad n_{12}(a_1 + b_2 + m) \quad N_{1\cdot}a_1 + n_{11}b_1 + n_{12}b_2 + N_{1\cdot}m = S_{1\cdot}$$

$$n_{21}(a_2 + b_1 + m) \quad n_{22}(a_2 + b_2 + m) \quad N_{2\cdot}a_2 + n_{21}b_1 + n_{22}b_2 + N_{2\cdot}m = S_{2\cdot}$$

Then

$$\bar{Y}_{1\cdot} = a_1 + \left(\frac{n_{11}}{N_{1\cdot}}\right) b_1 + \left(\frac{n_{12}}{N_{1\cdot}}\right) b_2 + m$$

$$\bar{Y}_{2\cdot} = a_2 + \left(\frac{n_{21}}{N_{2\cdot}}\right) b_1 + \left(\frac{n_{22}}{N_{2\cdot}}\right) b_2 + m \qquad 34$$

The response to A is

$$\bar{Y}_{2\cdot} - \bar{Y}_{1\cdot} = (a_2 - a_1) + \left(\frac{n_{21}}{N_{2\cdot}} - \frac{n_{11}}{N_{1\cdot}}\right) b_1 + \left(\frac{n_{22}}{N_{2\cdot}} - \frac{n_{12}}{N_{1\cdot}}\right) b_2 \qquad 35$$

which very clearly represents the effect of A plus 2 terms containing the numbers and b_1 and b_2.

We note first that if the numbers are equal or proportional,

$$\frac{n_{21}}{N_{2\cdot}} = \frac{n_{11}}{N_{1\cdot}} = \frac{n_{22}}{N_{2\cdot}} = \frac{n_{12}}{N_{1\cdot}} \qquad 36$$

the terms containing b_1 and b_2 disappear.

To note what happens when the numbers are disproportionate we can take a set of numbers as follows.

$$n_{11} = 2 \qquad n_{12} = 3 \qquad N_{1\cdot} = 5$$

$$n_{21} = 4 \qquad n_{22} = 5 \qquad N_{2\cdot} = 9$$

The terms in (35) containing b_1 and b_2 are

$$(\tfrac{4}{9} - \tfrac{2}{5})b_1 + (\tfrac{5}{9} - \tfrac{3}{5})b_2 = \tfrac{2}{45}(b_1 - b_2) \qquad 37$$

or in general the term containing b_1 and b_2 is

$$\frac{n_{12}n_{21} - n_{11}n_{22}}{N_{1\cdot}N_{2\cdot}}(b_1 - b_2)$$

This shows that the response to B is reflected in the means for A. Similarly we can show that the response to A is reflected in the means for B. Thus disproportionality is seen to have a definite effect on the orthogonality of the A and B responses as measured by the weighted means.

It is easy to see also that the unweighted means are not affected. For example

$$\text{Unweighted mean } (A_1) = \frac{\bar{Y}_{11} + \bar{Y}_{12}}{2} = 2a_1 + b_1 + b_2 + m$$

$$\text{Unweighted mean } (A_2) = \frac{\bar{Y}_{21} + \bar{Y}_{22}}{2} = 2a_2 + b_1 + b_2 + m$$

And the difference is $2(a_2 - a_1)$.

We inquire next into the effect of the presence of an interaction. To do this it is simpler to demonstrate the effect numerically than it is to work it out in algebraic form. We shall set up a series of tables with varying degrees of interaction, the first representing zero interaction, and the numbers remaining as in the first table. In the first table we take $a_2 = 2$, $a_1 = -2$, $b_2 = 1$, $b_1 = -1$, and $m = 10$. Then $28 = 4 \times (-2) + 4 \times (-1) + 4 \times 10$ and the mean is $28/4 = 7$, and so on for the remaining totals. In the other tables the means are changed so as to produce interactions.

Numbers			Means		Totals		Unweighted Means	Difference $A_2 - A_1$	Weighted Means	Difference $A_2 - A_1$
			− 1	*+ 1*						
4	8	*− 2*	7	9	28	72	8		8.33	
								4		3.92
6	10	*+ 2*	11	13	66	130	12		12.25	
4	8		5	11	20	88	8		9.00	
								4		2.75
6	10		13	11	78	110	12		11.75	
4	8		3	13	12	104	8		9.67	
								4		1.58
6	10		15	9	90	90	12		11.25	
4	8		1	15	4	120	8		10.33	
								4		0.42
6	10		17	7	102	70	12		10.75	

Note that the unweighted means remain the same throughout regardless of the interaction, whereas the weighted means not only change but, as the interaction increases, the response to A as measured by the difference between the weighted means decreases. It is easily verified that if the numbers are equal the unweighted and weighted means remain the same. By an algebraic procedure we can show that this is due to the interaction factor becoming entangled with means for the levels of A.

This brief discussion should be sufficient to show that for a given set of data with disproportionate numbers it is important to take into account the existence or non-existence of an interaction. It serves as a basis for a complete understanding of the methods that are applied. The following statement by Yates [6] summarizes the points to be taken into consideration.

> It is frequently reasonable to suppose that the interactions between the main effects are negligible. If this is so, the most efficient estimates of the magnitude of the main effects may be made by fitting constants to represent these effects only.
>
> If the interactions cannot be ignored the efficient estimates of the main effects are the means of the sub-class means (assuming the multiple classification to be complete). In orthogonal experiments these estimates are precisely the same as those obtained on fitting constants to represent the main effects only. In orthogonal experiments, therefore, there is no need to consider whether the interactions are in fact negligible, when estimating the main effects.

14. Methods of analysis appropriate for different conditions. Since there is more than one method for the analysis of data with disproportionate numbers, depending on different conditions and the assumptions made, the student will find it confusing unless the fundamentals outlined above are kept clearly in mind. In the first place the method known as the *fitting of constants* is basic to all other methods and would be applied almost exclusively except for the fact that other methods are less laborious, especially when the table contains more than 2 rows and columns. The first step, therefore, in a study of methods of analysis should be to become familiar with the method of fitting constants.

The second general method also developed by Yates is known as the *weighted squares of means.* It also has a sound theoretical background and its main application is in the analysis of data in which it is impossible to assume that the interaction is negligible.

15. Analysis of a 2 × 2 table with disproportionate sub-class numbers. In the first place we shall illustrate the application of the method of fitting constants. Assume that we have a 2 × 2 table as follows, using the notation described above.

	B			
A	n_{11}	n_{12}	$N_{1\cdot}$	$S_{1\cdot}$
	n_{21}	n_{22}	$N_{2\cdot}$	$S_{2\cdot}$
	$N_{\cdot 1}$	$N_{\cdot 2}$	N	
	$S_{\cdot 1}$	$S_{\cdot 2}$		S

The first step in all methods is to make a preliminary analysis of differences between the sub-class means. For a 2 × 2 table we have a simple analysis of the form

	DF
Sub-class means	3
Error	$N-4$
Total	$N-1$

Obviously, if the sub-class means are not significantly different, there is not much object in proceeding further. If the differences are significant, the sub-class means can be compared and this may provide all the information required. However, it may be desirable to have independent estimates and tests of the *A* and *B* effects and the interaction *AB*.

The fitting of constants follows the same general procedure as that outlined for the treatment of data with missing values. Here we have the equations

$$\begin{aligned} S_{1\cdot} &= N_{1\cdot}a_1 + n_{11}b_1 + n_{12}b_2 + N_{1\cdot}m \\ S_{2\cdot} &= N_{2\cdot}a_2 + n_{21}b_1 + n_{22}b_2 + N_{2\cdot}m \\ S_{\cdot1} &= N_{\cdot1}b_1 + n_{11}a_1 + n_{21}a_2 + N_{\cdot1}m \\ S_{\cdot2} &= N_{\cdot2}b_2 + n_{12}a_1 + n_{22}a_2 + N_{\cdot2}m \end{aligned} \qquad 38$$

Before illustrating how these simplify, we shall define

$$R_1 = \left(\frac{n_{11}}{N_{\cdot1}}\right) S_{\cdot1} + \left(\frac{n_{12}}{N_{\cdot2}}\right) S_{\cdot2} \qquad C_1 = \left(\frac{n_{11}}{N_{1\cdot}}\right) S_{1\cdot} + \left(\frac{n_{21}}{N_{2\cdot}}\right) S_{2\cdot} \qquad 39$$

$$R_{12} = \frac{n_{11}n_{21}}{N_{\cdot1}} + \frac{n_{12}n_{22}}{N_{\cdot2}} \qquad C_{12} = \frac{n_{11}n_{12}}{N_{1\cdot}} + \frac{n_{21}n_{22}}{N_{2\cdot}} \qquad 40$$

Then the simultaneous equations simplify to

$$S_{1\cdot} = R_1 + a_1R_{12} - a_2R_{12} \qquad S_{\cdot1} = C_1 + b_1C_{12} - b_2C_{12} \qquad 41$$

$$S_{2\cdot} = R_2 - a_1R_{12} + a_2R_{12} \qquad S_{\cdot2} = C_2 - b_1C_{12} + b_2C_{12} \qquad 42$$

and since according to a general principle in fitting constants

$$a_1 + a_2 = 0 \quad \text{and} \quad b_1 + b_2 = 0 \qquad 43$$

further simplification gives

$$a_1 = \frac{S_{1\cdot} - R_1}{2R_{12}} \qquad b_1 = \frac{S_{\cdot1} - C_1}{2C_{12}} \qquad 44$$

We can then solve for m, obtaining

$$m = \frac{S_{1\cdot}}{N_{1\cdot}} - a_1 - b_1\left(\frac{n_{11} - n_{12}}{N_{1\cdot}}\right) \qquad 45$$

In calculating R_1, R_{12}, C_1, and C_{12}, it is convenient to note that, if we write $n_{11}/N_{\cdot1}$, $n_{12}/N_{\cdot2}$, $n_{11}/N_{1\cdot}$, and $n_{21}/N_{2\cdot}$ in the margins of the table, the values required can be obtained by multiplying and summating on the machine.

The sum of squares for constants including the correction for the mean is given by

$$mS + (S_{1\cdot} - S_{2\cdot})a_1 + (S_{\cdot1} - S_{\cdot2})b_1 \qquad 46$$

The adjusted sums of squares for A, B, and the interaction are then obtained from

Between sub-classes — Constants = Interaction
Constants — A (unadjusted) = B (adjusted)
Constants — B (unadjusted) = A (adjusted)

The unadjusted sums of squares are of course given by

$$A \qquad \frac{(N_2.S_1. - N_1.S_2.)^2}{N_1.N_2.N} \qquad 47$$

$$B \qquad \frac{(N._2S._1 - N._1S._2)^2}{N._1N._2N} \qquad 48$$

The procedure given above can actually be abbreviated slightly, but it is reproduced in full here because it follows the general procedure of fitting constants to larger tables.

On testing the interaction and finding it insignificant, the constants for A and B can be taken as efficient estimates of the A and B responses. Since $a_1 + a_2 = 0$, we can take $2a_1$ to represent the A response and $2b_1$ to represent the B response. Possibly we should not take the evidence of the significance of the interaction too literally. Even if the interaction is significant, if we have good reason to believe that the interaction in the population is negligible, the constants are still efficient estimates of the main effects. Also, the interaction may not actually prove significant, but if we have reason to think that a real interaction effect exists in the population the A and B constants will not be efficient estimates. Generally speaking, however, it is sound practice to let the test of significance of the interaction be at least a guide to methods of estimating the main effects.

Assuming an interaction is present, more efficient tests of the main effects can be obtained by the method of weighted squares of means which is described below.

16. Analysis of 2 × 2 table using weighted squares of means. The table is most conveniently set up as follows, wherein the main calculations required are indicated.

	B		$\Sigma\left(\frac{1}{n}\right)$	$w_i.$	$\bar{Y}_i.$	$w_i.\bar{Y}_i.$
A	n_{11} $\bar{Y}_{11}$ $1/n_{11}$	n_{12} $\bar{Y}_{12}$ $1/n_{12}$				
	n_{21} $\bar{Y}_{21}$ $1/n_{21}$	n_{22} $\bar{Y}_{22}$ $1/n_{22}$				
$\Sigma\left(\frac{1}{n}\right)$				$\Sigma(w_i.)$		$\Sigma(w_i.\bar{Y}_i.)$
$w._j$			$\Sigma(w._j)$			
$\bar{Y}._j$						
$w._j\bar{Y}._j$			$\Sigma(w._j\bar{Y}._j)$			

$\bar{Y}_i.$ is the unweighted mean of $\bar{Y}_{11}$ and $\bar{Y}_{12}$, etc., $\bar{Y}._j$ is the unweighted mean of Y_{11} and Y_{21}, etc., $w_i.$ is the reciprocal of $\Sigma(1/n)$ in the same line, and similarly for $w._j$.

The sums of squares for the main effects are

$$A = 4\left\{\Sigma(w_{i}.\bar{Y}_{i}.^2) - \frac{[\Sigma(w_{i}.\bar{Y}_{i}.)]^2}{\Sigma(w_{i}.)}\right\} \qquad 49$$

$$B = 4\left\{\Sigma(w._{j}\bar{Y}._{j}^2) - \frac{[\Sigma(w._{j}\bar{Y}._{j})]^2}{\Sigma(w._{j})}\right\} \qquad 50$$

The sum of squares for interaction can be obtained as in fitting constants, but since we are dealing here with the unweighted means it is more conveniently calculated by setting up a column on the right containing values of $d_{i}.$ which are differences between the unweighted means in the same row. The interaction sum of squares is

$$AB = \Sigma(w_{i}.d_{i}.^2) - \frac{[\Sigma(w_{i}.d_{i}.)]^2}{\Sigma(w_{i}.)} \qquad 51$$

17. Analysis of an $r \times 2$ table with disproportionate sub-class numbers. In this notation the table will have r rows and 2 columns. It is convenient generally to set the table up in this way rather than with c columns and 2 rows.

The first step as with a 2×2 table is to make a preliminary analysis in order to test the significance of the mean square for sub-class means. Assuming this to be significant, we proceed to the more detailed analysis, illustrating first the method of fitting constants. The $r \times 2$ table can be represented as follows, with the same notation as in the previous section. It is convenient to illustrate with a 3×2 table, and it will be found easy to extend the method for any number of rows.

	B			
A	n_{11}	n_{12}	$N_{1}.$	$S_{1}.$
	n_{21}	n_{22}	$N_{2}.$	$S_{2}.$
	n_{31}	n_{32}	$N_{3}.$	$S_{3}.$
	$N._{1}$	$N._{2}$	N	
	$S._{1}$	$S._{2}$		S

The simultaneous equations are

$$\begin{aligned}
S_{1}. &= N_{1}.m + N_{1}.a_1 + n_{11}b_1 + n_{12}b_2 \\
S_{2}. &= N_{2}.m + N_{2}.a_2 + n_{21}b_1 + n_{22}b_2 \\
S_{3}. &= N_{3}.m + N_{3}.a_3 + n_{31}b_1 + n_{32}b_2 \\
S._{1} &= N._{1}m + N._{1}b_1 + n_{11}a_1 + n_{21}a_2 + n_{31}a_3 \\
S._{2} &= N._{2}m + N._{2}b_2 + n_{12}a_1 + n_{22}a_2 + n_{32}a_3
\end{aligned} \qquad 52$$

We then define

$$C_1 = \left(\frac{n_{11}}{N_{1.}}\right) S_{1.} + \left(\frac{n_{21}}{N_{2.}}\right) S_{2.} + \left(\frac{n_{31}}{N_{3.}}\right) S_{3.} \qquad 53$$

and

$$C_{12} = \left(\frac{n_{11}n_{12}}{N_{1.}}\right) + \left(\frac{n_{21}n_{22}}{N_{2.}}\right) + \left(\frac{n_{31}n_{32}}{N_{3.}}\right) \qquad 54$$

It can then be shown from the simultaneous equations that

$$b_1 = \frac{S_{.1} - C_1}{2C_{12}} \qquad 55$$

and, since $b_1 + b_2 = 0$, we have $b_2 = - b_1$, and substituting in the first three of the simultaneous equations we get

$$a_1 + m = \frac{S_{1.} - b_1(n_{11} - n_{12})}{N_{1.}}$$

$$a_2 + m = \frac{S_{2.} - b_1(n_{21} - n_{22})}{N_{2.}} \qquad 56$$

$$a_3 + m = \frac{S_{3.} - b_1(n_{31} - n_{32})}{N_{3.}}$$

The sum of squares for the fitted constants is

$$\Sigma(m + a_i)S_{i.} + b_1(S_{.1} - S_{.2}) \qquad 57$$

which includes the correction for the mean. We require also the sums of squares for

$$B \text{ (unadjusted)} = \frac{(N_{.1}S_{.2} - N_{.2}S_{.1})^2}{N_{.1}N_{.2}N} \qquad 58$$

$$A \text{ (unadjusted)} = \frac{S_{1.}^2}{N_{1.}} + \frac{S_{2.}^2}{N_{2.}} + \frac{S_{3.}^2}{N_{3.}} - \frac{S^2}{N} \qquad 59$$

The adjusted sums of squares orthogonal to the error are obtained from

Between sub-classes — Constants = Interaction AB

Constants — B (unadjusted) = A (adjusted)

Constants — A (unadjusted) = B (adjusted)

and the complete analysis can then be set up in the form below, where the degrees of freedom are given for the 3×2 and the $r \times 2$ table.

	3×2 DF	$r \times 2$ DF
A	2	$r - 1$
B	1	1
AB	2	$r - 1$
Error	$n - 6$	$n - 2r$

The full procedure of the method of fitting constants is given mainly for the purpose of illustrating principles. Certain abbreviations are possible in the actual analysis. For example, the first requisite of the analysis is to make a test of the interaction in order to decide on the method of estimating the main effects. It is convenient therefore to know that the sum of squares for B (adjusted) is given by $C_{12}(2b_1)^2$. By adding this to A (unadjusted) we get the sum of squares for constants directly and the interaction sum of squares is obtained as above. In short

$$\text{(Between sub-classes)} - C_{12}(2b_1)^2 - (A, \text{ unadjusted}) = \text{(Interaction)}$$

However, should the interaction prove to be insignificant, we will probably require the values of $a_i + m$ as estimates of the A effect.

On the other hand, if the data indicate that the interaction cannot be neglected in the estimation of the main effects, we shall probably proceed to the analysis by the weighted squares of means. For this purpose the table is set up as below. The last 2 columns are not essential if we have calculated the interaction from the fitting of constants. Note the subscripts $i = 1, 2, 3$, and $j = 1, 2$; and that $\bar{Y}_{i\cdot}$ and $\bar{Y}_{\cdot j}$ are unweighted means. Also $d_{1\cdot} = (\bar{Y}_{12} - \bar{Y}_{11})$ and $w_i = \dfrac{1}{\Sigma(1/n)}$.

	n_{i1}	$\bar{Y}_{i1}$	n_{i2}	$\bar{Y}_{i2}$	$\Sigma\left(\frac{1}{n}\right)$	$w_{1\cdot}$	$\bar{Y}_{i\cdot}$	$w_{1\cdot}.\bar{Y}_{i\cdot}$	$d_{i\cdot}$	$w_{i\cdot}d_{i\cdot}$
	n_{11}	$\bar{Y}_{11}$	n_{12}	$\bar{Y}_{12}$						
	$1/n_{11}$		$1/n_{12}$							
	n_{21}	$\bar{Y}_{21}$	n_{22}	$\bar{Y}_{22}$						
	$1/n_{21}$		$1/n_{22}$							
	n_{31}	$\bar{Y}_{31}$	n_{32}	$\bar{Y}_{32}$						
	$1/n_{31}$		$1/n_{32}$							
$\Sigma\left(\frac{1}{n}\right)$						$\Sigma(w_{i\cdot})$		$\Sigma(w_{i\cdot}.\bar{Y}_{i\cdot})$		$\Sigma(w_{i\cdot}d_{i\cdot})$
$w_{\cdot j}$					$\Sigma(w_{\cdot j})$					
$\bar{Y}_{\cdot j}$										
$w_{\cdot j}\bar{Y}_{\cdot j}$					$\Sigma(w_{\cdot j}\bar{Y}_{\cdot j})$					

From this table we calculate

$$A = 4\left\{\Sigma(w_{i\cdot}.\bar{Y}_{i\cdot}{}^2) - \frac{[\Sigma(w_{i\cdot}.\bar{Y}_{i\cdot})]^2}{\Sigma(w_{i\cdot})}\right\} \qquad 60$$

$$B = 9\left\{\Sigma(w_{\cdot j}\bar{Y}_{\cdot j}{}^2) - \frac{[\Sigma(w_{\cdot j}\bar{Y}_{\cdot j})]^2}{\Sigma(w_{\cdot j})}\right\} \qquad 61$$

where the numerical factor is the square of the number of rows or columns as the case may be. If the interaction sum of squares has not previously been calculated, we take

$$AB = \Sigma(w_{i}.d_{i}.^2) - \frac{[\Sigma(w_{i}.d_{i}.)]^2}{\Sigma(w_{i}.)} \qquad 62$$

The remainder of the analysis consists merely of setting up the sums of squares and degrees of freedom in the usual way and making tests of significance by comparison with the mean square for error arising from within sub-classes.

18. Analysis of an $r \times c$ table with disproportionate sub-class numbers. The preliminary analysis of a table with more than 2 rows or columns will take the usual form, the mean square for sub-class means being tested against the mean square for error. If significant effects are present, the analysis must be by the fitting of constants if an efficient test of the interaction effect is to be made.

A 4 × 3 table can be represented as follows, where $i = 1, 2, 3, 4$, and $j = 1, 2, 3$.

		B				
		n_{i1}	n_{i2}	n_{i3}	$N_{i\cdot}$	$S_{i\cdot}$
A	n_{1j}	n_{11}	n_{12}	n_{13}	$N_{1\cdot}$	$S_{1\cdot}$
	n_{2j}	n_{21}	n_{22}	n_{23}	$N_{2\cdot}$	$S_{2\cdot}$
	n_{3j}	n_{31}	n_{32}	n_{33}	$N_{3\cdot}$	$S_{3\cdot}$
	n_{4j}	n_{41}	n_{42}	n_{43}	$N_{4\cdot}$	$S_{4\cdot}$
	$N_{\cdot j}$	$N_{\cdot 1}$	$N_{\cdot 2}$	$N_{\cdot 3}$	N	
	$S_{\cdot j}$	$S_{\cdot 1}$	$S_{\cdot 2}$	$S_{\cdot 3}$		S

The method of writing down the simultaneous equations is similar to that for the 2 × 2 and the $r \times 2$ tables and therefore will not be given. It is sufficient to present the solution in terms of the constants. In the first place we define

$$C'_1 = \Sigma\left(\frac{n_{i1}S_{i\cdot}}{N_{i\cdot}}\right) - S_{\cdot 1} \quad C'_2 = \Sigma\left(\frac{n_{i2}S_{i\cdot}}{N_{i\cdot}}\right) - S_{\cdot 2} \quad C'_3 = \Sigma\left(\frac{n_{i3}S_{i\cdot}}{N_{i\cdot}}\right) - S_{\cdot 3} \qquad 63$$

$$C'_{11} = \Sigma\left(\frac{n_{i1}^2}{N_{i\cdot}}\right) - N_{\cdot 1} \quad C'_{22} = \Sigma\left(\frac{n_{i2}^2}{N_{i\cdot}}\right) - N_{\cdot 2} \quad C'_{33} = \Sigma\left(\frac{n_{i3}^2}{N_{i\cdot}}\right) - N_{\cdot 3} \qquad 64$$

$$C_{12} = \Sigma\left(\frac{n_{i1}n_{i2}}{N_{i\cdot}}\right) \quad C_{13} = \Sigma\left(\frac{n_{i1}n_{i3}}{N_{i\cdot}}\right) \quad C_{23} = \Sigma\left(\frac{n_{i2}n_{i3}}{N_{i\cdot}}\right) \qquad 65$$

We can then derive the simultaneous equations

$$\begin{aligned} C'_1 &= b_1C_{11} + b_2C_{12} + b_3C_{13} \\ C'_2 &= b_1C_{12} + b_2C_{22} + b_3C_{23} \\ C'_3 &= b_1C_{13} + b_2C_{23} + b_3C_{33} \end{aligned} \qquad 66$$

The solution of these equations is facilitated by the fact that $b_1 + b_2 + b_3 = 0$. Taking $b_3 = - b_1 - b_2$ and substituting, we have

$$\begin{aligned} C'_1 &= b_1(C'_{11} - C_{13}) + b_2(C_{12} - C_{13}) \\ C'_2 &= b_1(C_{12} - C_{23}) + b_2(C'_{22} - C_{23}) \end{aligned} \qquad 67$$

These can be solved by elimination, or in the determinant notation we can write

$$b_2 = \frac{\begin{vmatrix} C'_1 & (C_{12} - C_{13}) \\ C'_2 & (C'_{22} - C_{23}) \end{vmatrix}}{\begin{vmatrix} (C'_{11} - C_{13}) & (C_{12} - C_{13}) \\ (C_{12} - C_{23}) & (C'_{22} - C_{23}) \end{vmatrix}} \qquad 68$$

In other words in the general solution for an $r \times c$ table one of the equations can be eliminated by this device. After the values of b have been determined, the values of a_i are calculated from

$$\begin{aligned} a_1 + m &= \frac{S_{1\cdot}}{N_{1\cdot}} - \frac{n_{11}b_1}{N_{1\cdot}} - \frac{n_{12}b_2}{N_{1\cdot}} - \frac{n_{13}b_3}{N_{1\cdot}} \\ a_2 + m &= \frac{S_{2\cdot}}{N_{2\cdot}} - \frac{n_{21}b_1}{N_{2\cdot}} - \frac{n_{22}b_2}{N_{2\cdot}} - \frac{n_{23}b_3}{N_{2\cdot}} \\ a_3 + m &= \frac{S_{3\cdot}}{N_{3\cdot}} - \frac{n_{31}b_1}{N_{3\cdot}} - \frac{n_{32}b_2}{N_{3\cdot}} - \frac{n_{33}b_3}{N_{3\cdot}} \\ a_4 + m &= \frac{S_{4\cdot}}{N_{4\cdot}} - \frac{n_{41}b_1}{N_{4\cdot}} - \frac{n_{42}b_2}{N_{4\cdot}} - \frac{n_{43}b_3}{N_{4\cdot}} \end{aligned} \qquad 69$$

and finally

$$\sum_1^4 (a_i + m) = 4m$$

After obtaining the constants, we can proceed to the calculation of the sums of squares. First, the sum of squares for constants is

$$\Sigma(a_i + m)S_{i\cdot} + \Sigma(b_{\cdot j}S_{\cdot j}) - \frac{S^2}{N} \qquad 70$$

and the interaction sum of squares comes from subtracting this from the sum of squares for sub-classes. The general arrangement of the analysis is as follows in 4 groups.

	DF
Total	$N-1$
$-$ Between sub-classes	$rc-1$
$=$ Error	$N-rc$
Between sub-classes	$rc-1$
$-$ Constants	$r+c-2$
$=$ Interaction	$(r-1)(c-1)$
Constants	$r+c-2$
$-$ *A* (unadjusted)	$r-1$
$=$ *B* (adjusted)	$c-1$
Constants	$r+c-2$
$-$ *B* (unadjusted)	$c-1$
$=$ *A* (adjusted)	$r-1$

Should the interaction prove to be significant and we are unable therefore to neglect it, the test of significance of the main effects should be carried out by the weighted squares of means. The method of calculation is identical with that for the $r \times 2$ table and does not require repetition. The actual calculations can be followed in the examples.

19. Example 14–3. Analysis of an $r \times 2$ table with disproportionate sub-class numbers. The data given in Table 14–4 are for the milk yields of dairy cows in 2 seasons, fall and winter, and spring and summer. The variation in numbers is due to the individual cow's not freshening with equal frequency in the two seasons. For example, cow 2 freshened 7 times in the fall and winter season and only once in the spring and summer.

From Table 14–4 we obtain the sums of squares for the preliminary analysis. This is

	SS	DF	MS	*F*	5% Point
Sub-classes	409,129	15	27,275	2.71	1.93
Error	402,860	40	10,072		
Total	811,989	55			

There is evidence that significant differences between sub-class means exist, so we proceed to a study first of the interaction effect, and then of the main effects. It is convenient to make a new table of numbers and totals as in Table 14–5, allowing a column for entering values of $n_{i1}/N_{i\cdot}$ and another for $a_i + m$ to be entered at a later stage in the calculations.

TABLE 14–4

DATA FOR MILK YIELDS, IN POUNDS, OF COWS FRESHENING IN 2 SEASONS

Cow	Fall and Winter			N_{i1}	S_{i1}	Spring and Summer			N_{i2}	S_{i2}
1	378	591		2	969	336	296		2	632
2	480	210	465	7	2447	262			1	262
	174	432	344							
	342									
3	471	356		2	827	228	312		2	540
7	404	168		2	572	343	170	192	4	890
						185				
9	141	135	158	5	880	139	155	245	3	539
	169	277								
11	534	423	287	7	2703	404	318	216	4	1280
	380	343	354			342				
	382									
21	290	376	518	3	1184	318	418	458	3	1194
27	573	501	402	4	1753	506	313	293	5	1701
	277					434	155			
Total				32	11335				24	7038

TABLE 14–5

SUMMARIZED DATA FROM TABLE 14–4

Cow	n_{i1}	S_{i1}	n_{i2}	S_{i2}	$N_{i\cdot}$	$S_{i\cdot}$	$n_{i1}/N_{i\cdot}$	$a_i + m$
1	2	969	2	632	4	1,601	0.500 000	400.250
2	7	2,447	1	262	8	2,709	0.875 000	312.888
3	2	827	2	540	4	1,367	0.500 000	341.750
7	2	572	4	890	6	1,462	0.333 333	255.105
9	5	880	3	539	8	1,419	0.625 000	168.796
11	7	2,703	4	1,280	11	3,983	0.636 364	352.732
21	3	1,184	3	1,194	6	2,378	0.500 000	396.333
27	4	1,753	5	1,701	9	3,454	0.444 444	387.591
Total	32	11,335	24	7,038	56	18,373		
	$N_{\cdot 1}$	$S_{\cdot 1}$	$N_{\cdot 2}$	$S_{\cdot 2}$	N	S		

We calculate first

$$C_1 = (0.500\,000 \times 1601) + (0.875\,000 \times 2709) + \cdots + (0.444\,444 \times 3454) = 10{,}487.33$$

$$C_{12} = (0.500\,000 \times 2) + (0.875\,000 \times 7) + \cdots + (0.444\,444 \times 4) = 12.351\,01$$

Then

$$b_1 = \frac{11{,}335 - 10{,}487.33}{2 \times 12.35101} = 34.3158$$

At this stage the interaction sum of squares can be calculated. For this we require

$$A \text{ (unadjusted)} = \frac{1601^2}{4} + \frac{2709^2}{8} + \cdots + \frac{3454^2}{9} - \frac{18{,}373^2}{56} = 315{,}516$$

and

$$B \text{ (adjusted)} = C_{12}(2b_1)^2 = 12.351\,01 \times (68.6316)^2 = 58{,}177$$

Then

$$\text{Interaction} = \text{(Sub-classes)} - B \text{ (adjusted)} - A \text{ (unadjusted)}$$
$$= 409{,}129 - 58{,}177 - 315{,}516 = 35{,}436$$

The mean square for interaction is 35,436/7 = 5062, and since the error mean square is 10,072 there is no evidence of an interaction and we can complete the analysis by fitting constants. The sum of squares for fitting the constants is

$$B \text{ (adjusted)} + A \text{ (unadjusted)}$$
$$58{,}177 + 315{,}516 = 373{,}693$$

We now calculate B (unadjusted).

$$\frac{(11{,}335 \times 24 - 7038 \times 32)^2}{32 \times 24 \times 56} = 50{,}979$$

Then, to obtain A (adjusted),

$$\text{Constants} - B \text{ (unadjusted)}$$
$$373{,}693 - 50{,}979 = 322{,}714$$

and the complete analysis can be set up.

	SS	DF	MS	F	5% Point
A	322,714	7	46,102	4.58	2.25
B	58,177	1	58,177	5.78	4.08
AB	35,436	7	5,062		
Error	402,860	40	10,072		

The A and B effects are both significant, so we shall calculate the values of $a_i + m$.

$$a_1 + m = \frac{1601 - (34.3158 \times 0)}{4} = 400.250$$

$$a_2 + m = \frac{2709 - (34.3158 \times 6)}{8} = 312.888$$

$$a_3 + m = \frac{1367}{4} = 341.750$$

$$a_4 + m = \frac{1462 + (34.3158 \times 2)}{6} = 255.105$$

and so forth.

Having calculated the constants, the method given above for calculating the sum of squares for the fitted constants can be verified. We take

$$\Sigma(a_i + m)S_{i\cdot} + b(S_{\cdot 1} - S_{\cdot 2}) - \frac{S^2}{N} = 6{,}254{,}222 + 147{,}455 - 6{,}027{,}984$$

$$= 373{,}693$$

which is in perfect agreement with the figure obtained above.

In the actual calculations it is desirable to follow a scheme as outlined below in order to keep the work to a minimum.

1. Calculate sums of squares for total (T) and sub-classes (U). Then $E = T - U$, and make preliminary analysis.
2. Calculate C_1 and C_{12} giving b_1. Then B_a, the adjusted sum of squares for B, $= C_{12}(2b_1)^2$.
3. Calculate A_u, the unadjusted sum of squares for A, and obtain adjusted sum of squares for interaction AB_a from $AB_a = U - (B_a + A_u)$.
4. Adjusted sum of squares for A, (A_a), is obtained from $A_a = B_a - B_u + A_u$.

If the interaction proves to be significant, it is desirable to make estimates of the main effects from the unweighted means and to test the significance of these by the method of weighted squares of means. The necessary calculations are as shown in Table 14–6. Note that the table as set up enables us to complete the analysis by the weighted squares of means. The columns headed $d_{i\cdot}$ and $w_{i\cdot}d_{i\cdot}$ are for the calculation of the interaction and would not be required if we had obtained this by fitting constants. The two procedures for obtaining the interaction are

TABLE 14–6

CALCULATION OF ANALYSIS OF VARIANCE COMPONENTS FOR AN 8 × 2 TABLE BY WEIGHTED SQUARES OF MEANS

	n_{i1}	$\bar{Y}_{i1}$	n_{i2}	$\bar{Y}_{i2}$	$\Sigma\left(\frac{1}{n}\right)$	$w_{i\cdot}$	$d_{i\cdot} = \bar{Y}_{i1} - \bar{Y}_{i2}$	$w_{i\cdot}d_{i\cdot}$	$\frac{\bar{Y}_{i1} + \bar{Y}_{i2}}{\bar{Y}_{i\cdot}^2}$	$w_{i\cdot}\bar{Y}_{i\cdot}$
	2	484.50	2	316.00						
$1/n$		0.500 000		0.500 000	1.000 000	1.000 00	168.50	168.500	400.250	400.250
	7	349.57	1	262.00						
$1/n$		0.142 857		1.000 000	1.142 857	0.875 00	87.57	76.624	305.785	267.562
	2	413.50	2	270.00						
$1/n$		0.500 000		0.500 000	1.000 000	1.000 00	143.50	143.500	341.750	341.750
	2	286.00	4	222.50						
$1/n$		0.500 000		0.250 000	0.750 000	1.333 33	63.50	84.666	254.250	338.999
	5	176.00	3	179.67						
$1/n$		0.200 000		0.333 333	0.533 333	1.875 00	− 3.67	− 6.881	177.835	333.441
	7	386.14	4	320.00						
$1/n$		0.142 857		0.250 000	0.392 857	2.545 46	66.14	168.357	353.070	898.726
	3	394.67	3	398.00						
$1/n$		0.333 333		0.333 333	0.666 666	1.500 00	− 3.33	− 4.995	396.335	594.502
	4	438.25	5	340.20						
$1/n$		0.250 000		0.200 000	0.450 000	2.222 22	98.05	217.889	389.225	864.944
$\Sigma\left(\frac{1}{n}\right)$		2.569 047		3.366 666		12.351 01		847.660		4040.174

$w_{\cdot j}$ 0.389 249 + 0.297 030 = 0.686 279

$\bar{Y}_{\cdot j}$ 366.079   288.546

$w_{\cdot j}\bar{Y}_{\cdot j}$ 142.496 + 85.707 = 228.203

algebraically identical. The weighted squares of means gives the following analysis.

$$AB = \Sigma(w_{i}.d_{i}.^2) - \frac{[\Sigma(w_{i}.d_{i}.)]^2}{\Sigma(w_{i}.)} = 93{,}611.79 - 58{,}175.60 = 35{,}436$$

$$A = 4\left\{\Sigma(w_{i}.\bar{Y}_{i}.^2) - \frac{[\Sigma(w_{i}.\bar{Y}_{i}.)]^2}{\Sigma(w_{i}.)}\right\} = 4(1{,}393{,}890.5 - 1{,}321{,}592.8)$$

$$= 289{,}191$$

$$B = 64\left\{\Sigma(w_{.j}\bar{Y}_{.j}^2) - \frac{[\Sigma(w_{.j}\bar{Y}_{.j})]^2}{\Sigma(w_{.j})}\right\} = 64(76{,}895.21 - 75{,}882.56)$$

$$= 64{,}810$$

	SS	DF	MS	F	5% Point
A	289,191	7	41.313	4.10	2.25
B	64,810	1	64,810	6.43	4.08
AB	35,436	7	5,062		
Error	402,860	40	10,072		

Since the interaction is small, the end result is very much the same as by the method of fitting constants.

20. Example 14–4. Analysis of an $r \times c$ table with disproportionate sub-class numbers. Table 14–7 presents in summary form data on the protein content of barley obtained in a survey made by the Grain Research Laboratory, Winnipeg. The B classification represents 3 grades, and the A classification 4 of the chief barley-producing areas of Manitoba.

TABLE 14–7

PROTEIN CONTENT OF BARLEY, IN PERCENTAGE, FOR SAMPLES OF 3 GRADES AND FROM 4 AREAS IN MANITOBA

	B_1 Grade 2		B_2 Grade 3		B_3 Grade 6	
A_1	$n_{11} = 9$	$S_{11} = 96.2$	$n_{12} = 39$	$S_{12} = 437.8$	$n_{13} = 36$	$S_{13} = 392.7$
A_2	$n_{21} = 41$	$S_{21} = 451.5$	$n_{22} = 145$	$S_{22} = 1628.5$	$n_{23} = 96$	$S_{23} = 1102.0$
A_3	$n_{31} = 10$	$S_{31} = 115.8$	$n_{32} = 27$	$S_{32} = 307.1$	$n_{33} = 105$	$S_{33} = 1207.9$
A_4	$n_{41} = 29$	$S_{41} = 328.2$	$n_{42} = 31$	$S_{42} = 359.8$	$n_{43} = 99$	$S_{43} = 1145.3$

The preliminary analysis of the data gave the following results.

	SS	DF	MS	F	5% Point
Sub-classes	29.7164	11	2.7015	4.98	1.81
Error	355.4828	655	0.54272		
Total	385.1992	666			

On setting up the means for the sub-classes as below, no very marked interaction is indicated, but at the same time it is difficult to come to the

10.69	11.23	10.91
11.01	11.23	11.48
11.58	11.37	11.50
11.32	11.61	11.57

conclusion that the interaction is negligible. A complete analysis beginning with the fitting of constants in order to make a test of significance of the interaction seems to be necessary. For this purpose the data are set up as in Table 14–8.

TABLE 14–8

	B							
	n_{i1}	n_{i2}	n_{i3}	$N_{i\cdot}$	$n_{i1}/N_{i\cdot}$	$n_{i2}/N_{i\cdot}$	$n_{i3}/N_{i\cdot}$	$S_{i\cdot}$
A	9	39	36	84	0.107 1429	0.464 2857	0.428 5714	926.7
	41	145	96	282	0.145 3901	0.514 1844	0.340 4255	3182.0
	10	27	105	142	0.070 4225	0.190 1408	0.739 4366	1630.8
	29	31	99	159	0.182 3899	0.194 9686	0.622 6415	1833.3
$N_{\cdot j}$	89	242	336	667 = N				
$S_{\cdot j}$	991.7	2733.2	3847.9					7572.8 = S

Referring to formulas (63), (64), and (65), we calculate

$$C'_1 = 1011.1410 - 991.7 = 19.4410 \qquad C'_{11} = 12.9188 - 89 = -76.0812$$

$$C'_2 = 2733.905870 - 2733.2 = 0.705870 \qquad C'_{22} = 103.8417 - 242 = -138.1583$$

$$C'_3 = 3827.7529 - 3847.9 = -20.1471 \qquad C'_{33} = 187.3918 - 336 = -148.6082$$

$$C_{12} = 32.8156 \qquad C_{13} = 43.2656 \qquad C_{23} = 105.3427$$

These values are substituted in the simultaneous equations (66).

$$19.4410 = b_1(-76.0812) + b_2(32.8156) + b_3(43.2656)$$

$$0.705870 = b_1(32.8156) + b_2(-138.1583) + b_3(105.3427)$$

$$-20.1471 = b_1(43.2656) + b_2(105.3427) + b_3(-148.6082)$$

$$-0.0002 \qquad 0.0000 \qquad 0.0000 \qquad 0.0001 \quad \text{(Sum of columns)}$$

The sums of the coefficients in each column should equal zero except for errors in rounding decimals.

The next step is the solution of these equations, applying equations (67), derived from $b_1 + b_2 + b_3 = 0$. This gives

$$19.4410 = b_1(-119.3468) + b_2(-10.4500)$$

$$0.705870 = b_1(-72.5271) + b_2(-243.5010)$$

A simple solution then comes from the determinant method.*

$$b_1 = \frac{\begin{vmatrix} 19.4410 & -10.4500 \\ 0.705870 & -243.5010 \end{vmatrix}}{\begin{vmatrix} -119.3468 & -10.4500 \\ -72.5271 & -243.5010 \end{vmatrix}} = \frac{-243.5010 \times 19.4410 + 10.4500 \times 0.705870}{119.3468 \times 243.5010 - 72.5271 \times 10.4500}$$

$$= -0.166996$$

Substituting b_1 in the first equation, we have

$$19.4410 = 0.166\,996 \times 119.3468 - b_2(10.4500)$$

giving

$$b_2 = \frac{0.4895}{10.4500} = 0.046\,833$$

Finally

$$b_3 = -b_1 - b_2 = 0.166\,996 - 0.046\,833 = 0.120\,163$$

As a check we can substitute the determined values of b_1, b_2, and b_3 in the simultaneous equations.

Although they may not be essential, we shall find also the values of the constants a_1, a_2, a_3, a_4, and m. The simplest method is to solve equations (69) for $a_i + m$.

$$a_1 + m = 11.032\,143 + 0.107\,142\,8 \times 0.107\,142\,8 \times 0.166\,996$$
$$- 0.464\,285\,7 \times 0.046\,842 - 0.428\,571\,4 \times 0.120\,154$$
$$= 10.9768$$

---

* Briefly stated, if

$$c_1 = b_1x_1 + b_2y_1$$
$$c_2 = b_1x_2 + b_2y_2$$

then

$$b_1 = \frac{\begin{vmatrix} c_1 & y_1 \\ c_2 & y_2 \end{vmatrix}}{\begin{vmatrix} x_1 & y_1 \\ x_2 & y_2 \end{vmatrix}} = \frac{c_1y_2 - c_2y_1}{x_1y_2 - x_2y_1}$$

Also

$$a_2 + m = 11.2430$$

$$a_3 + m = 11.3985$$

$$a_4 + m = 11.4767$$

The value of $\Sigma(a_i + m) = 45.0950$, and, since $\Sigma(a_i) = 0$, we have

$$m = \frac{45.0950}{4} = 11.2738$$

The next step is to obtain the sum of squares for the fitted constants.

$$\Sigma(a_i + m)S_{i.} + \Sigma(b_{.j}S_{.j}) - \frac{S^2}{N}$$

$$85{,}576.3345 + 424.7692 - 85{,}977.9608 = 23.1429$$

We then require

$$A \text{ (unadjusted)} = \frac{926.7^2}{84} + \cdots + \frac{1833.3^2}{159} - 85{,}977.9608 = 17.4500$$

$$B \text{ (unadjusted)} = \frac{991.7^2}{89} + \cdots + \frac{3847.9^2}{336} - 85{,}977.9608 = 8.0710$$

and we get the adjusted sums of squares as follows.

Sub-classes — Constants = Interaction

29.7164 — 23.1429 = 6.5735

Constants — A (unadjusted) = B (adjusted)

23.1429 — 17.4500 = 5.6929

Constants — B (unadjusted) = A (adjusted)

23.1429 — 8.0710 = 15.0719

The complete analysis can then be set up.

	SS	DF	MS	F	5% Point
A	15.0719	3	5.0240	9.26	2.62
B	5.6929	2	2.8464	5.24	3.01
AB	6.5735	6	1.0956	2.02	2.11
Error	355.4828	655	0.54272		

The F for the interaction mean square is barely equal to the 5% point, but the existence of an interaction is certainly not inconceivable in this example, based not only on the results of the analysis but also on our knowledge of the behavior of protein contents of barley grades in previous experience. It is worth while, therefore, to examine the results of estimating the main effects from the weighted means and their significance from the weighted squares of means.

The necessary calculations are given in Table 14–9.

$$A \quad 9\left\{\Sigma(w\bar{Y}^2) - \frac{[\Sigma(w\bar{Y})]^2}{\Sigma w}\right\} = 9(6377.8804 - 6376.2691)$$
$$= 9 \times 1.6113 = 14.5017$$

$$B \quad 16\left\{\Sigma(w\bar{Y}^2) - \frac{[\Sigma(w\bar{Y})]^2}{\Sigma w}\right\} = 16(3961.4736 - 3961.3245)$$
$$= 2.3856$$

AB (from method of fitting constants, see page 349) = 6.5735

Analysis—Weighted Squares of Means

	SS	DF	MS	F	5% Point
A	14.5017	3	4.8339	8.91	2.62
B	2.3856	2	1.1928	2.20	3.01
AB	6.5735	6	1.0956	2.02	2.11
Error	355.4828	655	0.54272		

This analysis leaves some doubt as to the significance of the differences between grades since the F value is reduced to below the 5% point.

21. Exercise.

1. Table 14–10 gives the weights and numbers of lambs from 3 breeds of sheep over a period of 7 years. The table is in two sections, the left section showing the numbers and the right section the corresponding sub-totals.

Use the method of fitting constants to set up an analysis of variance. From your results decide as to the suitability of the adjusted means for representing the effects of breed and season. If the adjusted means are not satisfactory, state the action that should be taken. The total sum of squares for the data is 113,232.0.

$b_1 = -6.3464$. $b_2 = -3.2066$. $b_3 = 9.5530$.

Mean squares are:	*Breeds*	*13,905*
	Years	*2,408.5*
	Interaction	*320.0*
	Error	*101.3*

TABLE 14–9

	n_{i1}	$\bar{Y}_{i1}$	n_{i2}	$\bar{Y}_{i2}$	N	$\bar{Y}_{i\cdot}$	$\Sigma\left(\frac{1}{n}\right)$	$w_{i\cdot}$	$\bar{Y}_{i\cdot}$	$w_{i\cdot}\bar{Y}_{i\cdot}$
	9	10.6889	39	11.2256	36	10.9083				
$1/n$	0.111 111 1		0.025 641 0		0.027 777 8		0.164 529 9	6.077 923	10.9409	66.4979
	41	11.0122	145	11.2310	96	11.4792				
$1/n$	0.024 390 2		0.006 896 6		0.010 416 7		0.041 703 5	23.978 803	11.2408	169.5409
	10	11.5800	27	11.3741	105	11.5038				
$1/n$	0.100 000 0		0.037 037 0		0.009 523 8		0.146 560 8	6.823 107	11.4860	78.3702
	29	11.3172	31	11.6065	99	11.5687				
$1/n$	0.034 482 8		0.032 258 1		0.010 101 0		0.076 841 9	13.013 733	11.4975	149.6254
$\Sigma\left(\frac{1}{n}\right)$	0.269 984 1		0.101 832 7		0.057 819 3		0.429 636 1	49.893 566		564.0344
$w_{\cdot j}$	3.703 922		9.820 028		17.295 263		30.819 213			
$\bar{Y}_{\cdot j}$	11.1496		11.3593		11.3650					
$w_{\cdot j}\bar{Y}_{\cdot j}$	41.2972		111.5486		196.5607		349.4065			

TABLE 14–10

WEIGHTS OF SINGLE FEMALE LAMBS FROM 3 BREEDS FOR 7 YEARS*

		Breed					Breed			
		A	*B*	*C*			*A*	*B*	*C*	
		n_{i1}	n_{i2}	n_{i3}	$N_{i\cdot}$		S_{i1}	S_{i2}	S_{i3}	$S_{i\cdot}$
Year 1	n_{1j}	8	22	5	35	S_{1j}	464	1,361	369	2,194
2	n_{2j}	14	40	52	106	S_{2j}	845	2,758	3,778	7,381
3	n_{3j}	13	36	57	106	S_{3j}	707	2,310	4,281	7,298
4	n_{4j}	6	23	66	95	S_{4j}	411	1,595	5,465	7,471
5	n_{5j}	11	24	47	82	S_{5j}	756	1,618	4,003	6,377
6	n_{6j}	9	20	55	84	S_{6j}	489	1,016	3,915	5,420
7	n_{7j}	18	27	83	128	S_{7j}	1,227	1,798	6,813	9,838
	$N_{\cdot j}$	79	192	365	636 $= N_{\cdot\cdot}$	$S_{\cdot j}$	4,899	12,456	28,624	45,979 $= S_{\cdot\cdot}$

REFERENCES

1. F. E. Allan and J. Wishart, *J. Agr. Sci.*, **20**, 399–406, 1930.
2. R. L. Anderson, *Biometrics*, **2**, 41–47, 1946.
3. M. S. Bartlett, *J. Roy. Stat. Soc. Suppl.*, **14**, 137–170, 1937.
4. W. G. Cochran and Gertrude M. Cox, *Experimental Designs*, John Wiley and Sons, New York, 1950.
5. G. W. Snedecor, *Statistical Methods*, Iowa State College Press, Ames, Iowa, 4th ed., 1946.
6. F. Yates, *J. Agr. Sci.*, **23**, 108–145, 1933.
7. F. Yates, *Empire J. Exptl. Agr.*, **1**, 129–142, 1933.
8. F. Yates, *J. Am. Stat. Assoc.*, **29**, 51–66, 1934.
9. F. Yates, *J. Agr. Sci.*, **26**, 301–315, 1936.
10. F. Yates and R. W. Hale, *J. Roy. Stat. Soc. Suppl.*, **6**, 66–79, 1939.

---

* Data by courtesy of Dr. K. Rasmussen, Experimental Station, Lethbridge, Alta.

CHAPTER 15

Goodness of Fit

1. Two types of data. Generally speaking, the data from experiments, surveys, etc., may be classified into two types. To these types Snedecor [6] has applied the terms *measurement* and *enumeration*. We obtain measurement data when we measure individual variates for characteristics such as weight, height, and yield. Enumeration data arises from recording the number of variates falling into certain classes that are either descriptive or numerical. The average yields for a set of fertilizer treatments would be typical measurement data. The numbers of white and brown chaff plants in a segregating population of wheat plants would be typical enumeration data. In this chapter and in Chapter 16 we are concerned chiefly with methods of estimation and the making of tests of significance for data of the enumeration type.

2. Tests of goodness of fit. In many problems the test of significance requires the making of a comparison between a set of actual and a set of theoretical frequencies, the latter having been set up in accordance with the hypothesis that we wish to test. In an experiment in genetics an F_2 sample may be classified into 2 groups, as in a wheat experiment in which the F_2 sample of 132 plants is classified into 107 that are resistant to stem rust and 25 susceptible. These numbers suggest a simple genetic hypothesis, namely, that rust resistance is dependent on one pair of genes, with the gene for resistance dominant in the heterozygous condition. In order to test this hypothesis we must determine how often, if the hypothesis is true, we can expect to obtain a result that diverges from theory as much or more than the one observed. This would constitute a test of the goodness of fit of the actual to the theoretical ratio.

3. Goodness of fit for twofold classifications—numbers small. In the example to which we have just referred, the plants were classified as resistant and susceptible, giving a typical twofold classification. Because of certain problems that are characteristic of tests of goodness of fit when we have only 2 classes, these are discussed first. In the first place we should note that the varying conditions that may effect the structure of the test are:

1. Number in the sample.
2. Symmetry of theoretical distribution.

Let us suppose first that the number (n) in the sample is small, say 20, which is setting up a purely arbitrary dividing line and does not in any sense make a strict division between small and large samples. For enumeration data such small samples are rather rare, but suppose that a medical doctor has a record of only 16 cases with respect to a given disease and finds that 12 of these are men and 4 women.* It is perfectly legitimate for him to ask: Is this merely a random variation or does the population having this disease contain more men than women? Since the theoretical ratio is 1 : 1, or 8 : 8 in the sample of 16, this is a problem of testing the goodness of fit of the actual frequencies 12 : 4 with the theoretical frequencies of 8 : 8. At this point the student will recall that we have already solved problems of this kind by means of the binomial distribution, (Chapter 3, Section 8). We require merely the separate probabilities of all possible ratios which are given by the terms of the expanded binomial $(p_1 + p_2)^n$, where p_1 is the probability that a given individual in the sample will be a man, p_2 that the individual will be a woman, and n is the number in the sample. In this example $n = 16$, $p_1 = p_2 = {}^1/_2$, and therefore the binomial to be expanded is $\left(\frac{1}{2} + \frac{1}{2}\right)^{16}$. The calculations are given in Example 15–1.

4. Example 15–1. Goodness of fit of a 12 : 4 ratio to the theoretical 8 : 8. The expansion of the binomial is

$$\left(\frac{1}{2}\right)^{16} + 16\left(\frac{1}{2}\right)^{16} + \frac{16!}{2!\,14!}\left(\frac{1}{2}\right)^{16} + \frac{16!}{3!\,13!}\left(\frac{1}{2}\right)^{16} + \cdots + \left(\frac{1}{2}\right)^{16}$$

and the terms are very readily obtained by means of a table of logarithms of numbers and logarithms of factorials. Note that $\left(\frac{1}{2}\right)^{16}$ is a constant term. On the machine $\left(\frac{1}{2}\right)^{16}$ is obtained directly by negative multiplication of $\log 2 = 0.301\,030\,0$ by 16. The machine reads 995.183 520 0

* The 16 cases must constitute a random selection from the population of patients suffering from the disease. Therefore any 16 cases available for study do not necessarily constitute a sample from which reliable results can be obtained. It is essential, for example, that men and women have an equal chance of being infected or included in the sample.

which can be written down directly as $\bar{5}.183\ 520\ 0$. We require only the first 5 terms of the expansion as given below.

Number of Men	Probability of a Particular Ratio	P
16	0.000 015	0.000 015
15	0.000 244	0.000 259
14	0.001 831	0.000 290
13	0.008 545	0.010 635
12	0.027 771	0.038 406

In the third column P is the sum of the probabilities in the tail of the distribution. Thus 0.002 90 is the sum of the probabilities of the ratios 14 : 2, 15 : 1, and 16 : 0.

The data obtained enable us to test two different hypotheses. The probability 0.038 406 gives directly what is frequently referred to as a "one-tail" test. It tells us that, if a large number of samples of 16 are taken, the probability that the sample will contain 12 or more men is 0.0384. The implication in this example is that men are more likely to contract the disease than women, and the hypothesis to be tested is that, in the population sampled, *men are not more frequent than women.* Setting up our level of significance at the 5% point, we decide that the data tend to disprove the hypothesis. To test the validity of the reasoning in this problem and all problems wherein we have to decide between a one-tail and a two-tail test, it is useful to imagine the consequences of dealing with a large number of similar samples. It is clear that only 3.8% of the samples will have more men than the one corresponding to the 5% point; all others will have less and will be in agreement with the hypothesis. The samples that agree with the hypothesis will include those having 0 men and 16 women, 1 man and 15 women, and others which show a definite tendency in the opposite direction, but we are not testing for such a tendency and hence these samples are regarded as merely agreeing with the hypothesis.

The other hypothesis to be tested is that there is an equal sex ratio with respect to the incidence of the disease. The hypothesis is that men and women occur in equal numbers in the population sampled. On this basis we must consider both tails of the distribution because extremes in either direction disagree with the hypothesis. Our probability would be $0.0384 \times 2 = 0.0768$, and taking the level of significance at the 5% point we would have to conclude that the data were not violently in disagreement with the hypothesis, but open to question.

The question of which type of test to make is one that has caused considerable confusion, mainly on account of a lack of a clear understanding of the hypothesis to be tested. Suppose, for example, that we decide to test the first of the two hypotheses mentioned. Then we proceed to investigate a series of such samples, and to those that contain a preponderance of women we apply the same test in the opposite sense. Clearly we are utilizing for each test only one-half of the binomial distribution and as a result our level of significance should be set at the 2.5% point rather than at the 5% point.

Tests of goodness of fit when the classification is twofold can always be made by means of the binomial distribution, but we are confined in the exact method that has been outlined to examples in which the numbers are small. With large numbers the computations are onerous unless there are only a very few probabilities to compute at one tail of the distribution, and in that event the result would be obviously significant and the calculation of probabilities unnecessary.

With binomial distributions for which $p_1 \neq p_2$ and which are therefore skewed, the procedure is the same as given for the symmetrical binomial, but for a two-tailed test we have to calculate probabilities at both tails. For example, with $n = 20$, $p_1 = 3/4$, $p_2 = 1/4$, the theoretical ratio would be 15 : 5. For a sample giving a ratio of 18 : 2, the two-tailed test would involve the probabilities for the ratios 20 : 0, 19 : 1, 18 : 2, at one end, and 0 : 20, 1 : 19, · · ·, 12 : 8 at the other end. This would be a test of the probability of a deviation from the theoretical as great or greater than ± 3.

5. Goodness of fit for twofold classifications—numbers moderate to large. When the numbers are moderate to large, the most convenient goodness of fit test arises from the fact that the binomial distribution approximates to the normal distribution. This is true regardless of the inequality of p_1 and p_2; that is, as the numbers increase the binomial distribution approaches the normal even if $p_1 \neq p_2$, but if $p_1 = p_2$ the approach to the normal is more rapid and holds quite well for goodness of fit tests even when the numbers are small.

The approach of the binomial to the normal distribution for the case $p_1 \neq p_2$ can be gauged quite accurately by means of α_3, the measure of skewness discussed in Chapter 3, Section 8. We have

$$\alpha_3 = \frac{p_2 - p_1}{\sqrt{np_1p_2}} \qquad 1$$

and it is clear that if $p_1 = p_2$ the skewness is zero. If $p_1 \neq p_2$, however, the value of α_3 decreases fairly rapidly with increasing values of n.

To make a goodness of fit test we calculate first the theoretical ratio $t_1 : t_2$ and determine $|a_1 - t_1|$ or $|a_2 - t_2|$ where a_1, a_2 are the actual frequencies corresponding to the theoretical frequencies. Then we obtain

$$s = \sqrt{np_1p_2} \qquad 2$$

and

$$d = \frac{|a_1 - t_1|}{s} \qquad 3$$

which may be defined as the *relative deviate*. The significance of d is determined by entering the table of the probability integral and finding

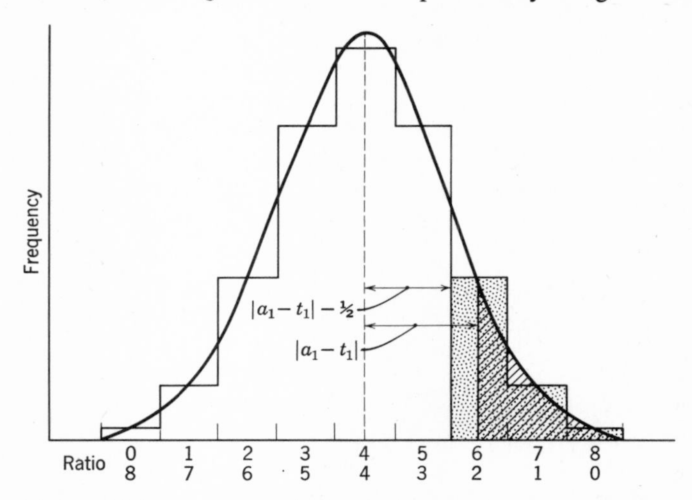

FIGURE 15–1. Frequency distribution of $(\frac{1}{2} + \frac{1}{2})^8$ and corresponding smooth curve. Shaded areas indicate the need for a correction to χ^2 for small samples.

the area of the normal curve beyond that point. If the table gives $^1/_2(1 + \alpha)$ we find $1 - {}^1/_2(1 + \alpha)$ for a one-tail test and $2[1 - {}^1/_2(1 + \alpha)]$ for a two-tail test.

Thus far, however, the assumption is of a closer agreement between the histogram of the binomial distribution and the smooth normal curve than is actually the case. Reference to Figure 15–1 illustrates this point. It represents the distribution obtained on expanding the binomial $\left(\frac{1}{2} + \frac{1}{2}\right)^8$.
The probability of 6 or more successes in a trial of 8 events would be given by the ratio of the dotted area to that of the whole. If a test based on the smooth normal curve is made, the probability would be the ratio of the cross-hatched area to the whole. This is evidently less than the dotted area by an amount equal approximately to one-half the area of the 6 : 2 ratio column. Consequently the calculated probability will be

too low. It is also clear from the figure that an approximate correction for the discrepancy can be made by calculating the required probability from the area underneath the smooth curve to the right of the line bordering the 5 : 3 and 6 : 2 columns. This will be given as indicated in the figure by taking $| a_1 - t_1 | - 1/2$ as the measure of the deviation from the theoretical. The working formula for the relative deviate will be

$$d = \frac{| a_1 - t_1 | - \frac{1}{2}}{s} \qquad 4$$

The work may be shortened slightly by writing equation (4) in the form

$$d = \frac{| a_1 - ra_2 | - (r + 1)/2}{\sqrt{r(a_1 + a_2)}} \qquad 5$$

where $r = t_1/t_2 = p_1/p_2$.

As the numbers become large there is less necessity for the correction, but in any event there will be a slight improvement, and consequently the making of the correction should be a routine procedure. The only exception to this will be demonstrated in connection with a method to be described later wherein the discrepancies for a series of ratios are summated and wherein the correction should not be made (see Section 9).

With the method just described for testing goodness of fit it is also possible to set up fiducial limits. From equation (4) and taking $d_{0.05} = 1.96$ from tables of the probability integral of the normal curve, we have

$$| a_1 - t_1 | = d_{0.05}s + \tfrac{1}{2}$$

Then l_1 and l_2 for a_1 are

$$l_1 = t_1 + d_{0.05}s + \tfrac{1}{2}$$
$$l_2 = t_1 - d_{0.05}s - \tfrac{1}{2} \qquad 6$$

The methods described for testing goodness of fit and setting up fiducial limits for a twofold classification where the numbers are moderate to large are applied in Example 15–2.

6. Example 15–2. Goodness of fit and fiducial limits for a twofold table —numbers moderate to large. The family of wheat plants referred to in the test above gave 107 resistant and 25 susceptible plants. This is to provide a test of the hypothesis that the genetic factor basis is such as to give a 3 : 1 ratio. Therefore $n = 132$, $p_1 = 0.75$, and $p_2 = 0.25$. Then

$$s = \sqrt{132 \times 0.75 \times 0.25} = 4.975$$

$$d = \frac{| 107 - 99 | - \frac{1}{2}}{4.975} = \frac{7.5}{4.975} = 1.51$$

Entering the tables of the probability integral, we find that 1.51 corresponds to $\alpha/2 = 0.4345$; therefore $P = 2 \times (0.5 - 0.4345) = 0.1310$. Although the fit is not particularly good, there is not sufficient information to disprove the hypothesis that the inheritance of rust resistance is based on a single pair of genes.

To obtain fiducial limits at the 5% point we look up $d_{0.05}$ in the tables corresponding to $P = 0.05$. The value is 1.96. Then

$$l_1 = 107 + 1.96 \times 4.975 + \tfrac{1}{2} = 117$$

$$l_2 = 107 - 1.96 \times 4.975 - \tfrac{1}{2} = 97$$

The approximate ratios for the fiducial limits are 117 : 15 and 97 : 35.

7. Goodness of fit—2 or more classes. For a large proportion of the problems involving goodness of fit the number of classes is greater than 2. For example in a genetic problem involving 2 pairs of genes the theoretical ratio may be 9 : 3 : 3 : 1. In comparing the goodness of fit of an actual frequency distribution to the theoretical normal the number of classes may be as large as 20. For the general case we assume 1, 2, 3, $\cdots$, k classes for which the corresponding probabilities are $p_1, p_2, p_3, \cdots, p_k$, and the total frequency is n. On this basis it is seen that the binomial distribution with only 2 classes is merely a special case. Just as the theoretical frequencies when we have only 2 classes are given by the expansion of the binomial $(p_1 + p_2)^n$, the theoretical frequencies for the general case are given by the terms of the expansion of the multinomial

$$(p_1 + p_2 + p_3 + \cdots + p_k)^n$$

The general term is

$$\left(\frac{n!}{n_1!n_2!n_3! \cdots n_k!}\right) p_1^{n_1} p_2^{n_2} p_3^{n_3} \cdots p_k^{n_k} \qquad 7$$

For example, if we have a population of black, white, and red balls in the ratio 1 : 2 : 1 we can set up

p_1 (probability of drawing a black ball) $= \frac{1}{4}$

p_2 (probability of drawing a white ball) $= \frac{1}{2}$

p_3 (probability of drawing a red ball) $= \frac{1}{4}$

Then, on drawing a sample of 8 balls, the probability of getting 1 black, 3 white, and 4 red is

$$\frac{8!}{1! \times 3! \times 4!}\left(\frac{1}{4}\right)\left(\frac{1}{2}\right)^3\left(\frac{1}{4}\right)^4 = 0.03418$$

For a particular problem with more than 2 classes the multinomial expansion enables us to determine the probability of each of the possible combinations as we did by means of the binomial expansion for 2 classes. However, one of the difficulties in making tests of goodness of fit is to classify the different combinations with respect to the degree of divergence from the theoretical. The binomial problem was simple because we could represent the theoretical and actual frequencies by means of a 2-dimensional graph. With 3 classes we require a 3-dimensional graph and for more than 3 classes the problem is one of N-dimensional geometry. This problem can best be visualized by setting up the possible combinations for a problem in which n is small and there are only 3 classes. Suppose that $n = 6$ and $p_1 = p_2 = p_3 = {}^1/_3$. The possible combinations and the corresponding probabilities are worked out below. For convenience the classes are represented by A, B, C.

Combinations *ABC*	Probability	Combinations *ABC*	Probability	Combinations *ABC*	Probability
6 0 0 0 6 0 0 0 6	0.001 372	4 2 0 4 0 2 0 4 2 2 4 0 0 2 4 2 0 4	0.020 576	4 1 1 1 4 1 1 1 4	0.041 152
5 1 0 5 0 1 0 5 1 1 5 0 1 0 5 0 1 5	0.008 230	3 3 0 3 0 3 0 3 3	0.027 435	3 2 1 3 1 2 1 3 2 2 3 1 1 2 3 2 1 3	0.082 304
				2 2 2	0.123 457

The theoretical ratio being 2 : 2 : 2 for a sample of 6 drawn from a population for which $p_1 = p_2 = p_3 = {}^1/_3$, a sample such as 1 : 4 : 1 would represent deviations of -1, $+2$, and -1, and to locate such a sample on a graph would require a 3-dimensional figure taking one axis for A, one for B, and one for C. The selection of the samples having a given divergence from the theoretical is a problem therefore of defining a region within which all samples would agree with the hypothesis and outside of which all samples would disagree. This is not a simple problem, and it is unnecessary to go into it in detail here. For an excellent discussion of this point the student is referred to Smith and Duncan [5], Chapter XIII. However, even assuming a simple solution to the problem of defining regions of rejection and acceptance of the hypothesis, the computations would be tremendous for appreciable values of n and k.

The solution of our difficulty came with the discovery of the χ^2 (chi square) distribution by Karl Pearson [4]. Its application to general problems involving various numbers of classes and with varying linear restrictions on the calculation of the theoretical frequencies was clarified by R. A. Fisher [2] who pointed out the necessity of taking the degrees of freedom into consideration. Pearson derived the theoretical distribution for the statistic χ^2 given by

$$\chi^2 = \Sigma \left\{ \frac{(m_i - n_i p_i)^2}{n_i p_i} \right\} \tag{8}$$

where n_i represents the numbers in the 1, 2, 3, $\cdots$, i, $\cdots$, k classes for which the probabilities are $p_1, p_2, p_3, \cdots, p_i, \cdots, p_k$. Thus the values of $n_i p_i$ are the theoretical and m_i are the actual frequencies. In general we shall take $a_1, a_2, \cdots, a_i, \cdots, a_k$ to represent the actual frequencies, and $t_1, t_2, \cdots, t_i, \cdots, t_k$ the theoretical frequencies,* so that

$$\chi^2 = \Sigma \left\{ \frac{(a_i - t_i)^2}{t_i} \right\} \tag{9}$$

By means of the statistic χ^2 the problem of testing goodness of fit with more than 2 classes is very much simplified since the distribution can be represented in the usual manner in 2 dimensions.

In the derivation of χ^2 from the multinomial distribution the necessity arises of substituting "Stirling's approximation" for factorial expressions. This approximation holds only when the factorials are large; hence the χ^2 distribution is not accurate when the theoretical frequencies are small. The general rule is not to have theoretical frequencies fewer than 5. This is accomplished by keeping the numbers dealt with as large as possible, but should low theoretical frequencies occur in any event it is desirable to rearrange the table by combining classes or, in certain cases, by eliminating the low frequency classes entirely. A full discussion of this point is given by Cochran [1] wherein it will be noted that setting the minimum for a theoretical frequency at 5 is being quite conservative. Cochran also describes methods of obtaining a reliable test when not more than one of the theoretical frequencies is quite small.

8. The χ^2 test for goodness of fit—2 classes. The test described in Section 5 for a twofold classification is fully adequate and gives the same result as the χ^2 test. However, there are certain practical and theoretical advantages in the application of χ^2 that will be brought out as we proceed.

---

* t will always be represented with a subscript and therefore is not to be confused with the statistic t.

χ^2 for 2 classes is equal to the square of d of Section 5. Therefore we have

$$\chi^2 = \frac{(a_1 - ra_2)^2}{r(a_1 + a_2)} \tag{10}$$

As in calculating d, it is necessary to apply the correction for continuity; hence the corrected χ_c^2 is given by

$$\chi_c^2 = \frac{\left[|\,a_1 - ra_2\,| - \left(\frac{r+1}{2}\right)\right]^2}{r(a_1 + a_2)} \tag{11}$$

The necessity of making this correction was first pointed out by Yates [7]. In this paper Yates discusses the need for the correction not only to a χ^2 based on 1 degree of freedom but to a χ^2 based on 2 or more degrees of freedom. A further discussion of the need and methods of applying the correction is given by Cochran [1].

For the simple twofold table there is only 1 degree of freedom for the estimation of χ^2. This follows from the fact that the total is fixed, i.e., we are concerned with the possible variation in samples of size $(a_1 + a_2)$. In such samples only one of the frequencies can be varied at will; hence we have only 1 degree of freedom.

For purposes of illustration we shall apply the χ^2 test to the data of Example 15–2. Here we have $a_1 = 107$, $a_2 = 25$, and $r = 3$. Then

$$\chi^2 = \frac{\left[(107 - 3 \times 25) - \frac{4}{2}\right]^2}{3 \times 132} = 2.27$$

In order to determine the corresponding probability we enter Table A–4 under $n = 1$ and note that P is approximately half-way between 0.20 and 0.10. The actual value as determined in Example 15–2 is 0.13.

It should be noted that the practical advantage here in calculating χ^2 as compared to calculating d is that it is not necessary to extract a square root.

9. The χ^2 test of heterogeneity and the addition theorem. An important property of the χ^2 distribution is that the sum of a series of independently determined values is itself distributed as χ^2 with degrees of freedom obtained from the sum of the degrees of freedom for the independent components. Thus, for a series of k samples,

Sample						Total
1	2	$\cdots$	i	$\cdots$	k	
a_{11}	a_{21}	$\cdots$	a_{i1}	$\cdots$	a_{k1}	A_1
a_{12}	a_{22}	$\cdots$	a_{i2}	$\cdots$	a_{k2}	A_2

each of these will provide a value of χ_i^2 estimated with 1 degree of freedom. Similarly we have

$$\chi_t^2 = \frac{(A_1 - rA_2)^2}{r(A_1 + A_2)} \quad 12$$

also estimated with 1 degree of freedom, and

$$\chi_s^2 = \Sigma(\chi_i^2) \quad 13$$

representing k degrees of freedom. We can now write

$$\chi_h^2 = \chi_s^2 - \chi_t^2 \quad 14$$

and the corresponding equation for degrees of freedom is

$$(k - 1) = k - 1 \quad 15$$

The value of χ_h^2 will be related to the variation in the ratios $a_{i1} : a_{i2}$. If these are all alike, $\chi_h^2 = 0$. If they are widely different, χ_h^2 becomes large. It is a measure of heterogeneity and is frequently referred to as the "heterogeneity" χ^2.

In connection with the test for heterogeneity the correction for continuity should not be made in obtaining the values of χ_i^2 that are summated (Cochran [1]). If a test of significance is to be applied to individual ratios or to χ_t^2, it is desirable to make the correction, but the addition theorem does not hold for corrected values.

Example 15–3 illustrates the points brought out in this section and also a convenient method of calculating the heterogeneity χ_h^2, given by Snedecor [6].

Since the distribution of χ^2 is dependent on the number of degrees of freedom, in theory we require a different probability table for each degree of freedom from 1 to ∞. The table prepared by Fisher [2] (Table A–4) overcomes this difficulty for practical purposes by giving the values of χ^2 for a series of different probability levels. Thus for 2 degrees of freedom the χ^2 and corresponding values of P for a few levels are

P	0.99	0.95	0.90	0.50	0.10	0.05	0.01	0.001
χ^2	0.02	0.10	0.21	1.39	4.60	5.99	9.21	13.82

For a particular problem, if we get a χ^2 of 7.21 we know that P is between 0.05 and 0.01, and this is sufficiently accurate for ordinary tests of significance.

The tables are made up for a range of degrees of freedom from 1 to 30. Beyond 30, we can make use of the fact that $\sqrt{2\chi^2}$ is approximately normally distributed about a mean of $\sqrt{2n - 1}$ with unit standard deviation, where n represents the degrees of freedom. This means that the relative deviate for entering the tables of the normal curve (Table A–1) is $\sqrt{2\chi^2} - \sqrt{2n-1}$.

10. Example 15–3. Goodness of fit for sex ratios with multiple classification. The data in Table 15–1 are numbers of male and female sawflies (*Cephus sp.*) emerging from wheat stubble. Counts were made on a number of varieties at several stations, and the data given are for the first 4 varieties at 2 stations.

TABLE 15–1*

FREQUENCY OF MALE AND FEMALE SAWFLIES EMERGING FROM WHEAT STUBBLE

	Swift Current		Scott		Both Stations	
Variety	Male	Female	Male	Female	Male	Female
1	574	369	503	459	1077	828
2	80	105	54	132	134	237
3	86	60	107	81	193	141
4	109	95	100	85	209	180
Total	849	629	764	757	1613	1386

We shall inquire first into the goodness of fit of the individual ratios to the theoretical 1 : 1 which is believed to be the situation existing in the normal wild population. The data indicate that the varieties have an effect on the sex ratio, and evidence of this can be obtained by a study of the heterogeneity of χ^2. It is convenient to list the values of χ^2 corresponding to the data in Table 15–1. These are given below.

	Variety	Swift Current	Scott	Both Stations	DF
	1	44.565**	2.012	32.546**	1
	2	3.378	32.710**	28.596**	1
	3	4.630*	3.596	8.096**	1
	4	0.961	1.216	2.162	1
Total	χ^2	53.534**	39.534**	71.400**	4
Pooled	χ_t^2	32.747**	0.032	17.182**	1
Heterogeneity	χ_h^2	20.787**	39.502**	54.218**	3

The χ^2's that exceed the 5% point are marked with a single asterisk, and those exceeding the 1% point with a double asterisk. The results for the heterogeneity χ_h^2 leave no room for doubt with respect to the differential

* Unpublished data furnished by A. W. Platt.

effect of the varieties on the sex ratio. At least there is some factor causing a serious disturbance in the theoretical 1 : 1 ratio, and this would appear to be a varietal effect. The results at Scott emphasize the need of care in interpreting the total χ_s^2. This total exceeds the 1% point, but we note that the greater portion of this is due to variety 2. For the other 3 varieties the fit to a 1 : 1 is reasonably good.*

A further test can be made with respect to the effect of environment on the sex ratio. In each line we can total the χ^2's for the 2 stations, and on subtracting the value obtained for the stations combined we have a measure of heterogeneity due to environment. The results are tabulated below.

Variety	Total	Both Stations	Heterogeneity
1	46.577	32.546	14.031**
2	36.088	28.596	7.492**
3	8.226	8.096	0.130
4	2.177	2.162	0.015
DF in each line =	2	1	1

For varieties 1 and 2 there is marked evidence of heterogeneity in the ratios at the 2 stations.

A convenient calculation procedure for the heterogeneity χ^2 when we wish to obtain it directly is given by Snedecor [6]. It is outlined below for the Swift Current data from Table 15–1.

	Number of Flies	Females	Proportion of Females
	N	a_1	p
	943	369	0.391 304
	185	105	0.567 568
	146	60	0.410 959
	204	95	0.465 686
Total	1478	629	0.425 575 $= \bar{p} = \frac{629}{1478}$

* Certain points should be noted in the analysis given above for the data of Table 15–1. In the first place it might be argued that a test of the heterogeneity of the ratios with respect to their fit to a 1 : 1 ratio is not logical at least for the Swift Current data, in view of the apparent contradiction of the totals of 849 male to 629 female flies. A test based on a 1 : 1 ratio is, however, the test having the most specific meaning here, as there is a definite expectation of equal numbers of males and females. In addition, it should be noted that having established heterogeneity a more correct test of the pooled χ^2 is one based on its relation to the heterogeneity χ^2. The latter can be converted into a variance based on 3 degrees of freedom and a test carried out as in the analysis of variance. Here, 20.787/3 = 6.929. Then $F = 32.747/6.929 = 4.73$, which is not significant for $n_1 = 1$ and $n_2 = 3$ degrees of freedom.

We calculate

$$\Sigma(a_1 p) = 272.8835$$
$$\Sigma(a_1)\bar{p} = 267.6867$$
$$\Sigma(a_1 p) - \Sigma(a_1)\bar{p} = \quad 5.1968$$

Then

$$\chi_h^2 = \frac{\Sigma(a_1 p) - \Sigma(a_1)\bar{p}}{PQ} = \frac{5.1968}{0.50 \times 0.50} = 20.787$$

where P and Q represent the probabilities $^1/_2$ and $^1/_2$ for the theoretical 1 : 1 ratio.

11. Example 15–4. Goodness of fit to a 9 : 3 : 3 : 1 ratio. In a cross between parents of the genetic constitution *BBcc* and *bbCC*, the F_2 sample is classified as follows. The first row represents the actual and the second row the theoretical frequencies according to a 9 : 3 : 3 : 1 ratio.

	BC	*Bc*	*Cb*	*cb*	Total
Actual	1260	625	610	5	2500
Theoretical	1406.25	468.75	468.75	156.25	2500
Deviations	– 146.25	156.25	141.25	– 151.25	0

The actual results differ quite widely from the theoretical, and χ^2 calculated as follows is quite large.

$$\chi^2 = \frac{146.25^2}{1406.25} + \frac{156.25^2}{468.75} + \frac{141.25^2}{468.75} + \frac{151.25^2}{156.25} = 256.2667$$

On examining the data for the source of the disturbance, we see that the end classes are deficient and the middle classes too large. This is an indication of linkage, so we proceed to analyze the data further. Fisher [2] gives a method that is particularly appropriate here for dividing the total χ^2 into 3 components, each representing 1 degree of freedom. If the observed frequencies are a_1, a_2, a_3, a_4, the χ^2 components represented by B, C, and linkage are

$$B \qquad \frac{[(a_1 + a_2) - 3(a_3 + a_4)]^2}{3n}$$

$$C \qquad \frac{[(a_1 + a_3) - 3(a_2 + a_4)]^2}{3n}$$

$$\text{Linkage} \qquad \frac{[a_1 - 3a_2 - 3a_3 + 9a_4]^2}{9n}$$

The figures are

$$
\begin{array}{lcl}
B & \dfrac{40^2}{7500} = & 0.2133 \\[2ex]
C & \dfrac{-20^2}{7500} = & 0.0533 \\[2ex]
\text{Linkage} & \dfrac{-2400^2}{22{,}500} = & 256.0000 \\[1ex]
\hline
\text{Total} & = & 256.2666
\end{array}
$$

It would seem suitable in this example to set up a hypothesis based on linkage. From the actual frequencies, applying a method given by Fisher and Balkmukand [3], we estimate that there is 9% crossing over and on this basis calculate a new set of theoretical frequencies and determine a new value of χ^2. The calculations are given below.

Class	Actual Frequency	Theoretical Frequency	$(a-t)^2/t$
BC	1260	1255	0.0199
Bc	625	620	0.0403
cB	610	620	0.1613
bc	5	5	0.0000
	Total	χ^2 =	0.2215

The theoretical frequencies for this test are obtained by using the figure of 9% crossing over which is calculated from the sample. This absorbs 1 degree of freedom; therefore we have only 2 degrees of freedom left for the estimation of χ^2. From Table A–4 we find that the 5% point of χ^2 for 2 degrees of freedom is 5.99. Therefore there is no question of disagreement with the hypothesis. In fact the value of P is close to 0.90, and as close a fit would be expected in only 10% of the trials. This is not a sufficiently close fit, however, to give us much concern.*

12. Exercises.

1. Test the goodness of fit of observation to theory for the following ratios. Calculate χ^2 to 3 decimal places for each ratio, making the correction for continuity, and look up the approximate values of P from Table A–4. Then determine $\sqrt{\chi^2} = \chi$ for

* Very close fits are generally to be regarded with suspicion as they usually reflect some unnatural condition either in the design of the experiment or the manner in which the data are obtained. Note that the ideal good fit gives $P = 0.5$.

each ratio to 2 decimal places and, entering tables of the probability integral, Table A–1, determine the corresponding values of P to 4 decimal places.

Sample	Observed		Theoretical Ratio	*Approximate*	*Exact*
	a_1	a_2	r	P	P
1	134	36	3	*0.30*	*0.2892*
2	240	120	3	< 0.01	*0.0004*
3	76	56	1	*0.10*	*0.0990*
4	240	13	15	> 0.50	*0.5484*

2. Find the fiducial limits for the ratios in Exercise 1.

(1) 146:24 and 122:48. (2) 257:103 and 223:137.
(3) 88:44 and 64:68. (4) 248:5 and 232:21.

3. In a certain cross the types represented by *BC*, *Bc*, *bC*, and *bc* are expected to occur in a 9 : 3 : 3 : 1 ratio. The observed frequencies were

BC	*Bc*	*bC*	*bc*
102	16	35	7

Determine the goodness of fit, and if the fit is poor analyze the data further to disclose the source of the discrepancy. See Example 15–4.

Total $\chi^2 = 9.87$. $P = 0.02$. *Components:* B $\chi^2 = 0.133$. $P = 0.70$.
C $\chi^2 = 9.633$. $P = < 0.01$.
Linkage $\chi^2 = 0.100$. $P = 0.75$.

4. The data given below represent segregations in 3 families of the same cross. Test the goodness of fit of each family to a 9 : 3 : 3 : 1 ratio and determine the heterogeneity χ^2.

Family	*AB*	*Ab*	*aB*	*ab*
1	94	25	26	15
2	102	17	36	5
3	72	43	39	6

$\chi_h^2 = 26.34$.

REFERENCES

1. W. G. Cochran, *Iowa State College J. Sci.*, **16**, 421–436, 1942.
2. R. A. Fisher, *Statistical Methods for Research Workers*, Oliver and Boyd, Edinburgh and London, 10th ed., 1948.
3. R. A. Fisher and Bhai Balkmukand, *J. Genetics*, **20**, 79–92, 1928.
4. K. Pearson, *Phil. Mag.*, **V, 1**, 157–175, 1900.
5. James G. Smith and A. J. Duncan, *Sampling Statistics and Applications*, McGraw-Hill Book Co., New York, 1945.
6. G. W. Snedecor, *Statistical Methods*, Iowa State College Press, Ames, Iowa, 4th ed., 1946.
7. F. Yates, *J. Roy. Stat. Soc. Suppl.*, **1**, 217–235, 1934.

CHAPTER 16

Tests of Independence

1. The nature of tests of independence. When enumeration data are classified in two ways, the data may indicate a state of dependence of one classification on the other. Table 16–1 contains data on 82 strains of oats which are divided into 2 groups according to the presence or absence

TABLE 16–1

CLASSIFICATION OF 82 STRAINS OF OATS FOR YIELD AND PRESENCE OR ABSENCE OF AWNS

	Yield Class, Weight in Grams			
	151–200	201–250	251–325	Total
Awned	6	7	21	34
Awnless	18	21	9	48
Total	24	28	30	82

of awns and into 3 groups for yield. On examining the frequencies we observe a tendency for more of the awned strains to occur in the high-yielding classes than the awnless strains. To test the significance of a result of this sort we have to find the theoretical frequencies for the 6 cells of the table on the assumption that the classes are independent. The basis for the calculation of the theoretical frequencies must be the marginal totals. In other words we say that, on the assumption of complete independence, the frequencies in the cells should be proportional to both sets of marginal totals. For example, in the cell containing 6 strains, if we let t_{11} be the theoretical frequency, then $t_{11} : 24 :: 34 : 82$, giving $t_{11} = (24 \times 34)/82 = 9.9512$. Similarly for all cells the products of the corresponding marginal totals, divided by the grand total, give the theoretical frequencies. Representing the actual frequencies by a, we have

$$\chi^2 = \Sigma \left[\frac{(a - t)^2}{t} \right] \qquad 1$$

It is worth while to inquire closely into the nature of the extremely interesting and practical test of significance arising from this procedure.

In the first place the marginal totals are accepted as part of the hypothesis, and consequently we are not testing anything in connection with them. For a population in which the distribution in the classes is as shown by the marginal totals and the classes are independent, we are asking what proportion of a large series of samples of 82 strains each will deviate as much or more from the theoretical as the one observed. This should clear up any difficulty that may present itself in connection with the method of calculating the theoretical frequencies. It is also obvious from these considerations that the frequencies in the margins together with the grand total are restrictions on degrees of freedom in the table. To find the number of degrees of freedom remaining for the estimation of χ^2 all we have to do is to see how many of the cells of the table can be filled up arbitrarily. On trying this for Table 16–1 we find that after 2 of the cells are filled the remainder are fixed, leaving 2 degrees of freedom. In general in an $r \times c$ table there are $(r-1)(c-1)$ degrees of freedom for the estimation of χ^2 in a test of independence.

2. Calculation of χ^2 in $r \times c$ tables when r and c are both > 2. The generalized table may be represented as follows.

	Column				Total
Row	a_{11}	a_{12}	$a_{13} \cdots$	a_{1c}	R_1
	a_{21}	a_{22}	$a_{23} \cdots$	a_{2c}	R_2
	$\vdots$	$\vdots$	$\vdots$	$\vdots$	$\vdots$
	a_{r1}	a_{r2}	$a_{r3} \cdots$	a_{rc}	R_r
Total	C_1	C_2	$C_3 \cdots$	C_c	G

The corresponding theoretical frequencies are $t_{11}, t_{12}, \cdots, t_{rc}$, which are calculated from

$$t_{11} = \frac{R_1 C_1}{G}$$

$$t_{12} = \frac{R_1 C_2}{G} \qquad 2$$

$$\vdots$$

$$t_{rc} = \frac{R_r C_c}{G}$$

etc.

Then χ^2 is given as usual by $\Sigma[(a-t)^2/t]$, and the degrees of freedom are $(r-1)(c-1)$.

3. χ^2 in an $r \times 2$ table. The $r \times 2$ table is

		Column		
		a_{i1}	a_{i2}	Total
Row	1	a_{11}	a_{12}	R_1
	2	a_{21}	a_{22}	R_2
	.	.	.	.
	.	.	.	.
	.	.	.	.
	i	a_{i1}	a_{i2}	R_i
	.	.	.	.
	.	.	.	.
	.	.	.	.
	r	a_{r1}	a_{r2}	R_r
Total		C_1	C_2	G

The shortest method is that given by Snedecor and Irwin [6]. We calculate

$$\chi^2 = \frac{G^2}{C_1C_2}\left[\Sigma\left(\frac{a_{i1}^{\ 2}}{R_i}\right) - \frac{C_1^{\ 2}}{G}\right] \qquad 3$$

wherein we can take either one of the columns for the basis of our calculations. In other words the same result would be obtained from

$$\frac{G^2}{C_1C_2}\left[\Sigma\left(\frac{a_{i2}^{\ 2}}{R_i}\right) - \frac{C_2^{\ 2}}{G}\right] \qquad 4$$

With a slight variation we may also apply Snedecor's formula as in Section 15–3. In applying this formula it is convenient to set the table up as follows.

			$p_i = \frac{a_{i1}}{R_i}$
	a_{11}	R_1	p_1
	a_{21}	R_2	p_2
	.	.	.
	.	.	.
	a_{i1}	R_i	p_i
	.	.	.
	.	.	.
	.	.	.
	a_{r1}	R_r	p_r
Total	C_1	G	

We calculate $\Sigma(a_{i1}p_i)$, $\bar{p} = C_1/G$, and $\bar{q} = 1 - \bar{p}$. Then

$$\chi^2 = \frac{\Sigma(a_{i1}p_i) - C_1\bar{p}}{\bar{p}\bar{q}} \qquad 5$$

This formula is almost the same as the one in Example 15–3 for calculating the heterogeneity χ^2, but in that case the denominator $\bar{p}\bar{q}$ came from the theoretical ratio for the goodness of fit test. It is important to know this as there may be examples in which we require χ^2 by both methods and it is only necessary to change the denominator.

4. χ^2 in 2 × 2 tables. Representing the 2 × 2 table by

a_{11}	a_{12}	R_1
a_{21}	a_{22}	R_2
C_1	C_2	G

we have χ^2 directly from

$$\chi^2 = \frac{(a_{11}a_{22} - a_{12}a_{21})^2 G}{C_1 C_2 R_1 R_2} \qquad 6$$

but, just as in testing simple ratios for goodness of fit, there is only 1 degree of freedom for estimating χ^2 and an improvement is brought about by making a correction for continuity. The correction for a 2 × 2 table in a test of independence amounts to subtracting $^1/_2$ from each of a_{11} and a_{22}, and adding $^1/_2$ to a_{21} and a_{12}, but this applies of course to the condition $a_{11}a_{22} > a_{21}a_{12}$. When $a_{11}a_{22} < a_{21}a_{22}$, the procedure is reversed. The easiest method is to incorporate the correction in the formula. For this we have

$$\chi^2 = \frac{\left(\mid a_{11}a_{22} - a_{12}a_{21} \mid - \dfrac{G}{2}\right)^2 G}{C_1 C_2 R_1 R_2} \qquad 7$$

showing that the correction $G/2$ must always reduce the numerical value of $(a_{11}a_{22} - a_{12}a_{21})$.

5. Exact tests for 2 × 2 tables. The discussion of Chapter 15, Section 7, emphasized that the use of the χ^2 method for examples in which we have only 1 degree of freedom is justified only when the numbers are quite large, or, if the numbers are limited, when we apply the correction for continuity. R. A. Fisher [1] has pointed out that when the numbers are small it is frequently possible to apply an exact test based on the direct calculation of the probabilities in a 2 × 2 table. Representing the 2 × 2 table by

a_{11}	a_{12}	R_1
a_{21}	a_{22}	R_2
C_1	C_2	G

Fisher has shown that the probability of obtaining this particular combination is

$$\frac{C_1!C_2!R_1!R_2!}{G!}\left(\frac{1}{a_{11}!a_{12}!a_{21}!a_{22}!}\right) \qquad 8$$

and with this in mind it may be comparatively easy to determine the separate probabilities for all the combinations required to make a test of significance. The procedure is most easily followed by its application to actual data as in Example 16–1.

6. Example 16–1. An exact test in a 2 × 2 table. In a study of the blood groups of the North American Indians, Grant [2] obtained the results given below.

	Blood Group				
	O	A	B	AB	Total
Fond du Lac	18	6	5	0	29
Chipewyan	13	0	1	0	14
Total	31	6	6	0	43

The essential feature of the data from the standpoint of the possibility of hybridization with the white race was the classification into 2 main groups, O and not O. We form therefore a 2 × 2 table

	O	Not O	Total
Fond du Lac	18	11	29
Chipewyan	13	1	14
Total	31	12	43

The various combinations of this table that can occur provided that the marginal totals remain the same are

$$\begin{vmatrix} 17 & 12 \\ 14 & 0 \end{vmatrix} \quad \begin{vmatrix} 18 & 11 \\ 13 & 1 \end{vmatrix} \quad \begin{vmatrix} 19 & 10 \\ 12 & 2 \end{vmatrix} \quad \begin{vmatrix} 20 & 9 \\ 11 & 3 \end{vmatrix} \quad \cdots \quad \begin{vmatrix} 28 & 1 \\ 3 & 11 \end{vmatrix} \quad \begin{vmatrix} 29 & 0 \\ 2 & 12 \end{vmatrix}$$

What we actually require in this test is the sum of the probabilities for the first 2 combinations on the left. It is taken as a test of the presence of a greater proportion of white race genes in the Indian race from Fond du Lac than in those from Chipewyan. Any result such as that obtained in the combinations on the right may be taken merely as lack of evidence on this point or tending to disprove the hypothesis.

The calculations are

$$\frac{31! \times 12! \times 29! \times 14!}{43!} \times \frac{1}{17! \times 14! \times 12!}$$

$$\frac{31! \times 12! \times 29! \times 14!}{43!} \times \frac{1}{18! \times 11! \times 13!}$$

For convenience in calculation we obtain first the logarithm of the constant factor which is 31.701 159 3. The logs of the 2 terms to be subtracted are 34.171 813 9 and 33.201 777 0, giving

Log term 1 = $\bar{3}.529\ 345\ 4$	Term 1 = 0.003 383
Log term 2 = $\bar{2}.499\ 382\ 3$	Term 2 = 0.031 578
	Total = 0.0350

It is of interest to calculate χ^2 for this same table in order to note the agreement with the exact method. The lowest theoretical frequency in this table is $(12 \times 14)/43 = 3.91$, and, since the general rule for χ^2 is that the lowest theoretical frequency should be about 5, this table is evidently just below the requirements. Here we have

$$\chi^2 = \frac{(13 \times 11 - 18 - 43/2)^2 43}{31 \times 12 \times 14 \times 29} = 3.0499$$

An easy method of obtaining the exact probability corresponding to a χ^2 based on 1 degree of freedom is to find

$$\chi = \sqrt{3.0499} = 1.75$$

which is equal to d, the relative deviate as described in Chapter 15, Section 5. Here we have

$$d = 1.75 \qquad \therefore\ \tfrac{1}{2}(1 + \alpha) = 0.9599$$

giving

$$P = 1 - \tfrac{1}{2}(1 + \alpha) = 0.0401$$

This is a reasonably close agreement and indicates that, when the correction for continuity is made, the χ^2 method can be depended on to give a fairly close approximation to the true probability even when the lowest frequency is 4.

7. Example 16–2. Test of independence in an $r \times 2$ table. The data are those of Table 16–1.

	R_i Number of Plants	a_{i1} Number of Awned Plants	p_i
Yield class	24	6	0.250 000
	28	7	0.250 000
	30	21	0.700 000
	82	$34 = C$	$0.414\ 634 = \bar{p}$

$$\Sigma(a_{i1}p_i) = 17.9500$$
$$C_1\bar{p} = 14.0976$$
$$\text{Difference} = 3.8524$$

$$\bar{q} = 1 - 0.414\ 634 = 0.585\ 366$$

$$\chi^2 = \frac{3.8524}{0.414\ 634 \times 0.585\ 366} = \frac{3.8524}{0.24271} = 15.87$$

The 1% point of χ^2 for 2 degrees of freedom is 9.21; therefore there is no question as to the significance of dependence in this table, or, in other words, that there is a significant increase in awned plants with higher yield.

8. Exercises.

1. Table 16–2 gives the data obtained during an epidemic of cholera (Greenwood and Yule [3]) on the effectiveness of inoculation as a means of preventing the disease. Test the hypothesis that inoculation has no prevention effect.

TABLE 16–2

FREQUENCIES OF ATTACKED AND NOT ATTACKED IN INOCULATED AND NOT INOCULATED GROUPS

	Not Attacked	Attacked
Inoculated	192	4
Not Inoculated	113	34

$\chi^2 = 35.81$. $P < 0.001$.

2. Kondra [4] studied the quality of feathering of chickens in an early and a late strain, obtaining the results given in Table 16–3, where *A*, *B*, and *C* are feather quality grade, *A* indicating those of superior quality. Study the dependence of earliness on feather quality in these data.

TABLE 16–3

QUALITY OF FEATHERING OF EARLY AND LATE STRAINS OF CHICKENS

Quality of Tail Feathers

1940

(*a*)	Early	Late
A	17	47
B	111	137
C	60	17

1941

(*b*)	Early	Late
A	11	41
B	74	64
C	23	6

Quality of Wing Feathers—1940

(*c*)	Early	Late
A	10	26
B	108	36
C	70	39

Quality of Back Feathers—1941

(*d*)	Early	Late
A	23	26
B	69	75
C	16	10

$\chi^2 =$ *40.41* (*a*); *27.96* (*b*); *18.73* (*c*); *1.78* (*d*).

3. *a*. From a study of the position of the polar bodies in the ova of the ferret, Mainland [5] gives the frequencies in the following table.

	Similar	Different
10μ apart	5	1
More than 10μ apart	1	6

Test the hypothesis that "similar" polar bodies are not more closely associated in position than "different" polar bodies. $p = 0.025$. *calculated by direct method.*

b. Twenty-two animals are suffering from a disease, and the severity of the disease is about the same in each case. In order to test the therapeutic value of a serum, it is administered to 10 animals, 12 remaining uninoculated as a control. The results are

	Recovered	Died
Inoculated	7	3
Not inoculated	3	9

Determine the probability of obtaining this result or one more favourable to the treatment. $P = 0.046$.

4. The data in Table 16–4 were obtained in a cross between a rust resistant and a susceptible variety of oats. The F_3 families were compared for rust reaction in the seedling stage and in the field under ordinary epidemic conditions.

TABLE 16–4

CLASSIFICATION OF SEEDLING AND FIELD REACTIONS OF 810 F_3 FAMILIES OF OATS

		Seedling Reaction		
		Resistant	Segregating	Susceptible
Field reaction	Resistant	142	51	3
	Segregating	13	404	2
	Susceptible	2	17	176

Calculate the value of χ^2 for this table, obtaining the theoretical frequencies to 2 decimal places of accuracy. Check the values of $a - t$ by noting that their sums are zero in each row and each column.

$\chi^2 = 1127.94.$

REFERENCES

1. R. A. Fisher, *Statistical Methods for Research Workers*, Oliver and Boyd, Edinburgh and London, 10th ed., 1948.
2. J. C. B. Grant, *Natl. Museum Can. Bull.*, **64**, 1930.
3. M. Greenwood and G. U. Yule, *Proc. Roy. Soc. Med.*, **8**, 113, 1915.
4. Kondra, Unpublished data, University of Manitoba, Poultry Department.
5. Donald Mainland, *Am. J. Anat.*, **47**, No. 2, 1931.
6. G. W. Snedecor and M. R. Irwin, *Iowa State Coll. J. Sci.*, **8**, 75, 1933.

CHAPTER 17

The Discriminant Function

1. The use of multiple measurements to discriminate between two groups. It is frequently important in biological work, on examining a single individual, or a small sample of individuals, to be able to decide in which of 2 groups the individual or small sample belongs. In botanical studies the problem might be one of deciding on the species. In plant breeding the problem might be to decide whether a plant or plant progeny belongs to a high-yielding or a low-yielding group.

Sometimes decisions can be made on the basis of a single variable, but more often the 2 groups differ in several variables, each of which gives some indication as to the group in which the individual should be placed. The problem of utilizing 2 or more variables, however, is obviously not simple unless either one is sufficient in itself for discrimination, in which case it is superfluous to consider more than one. The general problem is to set up a function of the form

$$Z = \lambda_1 X_1 + \lambda_2 X_2 + \lambda_3 X_3 + \cdots + \lambda_k X_k \qquad 1$$

where $X_1, X_2, \cdots, X_k$ are the variables measured and $\lambda_1, \lambda_2, \cdots, \lambda_k$ are the corresponding weights. The simplest type of function would be

$$Z = X_1 + X_2 + X_3 + \cdots + X_k \qquad 2$$

which assumes that the variables have the same mean and are of equal discriminating value. This is not likely to be the best discriminating function, however, as some of the variables may have much more discriminating power than others and should be weighted accordingly.

A solution to this problem was given by Fisher [3] in 1936, wherein the method was demonstrated for separating species of iris employing the variables sepal length, sepal breadth, petal length, and petal width. Fisher has shown how to devise the coefficients of equation (1) such that, if we were to make an analysis of variance of the Z values, the ratio of the variance between species to that within species would be a maximum.

Assuming that the 2 groups to be discriminated are A and B and that there are n_a sets of measurements in A and n_b in B, the coefficients of the discriminant function arise from maximizing the ratio.

$$G = \frac{(\bar{Z}_a - \bar{Z}_b)^2}{\sum_1^{n_a}(Z_i - \bar{Z}_a)^2 + \sum_1^{n_b}(Z_j - \bar{Z}_b)^2} \qquad 3$$

The numerator of this ratio is the square of the difference between the means of Z for the 2 groups, and the denominator is the sum of squares within groups. Fisher shows that maximizing the ratio G yields a set of simultaneous equations of the following form, assuming 3 variables, X_1, X_2, and X_3, are available for study.

$$\begin{aligned} \lambda_1\Sigma(x_1^2) + \lambda_2\Sigma(x_1x_2) + \lambda_3\Sigma(x_1x_3) &= d_1 \\ \lambda_1\Sigma(x_1x_2) + \lambda_2\Sigma(x_2^2) + \lambda_3\Sigma(x_2x_3) &= d_2 \\ \lambda_1\Sigma(x_1x_3) + \lambda_2\Sigma(x_2x_3) + \lambda_3\Sigma(x_3^2) &= d_3 \end{aligned} \qquad 4$$

where x_1, x_2, and x_3 represent deviations from their respective group means represented by $\bar{X}_a$ and $\bar{X}_b$ and

$$\begin{aligned} d_1 &= \bar{X}_{a1} - \bar{X}_{b1} \\ d_2 &= \bar{X}_{a2} - \bar{X}_{b2} \\ d_3 &= \bar{X}_{a3} - \bar{X}_{b3} \end{aligned} \qquad 5$$

The difference $\bar{Z}_a - \bar{Z}_b$ between the means for the groups, represented usually by D, is

$$D = \lambda_1 d_1 + \lambda_2 d_2 + \lambda_3 d_3 \qquad 6$$

When D has been calculated, a test can be made of the significance of the discriminant functions by means of the analysis of variance, taking

$$\left(\frac{n_a n_b}{n_a + n_b}\right) D^2 =$$ Sum of squares between groups for k degrees of freedom, where k = the number of characters measured 7

$D =$ Sum of squares within groups for $n_a + n_b - k - 1$ degrees of freedom

The partitioning of degrees of freedom is similar to that for multiple regression. The sum of squares for between groups is represented by k degrees of freedom because k of the λ coefficients are calculated from the data and applied as in equation (6) for estimating D.

In the actual calculations we may wish to know the correlations between the variables, in which case it is convenient as shown by Cox and Martin [1] to carry out the calculations in terms of the correlation coefficients. Since

$$r_{12} = \frac{\Sigma(x_1x_2)}{\sqrt{\Sigma(x_1^2)\Sigma(x_2^2)}} \qquad r_{13} = \frac{\Sigma(x_1x_3)}{\sqrt{\Sigma(x_1^2)\Sigma(x_3^2)}} \qquad r_{23} = \frac{\Sigma(x_2x_3)}{\sqrt{\Sigma(x_2^2)\Sigma(x_3^2)}} \qquad 8$$

it is possible to substitute for $\Sigma(x_1x_2)$, $\Sigma(x_1x_3)$, and $\Sigma(x_2x_3)$ in equations (4), and on simplifying we have

$$\begin{aligned} \lambda'_1 \quad + \lambda'_2 r_{12} + \lambda'_3 r_{13} &= d'_1 \\ \lambda'_1 r_{12} + \lambda'_2 \quad + \lambda'_3 r_{23} &= d'_2 \\ \lambda'_1 r_{13} + \lambda'_2 r_{23} + \lambda'_3 \quad &= d'_3 \end{aligned} \qquad 9$$

where

$$\begin{aligned} \lambda'_1 &= \lambda_1\sqrt{\Sigma(x_1^2)} \qquad & d'_1 &= d_1/\sqrt{\Sigma(x_1^2)} \\ \lambda'_2 &= \lambda_2\sqrt{\Sigma(x_2^2)} \qquad & d'_2 &= d_2/\sqrt{\Sigma(x_2^2)} \\ \lambda'_3 &= \lambda_3\sqrt{\Sigma(x_3^2)} \qquad & d'_3 &= d_3/\sqrt{\Sigma(x_3^2)} \end{aligned}$$

Finally

$$D' = \lambda'_1 d'_1 + \lambda'_2 d'_2 + \lambda'_3 d'_3 = \lambda_1 d_1 + \lambda_2 d_2 + \lambda_3 d_3 = D \qquad 10$$

The details of calculation are given in Example 17–1 below.

2. Example 17–1. The discriminant function applied to the differentiation of soil types. At the Iowa Agricultural Experiment Station, Cox and Martin [1] collected 286 samples of soil of which 100 contained the organism *Azotobacter* and 186 did not. Three characteristics of the soil were studied:

$X_1 = p\text{H}$

$X_2 =$ amount of readily available phosphate

$X_3 =$ total nitrogen content

A discriminant function was set up and was found to give a very good differentiation of the soils. In other words, knowledge of the 3 characters X_1, X_2, and X_3 could be combined in a discriminant function to give a very good indication as to whether or not the soil sample studied contained the organism *Azotobacter*.

A portion of the data from Cox and Martin is reproduced in Table 17–1 and is used here for a demonstration of the calculations required in order to set up a discriminant function and test its significance.

TABLE 17–1

DATA FROM COX AND MARTIN ON pH(X_1), AVAILABLE PHOSPHATE CONTENT (X_2), AND TOTAL NITROGEN CONTENT (X_3) OF 52 SAMPLES OF SOIL

	Group A ($n_a = 25$) containing *Azotobacter*			Group B ($n_b = 27$) without *Azotobacter*		
	X_1	X_2	X_3	X_1	X_2	X_3
	6.0	46	24	6.2	49	30
	7.0	35	17	5.6	31	23
	8.4	115	28	5.8	42	22
	5.8	35	17	5.7	42	14
	6.9	55	25	6.2	40	23
	7.8	52	29	6.4	49	18
	7.8	52	29	5.8	31	17
	6.9	208	58	6.4	31	19
	7.0	70	13	5.4	62	26
	6.7	35	16	5.4	42	16
	6.2	27	44	5.7	35	22
	6.9	52	27	5.6	33	24
	8.0	60	58	5.8	24	15
	8.0	156	68	7.3	70	14
	8.0	90	37	6.1	21	21
	6.1	44	27	6.2	36	26
	7.4	207	31	6.7	35	26
	7.4	120	32	5.9	33	21
	8.4	65	43	5.6	25	32
	8.1	237	45	5.8	31	30
	8.3	57	60	6.1	30	24
	7.0	94	43	6.1	21	25
	8.5	86	40	5.7	35	22
	8.4	52	48	5.8	37	24
	7.9	146	52	5.8	28	19
				5.7	34	20
				5.8	16	19
Total	184.9	2196	911	160.6	963	592
Mean	7.3960	87.8400	36.4400	5.9481	35.6667	21.9259

It is convenient to set up the sums of squares, sums of products, and correlation coefficients in the form given in Table 17–2. Examples of the calculation of sums of squares and products are

$$\Sigma X_1^2 = \Sigma(X_{a1}^2) + \Sigma(X_{b1}^2) = 1384.0500 + 959.7000 = 2343.7500$$

$$\text{C.T.} = \frac{(\Sigma X_{a1})^2}{25} + \frac{(\Sigma X_{b1})^2}{27} = \frac{(184.9)^2}{25} + \frac{(160.6)^2}{27} = 2322.7930$$

$$\Sigma(X_1 X_2) = \Sigma(X_{a1} X_{a2}) + \Sigma(X_{b1} X_{b2}) = 16{,}620.8000 + 5770.8000$$
$$= 22{,}391.6000$$

$$\text{C.T.} = \frac{\Sigma X_{a1} \cdot \Sigma X_{a2}}{25} + \frac{\Sigma X_{b1} \cdot \Sigma X_{b2}}{27} = \frac{184.9 \times 2196}{25} + \frac{160.6 \times 963}{27}$$
$$= 21{,}969.6827$$

TABLE 17–2

TABULAR ARRANGEMENT OF SUMS OF SQUARES, SUMS OF PRODUCTS, AND CORRELATION COEFFICIENTS

$\Sigma(X_1^2)$	2343.7500	$\Sigma(X_1X_2)$	22,391.6000	$\Sigma(X_1X_3)$	10,407.3000
C.T.	2322.7930	C.T.	21,969.6827	C.T.	10,259.0597
$\Sigma(x_1^2)$	20.9570	$\Sigma(x_1x_2)$	421.9173	$\Sigma(x_1x_3)$	148.2403
$\sqrt{\Sigma(x_1^2)}$	4.5779	r_{12}	0.309113	r_{13}	0.414946
		$\Sigma(X_2^2)$	316,141.0000	$\Sigma(X_2X_3)$	110,272.0000
		C.T.	227,243.6400	C.T.	101,136.9067
		$\Sigma(x_2^2)$	88,897.3600	$\Sigma(x_2x_3)$	9,135.0933
		$\sqrt{\Sigma(x_2^2)}$	298.1566	r_{23}	0.392608
				$\Sigma(X_3^2)$	52,267.0000
				C.T.	46,176.9881
				$\Sigma(x_3^2)$	6,090.0119
				$\sqrt{\Sigma(x_3^2)}$	78.0385

The next step is to carry out the calculations shown in Table 17–3. For the method, see Chapter 8, Section 7. The calculations lead to the Gauss multipliers. It will be remembered that these form a matrix inverse to the matrix of the correlation coefficients.

TABLE 17–3

CALCULATION OF INVERSE MATRIX TO CORRELATION COEFFICIENTS

1.0	0.309 113	0.414 946	1.0	0	0
	1.0	0.392 608	0	1.0	0
		1.0	0	0	1.0
1.0	0.309 113	0.414 946	1.0	0	0
1.0	0.309 113	0.414 946	1.0	0	0
	0.904 449	0.264 343	– 0.309 113	1.0	0
	1.0	0.292 270	– 0.341 769	1.105 646	0
		0.750 560	– 0.324 602	– 0.292 270	1.0
		1.0	– 0.432 480	– 0.389 403	1.332 339
			1.246 029	– 0.215 369	– 0.432 480
			– 0.215 369	1.219 457	– 0.389 403
			– 0.432 480	– 0.389 403	1.332 339

The matrix in the lower right portion of the table is

$$\begin{matrix} c_{11} & c_{12} & c_{13} \\ c_{12} & c_{22} & c_{23} \\ c_{13} & c_{23} & c_{33} \end{matrix}$$

These can be checked by substituting them in the original equations. Thus

$$(1.0 \times 1.246\,029) - (0.309\,113 \times 0.215\,369) - (0.414\,946 \times 0.432\,480) = 1.000\,000$$

$$-(0.309\,113 \times 0.215\,369) + (1.0 \times 1.219\,457) - (0.392\,608 \times 0.389\,403) = 1.000\,000$$

$$-(0.414\,946 \times 0.432\,480) - (0.392\,608 \times 0.389\,403) + (1.0 \times 1.332\,339) = 1.000\,000$$

We now require the values of d'_1, d'_2, and d'_3. These are calculated as follows.

$$d'_1 = \frac{7.3960 - 5.9481}{4.5779} = 0.316\,280$$

$$d'_2 = \frac{87.8400 - 35.667}{298.1566} = 0.174\,986$$

$$d'_3 = \frac{36.4400 - 21.9259}{78.0385} = 0.185\,986$$

The coefficients λ'_1, λ'_2, and λ'_3, are obtained by multiplying each line of the inverse matrix by d'_1, d'_2, d'_3.

$$\lambda'_1 = (0.316\,280 \times 1.246\,029) - (0.174\,986 \times 0.215\,369) - (0.185\,986 \times 0.432\,480) = 0.275\,972$$

$$\lambda'_2 = -(0.316\,280 \times 0.215\,369) + (0.174\,986 \times 1.219\,457) - (0.185\,986 \times 0.389\,403) = 0.072\,847\,5$$

$$\lambda'_3 = -(0.316\,280 \times 0.432\,480) - (0.174\,986 \times 0.389\,403) + (0.185\,986 \times 1.332\,339) = 0.042\,871\,6$$

Then

$$\lambda_1 = \frac{0.275\,972}{4.5779} = 0.060\,283\,5$$

$$\lambda_2 = \frac{0.072\,847\,5}{298.1566} = 0.000\,244\,326$$

$$\lambda_3 = \frac{0.042\,871\,6}{78.0385} = 0.000\,549\,365$$

The required discriminant function is then

$$Z = 0.060\,28X_1 + 0.000\,244\,3X_2 + 0.000\,549\,4X_3$$

and for convenience we can divide through by 0.000 243 3 on the right, giving a new equation which we can again put equal to Z because it is the final discriminant function.

$$Z = 247.8X_1 + X_2 + 2.258X_3$$

This equation shows very clearly the relative values of the 3 characters in distinguishing the soil types.

A complete analysis requires that we make a test of significance of the discriminant function. First we find D from equation (10).

$$D = (0.275\,972 \times 0.316\,280) + (0.072\,848 \times 0.174\,986) + (0.042\,872 \times 0.185\,986) = 0.108\,005$$

Then the sum of squares between groups is

$$\left(\frac{n_a n_b}{n_a + n_b}\right) D^2 = \frac{25 \times 27}{25 + 27}(0.108\,005)^2 = 0.151\,42$$

Since the sum of squares within groups is equal to D, the analysis of variance can now be set up.

	SS	DF	MS	F
Between groups	0.151 42	3	0.050 47	22.4
Within groups	0.108 00	48	0.002 25	

which leaves no doubt as to the discriminating power of the function.

3. Applications of the discriminant function for discriminating between two groups. It is of course not sufficient in itself to calculate a discriminant function and determine its significance. We might have, for example, a case of 3 variables wherein 1 variable alone would give complete discrimination without the assistance of the remaining variables. In such an example the discriminant function would obviously be significant. The error would lie actually in the application of a more complicated function than required by the data.

In other cases the discriminant function may be significant but some of the variables may not contribute anything of value to the function. Thus, if the function $Z_1 = \lambda_1 X_1 + \lambda_2 X_2$ gives a significant discrimination, it is most likely that the function $Z_2 = \lambda_1 X_1 + \lambda_2 X_2 + \lambda_3 X_3$ will also be significant even if X_3 does not in itself have any discriminating value.

Since in obtaining Z_1 and Z_2 we absorb 2 and 3 degrees of freedom, respectively, for the discriminant functions, it should be clear that the same technique for testing the significance of the additional information given by X_3 as employed in multiple regression analysis (Chapter 8, Section 14) can be applied. The procedure is to test the significance of the mean square corresponding to the additional degree of freedom.

4. Discriminant function for plant selection. The application of the discriminant function for plant selection was first described by Smith [5] in 1939. Smith points out that, in selecting for characters such as yield, differences due to genotype are very largely masked by non-heritable variations such as those due to soil and location. Plant breeders therefore select plants for yield on the basis of general vigor, number of culms, size of spike, etc., which they believe are associated with corresponding genes, but in doing this there is no basis for giving more or less weight to certain characters depending on the extent to which they really indicate a concentration of genes for yield. The method of approach suggested is the use of a discriminant function that will best indicate the genotypic value of a plant or line.

As a basis for the development of the required discriminant function for plant selection it can be assumed that the genotype of a given plant can be represented by a function of the type

$$\psi = a_1 X'_1 + a_2 X'_2 + a_3 X'_3 + \cdots \qquad 11$$

where X'_1, X'_2, X'_3, $\cdots$ are the values of the characters X_1, X_2, X_3, $\cdots$ to be expected due to genotype, and a_1, a_2, a_3, $\cdots$ are weights depending on the economic values of the corresponding characters. For example it might be worked out that number of tillers contributes twice as much to yield as size of spike. These characters would therefore be weighted in the proportion of 2 : 1. In any event there is no way in practice of avoiding the use of weights because we do actually assign weights in arbitrarily deciding on the relative value of the different characters.

Assuming that the genotype can be represented as in equation (11), the phenotype can be represented by

$$Y = b_1X_1 + b_2X_2 + b_3X_3 + \cdots \qquad 12$$

and the problem is to derive values of b such that the regression of Y on ψ will be a maximum because selection of phenotypes using Y as a discriminant function will then ensure a maximum concentration of the desired genes in the plants or lines selected. It can be shown that, if the plants or lines are replicated, and

t_{ij} represents variances and covariances for plants or lines

e_{ij} represents variances and covariances for error

$g_{ij} = t_{ij} - e_{ij}$, being an estimate of the component due to genotype

that maximizing the regression of Y on ψ yields the simultaneous equations (for 3 variables).

$$\begin{aligned} b_1t_{11} + b_2t_{12} + b_3t_{13} &= A_1 \\ b_1t_{12} + b_2t_{22} + b_3t_{23} &= A_2 \\ b_1t_{13} + b_2t_{23} + b_3t_{33} &= A_3 \end{aligned} \qquad 13$$

where

$$\begin{aligned} A_1 &= a_1g_{11} + a_2g_{12} + a_3g_{13} \\ A_2 &= a_1g_{12} + a_2g_{22} + a_3g_{23} \\ A_3 &= a_1g_{13} + a_2g_{23} + a_3g_{33} \end{aligned} \qquad 14$$

The A's are calculated from the data by substitution of the calculated values of g_{ij} and the assigned values of a. These are inserted in equations (13) which are then solved for b_1, b_2, and b_3.

5. Assigning weights in equation for genotype. Since it is necessary to assign weights of some sort, there are in general two courses that are open.

1. Without any basis for distinguishing between the characters with respect to their proportional economic value, the only course is to weight them equally. Since the means may differ, equal weighting is obtained by putting

$$a_1 = \frac{1}{\bar{X}_1} \qquad a_2 = \frac{1}{\bar{X}_2} \qquad a_3 = \frac{1}{\bar{X}_3} \qquad \text{etc.}$$

2. Assuming that there is a fair basis for assessing the actual economic value of each character either by reasoning or shrewd judgment, we assign the weights by modifying those given above. Thus, if the relative values of X_1, X_2, and X_3 are to be in the proportion of 2 : 1 : 3, we take

$$a_1 = \frac{2}{\bar{X}_1} \qquad a_2 = \frac{1}{\bar{X}_2} \qquad a_3 = \frac{3}{\bar{X}_3}$$

In any event it should be emphasized that the assigning of weights does not consist of a more arbitrary procedure than that followed in ordinary selection where the plant breeder merely selects those plants that show desirable characters. For example, in selecting for yield, he must pay attention to number of tillers and size of spike. In doing so, he must either assume these to be of equal importance or arbitrarily weight them, for example by assuming that numbers of tillers is of somewhat more importance than size of spike.

If it is more convenient the discriminant function can be calculated from the correlation coefficients by following the procedure outlined below.

Let $r_{12} = t_{12}/\sqrt{t_{11}t_{22}}$, $r_{23} = t_{23}/\sqrt{t_{22}t_{33}}$, etc. Then in equations (13) we can substitute $r_{12}\sqrt{t_{11}t_{22}}$ for t_{12}, $r_{23}\sqrt{t_{22}t_{33}}$ for t_{33}, etc., giving

$$\begin{aligned} b_1t_{11} \quad &+ b_2r_{12}\sqrt{t_{11}t_{22}} + b_3r_{13}\sqrt{t_{11}t_{33}} = A_1 \\ b_1r_{12}\sqrt{t_{11}t_{22}} &+ b_2t_{22} \quad + b_3r_{23}\sqrt{t_{22}t_{33}} = A_2 \\ b_1r_{13}\sqrt{t_{11}t_{33}} &+ b_2r_{23}\sqrt{t_{22}t_{33}} + b_3t_{33} \quad = A_3 \end{aligned}$$

Dividing the first equation by $\sqrt{t_{11}}$, the second by $\sqrt{t_{22}}$, and the third by $\sqrt{t_{33}}$ gives

$$\begin{aligned} b_1\sqrt{t_{11}} \quad &+ b_2r_{12}\sqrt{t_{22}} \quad + b_3r_{13}\sqrt{t_{33}} = \frac{A_1}{\sqrt{t_{11}}} \\ b_1r_{12}\sqrt{t_{11}} &+ b_2\sqrt{t_{22}} \quad + b_3r_{23}\sqrt{t_{33}} = \frac{A_2}{\sqrt{t_{22}}} \\ b_1r_{13}\sqrt{t_{11}} &+ b_2r_{23}\sqrt{t_{22}} \quad + b_3\sqrt{t_{33}} = \frac{A_3}{\sqrt{t_{33}}} \end{aligned}$$

Then, letting $b'_1 = b_1\sqrt{t_{11}}$, $b'_2 = b_2\sqrt{t_{22}}$, $b'_3 = b_3\sqrt{t_{33}}$, and

$$A'_1 = \frac{A_1}{\sqrt{t_{11}}} \qquad A'_2 = \frac{A_2}{\sqrt{t_{22}}} \qquad A'_3 = \frac{A_2}{\sqrt{t_{33}}}$$

the equations can be re-written in the following form.

$$b'_1 + r_{12}b'_2 + r_{13}b'_3 = A'_1$$
$$r_{12}b'_1 + \quad b'_2 + r_{23}b'_3 = A'_2$$
$$r_{13}b'_1 + r_{23}b'_2 + \quad b'_3 = A'_3$$

After calculating the c' matrix reciprocal to the r matrix, we have

$$\begin{matrix} c'_{11} & c'_{12} & c'_{13} \\ c'_{12} & c'_{22} & c'_{23} \\ c'_{13} & c'_{23} & c'_{33} \end{matrix}$$

The A's are best calculated from

$$A_1 = a_1g_{11} + a_2g_{12} + a_3g_{13}$$
$$A_2 = a_1g_{12} + a_2g_{22} + a_3g_{23}$$
$$A_3 = a_1g_{13} + a_2g_{23} + a_3g_{33}$$

and converted to A'_1, A'_2 and A'_3 by dividing by $\sqrt{t_{11}}$, $\sqrt{t_{22}}$, and $\sqrt{t_{33}}$. The b' values can then be obtained from

$$b'_1 = A'_1c'_{11} + A'_2c'_{12} + A'_3c'_{13}$$

and converted to b values by dividing by $\sqrt{t_{11}}$, $\sqrt{t_{22}}$, and $\sqrt{t_{33}}$.

6. Example 17–2. Use of discriminant function for plant selection. Table 17–4 gives the data obtained with 8 varieties of oats in a 3-replicate test. Root type is determined according to the scheme described by Hamilton [4]. The 3 characters measured contribute to lodging resistance, and the object of the analysis is to obtain a discriminant function that will discriminate between varieties for this character.

Analyses of variance and covariance are made as follows, using X_1 for the variance example and X_1X_2 for the covariance example.

(X_1)	SS	DF	MS
Replicates	2.400 833	2	
Varieties	46.259 583	7	6.608 512 = t_{11}
Error	4.799 167	14	0.342 798 = e_{11}
			6.265 714 = g_{11}

(X_1X_2)	SP	DF	Cov
Replicates	− 7.5125	2	
Varieties	− 14.0042	7	− 2.000 600 = t_{12}
Error	3.0792	14	0.219 943 = e_{12}
			− 2.220 543 = g_{12}

TABLE 17–4

DATA ON ROOT TYPE, HEIGHT, AND DIAMETER OF CULM FOR 8 VARIETIES IN A 3-REPLICATE TEST

	Root Type (X_1)			Total	Height (X_2)			Total	Diameter of Culm (X_3)			Total
	4.1	4.5	3.0	11.6	41	45	44	130	3.3	3.4	3.3	10.0
	3.0	3.1	3.7	9.8	38	40	42	120	3.3	3.4	3.2	9.9
	4.5	4.2	4.5	13.2	42	43	42	127	3.1	3.2	3.2	9.5
	4.1	3.2	3.7	11.0	42	46	49	137	3.1	3.3	3.2	9.6
	5.7	5.1	5.4	16.2	39	43	41	123	2.8	3.1	2.8	8.7
	4.1	3.3	3.8	11.2	53	51	53	157	3.0	3.1	3.1	9.2
	8.0	6.5	6.1	20.6	46	46	45	137	2.7	2.7	2.9	8.3
	8.3	6.8	6.0	21.1	41	42	45	128	3.0	3.0	3.1	9.1
Total	41.8	36.7	36.2	114.7	342	356	361	1059	24.3	25.2	24.8	74.3

The values of t_{ij}, e_{ij}, g_{ij}, and r_{ij} are conveniently tabulated as in Table 17–5. Note that, for convenience, the correlation coefficients are worked from the values of t_{ij}. Thus

$$r_{12} = \frac{-\,2.000\,600}{\sqrt{6.608\,512 \times 44.946\,429}} = -\,0.116\,081$$

TABLE 17–5

TABULATED VALUES OF t_{ij}, e_{ij}, AND r_{ij}

t_{ij}			e_{ij}		
6.608 512	− 2.000 600	− 0.680 298	0.342 798	0.219 943	− 0.012 887
	44.946 429	− 0.445 833		2.696 429	0.013 988
		0.113 7500			0.007 3214

g_{ij}			r_{ij}		
6.265 714	− 2.220 543	− 0.667 411	1.000 000	− 0.116 081	− 0.784 643
	42.250 000	− 0.459 821		1.000 000	− 0.197 174
		0.106 4286			1.000 000

We must now decide on the values of a. The object in this experiment is to obtain a discriminant function for the selection of those varieties having the greatest concentration of genes for resistance to lodging. It seems most logical here to assume that all 3 characters have equal weight; therefore

$$a_1 = \frac{1}{4.7792} \qquad a_2 = \frac{1}{44.125} \qquad a_3 = \frac{1}{3.0938}$$

or

$$a_1 = \frac{44.125}{4.7792} = 9.23 \qquad a_2 = 1 \qquad a_3 = \frac{44.125}{3.0958} = 14.25$$

The fractions are of no value, so we take $a_1 = 9$, $a_2 = 1$, and $a_3 = -14$. Note that a_1 and a_2 are opposite in sign to a_3 because of the way the 3 characters vary with lodging resistance.

It is convenient to carry out the remainder of the calculations as in Table 17–6.

TABLE 17–6

CALCULATION OF DISCRIMINANT FUNCTION FOR PLANT SELECTION. DATA OF TABLE 17–4 AND 17–5

	1.000 000	0.116 081	− 0.784 643	1.0	0	0	
		1.000 000	− 0.197 174	0	1.0	0	
			1.000 000	0	0	1.0	
	1.0	− 0.116 081	− 0.784 643	1.0	0	0	
	1.0	− 0.116 081	− 0.784 643	1.0	0	0	
		0.986 525	− 0.288 256	0.116 081	1.0	0	
		1.0	− 0.292 193	0.117 667	1.013 659	0	
			0.300 109	0.818 561	0.292 193	1.0	
			1.0	2.727 546	0.973 623	3.332 123	
	6.265 714	− 2.220 543	− 0.667 411	3.246 322	0.914 636	2.727 546	
g_{ij}	− 2.220 543	42.250 000	− 0.459 821	0.914 636	1.298 145	0.973 623	c_{ij}
	− 0.667 411	− 0.459 821	0.106 429	2.727 546	0.973 623	3.332 123	
a	9	1	− 14	A 63.5146	29.7026	− 7.9565	
				$\sqrt{t}$ 2.5707	6.7042	0.3373	
				A' 24.7071	4.2813	− 23.5916	
				λ' 19.7759	5.1864	− 7.0520	
				λ 7.693	0.774	− 20.91	
				10	1	− 27	

Note that the first step is to calculate the inverse matrix of the correlation coefficients. Then the values of g_{ij} and a_1, a_2, and a_3 are inserted in the table. From these we get

$$A_1 = 9 \times 6.265\,714 - 1 \times 2.220\,543 + 14 \times 0.667\,411 = 63.5146$$

$$A_2 = -9 \times 2.220\,543 + 1 \times 42.250\,000 + 14 \times 0.459\,821 = 28.7026$$

$$A_3 = -9 \times 0.667\,411 - 1 \times 0.459\,821 - 14 \times 0.106\,429 = -7.9565$$

We then enter the square root of t_{11}, t_{22}, and t_{33}. Using these as divisors gives A'_1, A'_2, and A'_3. Next we calculate

$$\lambda'_1 = 24.7071 \times 3.246\,322 + 4.2813 \times 0.914\,636 - 23.5916 \times 2.727\,546 = 19.7759$$

$$\lambda'_2 = 24.7071 \times 0.914\,636 + 4.2813 \times 1.298\,145 - 23.5916 \times 0.973\,623 = 5.1864$$

$$\lambda'_3 = 24.7071 \times 2.727\,546 + 4.2813 \times 0.973\,623 - 23.5916 \times 3.332\,123 = -7.0520$$

Then

$$\lambda_1 = \frac{19.7759}{2.5707} = 7.693$$

$$\lambda_2 = \frac{5.1864}{6.7042} = 0.774$$

$$\lambda_3 = \frac{-7.0520}{0.337\,26} = -20.91$$

The last line of the table shows the coefficients converted by dividing by λ_2 and writing down with the elimination of decimals.

Applying the discriminant function to the means of the first and last varieties in Table 17–4, we have

$$10 \times 3.87 + 43.3 - 27 \times 3.33 = -7.91$$

$$10 \times 7.03 + 42.7 - 27 \times 3.03 = 31.19$$

TABLE 17–7

VALUES OF EGG CHARACTERS FOR 2 GRADES

Grade A				Grade B			
Yolk Shadow X_1	Yolk Color X_2	Albumen Index X_3	Albumen Height X_4	Yolk Shadow X_1	Yolk Color X_2	Albumen Index X_3	Albumen Height X_4
8	13	30	17	12	12	40	16
7	11	30	20	9	14	20	26
7	14	35	14	10	15	25	20
7	14	20	25	13	17	35	14
7	13	20	25	10	17	30	16
8	16	20	28	10	15	25	22
6	13	25	26	10	17	30	18
8	16	20	27	12	16	35	12
8	14	20	26	10	17	20	27
8	16	25	24	12	15	35	18
7	12	20	27	10	14	25	22
8	17	20	25	11	15	45	12
7	13	25	24	10	16	25	22
7	15	15	36	9	15	25	22
7	14	20	26	12	16	35	16
7	8	15	34	10	15	25	24
7	14	20	27	12	16	35	17
6	15	15	33	11	14	30	19
8	14	20	24	9	13	25	24
6	14	20	26	10	16	30	18
8	13	20	28	10	17	25	23
6	13	25	24	10	14	25	22
7	16	20	31	10	18	30	19
6	14	20	26	11	14	30	20
8	16	20	28	10	15	30	20
				9	18	20	28
				9	14	20	26
				8	16	25	24
				10	15	25	20
				11	13	25	20
				11	15	35	16
				10	15	25	19
				11	16	25	20

7. Exercises.

1. The data of Table 17–7 are for samples of eggs of grade A and B. They are taken from a study made by A. Johnston, Poultry Division, Central Experimental Farm, Ottawa, on the value of 4 egg characters in determining grade. Each set of values is made up of means corresponding to one farm sampled for egg quality. This table gives the basic data required for the calculation of the discriminant function. Calculate λ_1, λ_2, λ_3, and λ_4 as in Example 17–1 and set up the actual equation corresponding to equation (7).

Make an analysis of variance and determine the significance of the discriminant function.

Calculate Z for 4 samples from grade A and 4 from grade B.

REFERENCES

1. Gertrude M. Cox and W. P. Martin, *Iowa State Coll. J. Sci.*, **11,** 323–331, 1937.
2. Prescott D. Crout, *Trans. Am. Inst. Elec. Eng.*, **60,** 1–7, 1941.
3. R. A. Fisher, The Use of Multiple Measurements in Taxonomic Problems, *Ann. Eugen.*, **7,** 179–188, 1936.
4. D. G. Hamilton, *Sci. Agr.*, **21,** 646–676, 1941.
5. H. Fairfield Smith, *Ann. Eugen.*, **7,** 240–250, 1936.

CHAPTER 18

Probit Analysis

1. Types of data appropriate for probit analysis. A great deal of biological work is now concerned with the assay of drugs, vitamins, sera, and other forms of stimuli. In these experiments the effect of the stimulus is determined according to the reaction of living organisms. Usually the stimulus is applied at a series of levels and the reaction of each level determined from its application to a batch of subjects.

Instead of speaking in general terms it is more convenient, in describing the kind of data obtained, to refer to one type of experiment such as the determination of the toxicity of a chemical preparation to a given type of insect. In such an experiment various concentrations are prepared and a batch of insects assigned at random to each concentration level. The substance is applied, and for each batch a count is made of the total number of insects (n) and the number killed (r). The results can be expressed either as a proportion (r/n) or as a percentage $100(r/n)$. This is the type of data to which the methods of the probit analysis are appropriate in assessing the value of different toxic substances, comparing relative potencies of different substances, applying tests of significance, and determining fiducial limits.

2. The distribution of tolerances. For any one subject there is a level of intensity of the stimulus below which response does not occur and above which it does occur. This level is referred to as the tolerance for that subject. For example, in considering a given insect there is a level of concentration for a certain poison such that if the concentration is less than this level the insect will live, but if the concentration is greater the insect will die.* Let this tolerance of a subject be represented by λ; then in a population of subjects we are concerned with the distribution of λ. It is generally true for most biological preparations that the distribution of λ is not normal but is at least approximately normal for

* It should be noted that this is the ideal situation from the standpoint of a mathematical model but one that is not strictly true on account of variability in the responses of individual insects.

$X = \log_{10} \lambda$. In the usual analysis, therefore, we deal with the log of the concentration. Following Finney [5], λ is referred to as the *dose* in terms of actual concentration such as milligrams per liter, and the $\log_{10}$ concentration is referred to as the *dosage* or *dose metameter*.

It should be noted that the log transformation does not necessarily normalize the distribution of tolerances. In certain cases other transformations are more appropriate, but the log transformation is found to apply in most experiments and there are chemical and biological reasons why this should be true.

3. The probit transformation. Assuming that the dosage in a population is normally distributed, we can picture the situation as in Figure 18–1. In the upper portion of the figure we have a normal curve in which the dosage deviations from the mean $(X - \bar{X})$ are replaced on the base line by $(X - \bar{X})/\sigma$ or the normal equivalent deviate (N.E.D.). In other words this can be regarded as a normal distribution with unit standard deviation. Above the graph of the normal distribution are the percentages of the total area from a given point on the base line to N.E.D. $= -\infty$. For example, at N.E.D. $= -1$, the area to the left of that point is 15.87% of the total. These percentages are represented in the lower half of the figure by the sigmoid curve.

It should be clear from the figure that, if we have a population in which the tolerance for a toxic substance is normally distributed and we apply the substance at a series of levels to different batches, the percentages killed when plotted against dosage should give a sigmoid curve. The analysis of results from the sigmoid curve present some rather serious difficulties; therefore it would seem to be desirable to use a transformation of the percentages such that with a normal distribution the transformed percentages would lie on a straight line. The obvious transformation for this purpose is the corresponding N.E.D. Thus, on obtaining a percentage kill at a given level of 15.87%, we would locate in a table the N.E.D. such that if the distribution is normal a kill of exactly 15.87% would be expected. The value would be -1. For a kill of 2.27% the N.E.D. would be -2, and so forth.

The suggestion that the N.E.D. be used as a transformation for percentage response seems to have been first made by Fechner [4] in 1860, but it was not considered seriously until it was again made by Gaddum [7] in 1933. Later, in 1934, Bliss [1, 2] suggested adding 5 to the N.E.D. in order to remove negative numbers, and he also suggested the term probit. At that time and since then Dr. Bliss has been responsible for a great deal of the development work with the probit transformation. At the present the best summary of the theory and application of probit analysis is *Probit Analysis* by D. J. Finney [5].

In Figure 18–1 the probit scale is shown on the right of the lower part of the figure and the straight line represents the probits of the percentages at all points along the normal curve.

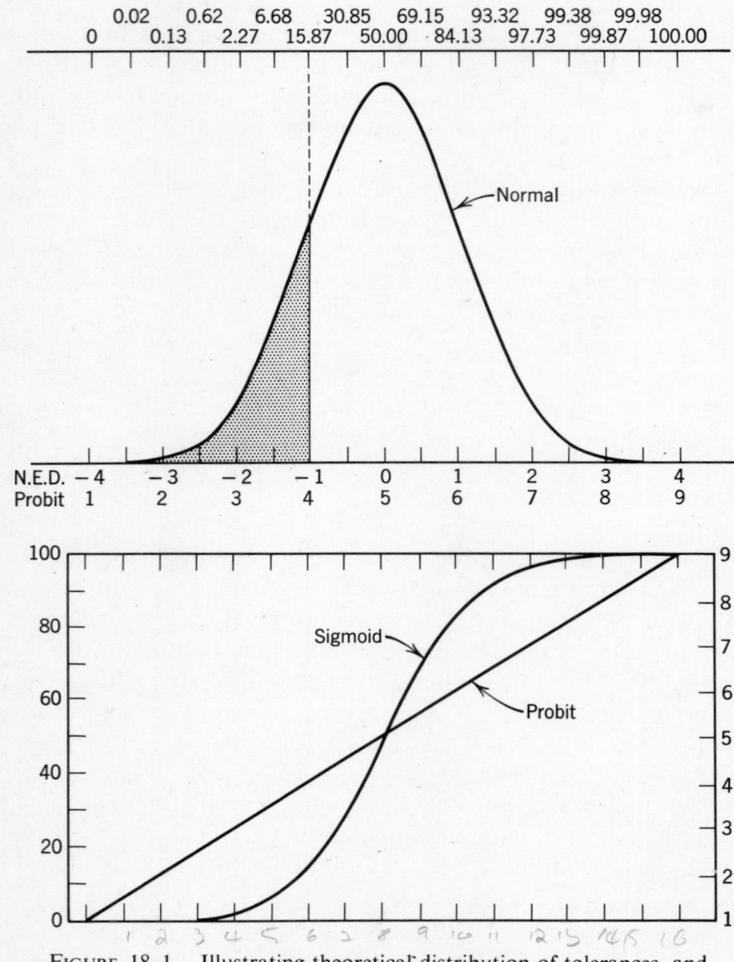

FIGURE 18–1. Illustrating theoretical distribution of tolerances, and relation of percentage kill to probits.

It should now be clear that, in a typical experiment wherein the tolerances are normally distributed, a graph of the probits corresponding to determined percentages will tend to be a straight line. Any variation from the normal curve will cause the plotted probits to vary from a straight line. Generally, the observed variations from a straight line are of two types. In the first place the batches of subjects may not be all uniform or the conditions for the batches may not be uniform. This will tend to produce an abnormal scatter of the points about the straight line. In the second place the transformation of the dose to dosage may not be suitable. Usually this will be indicated by trends towards curvilinear rather than linear regression.

4. Practical applications of probit analysis. Since we expect to get a straight-line graph when probits are plotted against dosage, the methods of linear regression are suggested. What we have to decide, however, is whether or not such methods are applicable: if they will yield estimates of required population parameters, if valid tests of significance can be applied, and if fiducial limits can be determined.

First we require a measure of the potency of the preparation. It has been concluded generally that the dosage giving a 50% kill is the most valuable statistic. It is referred to as the LD 50, (median lethal dose). In experiments where the response is not death we refer to the ED 50 (median effective dose). Whatever practical advantages there may be in knowing the LD 90 or some similar value, the fact is that much greater precision can be obtained in the measurement of the LD 50. This is obvious when we consider the measurement of a very high dosage such as the LD 100. Any levels administered beyond this point would give no information whatever. In the case of the LD 50, levels above and below contribute equally to the result.

Another factor to be measured is the range of the dosage required for a given range of percentage kill. This might be referred to as the sensitivity of the preparation tested. Obviously if small changes in concentrations give a wide range in the percentage kill, the sensitivity is high.

Referring now to a probit graph such as Figure 18–1, which will be described in detail later, it is clear that the LD 50 with respect to dosage is given by the dosage that corresponds to a probit value of 5.0. Therefore, if a straight line can be fitted, the LD 50 can be read directly from the graph.

Again on referring to the graph it is evident that sensitivity will be represented by the slope of the line. The greater the slope, the narrower the range in dosage for a given range in the percentage kill.

The geometry of the line would seem to give us therefore the required measures of potency and sensitivity. Locating 2 points X_1 and X_2, representing dosage, on the abscissa of the graph and finding the corresponding points Y_1 and Y_2 on the probit scale will give the slope of the line. If b represents the slope, we have

$$b = \frac{Y_2 - Y_1}{X_2 - X_1} \qquad 1$$

This makes it possible to set up a regression equation of the type $Y = a + bX$, where $a = Y_1 - bX_1$ or $Y_2 - bX_2$. This line can also be used to locate the LD 50 which we now represent by the symbol m. Putting $Y = 5$ and m for X, the regression equation is $5 = a + bm$, which can be solved for m.

5. Fitting a probit regression line. The fitting of a suitable straight-line regression would seem from the argument above to provide estimates of the required parameters. On making a close study of the problem of fitting such a line, however, we find that there is an essential difference between fitting a line to probit values and fitting a regression line to measure the relation between 2 variables in the ordinary case. It will be recalled from Chapter 6 that an essential assumption in the fitting of a regression line and testing its goodness of fit is that the variance of Y, the dependent variable, at all levels of X, the independent variable, should be the same. For the probit regression line this is definitely not the case. Actually, the variance is a minimum at the LD 50 and goes to infinity, on one end at the 100% kill, and on the other end at the 0% kill. In order to fit a regression line accurately it is necessary to weight the values at each point by the inverse of the variance. It has been shown that, if P represents the probability of kill at a given dosage level and $Q = (1 - P)$, the probability of survival, the correct weighting coefficient $w = Z^2/PQ$, where Z is the ordinate of the normal distribution corresponding to the probability P. Taking Y as a probit value on the straight line, the values of Z^2/PQ have been tabulated by Bliss [2] and reproduced by Fisher and Yates [6]. To illustrate the use of the weighting coefficients we must calculate the mean $\bar{X}$ from the formula $\Sigma(nwX)/\Sigma(nw)$ in place of the usual formula $\Sigma(nX)/\Sigma(n)$, where n represents the total number of insects in a batch.

One difficulty that arises in applying the weighting coefficients is that they are based on Z, P, and Q, which are parameters of the population and not estimates from the data of the experiment. In other words we must theoretically know the equation for the straight line in order to determine the values of w, which of course is an impossibility. In actual practice two things can be done to overcome the difficulty. First, many examples are such that a sufficiently good straight line can be fitted by obtaining what is known as an eye-fit. A straight edge is laid along the graph of probit points, and, if it is obvious that a close fit to the points can be obtained, this line is drawn and used for obtaining the required measures of potency and sensitivity, and further refinement is unnecessary. Second, a line fitted by eye (provisional line) will provide first approximations of Y and consequently of w. Substituting the approximate values of Y and w, another line is fitted which is a better fit than the provisional line. If further refinement is required, a third line can be fitted using the second line to provide estimates of Y and w. This process, if repeated, will lead very quickly to a line that does not change on further applications of the fitting process. This is known as an iterative process, and by suitable methods of fitting it can be made to give the maximum likelihood solution. It may appear to be tedious, but in actual practice there is little need to go beyond the second line.

The details of fitting and the formulas required are best observed from the actual examples given below. The same is true for learning the meaning of the terms and the interpretation of the data.

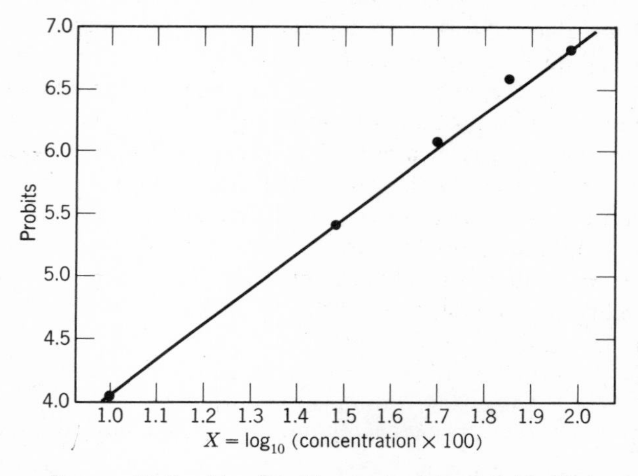

FIGURE 18–2. Line fitted by eye to data of Table 18–1.

6. Example 18–1. Fitting a provisional probit regression line. Table 18–1 is taken from data given by Morrison [10] for the effect of different concentrations of nicotine sulphate in a 1% saponin solution, on *Drosophila melanogaster*. The various steps in the calculations are best carried out as enumerated below.

1. Set up the data as in the first 3 columns of Table 18–1 and calculate % kill as in column (4).

2. Determine log concentrations after multiplying the concentrations by a suitable factor to remove negative values. These are entered in column (5).

3. Look up empirical probits in tables by Fisher and Yates, entering the table under % kill. Record these in column (6).

4. Draw Figure 18–2. First represent the empirical probits by dots, and then draw the straight line to give a good eye-fit. In this example it is fairly easy to draw a suitable line. One point that should be kept in

mind when it is difficult to decide where the line should be placed is that the most attention should be paid to those points representing kills of 40 to 60%, and percentage kills outside of the limits of 16 to 84 should be practically disregarded.*

5. From the regression line determine:

a. The LD 50 and LD 90. The LD 50 corresponds to a probit of 5.0, and the LD 90 to a probit of 6.28. In this figure we get m = LD 50 = 1.37 and LD 90 = 1.86.

b. The regression coefficient. Locate 2 convenient points at the ends of the line and write down corresponding values of X and Y. Thus

$$X_1 = 1.0 \qquad Y_1 = 4.02$$

$$X_2 = 2.0 \qquad Y_2 = 6.66$$

Then the increase in Y for unit increase in $X = \dfrac{Y_2 - Y_1}{X_2 - X_1} = 2.64 = b$.

6. In the regression equation $Y = a + bX$, put $a = Y_1 - bX_1 = 1.38$ and $b = 2.64$, giving the equation

$$Y = 1.38 + 2.64X$$

and from this equation obtain values of Y falling on the straight line for the levels of X required. The X's are entered in column (1) of Table 18–2, and the Y's in column (2). If the figure is accurately drawn, the Y values can be read from the figure instead of calculating them from the equation.

7. Reading backwards from Fisher and Yates' table of probits, find the corresponding values of P which are entered in column (3). Then complete the entries in columns (4) and (5), copying from Table 18–1.

8. Calculate the entries in columns (6), (7), and (8) as indicated. Note that P is a proportion and not a percentage. Thus a percentage of 16.4 is entered as 0.164. Add the last column to obtain $\chi^2 = 0.769$. This χ^2 is based on 3 degrees of freedom since we have adjusted for m and b. From Table A–4 we note that a χ^2 of 0.769 for 3 degrees of freedom corresponds to a probability of about 0.85. This is a better fit than can ordinarily be expected but is not sufficiently close to lead us to be suspicious of the data.

9. Tests of significance can now be applied to b and m, and fiducial limits calculated. The required preliminary calculations are shown in

---

* In Figure 18–2 it is possible that the line should have been drawn with more slope, giving greater weight to the percentage kill of 62.5 and 81.5.

Table 18–3. Note that Y is entered to the first decimal place only. The values of Y can be read to the second decimal place from the regression graph, but it can be shown that such a degree of accuracy is unnecessary at this point. The fourth column contains the weighting coefficients that are determined from Fisher and Yates' Table XI.

We require the sum of squares of X given by

$$\Sigma(nwx^2) = \Sigma(nwX^2) - \frac{\Sigma(nwX)^2}{\Sigma(nw)} = 31.5319 \qquad 2$$

Then the variance of b is

$$V_b = \frac{1}{\Sigma(nwx^2)} = \frac{1}{31.5319} = 0.031\,714 \qquad 3$$

$$s_b = \sqrt{0.031\,714} = 0.178 \qquad 4$$

and the fiducial limits are given by

$$b \pm ts_b$$

where $t = 1.96$. If χ^2 had indicated significant heterogeneity, it would have been necessary to make a correction in obtaining the fiducial limits. This will be demonstrated after first making the usual calculation of the limits.

$$2.64 \pm 1.96 \times 0.178 = 2.64 \pm 0.35$$

giving 2.29 to 2.99 as the required limits.

If heterogeneity is present, we calculate the heterogeneity factor

$$\mu = \frac{\chi^2}{\text{DF}} \qquad 5$$

where the degrees of freedom $= k - 2$, k being the number of batches tested. Then the variance of b is

$$V'_b = \frac{\mu}{\Sigma(nwx^2)} \qquad 6$$

and

$$s'_b = \sqrt{V'_b}$$

The fiducial limits are then

$$b \pm ts'_b$$

where t is the value required for significance at the 5% level for $k - 2$ degrees of freedom.

To get the fiducial limits of m we calculate

$$V_m = \frac{1}{b^2}\left[\frac{1}{\Sigma(nw)} + \frac{(m - \bar{X})^2}{\Sigma(nwx^2)}\right] \qquad 7$$

$$= \frac{1}{2.64^2}\left[\frac{1}{310.46} + \frac{(1.37 - 1.56)^2}{31.5319}\right]$$

$$= 0.000\,626\,4$$

$$s_m = \sqrt{0.000\,626\,4} = 0.025$$

The fiducial limits are then

$$m \pm ts_m \qquad 8$$

where $t = 1.96$ if there is no significant evidence of heterogeneity. Here we have

$$1.37 \pm 1.96 \times 0.025 = 1.37 \pm 0.05$$

giving 1.42 to 1.32 as the required limits.

The value of m and its fiducial limits should be expressed in actual concentrations, so we find their antilogs and divide by 100 to get back to the original scale. We get

$$\text{LD } 50 = 0.234$$

with fiducial limits 0.263 and 0.209.

A similar calculation gives the fiducial limits of the LD 90.

$$V_{\text{LD } 90} = \frac{1}{2.64^2}\left[\frac{1}{310.46} + \frac{(1.86 - 1.56)^2}{31.5319}\right] = 0.000\,871\,6$$

$$s_{\text{LD } 90} = \sqrt{0.000\,871\,6} = 0.0295$$

Then

$$1.86 \pm 1.96 \times 0.03 = 1.86 \pm 0.06$$

giving 1.92 to 1.80 as the fiducial limits. The corresponding doses are

$$\text{LD } 90 = 0.724$$

with fiducial limits 0.832 and 0.631.

Two points should be noted here in connection with fiducial limits. In the first place, formula (7) is merely a close approximation; and in the second place a correction for heterogeneity must be made whenever χ^2 is significant. The approximate formula is sufficiently accurate for this example, and also there is no evidence of heterogeneity, so further corrections will not be made. The exact formula for fiducial limits and the use of the heterogeneity factor will be demonstrated in the next example.

TABLE 18–1

DATA FROM AN EXPERIMENT ON THE EFFECT OF DIFFERENT CONCENTRATIONS OF NICOTINE SULPHATE ON *Drosophila melanogaster*. DETERMINATION OF EMPIRICAL PROBITS

(1) Nicotine Sulphate, gm/100 cc	(2) Number of Insects n	(3) Number Killed r	(4) % Kill p	(5) Log_{10} (Conc. × 100) X	(6) Empirical Probit Y_e
0.10	137	23	16.8	1.00	4.04
0.30	152	95	62.5	1.48	5.32
0.50	146	119	81.5	1.70	5.90
0.70	154	141	91.6	1.85	6.38
0.95	152	144	94.7	1.98	6.62

TABLE 18–2

CALCULATION OF χ^2—DATA OF TABLE 18–1

(1) X	(2) Y	(3) P	(4) n	(5) r	(6) nP	(7) $r - nP$	(8) $\frac{(r - nP)^2}{nP(1 - P)}$
1.00	4.02	16.4	137	23	22.5	+ 0.5	0.013
1.48	5.29	61.4	152	95	93.3	+ 1.7	0.080
1.70	5.87	80.8	146	119	118.0	+ 1.0	0.044
1.85	6.26	89.6	154	141	138.0	+ 3.0	0.627
1.98	6.61	94.6	152	144	143.8	+ 0.2	0.005
						χ^2 =	0.769

TABLE 18–3

CALCULATIONS—DATA OF TABLE 18–1

X	n	Y	w	nw	nwX
1.00	137	4.0	0.439	60.14	60.14
1.48	152	5.3	0.616	93.63	138.57
1.70	146	5.9	0.471	68.77	116.91
1.85	154	6.3	0.336	51.74	95.72
1.98	152	6.6	0.238	36.18	71.64
			Total	310.46	482.98

$$\bar{X} = \frac{482.98}{310.46} = 1.5557$$

$$\Sigma(nwX^2) = 782.8998$$

$$\text{C.T.} = 751.3679$$

$$\Sigma(nwx^2) = 31.5319$$

7. Example 18–2. Fitting a probit regression line by the method of maximum likelihood. The data of columns (1) to (5) of Table 18–4 were obtained from Dr. W. S. McLeod, being part of a published study [9] on refinements in the technique of testing insecticides. They represent percentage kill in batches of *Drosophila* treated with nicotine sulphate. The calculations for fitting a probit regression line by the method of maximum likelihood are enumerated below. It is assumed that the student is familiar with the methods of Example 18–1.

1. Enter data as in columns (1) to (5) of Table 18–4. Obtain empirical probits from the tables by Fisher and Yates, and enter in column (6).
2. Draw Figure 18–3, showing empirical probits plotted against X. Set up a straight line to give as good an eye-fit as possible. Then read off Y_0 on the probit scale to one decimal place and enter in column (7).
3. Obtain weighting coefficients from Fisher and Yates' Table XI or from Finney's Table II.
4. Calculate and enter nw in column (9).
5. Calculate working probits from Fisher and Yates' Table XI and enter in column (10). (Finney's Table IV is much more rapid than Fisher and Yates' Table XI and if available should be used.) The equation for the working probit is

$$Y_1 = \left(Y_0 - \frac{P}{Z}\right) + \frac{p}{Z}$$

Therefore for $Y_0 = 4.2$ and $p = 0.233$

$$Y_1 = 3.4687 + 0.233 \times 3.4519 = 4.27$$

It will be noted that the working probits in this example are identical with the empirical probits. This is not always the case, although it is to be expected that they will be closer to the empirical probits than to Y_0.

6. Calculate the entries for columns (11) and (12), and sum columns (9), (11), and (12). From these calculate

$$\frac{1}{\Sigma(nw)} \qquad \bar{X} = \frac{\Sigma(nwX)}{\Sigma(nw)} \qquad \bar{Y} = \frac{\Sigma(nwY_1)}{\Sigma(nw)} \qquad 9$$

7. Calculate

$$\Sigma(nwx^2) = \Sigma(nwX^2) - \frac{[\Sigma(nwX)]^2}{\Sigma(nw)} \qquad 10$$

$$\Sigma(nwxy_1) = \Sigma(nwXY_1) - \frac{(\Sigma nwX)(\Sigma nwY_1)}{\Sigma(nw)} \qquad 11$$

$$\Sigma(nwy_1^2) = \Sigma(nwY_1^2) - \frac{[\Sigma(nwY_1)]^2}{\Sigma(nw)} \qquad 12$$

$$\chi^2 = \Sigma(nwy_1^2) - \frac{[\Sigma(nwxy_1)]^2}{\Sigma(nwx^2)} \qquad 13$$

In this example $\chi^2 = 24.91$, and on referring to Table A–4 we note that this is a significant value for 4 degrees of freedom. Heterogeneity is obvious.

8. Compute

$$b = \frac{\Sigma(nwxy_1)}{\Sigma(nwx^2)} = \frac{312.86}{118.31} = 2.644 \qquad 14$$

and if heterogeneity were absent we would have

$$V_b = \frac{1}{\Sigma(nwx^2)} = \frac{1}{118.31} = 0.008\ 452$$

$$s_b = \sqrt{0.008\ 452} = 0.0919$$

but, heterogeneity being significant, we have

$$\mu = \frac{\chi^2}{\text{DF}} = \frac{24.91}{4} = 6.228$$

Therefore the corrected variance is

$$0.008\ 452 \times 6.228 = 0.052\ 639$$

and

$$s_b = \sqrt{0.052\ 639} = 0.2294$$

Since $t = 2.78$ at the 5% point for 4 degrees of freedom, the fiducial limits of b are obtained from

$$2.644 \pm 2.78 \times 0.2294 = 2.644 \pm 0.638$$

giving limits of 2.01 and 3.28.

9. From the regression equation

$$Y = \bar{Y}_1 + b(m - \bar{X}) \qquad 15$$

putting $Y = 5$, we get

$$m = \frac{5 - \bar{Y}_1}{b} + \bar{X} = \frac{5 - 5.0661}{2.644} + 1.0273 = 1.0023$$

The dose in original units of concentration expected to give a 50% kill is therefore (antilog 1.0023)/5 = 1.005.

Since χ^2 indicates significant heterogeneity, it is necessary to take this into account in determining the fiducial limits. Also in this example we shall apply the formula for the more exact fiducial limits.

First we have μ, as calculated in step 8, which must be introduced in order to take care of heterogeneity. Also we must obtain

$$g = \frac{t^2\mu}{b^2\Sigma(nwx^2)} = \frac{2.776^2 \times 6.228}{2.644^2 \times 118.31} = 0.0580 \qquad 16$$

Then the exact fiducial limits are given by

$$m + \frac{g}{1-g}(m - \bar{X}) \pm \frac{t}{b(1-g)}\sqrt{\left[\frac{1-g}{\Sigma(nw)} + \frac{(m-\bar{X})^2}{\Sigma(nwx^2)}\right]\mu} \qquad 17$$

which for purposes of calculation is most conveniently broken down into three parts.

$$m + \frac{g}{1-g}(m - \bar{X}) = 1.0023 + \frac{0.0580}{0.9420}(1.0023 - 1.0273) = 1.0038$$

$$\frac{t}{b(1-g)} = \frac{2.776}{2.644 \times 0.9420} = 1.1146$$

$$\sqrt{\mu\left[\frac{1-g}{\Sigma(nw)} + \frac{(m-\bar{X})^2}{\Sigma(nwx^2)}\right]} = \sqrt{\left[\frac{0.9420}{3827} + \frac{(1.0023 - 1.0273)^2}{118.31}\right]6.228}$$

$$= 0.039\,53$$

Finally

$$1.0008 \pm 1.1144 \times 0.03953 = 1.0008 \pm 0.0441$$

giving fiducial limits of 1.045 to 0.957 in dosage terms and 1.11 to 0.91 in actual concentrations.

The procedure and methods for calculating fiducial limits of m may be summarized as follows.

a. No heterogeneity (χ^2 not significant).

(i) g small with respect to unity, where

$$g = \frac{t^2\mu}{b^2\Sigma(nws^2)} \quad \text{(taking } t = 1.96\text{)}$$

Limits given by

$$m \pm 1.96\sqrt{\frac{1}{b^2}\left[\frac{1}{\Sigma(nw)} + \frac{(m-\bar{X})^2}{\Sigma(nwx^2)}\right]}$$

(ii) g appreciable with respect to unity.

Limits given by

$$m + \frac{g}{1-g}(m - \bar{X}) \pm \frac{t}{b(1-g)}\sqrt{\left[\frac{1-g}{\Sigma(nw)} + \frac{(m-\bar{X})^2}{\Sigma(nwx^2)}\right]}$$

b. Significant heterogeneity.
Calculate

$$\mu = \frac{\chi^2}{\text{DF}} \quad \text{and} \quad g = \frac{t^2\mu}{b^2\Sigma(nwx^2)}$$

Limits given by

$$m + \frac{g}{1-g}(m - \bar{X}) \pm \frac{t}{b(1-g)}\sqrt{\left[\frac{1-g}{\Sigma(nw)} + \frac{(m - \bar{X})^2}{\Sigma(nwx^2)}\right]\mu}$$

At this point the student might refer to Section 10 on Experimental Design with a view to assessing the design of the experiment just analyzed.

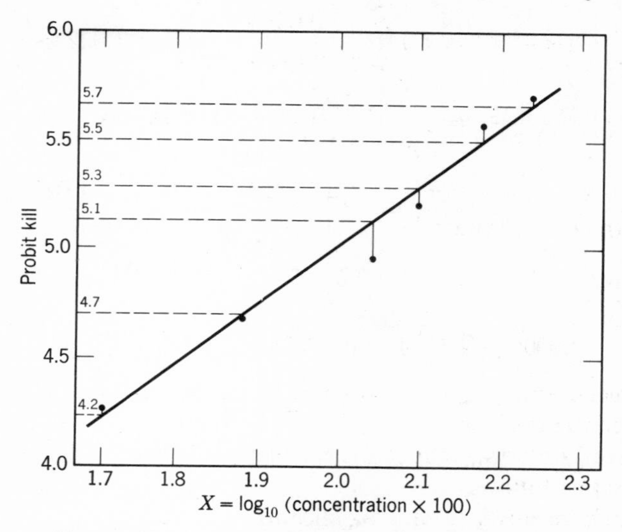

FIGURE 18–3. Fitting of probit regression line to data of Table 18–4.

It will be noted that the dosage range is very good in that the percentage kills range from 23 to 75%. Also, the number of insects in each batch is quite satisfactory. In this experiment there is no control level and hence no measure of natural mortality. This might be considered a weakness in the design, but it is of course possible that the experimenter may have had natural mortality in good control and considered that a measure of it was not required. A significant feature of this experiment is the heterogeneity, and an examination of Figure 18–3 indicates a curvilinear trend. Possibly some relation between dose and dosage other than the logarithmic one tried would be better, and this point at least requires investigation.

TABLE 18–4

DATA ON EFFECT OF DIFFERENT CONCENTRATIONS OF NICOTINE SULPHATE ON *Drosophila melanogaster*, FROM McLEOD [9]

(1) Dose	(2) Log_{10} 10X X	(3) Number of Insects n	(4) Number Killed r	(5) % Kill p	(6) Empirical Probit	(7) Provisional Probit Y_0	(8) Weighting Coefficient w	(9) nw	(10) Working Probit Y_1	(11) nwX	(12) nwY_1
0.50	0.70	1048	244	23.3	4.27	4.2	0.503	527	4.27	368.90	2,250.29
0.75	0.88	1202	451	37.5	4.68	4.7	0.616	740	4.68	651.20	3,463.20
1.10	1.04	1039	503	48.4	4.96	5.1	0.634	659	4.96	685.36	3,268.64
1.25	1.10	1102	638	57.9	5.20	5.3	0.616	679	5.20	746.90	3,530.80
1.50	1.18	1034	736	71.2	5.56	5.5	0.581	601	5.56	709.18	3,341.56
1.75	1.24	1167	880	75.4	5.69	5.7	0.532	621	5.69	770.04	3,533.49
								3827		3931.58	19,387.98

$$\frac{1}{\Sigma nw} = 0.000\,261\,3 \qquad \bar{X} = 1.0273 \qquad \bar{Y}_1 = 5.0661$$

$$\Sigma(nwX^2) = 4157.33 \qquad \Sigma(nwXY_1) = 20{,}230.65 \qquad \Sigma(nwY_1^2) = 99{,}073.76$$

$$\text{C.T.} = 4039.02 \qquad \text{C.T.} = 19{,}917.79 \qquad \text{C.T.} = 98{,}221.52$$

$$118.31 \qquad 312.86 \qquad 852.24$$

$$\text{C.T.} = 827.33$$

$$\chi^2 = 24.91$$

8. Example 18–3. Determination of relative potency of biological preparations. In the measurement of the effect of toxic substances, effectiveness of sera for the prevention of disease, and so forth, one of the common problems is to compare the potency of two or more preparations. In some experiments the preparations may be new ones, but the usual problem is that of comparing one or more new preparations with a standard. In biological work of this sort it is very difficult to obtain exactly similar conditions in experiments carried out at different times and with different insects or animals. The inclusion of a standard in an experiment is therefore a routine procedure.

Irwin [8] quotes an example from Smith [12] in which two antipneumococcus sera are tested for the prevention of disease in mice. The data are given in Table 18–5. The symbols α and β distinguish the sera, and for our purpose β can be considered as the standard. Note that the data are for percentage survival and not for percentage mortality as in previous examples. The calculations are conveniently carried out in the steps enumerated below.

1. Set up the data as in the first four columns of Table 18–5 and calculate p (the percentage survival). Empirical probits are then found from Fisher and Yates' Table IX, noting that for $p = 0$ the empirical probit is $-\infty$.

2. Draw Figure 18–4, locating the points corresponding to the empirical probits but neglecting $-\infty$. On this graph draw two *parallel* lines giving

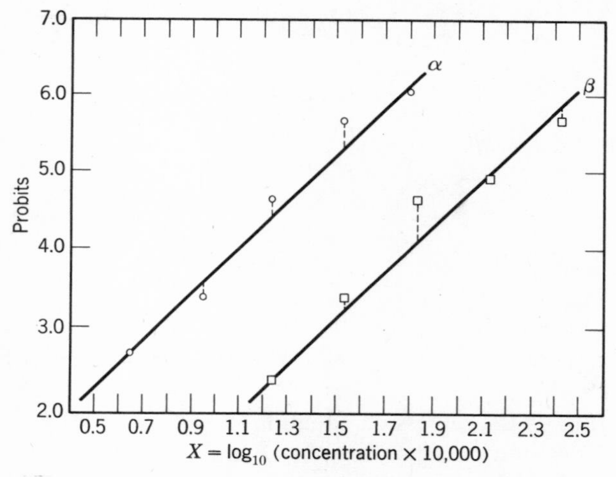

FIGURE 18–4. Probit regression lines for data of Table 18–5.

a good eye-fit. Then for each point on the graph find the corresponding point on the straight line and from these read off the provisional probits (Y_0) on the probit scale. Enter these in column (7). For the empirical probit $-\infty$, note that the figure is entered at $X = 0.64$ for α and $X = 1.24$ for β.

3. Enter weighting coefficients in column (8) from Fisher and Yates' Table XI.

Calculate and enter nw in column (9).

4. The working probits of column (10) are obtained from Fisher and Yates' Table IX. For $Y_0 = 2.7$, $Y_1 = 2.32$ from the formula for a *minimum working probit*; that is, $Y_1 = Y - P/Z$. For $Y_0 = 3.6$ we have

$$Y_1 = \left(Y - \frac{P}{Z}\right) + \frac{p}{Z} = 3.0606 + 0.05 \times 6.6788 = 3.39$$

5. Calculate and enter nwX and nwY_1 in columns (11) and (12). Then sum columns (9), (11), (12) separately for α and β, and calculate $1/\Sigma(nw)$, $\bar{X}$, and $\bar{Y}_1$.

6. Provisional values of b_1, m_α, m_β, $M_{\alpha\beta}$ and $\rho_{\alpha\beta}$ may now be calculated.

$$M_{\alpha\beta} = m_\beta - m_\alpha \quad \text{(relative potency in dosage)}$$

$$\rho_{\alpha\beta} = 10^{M_{\alpha\beta}} \quad \text{(relative potency in units of concentration)}$$

From the graph for α

$$\begin{array}{lll} X_2 = 1.80 & Y_2 = 6.01 & \\ X_1 = 0.45 & Y_1 = 2.12 & b = \dfrac{3.89}{1.35} = 2.88 \\ \hline \text{Difference} = 1.35 & 3.89 & \end{array}$$

From the graph for β

$$\begin{array}{lll} X_2 = 2.40 & Y_2 = 5.70 & \\ X_1 = 1.15 & Y_1 = 2.10 & b = \dfrac{3.60}{1.25} = 2.88 \\ \hline \text{Difference} = 1.25 & 3.60 & \end{array}$$

The two estimates of b must of course agree if the two lines have been drawn parallel.

Then, setting up the regression equation $Y = \bar{Y}_1 + b(X - \bar{X})$ for both α and β and substituting m_α and m_β for X and 5 for Y gives

$$\alpha \qquad Y = 4.96 + 2.88(X - 1.39) = 0.96 + 2.88X$$

$$5 = 0.96 + 2.88m_\alpha \qquad m_\alpha = \frac{4.04}{2.88} = 1.40$$

$$\beta \qquad Y = 4.87 + 2.88(X - 2.08) = -1.12 + 2.88X$$

$$5 = -1.12 + 2.88m_\beta \qquad m_\beta = \frac{6.12}{2.88} = 2.12$$

$$M_{\alpha\beta} = 2.12 - 1.40 = 0.72$$

$$\rho_{\alpha\beta} = 10^{0.72} = 5.2$$

The provisional estimate indicates that 5.2 times the concentration of β is required to give the same protection as 1 unit of concentration of α.

7. Complete the calculations given below in order to obtain new estimates of the parameters, and to test their significance and the goodness of fit of the new regression lines.

		α		β		$\alpha + \beta$
$\Sigma(nwX^2)$	=	160.1200		322.5672		
C.T.	=	151.4806		315.4643		
$\Sigma(nwx^2)$	=	8.6394	+	7.1029	=	15.7423
$\Sigma(nwXY_1)$	=	566.2667		756.1954		
C.T.	=	540.0853		739.8953		
$\Sigma(nwxy_1)$	=	26.1814	+	16.3001	=	42.4815
$\Sigma(nwY_1^2)$	=	2009.2773		1777.4078		
C.T.	=	1925.6069		1735.3626		
		83.6704		42.0452	=	125.7156
Regression	=	79.3418		37.4063		
χ^2	=	4.3286	+	4.6389	=	8.9675
DF	=	3	+	3		6
5% point	=	7.815		7.815		12.592

A complete analysis of χ^2 can be made by calculating a total χ^2 for 7 degrees of freedom as follows:

$$\chi^2 = 125.7156 - \frac{(42.4815)^2}{15.7423} = 11.0768$$

giving the analysis

	χ^2	DF	MS	5% Point χ^2
Parallelism of regressions	2.1093	1	2.109	3.84
Heterogeneity	8.9675	6	1.494	12.59
Total	11.0768	7	1.582	14.07

None of the χ^2 values is significant at the 5% point although there is some indication of heterogeneity. This seems to be due to a tendency of the α regression to be somewhat curvilinear and to one point on the β

regression that deviates rather widely from the straight line. The parallelism is also only reasonably satisfactory. Note that heterogeneity as measured here is a residual effect—that is, it represents total lack of agreement with the straight line within the two regressions.

Due to some indication of heterogeneity the heterogeneity factor will be used in setting up fiducial limits although it is not expected that they will be greatly affected.

8. Obtain new estimates of the parameters and set up fiducial limits.

$$b = \frac{42.4815}{15.7423} = 2.6986$$

$$\mu = \frac{8.9675}{4} = 2.2419$$

$$V_{(b)} = \frac{\mu}{\Sigma(nwx^2)} = \frac{2.2419}{15.7423} = 0.1424$$

$$s_b = \sqrt{0.1424} = 0.377$$

Fiducial limits are $2.699 \pm 2.776 \times 0.377$, giving 3.75 and 1.65. Then from

$$Y_\alpha = 4.9597 + 2.6986(X - 1.3911) = 1.2057 + 2.6986X$$

the value of m_α is calculated by putting $m_\alpha = X$, and $Y_\alpha = 5$.

$$m_\alpha = \frac{5 - 1.2057}{2.6986} = 1.4060$$

Similarly

$$Y_\beta = 4.8677 + 2.6986(X - 2.0754) = -0.7330 + 2.6986X$$

$$\therefore \qquad m_\beta = \frac{5 + 0.7330}{2.6986} = 2.1244$$

Then

$$M_{\alpha\beta} = 2.1244 - 1.4060 = 0.7184$$

$$\rho_{\alpha\beta} = 10^{0.72} = 5.2$$

The fiducial limits of $M_{\alpha\beta}$ are given by

$$M + \frac{g}{1-g}[M - (\bar{X}_\beta - \bar{X}_\alpha)] \pm \frac{t}{b(1-g)} \sqrt{(1-g)(V_{\bar{Y}\alpha} + V_{\bar{Y}\beta}) + [(\bar{X}_\beta - \bar{X}_\alpha) - M]^2 V_b}$$

where g and the variances must in this example, be increased by the heterogeneity factor. We have to find:

$$g = \frac{2.776^2 \times 2.2419}{2.6986^2 \times 15.7423} = \frac{17.2765}{114.6424} = 0.1507$$

$$V_{\bar{Y}\alpha} = \frac{2.2419}{78.28} = 0.028\ 64$$

$$V_{\bar{Y}\beta} = \frac{2.2419}{73.24} = 0.030\ 61$$

$$V_b = 0.1424 \quad \text{(step 8, above)}$$

$$\frac{g}{1-g}[M - (\bar{X}_\beta - \bar{X}_\alpha)] = \frac{0.1507}{0.8493}(0.7184 - 0.6843) = 0.006\ 051$$

$$\frac{t}{b(1-g)} = \frac{2.776}{2.6986 \times 0.8493} = 1.2112$$

$$\sqrt{(1-g)(V_{\bar{Y}\beta} + V_{\bar{Y}\alpha}) + [(\bar{X}_\beta - \bar{X}_\alpha) - M]^2 V_b}$$

$$= \sqrt{(0.8493 \times 0.059\ 25) + (0.6843 - 0.7184)^2 \times 0.1424}$$

$$= \sqrt{0.050\ 49} = 0.2247$$

Finally the fiducial limits are

$$0.7184 + 0.0061 \pm 1.2112 \times 0.2247 = 0.7245 \pm 0.2722$$

giving 0.9967 and 0.4523. The corresponding relative potencies are $10^{0.997} = 9.93$ and $10^{0.452} = 2.83$.

Owing largely to lack of homogeneity the final result in terms of relative potency of the two preparations is not very satisfactory.

9. Other developments of probit analysis. The theory and examples given in this chapter are merely an introduction to probit analysis. The student who wishes to obtain a full treatment should refer to *Probit Analysis* by D. J. Finney [5].

One feature not covered in this chapter but which may be of great importance is the treatment of data containing a check in which mortality occurs. This requires a correction throughout the data. The method in detail is given by Finney.

Mortality-dosage experiments can be carried out in factorial design. For example an insect spray may be applied in two forms, each at two or more concentrations. The analysis of the data involves fitting probit planes.

Another interesting development is the application of graphical methods in order to reduce calculations to a minimum. A very complete graphical method involving nomograms for simplifying most of the calculations has been given by Wilcoxon and Litchfield [11]. These methods have considerable value when an appreciable number of analyses are to be made.

These and many other phases of the probit analysis technique are available to the experimenter who wishes to take advantage of them.

TABLE 18–5

CALCULATION OF RELATIVE POTENCY OF TWO ANTI-PNEUMOCOCCUS SERA

	(1)	(2)	(3)	(4)	(5)	(6)	(7)	(8)	(9)	(10)	(11)	(12)
		Log_{10} $\times$ 10,000		Number Surviving		Empirical Probit						
	λ	X	n	r	p		Y_0	w	nw	Y_1	nwX	nwY_1
α	0.000 4375	0.64	40	0	0	$-\infty$	2.7	0.076	3.04	2.32	1.946	7.053
	0.000 875	0.94	40	2	5	3.36	3.6	0.302	12.08	3.39	11.355	40.951
	0.001 75	1.24	40	14	35	4.61	4.4	0.558	22.32	4.63	27.677	103.342
	0.003 5	1.54	40	30	75	5.67	5.3	0.616	24.64	5.65	37.946	139.216
	0.007	1.85	40	34	85	6.04	6.1	0.405	16.20	6.03	29.970	97.686
									78.28		108.894	388.248
β	0.001 75	1.24	40	0	0	$-\infty$	2.4	0.040	1.60	2.06	1.984	3.296
	0.003 5	1.54	40	2	5	3.36	3.2	0.180	7.20	3.38	11.088	24.336
	0.007	1.85	40	14	35	4.61	4.1	0.471	18.84	4.72	34.854	88.925
	0.014	2.15	40	19	47.5	4.94	5.0	0.637	25.48	4.94	54.782	125.871
	0.028	2.45	40	30	75	5.67	5.8	0.503	20.12	5.67	49.294	114.080
									73.24		152.002	356.508

$$\frac{1}{\Sigma nw_\alpha} = \frac{1}{78.28} = 0.012\,775 \qquad \bar{X}_\alpha = \frac{108.894}{78.280} = 1.3911 \qquad \bar{Y}_\alpha = 4.9597$$

$$\frac{1}{\Sigma nw_\beta} = \frac{1}{73.240} = 0.013\,654 \qquad \bar{X}_\beta = \frac{152.002}{73.240} = 2.0754 \qquad \bar{Y}_\beta = 4.8677$$

10. Experimental design. After having worked through the examples and learned the fundamentals of the probit analysis method, the student is in a position to make some decisions as to how new experiments should be set up. Two questions normally arise in the minds of investigators planning experiments of this type. In the first place they ask: "What should be the range and number of concentrations?" And in the second place: "How many insects or animals, etc., should be treated at each level?"

The range of dose is obviously something that cannot be answered without some preliminary information, and in dealing with an entirely new substance it would seem to be desirable to get preliminary data on roughly approximate levels for the LD 10, LD 50, and LD 90. It should then be possible to set up a series of satisfactory dose levels for a well-controlled experiment, keeping in mind that the least information with respect to potency is given by the levels that give very low and very high percentage kills. The most valuable points are those giving kills from 25 to 75%. Kills lower than 16% and higher than 84% give so little information with respect to the LD 50 that they can practically be disregarded. Their precision is so low that a much larger number of insects is required to estimate them with the accuracy ordinarily obtained in the region of the LD 50.

The question of how many insects there should be in each batch is related to the number of batches, but in any event it is preferable with a given number of insects available to spread these over several batches at different levels rather than to have only 3 or 4 larger batches at 3 or 4 levels. The general accuracy of the experiment is of course increased by increasing the number of insects in each batch. Perhaps certain published results of probit analysis with 20 to 30 insects in each batch have led investigators to think that a greater number is unnecessary. This is of course incorrect, and the greatest number should be used that does not make the experiment too expensive and unwieldly relative to the value of the information to be obtained. It must be recognized that in experimenting with animals the numbers may have to be small. The chief point to remember, however, is that the probit method or any other type of analysis does not make up for lack of accuracy in the experiment or unsatisfactory techniques.

In most experiments of the biological assay type it is important to have some measure of natural mortality. This is usually accomplished by having a control level. When mortality occurs at this level it is advisable to make a correction in the analysis. The method for this is described by Finney [5] in some detail.

11. Exercises.

1. Table 18–6 gives data from Morrison [10] on results in applying different concentrations of nicotine sulphate to batches of *Drosophila* of 150 flies each.

Obtain a provisional regression line for the data and calculate χ^2 for goodness of fit. Estimate b and m from the graph.

TABLE 18–6

Concentration	Insects Killed r	% Kill p
0.6	97	64.7
0.8	120	80.0
1.1	133	88.7
1.4	137	91.3
1.8	145	96.7

2. Table 18–7 gives data from Morrison [10] in an experiment for comparing the effect of containers in the treatment of *Drosophila* with nicotine sulphate. A batch consists of 150 flies, but in the α series the flies were treated in 10 containers of 15 flies each.

Complete the analysis of the data as in Example 18–3, obtaining $M_{\alpha\beta}$ and its fiducial limits.

TABLE 18–7

α Series		β Series	
Concentration	% Kill	Concentration	% Kill
0.6	31.4	0.6	64.8
0.8	39.7	0.8	79.8
1.1	56.6	1.1	88.6
1.4	63.8	1.4	91.6
1.8	77.7	1.8	96.8

REFERENCES

1. C. I. Bliss, The Method of Probits, *Science*, **79**, 38–39, 1934.
2. C. I. Bliss, The Calculation of the Dosage-Mortality Curve, *Ann. Applied Biol.*, **22**, 134–167, 1935.
3. C. I. Bliss, The Comparison of Dosage-Mortality Data, *Ann. Applied Biol.*, **22**, 307–333, 1935.
4. G. T. Fechner, *Elemente der Psychophysik*, Breitkopf and Härtel, Leipzig, 1860.
5. D. J. Finney, *Probit Analysis*, Cambridge University Press, Cambridge, 2nd ed., 1951.
6. R. A. Fisher and F. Yates, *Statistical Tables*, Oliver and Boyd, Edinburgh and London, 3rd ed., 1949.
7. J. H. Gaddum, Reports on Biological Standards, *Med. Research Council Brit. Special Rept. Ser.*, **183**, 1933.

8. J. O. Irwin, Statistical Method Applied to Biological Assay, *J. Roy. Stat. Soc. Suppl.*, **4,** 1–60, 1937.
9. W. S. McLeod, Further Refinements of a Technique for Testing Contact Insecticides, *Can. J. Research*, **D, 22,** 87–104, 1944.
10. F. O. Morrison, The Standardizing of a Laboratory Method for Comparing Toxicity of Contact Insecticides, *Can. J. Research*, **D, 21,** 35–75, 1943.
11. F. Wilcoxon and J. T. Litchfield, *A Simplified Method of Evaluating Dose-Effect Experiments*, publication of American Cyanamid Company, Stamford Research Laboratories, reprinted from *Journal of Pharmacology and Therapeutics*, **97,** 99–113, 1949.
12. Wilson Smith, *J. Path. Bact.*, **35,** 309, 1932.

CHAPTER 19

Quality Control and Sampling for Inspection and Verification

1. Definition of quality control. Quality control is considered here to be the maintenance of quality in a uniform flow of manufactured products. This is essentially what the term quality control has come to mean in recent years, but this does not imply that the same principles cannot be applied in other fields. Actually, as we shall see later, the principles of quality control can be applied wherever we are concerned with the establishment of uniform standards of quality in a continuous flow of products, or, in other words, where the units or parts of the flow are spaced consecutively in time.

In quality control more emphasis is placed on the time element than in many other types of statistical applications. Of course we have time trends in economic and business statistics, and time is often a factor in research experiments, but our interest in such studies is usually to measure, interpret, and test the significance of the trends. In quality control the objective is to study the trend with sufficient accuracy to observe any deviations from an even course, and, when such deviations are observed, to take the action necessary to prevent future occurrences.

2. The control chart. Although there are many phases of quality control, one of the basic applications is the use of control charts. To illustrate the control chart let us suppose that the product is bread and that loaves are produced in batches of 100 at a time. Any variable may be the subject of quality control, and there may be as many variables as we wish to measure, but for each a separate chart will be required. Let us suppose that the variable in this case is loaf weight. We chose this variable for the first example because it is easy to measure and does not involve destructive sampling. From each batch we form a sub-group or sample, the selection of loaves for the sample being purely random. The first problem to be solved is the number of loaves required. Since sampling is not destructive, the chief determining factors will be time and expense, but in any event the minimum number of loaves will be 2 as otherwise the control chart will be of no value. A very common practice, unless there are very good reasons for choosing a different number, is to take 4 loaves. The weights of the individual loaves are determined and the mean ($\bar{X}$) and the standard deviation (s') calculated. We now set up two charts with time as the abscissas, and on one of these we plot means and on the other the standard deviations. The plotting of one such set of determinations is of no value, but we proceed to plot similar determinations as the batches come forward. Obviously, uniformity of product will be represented by a horizontal row of points and a widely deviating flow of products by a scatter. After plotting 10 to 20 batches a calculation can be made of what is known as control limits, the purpose being to study the relation between chance causes of variation and those due to definite assignable causes.

Assuming that k samples of n each have been taken, we have the k means $\bar{X}_1, \bar{X}_2, \cdots, \bar{X}_k$, and the k standard deviations $s'_1, s'_2, \cdots, s'_k$, where s'_i is calculated from

$$s'_i = \sqrt{\frac{\Sigma(X - \bar{X})^2}{n}}$$

On the chart for means we plot the mean of all samples given by

$$\bar{X}_t = \frac{\bar{X}_1 + \bar{X}_2 + \cdots + \bar{X}_k}{k}$$

With respect to control limits for the mean it is customary to set these so that the probability of a mean's going beyond them due to chance variation only is quite small. Shewhart [4] of the Bell Telephone Laboratories takes it as a general rule based on both theoretical and practical grounds that the limits should be

Lower limit $\qquad L_1 = \bar{X}_t - 3s'_{\bar{X}}$

Upper limit $\qquad L_2 = \bar{X}_t + 3s'_{\bar{X}}$

where $s'_{\bar{X}}$, the standard deviation of a mean of a sample of size n, is calculated as follows.

$$\bar{s}' = \frac{s'_1 + s'_2 + \cdots + s'_k}{k}$$

$$s'_{\bar{X}} = \frac{\bar{s}'}{c_2\sqrt{n}}$$

where

$$c_2 = \sqrt{\frac{2}{n}}\,\frac{\left(\frac{n-2}{2}\right)!}{\left(\frac{n-3}{2}\right)!}$$

For practical calculations Shewhart [4] has tabulated a series of values of c_2. These are reproduced in Table A–5 in the Appendix.

On the chart for standard deviations we plot the mean $\bar{s}'$ and determine the limits from

$$L_1 = \bar{s}' - 3s'_s$$

$$L_2 = \bar{s}' + 3s'_s$$

where

$$s'_s = \frac{\bar{s}'}{c_2\sqrt{2n}}$$

Whenever L_1 turns out to be negative, it is taken as zero.

We now examine Figure 19–1 taken from Pearson [2] in a monograph on industrial standardization and quality control. It represents a control

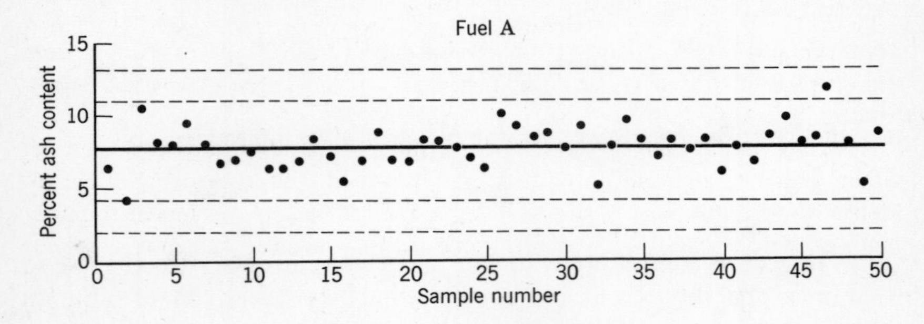

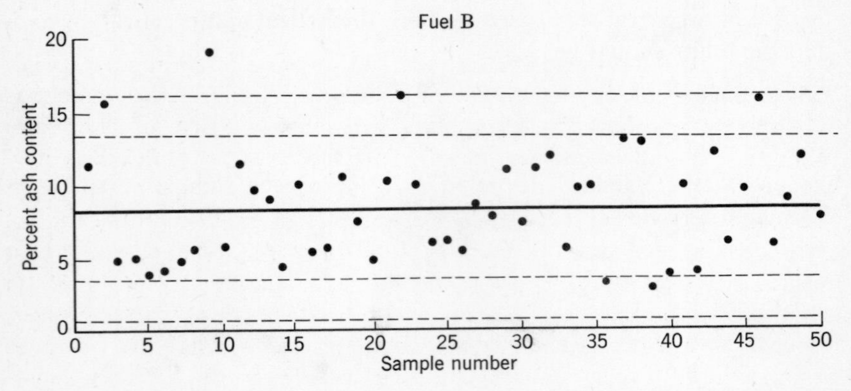

FIGURE 19–1. Control charts for mean ash content of coal delivered by two companies. Extracted with permission from *Applications of Statistical Methods to Industrial Standardization and Quality Control*, by E. S. Pearson, B.S. 600, 1935; reproduced by permission of the British Standards Institution, 24/28 Victoria Street, Westminster, London, S.W.1, from whom official copies can be obtained, price 12/6*d*, post free.

chart for means taken by a consumer of coal who was receiving it from two companies. In this instance the means and standard deviations were calculated from consecutive pairs of loads delivered, so that $n = 2$. We note that for fuel A the limits of ash content are much narrower than for fuel B and only one sample falls outside the inner limits representing a probability of 0.025 and none outside the outer limits representing a probability of 0.001.

The charts of Figure 19–1 show very clearly that fuel B was varying because of definitely assignable causes which could probably have been removed by attention to engineering details.

At this point, it is worth while to return to an emphasis of the importance of the order in which the data are studied. To demonstrate this point Shewhart [5] gives a chart showing results for 204 observations in groups of 4 of the resistance in 10^2 megohms of pieces of insulating material. In the first instance the data are plotted as the pieces were obtained in production, and in the second instance the data for the 204 pieces were written on chips and drawn at random in groups of 4. These charts are reproduced in Figure 19–2.

It is obvious from Figure 19–2 that there is evidence of lack of control when the data are plotted in consecutive order, i.e., of the presence of definite assignable causes of variation. When the data are mixed together and drawn at random, the limits are closer and there is no evidence whatever of lack of control. The latter result is of course to be expected as the process of mixing the results and drawing at random has completely eliminated the distinction between chance errors and those arising from assignable causes. The entire purpose of the control chart is in this way defeated. This example brings out the essential importance of the time element as portrayed in a control chart. It is analogous to bringing another dimension into the representation of the data. Without this dimension the important characteristics of the data may be lost.

Violent fluctuations in the means of samples as detected by the control chart show that the products are fluctuating in average quality and as a result consumers may be provided with lots that fall below a certain definite desirable standard. There is another factor in quality, however, which is frequently of considerable importance. This is the factor of variation itself, even when the level does not fall below a certain established standard. Information on variability is given by the control chart of standard deviations. In general, when the means fluctuate violently the standard deviations can be expected to fluctuate in a similar manner, but in certain cases the means appear to be in control whereas the standard deviations are not. This represents an undesirable condition with respect

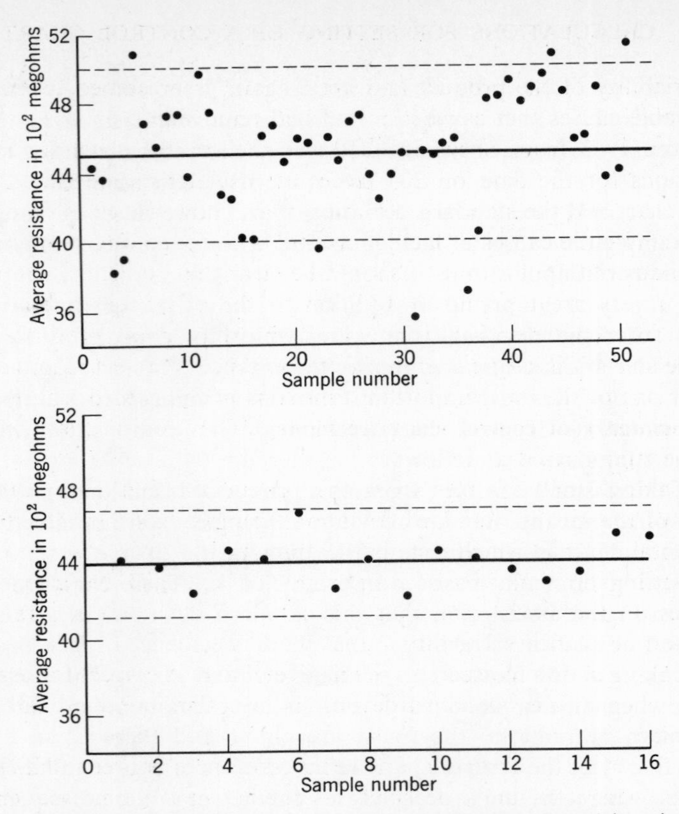

FIGURE 19–2. Control chart from Shewhart [5] for 204 observations in groups of 4, of the resistance in 10^2 megohms of pieces of insulating material. Upper chart represents data as actually taken from the production line. Lower chart represents data after mixing and drawing out groups of 4 at random. Reproduced from *Statistical Methods from the Viewpoint of Quality Control*, W. A. Shewhart, U.S. Dept. of Agriculture, Graduate School, 1939.

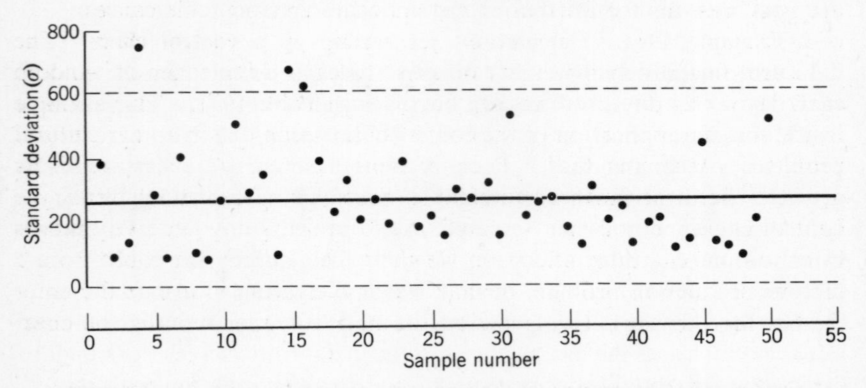

FIGURE 19–3. Control chart for standard deviations. Data from Shewhart [5], as in Figure 19–2. Reproduced from *Statistical Methods from the Viewpoint of Quality Control*, W. A. Shewhart, U.S. Dept. of Agriculture, Graduate School, 1939.

to variability of the product and here, again, is presumed to arise from assignable causes that can be located and removed.

Figure 19–3 from Shewhart [5] gives the control chart for standard deviations for the data on 204 pieces of insulating material. Both the mean chart and the standard deviation chart showed lack of control. In this example the causes of lack of control were found and removed.

In industrial applications it should be clear that statistical control may mean a very great saving in addition to the enhanced reputation that comes from the merchandising of a uniformly good product. When trouble starts it is of great economic importance to detect it immediately. This is one of the most important functions of the control chart.

3. Summary of control chart technique. The control chart technique may be summarized as follows:

1. Taking small samples from the production line and plotting the values of the means, standard deviations, ranges, or other statistics on a horizontal chart in which time is the abscissa.

2. Setting up limits based on the pooled standard deviations of the samples on the assumption that this standard deviation is a fair representation of chance variability.

3. Taking action to ascertain the nature of and to correct for assignable causes when means, standard deviations, or other statistics, fall outside the limits.

The theory of the control chart is that differences between units in small samples, where the units occur close together in the time sequence, are much more likely to represent chance deviations than would be the case if large samples were taken consisting of units spread widely along the production line. Assuming that a good approximation to the standard deviation representing chance variation has been made, the limits set up are such that, if the statistic charted wanders out of these limits, there are good reasons for attributing the variation to assignable causes.

4. Example 19–1. Calculations for setting up a control chart. The data are on individual weights of eggs, 10 eggs being taken at random each day for 24 days.* The data are given in Table 19–1. This example is useful as an application of the control chart technique in an agricultural problem. Assuming that a flock of hens has reached the stage in its growth where the mean egg weight is not showing a distinct trend, the control chart method can be employed to indicate any decisive changes in conditions that may affect egg weight. This differs somewhat from a factory production problem in that seasonal trends will eventually enter in, but for the usual laying period during the winter months the chart

* Data obtained by courtesy of the University of Manitoba, Poultry Department.

may be quite effective in giving an indication of the general condition of the flock. Of course other egg characters could be charted. Weight was taken in this example because it was an important but easily determined character.

The calculations shown in Table 19–2 would ordinarily be computed in the order that the data are obtained. Each day the mean and standard deviation would be plotted on the control chart as in Figure 19–4. A preliminary check on the state of control might be made after a period of

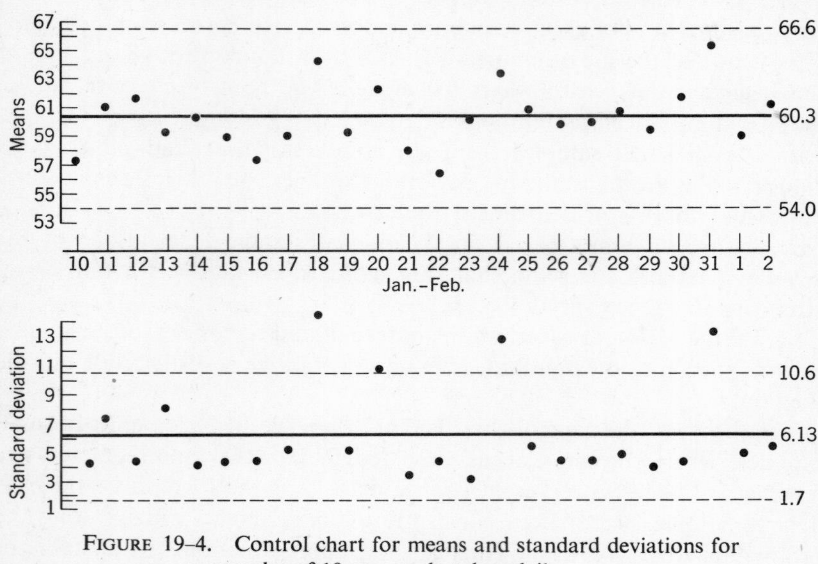

FIGURE 19–4. Control chart for means and standard deviations for samples of 10 eggs each, taken daily.

about 10 days. Here we have assumed that the trial has been operating for 24 days, and we wish to set up the limits of variation on the control chart which will then remain for another period of about 20 days, at which time the data are to be again summarized and new limits set up.

Note that in calculating s' we apply the formula for large samples; i.e., the divisor is the number in the sample. This is in accord with the recommendations made by Shewhart [4]. In determining the $3s'_{\bar{x}}$ limits for the mean, the bias in s' is removed by dividing by the factor c_2.

On studying the control chart of the means in this example it is clear that there is very little evidence of lack of control. The chart for standard deviations, however, shows 4 values that are beyond the upper limits. An examination of individual weights shows that on these days a single exceptionally large egg occurred in the sample. These are undoubtedly double-yolked eggs which are known to occur in practically all flocks but probably with greater frequency under conditions where the hens are being forced beyond the capacity of their egg-laying apparatus. This might be regarded by the poultryman as a type of abnormality on which it would be valuable to have a check, and, although it might not be possible to eliminate the double-yolked eggs completely, if they seemed to occur too frequently action of some sort would be indicated, either by varying the diet or by eliminating the offending birds.

Although this example seems to indicate that egg weight alone is of value for control purposes, it should be obvious that other egg characters could be used. With a fairly large flock it might be quite profitable to employ destructive sampling in which case quality factors could be accurately studied. A control chart would be set up for each character, and a complete check obtained on the output of the flock. Trouble would be observed at an early stage, and action taken before economic losses were involved.

There is a specific problem to be considered in applying control charts to the output of animals or plants in that definite and normal seasonal trends may take place. Although it might be possible to set up normal trends and study the deviations from these, it would seem to be more

TABLE 19–1

DATA ON EGG WEIGHTS—SAMPLES OF 10 EACH TAKEN ON 24 CONSECUTIVE DAYS

Dec. 10	55	53	56	63	66	58	53	57	61	53
11	59	62	56	51	61	75	57	60	55	74
12	55	61	62	55	64	59	60	65	66	70
13	74	44	60	63	56	51	63	55	58	68
14	55	57	63	67	61	64	65	57	55	58
15	62	62	54	59	61	56	54	68	57	55
16	50	53	58	57	58	56	68	57	61	56
17	61	58	61	50	60	61	54	63	69	53
18	59	50	55	51	75	57	63	95	78	60
19	64	62	55	53	60	55	56	71	60	57
20	58	93	60	60	57	63	60	53	63	54
21	56	57	58	62	55	57	63	53	55	64
22	55	51	61	52	61	55	61	51	63	55
23	60	64	57	58	66	59	57	61	56	63
24	98	63	56	62	67	62	52	50	57	66
25	64	66	64	65	55	67	62	59	54	51
26	52	60	57	65	65	57	65	54	60	64
27	64	61	69	61	54	55	60	62	54	60
28	67	61	59	60	61	62	71	56	56	54
29	65	65	63	63	60	55	54	56	55	60
30	65	60	66	60	56	70	60	54	64	63
31	58	64	58	64	103	65	64	67	51	60
Jan. 1	64	63	64	55	57	64	55	63	56	49
2	66	57	70	59	55	54	62	61	59	69

practical to establish a new mean at frequent intervals. With egg production, for example, it might be advisable to operate with 10-day periods. The most efficient method would arise from actual experience and could be developed while the control chart work is in progress.

TABLE 19–2

CALCULATION OF MEANS AND STANDARD DEVIATIONS AND $3s'$ LIMITS FOR CONTROL CHART

	Total	Mean	$\Sigma(X^2)$	Σx^2	s'
Dec. 10	575	57.5	33,247	184.5	4.30
11	610	61.0	37,758	548.0	7.40
12	617	61.7	38,273	204.1	4.52
13	592	59.2	35,700	653.6	8.08
14	602	60.2	36,412	171.6	4.14
15	588	58.8	34,756	181.6	4.26
16	574	57.4	33,152	204.4	4.52
17	590	59.0	35,082	272.0	5.22
18	643	64.3	43,159	1814.1	13.47
19	593	59.3	35,425	260.1	5.10
20	621	62.1	39,725	1160.9	10.77
21	580	58.0	33,766	126.0	3.55
22	565	56.5	32,113	190.5	4.36
23	601	60.1	36,221	100.9	3.18
24	633	63.3	41,695	1626.1	12.75
25	607	60.7	37,129	284.1	5.33
26	599	59.9	36,089	208.9	4.57
27	600	60.0	36,200	200.0	4.47
28	607	60.7	37,085	240.1	4.90
29	596	59.6	35,690	168.4	4.10
30	618	61.8	38,398	205.6	4.53
31	654	65.4	44,540	1768.4	13.30
Jan. 1	590	59.0	35,062	252.0	5.02
2	612	61.2	37,734	279.6	5.29
Total		1446.7			147.13

$$\bar{X} = \frac{1446.7}{24} = 60.28 \qquad \bar{X} + 3s'_{\bar{X}} = 60.28 + 6.30 = 66.58$$

$$\bar{s}' = \frac{147.13}{24} = 6.130 \qquad \bar{X} - 3s'_{\bar{X}} = 60.28 - 6.30 = 53.98$$

$$s'_{\bar{X}} = \frac{6.130}{0.9228 \times 3.162} = 2.101 \qquad \bar{s}' + 3s'_{s'} = 6.130 + 4.455 = 10.58$$

$$s'_{s'} = \frac{6.130}{0.9228 \times 4.472} = 1.485 \qquad \bar{s}' - 3s'_{s'} = 6.130 - 4.455 = 1.68$$

5. Sampling for inspection. The problems of sampling for purposes of inspection are much the same regardless of the nature of the material inspected. For this reason the inspection of lots of manufactured products for the detection of poor quality articles is essentially similar to inspecting herds of cattle for disease or fields of grain for the presence of off-types or other varieties. It appears to be generally true, however, that in the manufacturing process the efficiency of inspection procedures are more readily interpreted in terms of costs and savings. Consequently the techniques of sampling and inspection for factory outputs have been studied extensively and practical procedures have been worked out that are now being widely employed. The inspection of agricultural products has not been studied as extensively, and in many cases procedures are followed that are not the most efficient or the most economical.

Although the principles of sampling for inspection purposes are essentially the same irrespective of the material inspected, in every inspection procedure there are certain basic statistical problems to be worked out. For example we must find the appropriate theoretical distribution of defective units. In considering the probability of obtaining a defective unit from a production line in which the proportion of defectives is 10%, we are obviously dealing with a binomial distribution. In seed sampling, if the proportion of foreign seeds is 1 in 10,000, the Poisson distribution is more appropriate. In other examples we may have a normal distribution, or a negative binomial, and so forth. Also we have to consider the cost of inspection, the importance of accuracy in inspection, and the value of the data provided by the inspection as a basis for control of quality by the producer.

It is not possible, therefore, to take procedures developed in a factory for inspecting lots for defective parts and apply them directly for example to inspection of fields of seed grain. In all cases there is preliminary work to be done and data collected before an adequate sampling and inspection program can be developed.

Since the greatest developments in sampling and inspection have taken place in the control of quality of manufactured products, the principles can best be studied by a brief examination of the procedures developed in this field.

6. Single sampling. This is the term applied to a method of sampling worked out by Dodge and Romig [1] of the Bell Telephone System. We should visualize in the first place a factory in continuous operation and articles of varying quality being produced. For convenience it can be assumed that the articles are being collected in lots of 1000, and the job of the inspectors is to draw a sample from each lot and decide whether or not the lot meets specifications as to their containing not more than a given proportion of defectives. An efficient, but not necessarily the most efficient, method* from the standpoint of the average outgoing quality is to inspect every item and remove the defectives. This, however, automatically places inspection costs at a maximum, and if the average quality is high a great deal of this is wasted effort. On the other hand such great care might be taken in the factory as to render inspection unnecessary, but this requires very specialized procedures and a large proportion of highly skilled workers, and the cost of the articles is increased to a point where all profits are absorbed. There is obviously a balance somewhere between production costs and inspection costs, for a given average outgoing quality, that will result in maximum economy. It is this balance which the statistician must work out.

In single sampling the first step is to decide on the sample size and the acceptance number. The acceptance number is the number of defective units tolerated in a sample of a given size. These are worked out from data available on the average quality of the lots submitted, the specified tolerance percentage of defective units, and a specified risk of accepting a lot having the tolerance percentage of defectives. For example, the lots may contain 1000 articles and the specified tolerance limit is 5%. The average quality of lots submitted is 1%, and it may be agreed that for those lots having exactly 5% defectives the probability of acceptance is 1/10. The latter is defined as the consumer's risk. Since the sampling of the lot is without replacement, the hypergeometric series provides the mathematical basis for arriving at the sample size and the acceptance number for varying values of the three determining factors. These have been worked out by Dodge and Romig [1] in the form of tables and charts. In a specific example using the values given above the sample size is 130 and the acceptance number is 3.

The procedure is then as follows.

1. Inspect a sample.
2. If the acceptance number is not exceeded, accept the lot.
3. If the acceptance number is exceeded, inspect the remainder of the lot.

It is obvious that if there are very few poor lots it will rarely be necessary to make a complete inspection, and inspection costs are kept at the minimum. If there are many poor lots, inspection costs will increase, but in any event the probability of a consumer's obtaining a poor lot is not increased.

The consumer's risk has already been defined. In addition there is a

* Heavy routine may lead to errors, and inspectors generally are more alert and accurate when dealing with samples.

producer's risk which arises from the probability that a lot that is better than the tolerance limit will be rejected and therefore must be inspected in detail. The relation between the consumer's risk and the producer's risk is illustrated in Figure 19–5, taken from Dodge and Romig [1]. In this case the process average is 0.45%, the lot tolerance is 3%, and the consumer's risk is 1%. Notice that the distribution having a mean of 3%

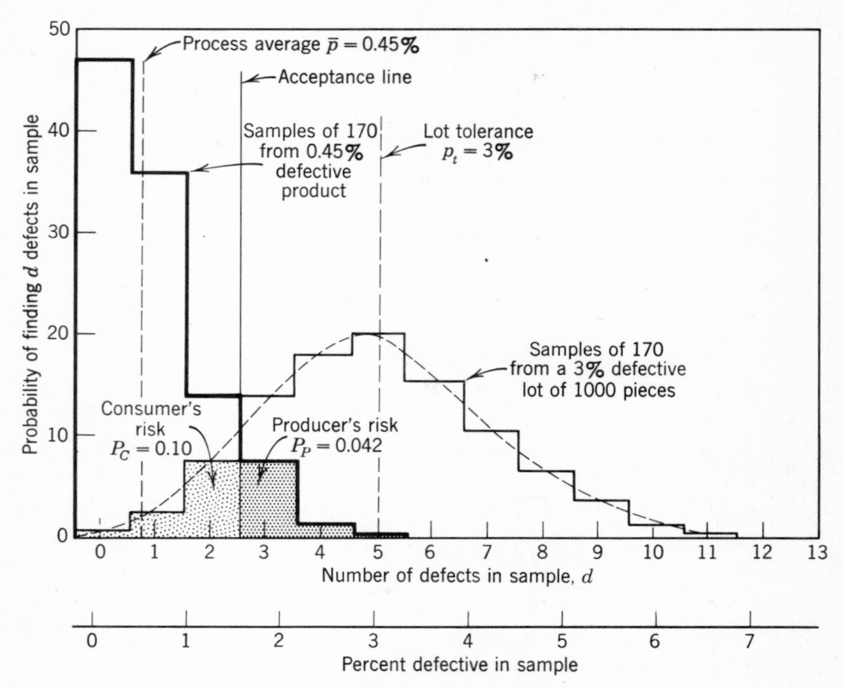

FIGURE 19–5. Illustrating consumer's risk and producer's risk. From Dodge and Romig [1], with permission.

overlaps the distribution having a mean of 0.45%. This gives a graphical picture of the two types of risks.

7. Double sampling. Experience has shown that a more complex method than that of single sampling, wherein the results of the sampling procedure more closely controls the extent of the sampling required, may be more efficient. This has resulted in the method described by Dodge and Romig [1] as double sampling. The basic principles are the same as in single sampling in that the same considerations enter into the design. However, the procedure as illustrated in Figure 19–6 is different.

Note first that two numbers c_1 and c_2 are set up for the allowable number of defectives in a sample. If the number in the first sample is

c_1 or less, the lot is accepted without question. If the number is c_2 or greater, the lot is presumed bad and all articles must be examined. When the number is between c_1 and c_2, a second sample is examined from which a final decision is made as to acceptance or complete inspection.

Allowing the results of the first sample to influence the extent of sampling is essentially sound in principle when minimum inspection costs

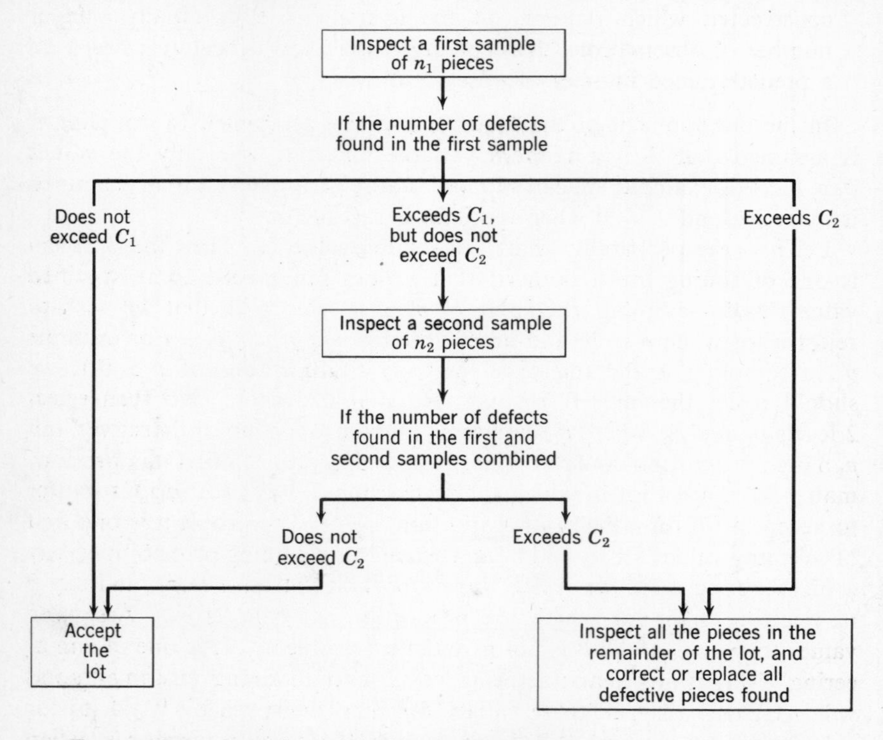

FIGURE 19–6. Procedure of double sampling. Reproduced with permission from Dodge and Romig [1].

are an important feature of the sampling process. This principle is carried to the limit of its application in the next method to be described.

8. Sequential sampling. In this method the principle of allowing the results obtained to determine the extent of the sampling is carried to its logical conclusion, i.e., to the point of allowing the results obtained to determine exactly the extent of the sampling required to reach a decision. The method has been developed largely by the late Professor Abraham Wald of Columbia University, and the theory is summarized in his book, *Sequential Analysis* [6]. In the introduction to this book Prof. Wald states:

Sequential analysis is a method of statistical inference whose characteristic feature is that the number of observations required by the procedure is not determined in advance of the experiment. The decision to terminate the experiment depends, at each stage, on the results of the observations previously made. The merit of the sequential method, as applied to testing statistical hypotheses, is that test procedures can be constructed which require, on the average, a substantially smaller number of observations than equally reliable test procedures based on a predetermined number of observations.

In the development of the sequential theory as applied to sampling it is assumed that X is a random variable that can take only the values 0 or 1. For example, we can suppose that $X = 1$ when an item examined is defective and $X = 0$ when the item is satisfactory.

Let $p =$ the probability that X takes the value 1. Then the problem is one of testing the hypothesis that p does not exceed some specified value p'. In sampling, the value of p' is selected such that we wish to reject a lot when $p > p'$ and accept the lot when $p \leq p'$. For example p' in sampling is the tolerance limit, say $1/10 = 0.1$. If $p > 0.1$, we should reject the lot. If $p \leq 0.1$, we should accept. We then select 2 levels p_1 and p_0, where p_0 represents a low proportion of defectives and p_1 a high proportion, and the values of p_0 and p_1 are such that it is a serious matter to reject a lot in which the proportion is p_0 and a serious matter to accept a lot for which the proportion is p_1. The problem is one first of selecting values for p_0 and p_1 and second of assigning probabilities, say α of accepting a lot for which the proportion defective is p_1, and say β of rejecting a lot for which the proportion defective is p_0. Assigning values to p_0, p_1, α, and β is not a statistical problem. It is one of engineering, establishing manufacturing costs, and retaining customer good will. Having assigned these values, formulas are given by Wald [6] for calculating the acceptance number n_a and the rejection number n_r when a given sequential procedure of sampling is followed. These are

$$n_a = \frac{\log\left(\dfrac{\beta}{1-\alpha}\right)}{\log\dfrac{p_1}{p_0} - \log\left(\dfrac{1-p_1}{1-p_0}\right)} + m\left[\frac{\log\left(\dfrac{1-p_0}{1-p_1}\right)}{\log\dfrac{p_1}{p_0} - \log\left(\dfrac{1-p_1}{1-p_0}\right)}\right] \qquad 1$$

$$n_r = \frac{\log\left(\dfrac{1-\beta}{\alpha}\right)}{\log\dfrac{p_1}{p_0} - \log\left(\dfrac{1-p_1}{1-p_0}\right)} + m\left[\frac{\log\left(\dfrac{1-p_0}{1-p_1}\right)}{\log\dfrac{p_1}{p_0} - \log\left(\dfrac{1-p_1}{1-p_0}\right)}\right] \qquad 2$$

where m is the number in the sample. These rather heavy-looking formulas are actually quite easy for calculation and can be simplified by putting

$$B = \frac{\beta}{1-\alpha} \qquad A = \frac{1-\beta}{\alpha} \qquad r_1 = \frac{p_1}{p_0} \qquad r_2 = \frac{1-p_1}{1-p_0}$$

Then

$$n_a = \frac{\log B - m \log r_2}{\log r_1 - \log r_2} \tag{3}$$

$$n_r = \frac{\log A - m \log r_2}{\log r_1 - \log r_2} \tag{4}$$

In order to apply these formulas it is necessary to make up a table for each value of m showing the corresponding values of n_a and n_r required to accept or reject. It is more convenient, however, to follow a graphical method wherein the cumulative results of examining each unit are marked on a graph and acceptance or rejection decided in accordance with the graph passing over the lower or upper of two parallel lines. To construct the graph we require

$$h_0 = \frac{\log B}{\log r_1 - \log r_2}$$

$$h_1 = \frac{\log A}{\log r_1 - \log r_2}$$

$$S = \frac{-\log r_2}{\log r_1 - \log r_2}$$

$$E_s(n) = \frac{-\log B \log A}{-\log r_1 \log r_2}$$

where h_0 and h_1 govern the position of the parallel lines, S the slope, and $E_s(n)$ gives a measure of the maximum number in the sample that will be required in order to reach a decision.

We shall construct the graph for the values $p_0 = 0.1$, $p_1 = 0.3$, $\alpha = 0.02$, and $\beta = 0.03$. This graph is shown in Figure 19–7.

First we find

$$B = 0.03061 \qquad \log B = \bar{1}.5141$$

$$A = 48.5 \qquad \log A = 1.6857$$

$$r_1 = 3 \qquad \log r_1 = 0.4771$$

$$r_2 = 0.7778 \qquad \log r_2 = -0.1091$$

Then

$$h_0 = \frac{-1.5141}{0.4771 + 0.1091} = \frac{-1.5141}{0.5862} = -2.58$$

$$h_1 = \frac{1.6857}{0.5862} = 2.88$$

$$S = \frac{0.1091}{0.5862} = 0.186$$

$$E_s(n) = \frac{1.5141 \times 1.6857}{0.4771 \times 0.1091} = \frac{2.5523}{0.0521} = 49$$

It should be pointed out that the formulas given in (1), (2), (3), and (4) are based on the binomial distribution. In other words, it is assumed that, with $p =$ fraction defective and $(1 - p) = q$, the fraction not defective, the distribution of defectives in samples of size n is given by the expansion of $(q + p)^n$. When p is quite small the Poisson distribution is more suitable than the binomial, but different formulas for h_0, h_1, and $E_s(n)$ are required. These are given below.*

$$h_1 = \frac{l_n\left(\frac{1-\beta}{\alpha}\right)}{l_n\left(\frac{m_1}{m_0}\right)}$$

$$h_0 = \frac{l_n\left(\frac{\beta}{1-\alpha}\right)}{l_n\left(\frac{m_1}{m_0}\right)}$$

$$s = \frac{m_1 - m_0}{l_n\left(\frac{m_1}{m_0}\right)}$$

where m_0 and m_1 are the means of the Poisson between which we want to distinguish and l_n represents the natural logarithm.

These formulas can best be understood by an application to a practical example. Suppose that seed samples are being drawn and the problem is to reject lots having a weed seed content of 3 or more per pound and

* Worked out and supplied by the courtesy of G. B. Oakland, Science Service Branch, Department of Agriculture, Ottawa.

to accept lots having a content of 1 or less per pound. Then $m_0 = 1$ and $m_1 = 3$. The probabilities of acceptance and rejection have to be determined arbitrarily as this is a commercial rather than a statistical problem. For illustration we shall take $\alpha = 0.1$ and $\beta = 0.1$.

$$h_1 = \frac{l_n 9}{l_n 3} = \frac{2.1972}{1.0986} = 2.00$$

$$h_0 = \frac{l_n(1/9)}{l_n 3} = -\,2.00$$

$$S = \frac{2}{l_n 3} = \frac{2}{1.0986} = 1.82$$

The graph is shown in Figure 19–8. Before calculating the values for the graph it is useful to determine $\bar{n}_0$ and $\bar{n}_1$, the number of drawings required on the average to reach a decision, first when the lot contains 1 weed seed or less per pound and second when the lot contains 3 weed seeds or more per pound. These are given by

$$\bar{n}_0 = \frac{(1-\alpha)\, l_n\left(\frac{\beta}{1-\alpha}\right) + \alpha l_n\left(\frac{1-\beta}{\alpha}\right)}{(m_0 - m_1) + m_0 l_n\left(\frac{m_1}{m_0}\right)}$$

$$\bar{n}_1 = \frac{\beta l_n\left(\frac{\beta}{1-\alpha}\right) + (1-\beta)\, l_n\left(\frac{1-\beta}{\alpha}\right)}{(m_0 - m_1) + m_1 l_n\left(\frac{m_1}{m_0}\right)}$$

Here we have

$$\bar{n}_0 = \frac{0.9 \times l_n(1/9) + 0.1 \times l_n 9}{(1-3) + l_n 3} = \frac{-\,1.9775 + 0.2197}{-\,2 + 1.0986} = \frac{-\,1.7578}{-\,0.9014} = 1.95$$

$$\bar{n}_1 = \frac{0.1 \times l_n(1/9) + 0.9 \times l_n 9}{(1-3) + 3l_n 3} = \frac{-\,0.2197 + 1.9775}{-\,2 + 3.2958} = \frac{1.7578}{1.2958} = 1.36$$

It would appear that 2 one-pound samples will be sufficient on the average to obtain a decision. If a decision is not reached after taking 3×1.95 samples $= 6$ approximately, the rule is to stop the sampling procedure and take the mean of all samples drawn. If this is closest to m_0 the lot is accepted, and if closest to m_1 the lot is rejected.

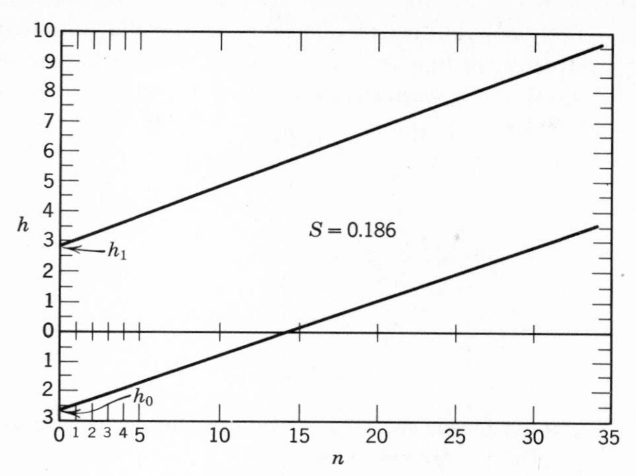

FIGURE 19–7. Graph prepared for a sequential sampling procedure.

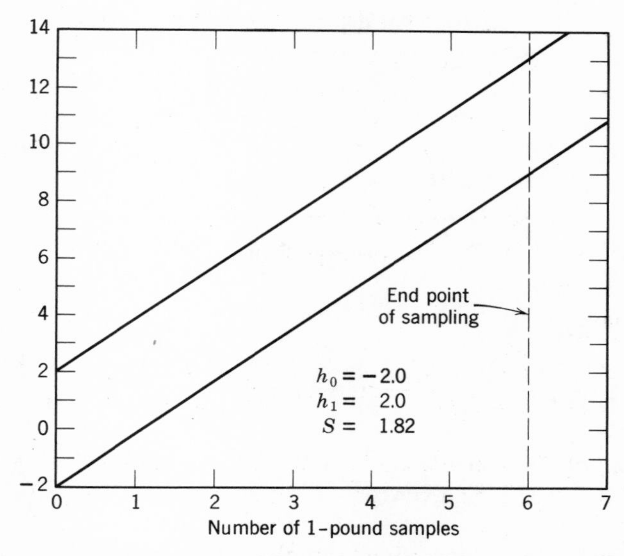

FIGURE 19–8. Sequential sampling diagram for distinguishing between lots having $m_0 = 1$ weed seed per pound and lots having $m_1 = 3$ weed seeds per pound. $\alpha = 0.1$, $\beta = 0.1$.

9. Verification trials. Fundamentally the verification trial as applied to registered plant stocks consists in taking a random sample of seed from a given lot, placing this sample in a growing test, and making counts to obtain an estimate of the proportion of off-types in the lot. This type of test differs from seed sampling or field inspection in that the number of plants grown must be determined in advance, and only 1 sample can be taken. The statistical problem is one of deciding on the size of sample required based on the tolerance limit for off-types and the accuracy with which estimates should be made.

Tolerance limits differ according to the crop. A few of the tolerance limits for off-types of different crops are given below, based on standards for foundation stock in the Canadian Seed Growers' Association.

Cereals	1 in 20,000
Cucumber	1 in 1,000
Beans (vegetable)	1 in 500
Carrots	1 in 10

We note that there is a very wide range, but for cereals and the most of the vegetable crops the tolerance limits are such that, in samples taken from lots in which the proportion of off-types is in the range of the tolerance limit, the distribution will be of the Poisson type.

Defining a sample unit as the number in which the tolerance limit is 1 off-type, the basic Poisson distribution for verification trials of 1 sampling unit is given in Figure 19–9. It is used in this manner. Suppose that the tolerance limit of off-types is 1:1000. If we take a large number of samples of 1000 each from a lot in which the proportion of off-types is exactly 1:1000, the chart shows that in 36.8% of these samples we will expect to get 0 off-types, in 36.8% 1 off-type, in 18.4% 2 off-types, and so forth. Notice that in 73.6% of the trials we will get samples coming within the tolerance limit. This means that, if 1000 farmers submitted samples for verification trials all from lots containing exactly the tolerance limit, it would be expected on the basis of random sampling and taking 1 sampling unit from each lot that 74% of the lots would be accepted and 26% rejected.

Suppose now that in the verification trials 2 sampling units are used. For example, in verifying cereals we would grow 40,000 plants, and for cucumbers, 2000 plants. The distribution of off-types would be as in Figure 19–10.

We note now that 2 off-types is the tolerance limit because we are using 2 sampling units. Totaling the first 3 columns, we have 67.7% as the percentage of lots that would be accepted and 32.3% that would be rejected, provided that all lots sampled contained exactly the tolerance

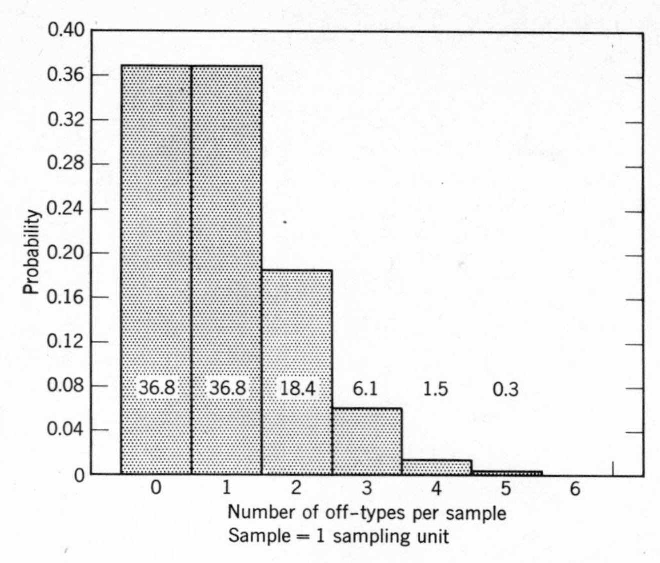

FIGURE 19–9. Basic Poisson distribution for verification trials of 1 sampling unit.

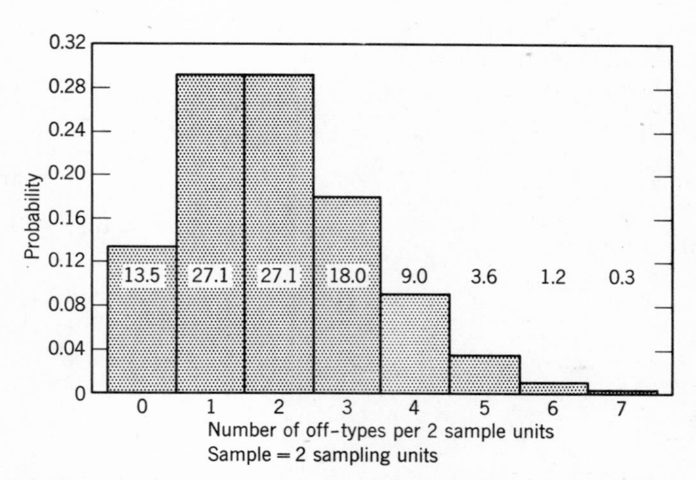

FIGURE 19–10. Basic Poisson distribution for verification trials of 2 sampling units.

limit. For other numbers of sampling units the data can be summarized as in Table 19–3. This table reflects merely the greater accuracy attained with larger numbers of plants. Since the increase in accuracy is very slow after reaching 5 sampling units, it would seem that there is not a great deal to be gained in going beyond this point.

A more valuable point of view in deciding on the number of sampling units required is to determine limits p_0 and p_1 for the proportion of off-types in lots from which samples are taken such that if the lot contains

TABLE 19–3

PERCENTAGE OF SAMPLES ACCEPTED OR REJECTED ACCORDING TO NUMBER OF SAMPLING UNITS

Number of Sampling Units	% Accepted	% Rejected
1	73.6	26.4
2	67.7	32.3
3	64.7	35.3
4	62.9	37.1
5	61.6	38.4
6	60.6	39.4
7	59.9	40.1
8	59.2	40.8
9	58.7	41.3
10	58.3	41.7

the proportion p_0 it will be rejected in only a certain small percentage of the trials and if the proportion is p_1 the lot will be accepted in only a certain small percentage of the trials.

This can be done by examining the range of Poisson distributions for different proportions of off-types. For example, suppose that we set the probability of acceptance of a poor lot at $P = 0.10$; what we want to know is just how poor this lot can be in order to have 1 chance in 10 of being accepted, with different numbers of sampling units. With 1 sampling unit the lot is accepted when 1 or 0 off-types are found. We then determine the Poisson distribution with a value of m such that the 0 and 1 columns of the histogram contain 10% of the total area. The value of m for this distribution corresponds to p_1, the proportion in the lot such that it has only 1 chance in 10 of being accepted. With 2 sampling units the lot is accepted when 2, 1, or 0 off-types are found. The corresponding Poisson distribution required is that in which the 0, 1, and 2 columns add to 10% of the total area. In a similar manner p_1 values can be found for any number of sampling units.

The values of p_0 are found in a corresponding manner. With 1 sampling unit a lot is accepted when either 0 or 1 off-type is found, and in this case a distribution must be selected such that 90% of the area falls in the columns 0 and 1.

Figure 19–11 results from an examination of the Poisson distributions for 3 probability levels, $P = 0.01$, 0.05, and 0.10. The A curves show for different numbers of sampling units the lot values (p_1) such that the chances of acceptance are 0.01 on the $A_{0.01}$ curve, 0.05 on the $A_{0.05}$ curve,

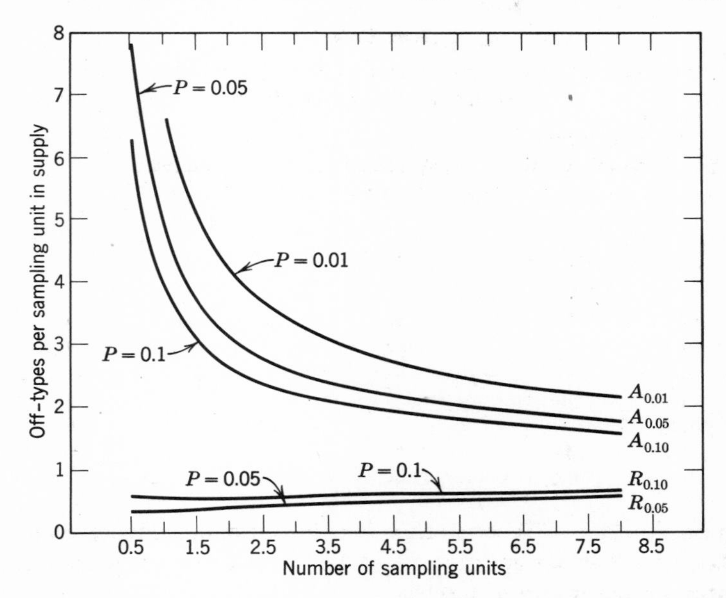

FIGURE 19–11. Limits of accuracy of verification trials with different numbers of sampling units.

and 0.10 on the $A_{0.10}$ curve. For example, if 2 sampling units are taken for the verification of a lot containing an average of 3.1 off-types per sampling unit, the probability of acceptance as read on the $A_{0.05}$ curve is 0.05, and conversely the probability of rejection is 0.95. The A curves therefore are thought of in terms of the probability of acceptance of lots that are poorer than the tolerance limit. The R curves show the probability of rejection (p_0) of lots that are better than the tolerance limit. For example, a lot containing an average of 0.04 off-types per sampling unit will have only 1 chance in 20 of being rejected.

The curves show also the limits of accuracy within which the verification trials with different numbers of sampling units are determined. For example, with 3 sampling units it can be said with a reasonable degree of certainty that the stocks accepted do not contain more than 2.58 off-types per sampling unit and those that are rejected do not contain less than 0.45 off-types per sampling unit. In addition, Figure 19–11 summarizes the information required for selecting sample sizes in verification trials. For most verification work the $A_{0.05}$ and $A_{0.10}$ curves are probably of the greatest importance. These curves enable us to arrive at a very simple conclusion with respect to all such trials. There is a very rapid improvement in accuracy as the sampling units are increased from $^1/_2$ to 2, but beyond 2 the improvement is slow. It would seem that a general conclusion can be drawn to the effect that 2 sampling units are the minimum for verification trials and that beyond 4 sampling units the increase in accuracy is not sufficient to warrant the additional labor involved. A safe working rule would be to take 3 units for an average testing procedure, to reduce this to 2 units when the work involved is heavy, and to increase it to 4 units whenever conditions are such as to make this possible.

10. Exercises.

1. Make a control chart from the first 5 columns of the data of Table 19–1, calculating the required values from the results for the first 10 days. Plot the complete data for the means and standard deviations on this chart.

2. Set up a sequential sampling chart for $p_0 = 0.05$, $p_1 = 0.2$, $\alpha = 0.05$, $\beta = 0.10$.

3. By coloring seeds to represent impurities, make up a 10-pound sample containing approximately 10 impurities per ounce. Letting $m_0 = 1$, $m_1 = 5$, $\alpha = 0.05$, $\beta = 0.1$, calculate and set up the sequential sampling graph, and then inspect the 10-pound sample by drawing 1-ounce samples in succession until a decision is reached.

REFERENCES

1. H. F. Dodge and H. G. Romig, *Sampling Inspection Tables*, John Wiley and Sons, New York, 1944.
2. E. S. Pearson, *The Application of Statistical Methods to Industrial Standardization and Quality Control*, British Standards Institution, London, 1935.
3. Statistical Research Group, Columbia University, *Sequential Analysis of Statistical Data*, Columbia University Press, New York, 1945.
4. W. A. Shewhart, *Economic Control of Quality of Manufactured Product*, D. Van Nostrand Co., New York, 1931.
5. W. A. Shewhart, *Statistical Methods from the Viewpoint of Quality Control*, U.S. Dept. of Agriculture, Graduate School, 1939.
6. Abraham Wald, *Sequential Analysis*, John Wiley and Sons, New York, 1947.

TABLE A–1

AREAS, $\frac{1}{2}(1 + \alpha)$ OF THE NORMAL CURVE IN TERMS OF THE NORMAL DEVIATE

	.00	.01	.02	.03	.04	.05	.06	.07	.08	.09
0.0	.5000	.5040	.5080	.5120	.5160	.5199	.5239	.5279	.5319	.5359
0.1	.5398	.5438	.5478	.5517	.5557	.5596	.5636	.5675	.5714	.5753
0.2	.5793	.5832	.5871	.5910	.5948	.5987	.6026	.6064	.6103	.6141
0.3	.6179	.6217	.6255	.6293	.6331	.6368	.6406	.6443	.6480	.6517
0.4	.6554	.6591	.6628	.6664	.6700	.6736	.6772	.6808	.6844	.6879
0.5	.6915	.6950	.6985	.7019	.7054	.7088	.7123	.7157	.7190	.7224
0.6	.7257	.7291	.7324	.7357	.7389	.7422	.7454	.7486	.7517	.7549
0.7	.7580	.7611	.7642	.7673	.7704	.7734	.7764	.7794	.7823	.7852
0.8	.7881	.7910	.7939	.7967	.7995	.8023	.8051	.8078	.8106	.8133
0.9	.8159	.8186	.8212	.8238	.8264	.8289	.8315	.8340	.8365	.8389
1.0	.8413	.8438	.8461	.8485	.8508	.8531	.8554	.8577	.8599	.8621
1.1	.8643	.8665	.8686	.8708	.8729	.8749	.8770	.8790	.8810	.8830
1.2	.8849	.8869	.8888	.8907	.8925	.8944	.8962	.8980	.8997	.9015
1.3	.9032	.9049	.9066	.9082	.9099	.9115	.9131	.9147	.9162	.9177
1.4	.9192	.9207	.9222	.9236	.9251	.9265	.9279	.9292	.9306	.9319
1.5	.9332	.9345	.9357	.9370	.9382	.9394	.9406	.9418	.9429	.9441
1.6	.9452	.9463	.9474	.9484	.9495	.9505	.9515	.9525	.9535	.9545
1.7	.9554	.9564	.9573	.9582	.9591	.9599	.9608	.9616	.9625	.9633
1.8	.9641	.9649	.9656	.9664	.9671	.9678	.9686	.9693	.9699	.9706
1.9	.9713	.9719	.9726	.9732	.9738	.9744	.9750	.9756	.9761	.9767
2.0	.9772	.9778	.9783	.9788	.9793	.9798	.9803	.9808	.9812	.9817
2.1	.9821	.9826	.9830	.9834	.9838	.9842	.9846	.9850	.9854	.9857
2.2	.9861	.9864	.9868	.9871	.9875	.9878	.9881	.9884	.9887	.9890
2.3	.9893	.9896	.9898	.9901	.9904	.9906	.9909	.9911	.9913	.9916
2.4	.9918	.9920	.9922	.9925	.9927	.9929	.9931	.9932	.9934	.9936
2.5	.9938	.9940	.9941	.9943	.9945	.9946	.9948	.9949	.9951	.9952
2.6	.9953	.9955	.9956	.9957	.9959	.9960	.9961	.9962	.9963	.9964
2.7	.9965	.9966	.9967	.9968	.9969	.9970	.9971	.9972	.9973	.9974
2.8	.9974	.9975	.9976	.9977	.9977	.9978	.9979	.9979	.9980	.9981
2.9	.9981	.9982	.9982	.9983	.9984	.9984	.9985	.9985	.9986	.9986
3.0	.9987	.9987	.9987	.9988	.9988	.9989	.9989	.9989	.9990	.9990
3.1	.9990	.9991	.9991	.9991	.9992	.9992	.9992	.9992	.9993	.9993
3.2	.9993	.9993	.9994	.9994	.9994	.9994	.9994	.9995	.9995	.9995
3.3	.9995	.9995	.9995	.9996	.9996	.9996	.9996	.9996	.9996	.9997
3.4	.9997	.9997	.9997	.9997	.9997	.9997	.9997	.9997	.9997	.9998
3.5	.9998	.9998	.9998	.9998	.9998	.9998	.9998	.9998	.9998	.9998
3.6	.9998	.9998	.9999	.9999	.9999	.9999	.9999	.9999	.9999	.9999
3.7	.9999	.9999	.9999	.9999	.9999	.9999	.9999	.9999	.9999	.9999
3.8	.9999	.9999	.9999	.9999	.9999	.9999	.9999	.9999	.9999	1.0000

TABLE A–2

Ordinates of the Normal Curve in Terms of the Normal Deviate

	.00	.01	.02	.03	.04	.05	.06	.07	.08	.09
0.0	.3989	.3989	.3989	.3988	.3986	.3984	.3982	.3980	.3977	.3973
0.1	.3970	.3965	.3961	.3956	.3951	.3945	.3939	.3932	.3925	.3918
0.2	.3910	.3902	.3894	.3885	.3876	.3867	.3857	.3847	.3836	.3825
0.3	.3814	.3802	.3790	.3778	.3765	.3752	.3739	.3725	.3712	.3697
0.4	.3683	.3668	.3653	.3637	.3621	.3605	.3589	.3572	.3555	.3538
0.5	.3521	.3503	.3485	.3467	.3448	.3429	.3410	.3391	.3372	.3352
0.6	.3332	.3312	.3292	.3271	.3251	.3230	.3209	.3187	.3166	.3144
0.7	.3123	.3101	.3079	.3056	.3034	.3011	.2989	.2966	.2943	.2920
0.8	.2897	.2874	.2850	.2827	.2803	.2780	.2756	.2732	.2709	.2685
0.9	.2661	.2637	.2613	.2589	.2565	.2541	.2516	.2492	.2468	.2444
1.0	.2420	.2396	.2371	.2347	.2323	.2299	.2275	.2251	.2227	.2203
1.1	.2179	.2155	.2131	.2107	.2083	.2059	.2036	.2012	.1989	.1965
1.2	.1942	.1919	.1895	.1872	.1849	.1826	.1804	.1781	.1758	.1736
1.3	.1714	.1691	.1669	.1647	.1626	.1604	.1582	.1561	.1539	.1518
1.4	.1497	.1476	.1456	.1435	.1415	.1394	.1374	.1354	.1334	.1315
1.5	.1295	.1276	.1257	.1238	.1219	.1200	.1182	.1163	.1145	.1127
1.6	.1109	.1092	.1074	.1057	.1040	.1023	.1006	.0989	.0973	.0957
1.7	.0940	.0925	.0909	.0893	.0878	.0863	.0848	.0833	.0818	.0804
1.8	.0790	.0775	.0761	.0748	.0734	.0721	.0707	.0694	.0681	.0669
1.9	.0656	.0644	.0632	.0620	.0608	.0596	.0584	.0573	.0562	.0551
2.0	.0540	.0529	.0519	.0508	.0498	.0488	.0478	.0468	.0459	.0449
2.1	.0440	.0431	.0422	.0413	.0404	.0400	.0387	.0379	.0371	.0363
2.2	.0355	.0347	.0339	.0332	.0325	.0317	.0310	.0303	.0297	.0290
2.3	.0283	.0277	.0270	.0264	.0258	.0252	.0246	.0241	.0235	.0229
2.4	0.224	.0219	.0213	.0208	.0203	.0198	.0194	.0189	.0184	.0180
2.5	.0175	.0171	.0167	.0163	.0158	.0154	.0151	.0147	.0143	.0139
2.6	.0136	.0132	.0129	.0126	.0122	.0119	.0116	.0113	.0110	.0107
2.7	.0104	.0101	.0099	.0096	.0093	.0091	.0088	.0086	.0084	.0081
2.8	.0079	.0077	.0075	.0073	.0071	.0069	.0067	.0065	.0063	.0061
2.9	.0060	.0058	.0056	.0055	.0053	.0051	.0050	.0048	.0047	.0046
3.0	.0044	.0043	.0042	.0040	.0039	.0038	.0037	.0036	.0035	.0034
3.1	.0033	.0032	.0031	.0030	.0029	.0028	.0027	.0026	.0025	.0025
3.2	.0024	.0023	.0022	.0022	.0021	.0020	.0020	.0019	.0018	.0018
3.3	.0017	.0017	.0016	.0016	.0015	.0015	.0014	.0014	.0013	.0013
3.4	.0012	.0012	.0012	.0011	.0011	.0010	.0010	.0010	.0009	.0009
3.5	.0009	.0008	.0008	.0008	.0008	.0007	.0007	.0007	.0007	.0006
3.6	.0006	.0006	.0006	.0005	.0005	.0005	.0005	.0005	.0005	.0004
3.7	.0004	.0004	.0004	.0004	.0004	.0004	.0003	.0003	.0003	.0003
3.8	.0003	.0003	.0003	.0003	.0003	.0002	.0002	.0002	.0002	.0002
3.9	.0002	.0002	.0002	.0002	.0002	.0002	.0002	.0002	.0001	.0001
4.0	.0001									

TABLE A–3

TABLE OF t*

DF	Probability 0.50	0.10	0.05	0.02	0.01	0.001
1	1.000	6.31	12.71	31.82	63.66	63.7
2	0.816	2.92	4.30	6.96	9.92	31.6
3	.765	2.35	3.18	4.54	5.84	12.9
4	.741	2.13	2.78	3.75	4.60	8.61
5	.727	2.02	2.57	3.36	4.03	6.86
6	.718	1.94	2.45	3.14	3.71	5.96
7	.711	1.90	2.36	3.00	3.50	5.40
8	.706	1.86	2.31	2.90	3.36	5.04
9	.703	1.83	2.26	2.82	3.25	4.78
10	.700	1.81	2.23	2.76	3.17	4.59
11	.697	1.80	2.20	2.72	3.11	4.44
12	.695	1.78	2.18	2.68	3.06	4.32
13	.694	1.77	2.16	2.65	3.01	4.22
14	.692	1.76	2.14	2.62	2.98	4.14
15	.691	1.75	2.13	2.60	2.95	4.07
16	.690	1.75	2.12	2.58	2.92	4.02
17	.689	1.74	2.11	2.57	2.90	3.96
18	.688	1.73	2.10	2.55	2.88	3.92
19	.688	1.73	2.09	2.54	2.86	3.88
20	.687	1.72	2.09	2.53	2.84	3.85
21	.686	1.72	2.08	2.52	2.83	3.82
22	.686	1.72	2.07	2.51	2.82	3.79
23	.685	1.71	2.07	2.50	2.81	3.77
24	.685	1.71	2.06	2.49	2.80	3.74
25	.684	1.71	2.06	2.48	2.79	3.72
26	.684	1.71	2.06	2.48	2.78	3.71
27	.684	1.70	2.05	2.47	2.77	3.69
28	.683	1.70	2.05	2.47	2.76	3.67
29	.683	1.70	2.04	2.46	2.76	3.66
30	.683	1.70	2.04	2.46	2.75	3.65
35	.682	1.69	2.03	2.44	2.72	3.59
40	.681	1.68	2.02	2.42	2.71	3.55
45	.680	1.68	2.02	2.41	2.69	3.52
50	.679	1.68	2.01	2.40	2.68	3.50
60	.678	1.67	2.00	2.39	2.66	3.46
70	.678	1.67	2.00	2.38	2.65	3.44
80	.677	1.66	1.99	2.38	2.64	3.42
90	.677	1.66	1.99	2.37	2.63	3.40
100	.677	1.66	1.98	2.36	2.63	3.39
120	.676	1.66	1.98	2.36	2.62	3.37
150	.676	1.66	1.98	2.35	2.61	3.36
200	.675	1.65	1.97	2.35	2.60	3.34
300	.675	1.65	1.97	2.34	2.59	3.32
400	.675	1.65	1.97	2.34	2.59	3.32
500	.674	1.65	1.96	2.33	2.59	3.31
1000	.674	1.65	1.96	2.33	2.58	3.30
∞	.674	1.64	1.96	2.33	2.58	3.29

* The data of this table extracted from Table IV of R. A. Fisher's *Statistical Methods for Research Workers* with the permission of the author and his publishers, Oliver and Boyd, Edinburgh.

TABLE A–4

TABLE OF χ^{2*}

	Probability									
DF	0.99	0.95	0.50	0.30	0.20	0.10	0.05	0.02	0.01	0.001
1	0.0002	0.004	0.46	1.07	1.64	2.71	3.84	5.41	6.64	10.83
2	0.020	0.103	1.39	2.41	3.22	4.60	5.99	7.82	9.21	13.82
3	0.115	0.35	2.37	3.66	4.64	6.25	7.82	9.84	11.34	16.27
4	0.30	0.71	3.36	4.88	5.99	7.78	9.49	11.67	13.28	18.46
5	0.55	1.14	4.35	6.06	7.29	9.24	11.07	13.39	15.09	20.52
6	0.87	1.64	5.35	7.23	8.56	10.64	12.59	15.03	16.81	22.46
7	1.24	2.17	6.35	8.38	9.80	12.02	14.07	16.62	18.48	24.32
8	1.65	2.73	7.34	9.52	11.03	13.36	15.51	18.17	20.09	26.12
9	2.09	3.32	8.34	10.66	12.24	14.68	16.92	19.68	21.67	27.88
10	2.56	3.94	9.34	11.78	13.44	15.99	18.31	21.16	23.21	29.59
11	3.05	4.58	10.34	12.90	14.63	17.28	19.68	22.62	24.72	31.26
12	3.57	5.23	11.34	14.01	15.81	18.55	21.03	24.05	26.22	32.91
13	4.11	5.89	12.34	15.12	16.98	19.81	22.36	25.47	27.69	34.53
14	4.66	6.57	13.34	16.22	18.15	21.06	23.68	26.87	29.14	36.12
15	5.23	7.26	14.34	17.32	19.31	22.31	25.00	28.26	30.58	37.70
16	5.81	7.96	15.34	18.42	20.46	23.54	26.30	29.63	32.00	39.25
17	6.41	8.67	16.34	19.51	21.62	24.77	27.59	31.00	33.41	40.79
18	7.02	9.39	17.34	20.60	22.76	25.99	28.87	32.35	34.80	42.31
19	7.63	10.12	18.34	21.69	23.90	27.20	30.14	33.69	36.19	43.82
20	8.26	10.85	19.34	22.78	25.04	28.41	31.41	35.02	37.57	45.32
21	8.90	11.59	20.34	23.86	26.17	29.62	32.67	36.34	38.93	46.80
22	9.54	12.34	21.34	24.94	27.30	30.81	33.92	37.66	40.29	48.27
23	10.20	13.09	22.34	26.02	28.43	32.01	35.17	38.97	41.64	49.73
24	10.86	13.85	23.34	27.10	29.55	33.20	36.42	40.27	42.98	51.18
25	11.52	14.61	24.34	28.17	30.68	34.38	37.65	41.57	44.31	52.62
26	12.20	15.38	25.34	29.25	31.80	35.56	38.88	42.86	45.64	54.05
27	12.88	16.15	26.34	30.32	32.91	36.74	40.11	44.14	46.96	55.48
28	13.56	16.93	27.34	31.39	34.03	37.92	41.34	45.42	48.28	56.89
29	14.26	17.71	28.34	32.46	35.14	39.09	42.56	46.69	49.59	58.30
30	14.95	18.49	29.34	33.53	36.25	40.26	43.77	47.96	50.89	59.70

* The data of this table extracted from Table III of R. A. Fisher's *Statistical Methods for Research Workers* with the permission of the author and his publishers, Oliver and Boyd, Edinburgh.

TABLE A–5

Correction Factor c_2 for Calculation of Average Standard Deviations

n	c_2	n	c_2
3	0.72360	22	0.96545
4	0.79788	23	0.96697
5	0.84069	24	0.96837
6	0.86863	25	0.96965
7	0.88820	30	0.97475
8	0.90270	35	0.97839
9	0.91388	40	0.98111
10	0.92275	45	0.98322
11	0.92996	50	0.98491
12	0.93594	55	0.98629
13	0.94098	60	0.98744
14	0.94529	65	0.98841
15	0.94901	70	0.98924
16	0.95225	75	0.98996
17	0.95511	80	0.99059
18	0.95765	85	0.99115
19	0.95991	90	0.99164
20	0.96194	95	0.99208
21	0.96378	100	0.99248

TABLE A–6

5% (Roman Type) and 1% (Bold-Face Type) Points for the Distribution of F*

n_2	n_1 Degrees of Freedom for Greater Mean Square: 1	2	3	4	5	6	7	8	9	10	11	12	14	16	20	24	30	40	50	75	100	200	500	∞
1	161 **4052**	200 **4999**	216 **5403**	225 **5625**	230 **5764**	234 **5859**	237 **5928**	239 **5981**	241 **6022**	242 **6056**	243 **6082**	244 **6106**	245 **6142**	246 **6169**	248 **6208**	249 **6234**	250 **6258**	251 **6286**	252 **6302**	253 **6323**	253 **6334**	254 **6352**	254 **6361**	254 **6366**
2	18.51 **98.49**	19.00 **99.00**	19.16 **99.17**	19.25 **99.25**	19.30 **99.30**	19.33 **99.33**	19.36 **99.34**	19.37 **99.36**	19.38 **99.38**	19.39 **99.40**	19.40 **99.41**	19.41 **99.42**	19.42 **99.43**	19.43 **99.44**	19.44 **99.45**	19.45 **99.46**	19.46 **99.47**	19.47 **99.48**	19.47 **99.48**	19.48 **99.49**	19.49 **99.49**	19.49 **99.49**	19.50 **99.50**	19.50 **99.50**
3	10.13 **34.12**	9.55 **30.82**	9.28 **29.46**	9.12 **28.71**	9.01 **28.24**	8.94 **27.91**	8.88 **27.67**	8.84 **27.49**	8.81 **27.34**	8.78 **27.23**	8.76 **27.13**	8.74 **27.05**	8.71 **26.92**	8.69 **26.83**	8.66 **26.69**	8.64 **26.60**	8.62 **26.50**	8.60 **26.41**	8.58 **26.35**	8.57 **26.27**	8.56 **26.23**	8.54 **26.18**	8.54 **26.14**	8.53 **26.12**
4	7.71 **21.20**	6.94 **18.00**	6.59 **16.69**	6.39 **15.98**	6.26 **15.52**	6.16 **15.21**	6.09 **14.98**	6.04 **14.80**	6.00 **14.66**	5.96 **14.54**	5.93 **14.45**	5.91 **14.37**	5.87 **14.24**	5.84 **14.15**	5.80 **14.02**	5.77 **13.93**	5.74 **13.83**	5.71 **13.74**	5.70 **13.69**	5.68 **13.61**	5.66 **13.57**	5.65 **13.52**	5.64 **13.48**	5.63 **13.46**
5	6.61 **16 26**	5.79 **13.27**	5.41 **12.06**	5.19 **11.39**	5.05 **10.97**	4.95 **10.67**	4.88 **10.45**	4.82 **10.27**	4.78 **10.15**	4.74 **10.05**	4.70 **9.96**	4.68 **9.89**	4.64 **9.77**	4.60 **9.68**	4.56 **9.55**	4.53 **9.47**	4.50 **9.38**	4.46 **9.29**	4.44 **9.24**	4.42 **9.17**	4.40 **9.13**	4.38 **9.07**	4.37 **9.04**	4.36 **9.02**
6	5.99 **13.74**	5.14 **10.92**	4.76 **9.78**	4.53 **9.15**	4.39 **8.75**	4.28 **8.47**	4.21 **8.26**	4.15 **8.10**	4.10 **7.98**	4.06 **7.87**	4.03 **7.79**	4.00 **7.72**	3.96 **7.60**	3.92 **7.52**	3.87 **7.39**	3.84 **7.31**	3.81 **7.23**	3.77 **7.14**	3.75 **7.09**	3.72 **7.02**	3.71 **6.99**	3.69 **6.94**	3.68 **6.90**	3.67 **6.88**
7	5.59 **12.25**	4.74 **9.55**	4.35 **8.45**	4.12 **7.85**	3.97 **7.46**	3.87 **7.19**	3.79 **7.00**	3.73 **6.84**	3.68 **6.71**	3.63 **6.62**	3.60 **6.54**	3.57 **6.47**	3.52 **6.35**	3.49 **6.27**	3.44 **6.15**	3.41 **6.07**	3.38 **5.98**	3.34 **5.90**	3.32 **5.85**	3.29 **5.78**	3.28 **5.75**	3.25 **5.70**	3.24 **5.67**	3.23 **5.65**
8	5.32 **11.26**	4.46 **8.65**	4.07 **7.59**	3.84 **7.01**	3.69 **6.63**	3.58 **6.37**	3.50 **6.19**	3.44 **6.03**	3.39 **5.91**	3.34 **5.82**	3.31 **5.74**	3.28 **5.67**	3.23 **5.56**	3.20 **5.48**	3.15 **5.36**	3.12 **5.28**	3.08 **5.20**	3.05 **5.11**	3.03 **5.06**	3.00 **5.00**	2.98 **4.96**	2.96 **4.91**	2.94 **4.88**	2.93 **4.86**
9	5.12 **10.56**	4.26 **8.02**	3.86 **6.99**	3.63 **6.42**	3.48 **6.06**	3.37 **5.80**	3.29 **5.62**	3.23 **5.47**	3.18 **5.35**	3.13 **5.26**	3.10 **5.18**	3.07 **5.11**	3.02 **5.00**	2.98 **4.92**	2.93 **4.80**	2.90 **4.73**	2.86 **4.64**	2.82 **4.56**	2.80 **4.51**	2.77 **4.45**	2.76 **4.41**	2.73 **4.36**	2.72 **4.33**	2.71 **4.31**
10	4.96 **10.04**	4.10 **7.56**	3.71 **6.55**	3.48 **5.99**	3.33 **5.64**	3.22 **5.39**	3.14 **5.21**	3.07 **5.06**	3.02 **4.95**	2.97 **4.85**	2.94 **4.78**	2.91 **4.71**	2.86 **4.60**	2.82 **4.52**	2.77 **4.41**	2.74 **4.33**	2.70 **4.25**	2.67 **4.17**	2.64 **4.12**	2.61 **4.05**	2.59 **4.01**	2.56 **3.96**	2.55 **3.93**	2.54 **3.91**
11	4.84 **9.65**	3.98 **7.20**	3.59 **6.22**	3.36 **5.67**	3.20 **5.32**	3.09 **5.07**	3.01 **4.88**	2.95 **4.74**	2.90 **4.63**	2.86 **4.54**	2.82 **4.46**	2.79 **4.40**	2.74 **4.29**	2.70 **4.21**	2.65 **4.10**	2.61 **4.02**	2.57 **3.94**	2.53 **3.86**	2.50 **3.80**	2.47 **3.74**	2.45 **3.70**	2.42 **3.66**	2.41 **3.62**	2.40 **3.60**
12	4.75 **9.33**	3.88 **6.93**	3.49 **5.95**	3.26 **5.41**	3.11 **5.06**	3.00 **4.82**	2.92 **4.65**	2.85 **4.50**	2.80 **4.39**	2.76 **4.30**	2.72 **4.22**	2.69 **4.16**	2.64 **4.05**	2.60 **3.98**	2.54 **3.86**	2.50 **3.78**	2.46 **3.70**	2.42 **3.61**	2.40 **3.56**	2.36 **3.49**	2.35 **3.46**	2.32 **3.41**	2.31 **3.38**	2.30 **3.36**
13	4.67 **9.07**	3.80 **6.70**	3.41 **5.74**	3.18 **5.20**	3.02 **4.86**	2.92 **4.62**	2.84 **4.44**	2.77 **4.30**	2.72 **4.19**	2.67 **4.10**	2.63 **4.02**	2.60 **3.96**	2.55 **3.85**	2.51 **3.78**	2.46 **3.67**	2.42 **3.59**	2.38 **3.51**	2.34 **3.42**	2.32 **3.37**	2.28 **3.30**	2.26 **3.27**	2.24 **3.21**	2.22 **3.18**	2.21 **3.16**

* This table taken from G. W. Snedecor's *Statistical Methods*, Iowa State College Press, 4th ed., 1946, reproduced by permission of the author and his publishers. Calculated by G. W. Snedecor from Table VI of R. A. Fisher's *Statistical Methods for Research Workers*.

TABLE A-6 (*continued*)

n_2	n_1 Degrees of Freedom for Greater Mean Square																							
	1	2	3	4	5	6	7	8	9	10	11	12	14	16	20	24	30	40	50	75	100	200	500	∞
14	4.60 **8.86**	3.74 **6.51**	3.34 **5.56**	3.11 **5.03**	2.96 **4.69**	2.85 **4.46**	2.77 **4.28**	2.70 **4.14**	2.65 **4.03**	2.60 **3.94**	2.56 **3.86**	2.53 **3.80**	2.84 **3.70**	2.44 **3.62**	2.39 **3.51**	2.35 **3.43**	2.31 **3.34**	2.27 **3.26**	2.24 **3.21**	2.21 **3.14**	2.19 **3.11**	2.16 **3.06**	2.14 **3.02**	2.13 **3.00**
15	4.54 **8.68**	3.68 **6.36**	3.29 **5.42**	3.06 **4.89**	2.90 **4.56**	2.79 **4.32**	2.70 **4.14**	2.64 **4.00**	2.59 **3.89**	2.55 **3.80**	2.51 **3.73**	2.48 **3.67**	2.43 **3.56**	2.39 **3.48**	2.33 **3.36**	2.29 **3.29**	2.25 **3.20**	2.21 **3.12**	2.18 **3.07**	2.15 **3.00**	2.12 **2.97**	2.10 **2.92**	2.08 **2.89**	2.07 **2.87**
16	4.49 **8.53**	3.63 **6.23**	3.24 **5.29**	3.01 **4.77**	2.85 **4.44**	2.74 **4.20**	2.66 **4.03**	2.59 **3.89**	2.54 **3.78**	2.49 **3.69**	2.45 **3.61**	2.42 **3.55**	2.37 **3.45**	2.33 **3.37**	2.28 **3.25**	2.24 **3.18**	2.20 **3.10**	2.16 **3.01**	2.13 **2.96**	2.09 **2.89**	2.07 **2.86**	2.04 **2.80**	2.02 **2.77**	2.01 **2.75**
17	4.45 **8.40**	3.59 **6.11**	3.20 **5.18**	2.96 **4.67**	2.81 **4.34**	2.70 **4.10**	2.62 **3.93**	2.55 **3.79**	2.50 **3.68**	2.45 **3.59**	2.41 **3.52**	2.38 **3.45**	2.33 **3.35**	2.29 **3.27**	2.23 **3.16**	2.19 **3.08**	2.15 **3.00**	2.11 **2.92**	2.08 **2.86**	2.04 **2.79**	2.02 **2.76**	1.99 **2.70**	1.97 **2.67**	1.96 **2.65**
18	4.41 **8.28**	3.55 **6.01**	3.16 **5.09**	2.93 **4.58**	2.77 **4.25**	2.66 **4.01**	2.58 **3.85**	2.51 **3.71**	2.46 **3.60**	2.41 **3.51**	2.37 **3.44**	2.34 **3.37**	2.29 **3.27**	2.25 **3.19**	2.19 **3.07**	2.15 **3.00**	2.11 **2.91**	2.07 **2.83**	2.04 **2.78**	2.00 **2.71**	1.98 **2.68**	1.95 **2.62**	1.93 **2.59**	1.92 **2.57**
19	4.38 **8.18**	3.52 **5.93**	3.13 **5.01**	2.90 **4.50**	2.74 **4.17**	2.63 **3.94**	2.55 **3.77**	2.48 **3.63**	2.43 **3.52**	2.38 **3.43**	2.34 **3.36**	2.31 **3.30**	2.26 **3.19**	2.21 **3.12**	2.15 **3.00**	2.11 **2.92**	2.07 **2.84**	2.02 **2.76**	2.00 **2.70**	1.96 **2.63**	1.94 **2.60**	1.91 **2.54**	1.90 **2.51**	1.88 **2.49**
20	4.35 **8.10**	3.49 **5.85**	3.10 **4.94**	2.87 **4.43**	2.71 **4.10**	2.60 **3.87**	2.52 **3.71**	2.45 **3.56**	2.40 **3.45**	2.35 **3.37**	2.31 **3.30**	2.28 **3.23**	2.23 **3.13**	2.18 **3.05**	2.12 **2.94**	2.08 **2.86**	2.04 **2.77**	1.99 **2.69**	1.96 **2.63**	1.92 **2.56**	1.90 **2.53**	1.87 **2.47**	1.85 **2.44**	1.84 **2.42**
21	4.32 **8.02**	3.47 **5.78**	3.07 **4.87**	2.84 **4.37**	2.68 **4.04**	2.57 **3.81**	2.49 **3.65**	2.42 **3.51**	2.37 **3.40**	2.32 **3.31**	2.28 **3.24**	2.25 **3.17**	2.20 **3.07**	2.15 **2.99**	2.09 **2.88**	2.05 **2.80**	2.00 **2.72**	1.96 **2.63**	1.93 **2.58**	1.89 **2.51**	1.87 **2.47**	1.84 **2.42**	1.82 **2.38**	1.81 **2.36**
22	4.30 **7.94**	3.44 **5.72**	3.05 **4.82**	2.82 **4.31**	2.66 **3.99**	2.55 **3.76**	2.47 **3.59**	2.40 **3.45**	2.35 **3.35**	2.30 **3.26**	2.26 **3.18**	2.23 **3.12**	2.18 **3.02**	2.13 **2.94**	2.07 **2.83**	2.03 **2.75**	1.98 **2.67**	1.93 **2.58**	1.91 **2.53**	1.87 **2.46**	1.84 **2.42**	1.81 **2.37**	1.80 **2.33**	1.78 **2.31**
23	4.28 **7.88**	3.42 **5.66**	3.03 **4.76**	2.80 **4.26**	2.64 **3.94**	2.53 **3.71**	2.45 **3.54**	2.38 **3.41**	2.32 **3.30**	2.28 **3.21**	2.24 **3.14**	2.20 **3.07**	2.14 **2.97**	2.10 **2.89**	2.04 **2.78**	2.00 **2.70**	1.96 **2.62**	1.91 **2.53**	1.88 **2.48**	1.84 **2.41**	1.82 **2.37**	1.79 **2.32**	1.77 **2.28**	1.76 **2.26**
24	4.26 **7.82**	3.40 **5.61**	3.01 **4.72**	2.78 **4.22**	2.62 **3.90**	2.51 **3.67**	2.43 **3.50**	2.36 **3.36**	2.30 **3.25**	2.26 **3.17**	2.22 **3.09**	2.18 **3.03**	2.13 **2.93**	2.09 **2.85**	2.02 **2.74**	1.98 **2.66**	1.94 **2.58**	1.89 **2.49**	1.86 **2.44**	1.82 **2.36**	1.80 **2.33**	1.76 **2.27**	1.74 **2.23**	1.73 **2.21**
25	4.24 **7.77**	3.38 **5.57**	2.99 **4.68**	2.76 **4.18**	2.60 **3.86**	2.49 **3.63**	2.41 **3.46**	2.34 **3.32**	2.28 **3.21**	2.24 **3.13**	2.20 **3.05**	2.16 **2.99**	2.11 **2.89**	2.06 **2.81**	2.00 **2.70**	1.96 **2.62**	1.92 **2.54**	1.87 **2.45**	1.84 **2.40**	1.80 **2.32**	1.77 **2.29**	1.74 **2.23**	1.72 **2.19**	1.71 **2.17**
26	4.22 **7.72**	3.37 **5.53**	2.98 **4.64**	2.74 **4.14**	2.59 **3.82**	2.47 **3.59**	2.39 **3.42**	2.32 **3.29**	2.27 **3.17**	2.22 **3.09**	2.18 **3.02**	2.15 **2.96**	2.10 **2.86**	2.05 **2.77**	1.99 **2.66**	1.95 **2.58**	1.90 **2.50**	1.85 **2.41**	1.82 **2.36**	1.78 **2.28**	1.76 **2.25**	1.72 **2.19**	1.70 **2.15**	1.69 **2.13**

TABLE A–6 (*continued*)

n_2	n_1 Degrees of Freedom for Greater Mean Square																							
	1	2	3	4	5	6	7	8	9	10	11	12	14	16	20	24	30	40	50	75	100	200	500	∞
27	4.21 **7.68**	3.35 **5.49**	2.96 **4.60**	2.73 **4.11**	2.57 **3.79**	2.46 **3.56**	2.37 **3.39**	2.30 **3.26**	2.25 **3.14**	2.20 **3.06**	2.16 **2.98**	2.13 **2.93**	2.08 **2.83**	2.03 **2.74**	1.97 **2.63**	1.93 **2.55**	1.88 **2.47**	1.84 **2.38**	1.80 **2.33**	1.76 **2.25**	1.74 **2.21**	1.71 **2.16**	1.68 **2.12**	1.67 **2.10**
28	4.20 **7.64**	3.34 **5.45**	2.95 **4.57**	2.71 **4.07**	2.56 **3.76**	2.44 **3.53**	2.36 **3.36**	2.29 **3.23**	2.24 **3.11**	2.19 **3.03**	2.15 **2.95**	2.12 **2.90**	2.06 **2.80**	2.02 **2.71**	1.96 **2.60**	1.91 **2.52**	1.87 **2.44**	1.81 **2.35**	1.78 **2.30**	1.75 **2.22**	1.72 **2.18**	1.69 **2.13**	1.67 **2.09**	1.65 **2.06**
29	4.18 **7.60**	3.33 **5.42**	2.93 **4.54**	2.70 **4.04**	2.54 **3.73**	2.43 **3.50**	2.35 **3.33**	2.28 **3.20**	2.22 **3.08**	2.18 **3.00**	2.14 **2.92**	2.10 **2.87**	2.05 **2.77**	2.00 **2.68**	1.94 **2.57**	1.90 **2.49**	1.85 **2.41**	1.80 **2.32**	1.77 **2.27**	1.73 **2.19**	1.71 **2.15**	1.68 **2.10**	1.65 **2.06**	1.64 **2.03**
30	4.17 **7.56**	3.32 **5.39**	2.92 **4.51**	2.69 **4.02**	2.53 **3.70**	2.42 **3.47**	2.34 **3.30**	2.27 **3.17**	2.21 **3.06**	2.16 **2.98**	2.12 **2.90**	2.09 **2.84**	2.04 **2.74**	1.99 **2.66**	1.93 **2.55**	1.89 **2.47**	1.84 **2.38**	1.79 **2.29**	1.76 **2.24**	1.72 **2.16**	1.69 **2.13**	1.66 **2.07**	1.64 **2.03**	1.62 **2.01**
32	4.15 **7.50**	3.30 **5.34**	2.90 **4.46**	2.67 **3.97**	2.51 **3.66**	2.40 **3.42**	2.32 **3.25**	2.25 **3.12**	2.19 **3.01**	2.14 **2.94**	2.10 **2.86**	2.07 **2.80**	2.02 **2.70**	1.97 **2.62**	1.91 **2.51**	1.86 **2.42**	1.82 **2.34**	1.76 **2.25**	1.74 **2.20**	1.69 **2.12**	1.67 **2.08**	1.64 **2.02**	1.61 **1.98**	1.59 **1.96**
34	4.13 **7.44**	3.28 **5.29**	2.88 **4.42**	2.65 **3.93**	2.49 **3.61**	2.38 **3.38**	2.30 **3.21**	2.23 **3.08**	2.17 **2.97**	2.12 **2.89**	2.08 **2.82**	2.05 **2.76**	2.00 **2.66**	1.95 **2.58**	1.89 **2.47**	1.84 **2.38**	1.80 **2.30**	1.74 **2.21**	1.71 **2.15**	1.67 **2.08**	1.64 **2.04**	1.61 **1.98**	1.59 **1.94**	1.57 **1.91**
36	4.11 **7.39**	3.26 **5.25**	2.86 **4.38**	2.63 **3.89**	2.48 **3.58**	2.36 **3.35**	2.28 **3.18**	2.21 **3.04**	2.15 **2.94**	2.10 **2.86**	2.06 **2.78**	2.03 **2.72**	1.98 **2.62**	1.93 **2.54**	1.87 **2.43**	1.82 **2.35**	1.78 **2.26**	1.72 **2.17**	1.69 **2.12**	1.65 **2.04**	1.62 **2.00**	1.59 **1.94**	1.56 **1.90**	1.55 **1.87**
38	4.10 **7.35**	3.25 **5.21**	2.85 **4.34**	2.62 **3.86**	2.46 **3.54**	2.35 **3.32**	2.26 **3.15**	2.19 **3.02**	2.14 **2.91**	2.09 **2.82**	2.05 **2.75**	2.02 **2.69**	1.96 **2.59**	1.92 **2.51**	1.85 **2.40**	1.80 **2.32**	1.76 **2.22**	1.71 **2.14**	1.67 **2.08**	1.63 **2.00**	1.60 **1.97**	1.57 **1.90**	1.54 **1.86**	1.53 **1.84**
40	4.08 **7.31**	3.23 **5.18**	2.84 **4.31**	2.61 **3.83**	2.45 **3.51**	2.34 **3.29**	2.25 **3.12**	2.18 **2.99**	2.12 **2.88**	2.07 **2.80**	2.04 **2.73**	2.00 **2.66**	1.95 **2.56**	1.90 **2.49**	1.84 **2.37**	1.79 **2.29**	1.74 **2.20**	1.69 **2.11**	1.66 **2.05**	1.61 **1.97**	1.59 **1.94**	1.55 **1.88**	1.53 **1.84**	1.51 **1.81**
42	4.07 **7.27**	3.22 **5.15**	2.83 **4.29**	2.59 **3.80**	2.44 **3.49**	2.32 **3.26**	2.24 **3.10**	2.17 **2.96**	2.11 **2.86**	2.06 **2.77**	2.02 **2.70**	1.99 **2.64**	1.94 **2.54**	1.89 **2.46**	1.82 **2.35**	1.78 **2.26**	1.73 **2.17**	1.68 **2.08**	1.64 **2.02**	1.60 **1.94**	1.57 **1.91**	1.54 **1.85**	1.51 **1.80**	1.49 **1.78**
44	4.06 **7.24**	3.21 **5.12**	2.82 **4.26**	2.58 **3.78**	2.43 **3.46**	2.31 **3.24**	2.23 **3.07**	2.16 **2.94**	2.10 **2.84**	2.05 **2.75**	2.01 **2.68**	1.98 **2.62**	1.92 **2.52**	1.88 **2.44**	1.81 **2.32**	1.76 **2.24**	1.72 **2.15**	1.66 **2.06**	1.63 **2.00**	1.58 **1.92**	1.56 **1.88**	1.52 **1.82**	1.50 **1.78**	1.48 **1.75**
46	4.05 **7.21**	3.20 **5.10**	2.81 **4.24**	2.57 **3.76**	2.42 **3.44**	2.30 **3.22**	2.22 **3.05**	2.14 **2.92**	2.09 **2.82**	2.04 **2.73**	2.00 **2.66**	1.97 **2.60**	1.91 **2.50**	1.87 **2.42**	1.80 **2.30**	1.75 **2.22**	1.71 **2.13**	1.65 **2.04**	1.62 **1.98**	1.57 **1.90**	1.54 **1.86**	1.51 **1.80**	1.48 **1.76**	1.46 **1.72**
48	4.04 **7.19**	3.19 **5.08**	2.80 **4.22**	2.56 **3.74**	2.41 **3.42**	2.30 **3.20**	2.21 **3.04**	2.14 **2.90**	2.08 **2.80**	2.03 **2.71**	1.99 **2.64**	1.96 **2.58**	1.90 **2.48**	1.86 **2.40**	1.79 **2.28**	1.74 **2.20**	1.70 **2.11**	1.64 **2.02**	1.61 **1.96**	1.56 **1.88**	1.53 **1.84**	1.50 **1.78**	1.47 **1.73**	1.45 **1.70**

TABLE A–6 (*continued*)

n_2	n_1 Degrees of Freedom for Greater Mean Square 1	2	3	4	5	6	7	8	9	10	11	12	14	16	20	24	30	40	50	75	100	200	500	∞
50	4.03 **7.17**	3.18 **5.06**	2.79 **4.20**	2.56 **3.72**	2.40 **3.41**	2.29 **3.18**	2.20 **3.02**	2.13 **2.88**	2.07 **2.78**	2.02 **2.70**	1.98 **2.62**	1.95 **2.56**	1.90 **2.46**	1.85 **2.39**	1.78 **2.26**	1.74 **2.18**	1.69 **2.10**	1.63 **2.00**	1.60 **1.94**	1.55 **1.86**	1.52 **1.82**	1.48 **1.76**	1.46 **1.71**	1.44 **1.68**
55	4.02 **7.12**	3.17 **5.01**	2.78 **4.16**	2.54 **3.68**	2.38 **3.37**	2.27 **3.15**	2.18 **2.98**	2.11 **2.85**	2.05 **2.75**	2.00 **2.66**	1.97 **2.59**	1.93 **2.53**	1.88 **2.43**	1.83 **2.35**	1.76 **2.23**	1.72 **2.15**	1.67 **2.06**	1.61 **1.96**	1.58 **1.90**	1.52 **1.82**	1.50 **1.78**	1.46 **1.71**	1.43 **1.66**	1.41 **1.64**
60	4.00 **7.08**	3.15 **4.98**	2.76 **4.13**	2.52 **3.65**	2.37 **3.34**	2.25 **3.12**	2.17 **2.95**	2.10 **2.82**	2.04 **2.72**	1.99 **2.63**	1.95 **2.56**	1.92 **2.50**	1.86 **2.40**	1.81 **2.32**	1.75 **2.20**	1.70 **2.12**	1.65 **2.03**	1.59 **1.93**	1.56 **1.87**	1.50 **1.79**	1.48 **1.74**	1.44 **1.68**	1.41 **1.63**	1.39 **1.60**
65	3.99 **7.04**	3.14 **4.95**	2.75 **4.10**	2.51 **3.62**	2.36 **3.31**	2.24 **3.09**	2.15 **2.93**	2.08 **2.79**	2.02 **2.70**	1.98 **2.61**	1.94 **2.54**	1.90 **2.47**	1.85 **2.37**	1.80 **2.30**	1.73 **2.18**	1.68 **2.09**	1.63 **2.00**	1.57 **1.90**	1.54 **1.84**	1.49 **1.76**	1.46 **1.71**	1.42 **1.64**	1.39 **1.60**	1.37 **1.56**
70	3.98 **7.01**	3.13 **4.92**	2.74 **4.08**	2.50 **3.60**	2.35 **3.29**	2.23 **3.07**	2.14 **2.91**	2.07 **2.77**	2.01 **2.67**	1.97 **2.59**	1.93 **2.51**	1.89 **2.45**	1.84 **2.35**	1.79 **2.28**	1.72 **2.15**	1.67 **2.07**	1.62 **1.98**	1.56 **1.88**	1.53 **1.82**	1.47 **1.74**	1.45 **1.69**	1.40 **1.62**	1.37 **1.56**	1.35 **1.53**
80	3.96 **6.96**	3.11 **4.88**	2.72 **4.04**	2.48 **3.56**	2.33 **3.25**	2.21 **3.04**	2.12 **2.87**	2.05 **2.74**	1.99 **2.64**	1.95 **2.55**	1.91 **2.48**	1.88 **2.41**	1.82 **2.32**	1.77 **2.24**	1.70 **2.11**	1.65 **2.03**	1.60 **1.94**	1.54 **1.84**	1.51 **1.78**	1.45 **1.70**	1.42 **1.65**	1.38 **1.57**	1.35 **1.52**	1.32 **1.49**
100	3.94 **6.90**	3.09 **4.82**	2.70 **3.98**	2.46 **3.51**	2.30 **3.20**	2.19 **2.99**	2.10 **2.82**	2.03 **2.69**	1.97 **2.59**	1.92 **2.51**	1.88 **2.43**	1.85 **2.36**	1.79 **2.26**	1.75 **2.19**	1.68 **2.06**	1.63 **1.98**	1.57 **1.89**	1.51 **1.79**	1.48 **1.73**	1.42 **1.64**	1.39 **1.59**	1.34 **1.51**	1.30 **1.46**	1.28 **1.43**
125	3.92 **6.84**	3.07 **4.78**	2.68 **3.94**	2.44 **3.47**	2.29 **3.17**	2.17 **2.95**	2.08 **2.79**	2.01 **2.65**	1.95 **2.56**	1.90 **2.47**	1.86 **2.40**	1.83 **2.33**	1.77 **2.23**	1.72 **2.15**	1.65 **2.03**	1.60 **1.94**	1.55 **1.85**	1.49 **1.75**	1.45 **1.68**	1.39 **1.59**	1.36 **1.54**	1.31 **1.46**	1.27 **1.40**	1.25 **1.37**
150	3.91 **6.81**	3.06 **4.75**	2.67 **3.91**	2.43 **3.44**	2.27 **3.14**	2.16 **2.92**	2.07 **2.76**	2.00 **2.62**	1.94 **2.53**	1.89 **2.44**	1.85 **2.37**	1.82 **2.30**	1.76 **2.20**	1.71 **2.12**	1.64 **2.00**	1.59 **1.91**	1.54 **1.83**	1.47 **1.72**	1.44 **1.66**	1.37 **1.56**	1.34 **1.51**	1.29 **1.43**	1.25 **1.37**	1.22 **1.33**
200	3.89 **6.76**	3.04 **4.71**	2.65 **3.88**	2.41 **3.41**	2.26 **3.11**	2.14 **2.90**	2.05 **2.73**	1.98 **2.60**	1.92 **2.50**	1.87 **2.41**	1.83 **2.34**	1.80 **2.28**	1.74 **2.17**	1.69 **2.09**	1.62 **1.97**	1.57 **1.88**	1.52 **1.79**	1.45 **1.69**	1.42 **1.62**	1.35 **1.53**	1.32 **1.48**	1.26 **1.39**	1.22 **1.33**	1.19 **1.28**
400	3.86 **6.70**	3.02 **4.66**	2.62 **3.83**	2.39 **3.36**	2.23 **3.06**	2.12 **2.85**	2.03 **2.69**	1.96 **2.55**	1.90 **2.46**	1.85 **2.37**	1.81 **2.29**	1.78 **2.23**	1.72 **2.12**	1.67 **2.04**	1.60 **1.92**	1.54 **1.84**	1.49 **1.74**	1.42 **1.64**	1.38 **1.57**	1.32 **1.47**	1.28 **1.42**	1.22 **1.32**	1.16 **1.24**	1.13 **1.19**
1000	3.85 **6.66**	3.00 **4.62**	2.61 **3.80**	2.38 **3.34**	2.22 **3.04**	2.10 **2.82**	2.02 **2.66**	1.95 **2.53**	1.89 **2.43**	1.84 **2.34**	1.80 **2.26**	1.76 **2.20**	1.70 **2.09**	1.65 **2.01**	1.58 **1.89**	1.53 **1.81**	1.47 **1.71**	1.41 **1.61**	1.36 **1.54**	1.30 **1.44**	1.26 **1.38**	1.19 **1.28**	1.13 **1.19**	1.08 **1.11**
∞	3.84 **6.64**	2.99 **4.60**	2.60 **3.78**	2.37 **3.32**	2.21 **3.02**	2.09 **2.80**	2.01 **2.64**	1.94 **2.51**	1.88 **2.41**	1.83 **2.32**	1.79 **2.24**	1.75 **2.18**	1.69 **2.07**	1.64 **1.99**	1.57 **1.87**	1.52 **1.79**	1.46 **1.69**	1.40 **1.59**	1.35 **1.52**	1.28 **1.41**	1.24 **1.36**	1.17 **1.25**	1.11 **1.15**	1.00 **1.00**

TABLE A–7

Random Numbers*

22 17 68 65 84	68 95 23 92 35	87 02 22 57 51	61 09 43 95 06	58 24 82 03 47
19 36 27 59 46	13 79 93 37 55	39 77 32 77 09	85 52 05 30 62	47 83 51 62 74
16 77 23 02 77	09 61 87 25 21	28 06 24 25 93	16 71 13 59 78	23 05 47 47 25
78 43 76 71 61	20 44 90 32 64	97 67 63 99 61	46 38 03 93 22	69 81 21 99 21
03 28 28 26 08	73 37 32 04 05	69 30 16 09 05	88 69 58 28 99	35 07 44 75 47
93 22 53 64 39	07 10 63 76 35	87 03 04 79 88	08 13 13 85 51	55 34 57 72 69
78 76 58 54 74	92 38 70 96 92	52 06 79 79 45	82 63 18 27 44	69 66 92 19 09
23 68 35 26 00	99 53 93 61 28	52 70 05 48 34	56 65 05 61 86	90 92 10 70 80
15 39 25 70 99	93 86 52 77 65	15 33 59 05 28	22 87 26 07 47	86 96 98 29 06
58 71 96 30 24	18 46 23 34 27	85 13 99 24 44	49 18 09 79 49	74 16 32 23 02
57 35 27 33 72	24 53 63 94 09	41 10 76 47 91	44 04 95 49 66	39 60 04 59 81
48 50 86 54 48	22 06 34 72 52	82 21 15 65 20	33 29 94 71 11	15 91 29 12 03
61 96 48 95 03	07 16 39 33 66	98 56 10 56 79	77 21 30 27 12	90 49 22 23 62
36 93 89 41 26	29 70 83 63 51	99 74 20 52 36	87 09 41 15 09	98 60 16 03 03
18 87 00 42 31	57 90 12 02 07	23 47 37 17 31	54 08 01 88 63	39 41 88 92 10
88 56 53 27 59	33 35 72 67 47	77 34 55 45 70	08 18 27 38 90	16 95 86 70 75
09 72 95 84 29	49 41 31 06 70	42 38 06 45 18	64 84 73 31 65	52 53 37 97 15
12 96 88 17 31	65 19 69 02 83	60 75 86 90 68	24 64 19 35 51	56 61 87 39 12
85 94 57 24 16	92 09 84 38 76	22 00 27 69 85	29 81 94 78 70	21 94 47 90 12
38 64 43 59 98	98 77 87 68 07	91 51 67 62 44	40 98 05 93 78	23 32 65 41 18
53 44 09 42 72	00 41 86 79 79	68 47 22 00 20	35 55 31 51 51	00 83 63 22 55
40 76 66 26 84	57 99 99 90 37	36 63 32 08 58	37 40 13 68 97	87 64 81 07 83
02 17 79 18 05	12 59 52 57 02	22 07 90 47 03	28 14 11 30 79	20 69 22 40 98
95 17 82 06 53	31 51 10 96 46	92 06 88 07 77	56 11 50 81 69	40 23 72 51 39
35 76 22 42 92	96 11 83 44 80	34 68 35 48 77	33 42 40 90 60	73 96 53 97 86
26 29 13 56 41	85 47 04 66 08	34 72 57 59 13	82 43 80 46 15	38 26 61 70 04
77 80 20 75 82	72 82 32 99 90	63 95 73 76 63	89 73 44 99 05	48 67 26 43 18
46 40 66 44 52	91 36 74 43 53	30 82 13 54 00	78 45 63 98 35	55 03 36 67 68
37 56 08 18 09	77 53 84 46 47	31 91 18 95 58	24 16 74 11 53	44 10 13 85 57
61 65 61 68 66	37 27 47 39 19	84 83 70 07 48	53 21 40 06 71	95 06 79 88 54
93 43 69 64 07	34 18 04 52 35	56 27 09 24 86	61 85 53 83 45	19 90 70 99 00
21 96 60 12 99	11 20 99 45 18	48 13 93 55 34	18 37 79 49 90	65 97 38 20 46
95 20 47 97 97	27 37 83 28 71	00 06 41 41 74	45 89 09 39 84	51 67 11 52 49
97 86 21 78 73	10 65 81 92 59	58 76 17 14 97	04 76 62 16 17	17 95 70 45 80
69 92 06 34 13	59 71 74 17 32	27 55 10 24 19	23 71 82 13 74	63 52 52 01 41
04 31 17 21 56	33 73 99 19 87	26 72 39 27 67	53 77 57 68 93	60 61 97 22 61
61 06 98 03 91	87 14 77 43 96	43 00 65 98 50	45 60 33 01 07	98 99 46 50 47
85 93 85 86 88	72 87 08 62 40	16 06 10 89 20	23 21 34 74 97	76 38 03 29 63
21 74 32 47 45	73 96 07 94 52	09 65 90 77 47	25 76 16 19 33	53 05 70 53 30
15 69 53 82 80	79 96 23 53 10	65 39 07 16 29	45 33 02 43 70	02 87 40 41 45
02 89 08 04 49	20 21 14 68 86	87 63 93 95 17	11 29 01 95 80	35 14 97 35 33
87 18 15 89 79	85 43 01 72 73	08 61 74 51 69	89 74 39 82 15	94 51 33 41 67
98 83 71 94 22	59 97 50 99 52	08 52 85 08 40	87 80 61 65 31	91 51 80 32 44
10 08 58 21 66	72 68 49 29 31	89 85 84 46 06	59 73 19 85 23	65 09 29 75 63
47 90 56 10 08	88 02 84 27 83	42 29 72 23 19	66 56 45 65 79	20 71 53 20 25
22 85 61 68 90	49 64 92 85 44	16 40 12 89 88	50 14 49 81 06	01 82 77 45 12
67 80 43 79 33	12 83 11 41 16	25 58 19 68 70	77 02 54 00 52	53 43 37 15 26
27 62 50 96 72	79 44 61 40 15	14 53 40 65 39	27 31 58 50 28	11 39 03 34 25
33 78 80 87 15	38 30 06 38 21	14 47 47 07 26	54 96 87 53 32	40 36 40 96 76
13 13 92 66 99	47 24 49 57 74	32 25 43 62 17	10 97 11 69 84	99 63 22 32 98

* Reprinted from Table XXXIII of Fisher and Yates' *Statistical Tables*, with the permission of the authors and publishers, Oliver and Boyd, Edinburgh.

SOME MATRIX CALCULATION METHODS

1. Evaluation of determinants.

a. Unsymmetrical.

Let the determinant be as shown on the left. The main calculations involve setting up the *auxiliary matrix* as on the right.

Given Matrix

a_{11}	a_{12}	a_{13}	a_{14}
a_{21}	a_{22}	a_{23}	a_{24}
a_{31}	a_{32}	a_{33}	a_{34}
a_{41}	a_{42}	a_{43}	a_{44}

Auxiliary Matrix

a_{11}	x_{12}	x_{13}	x_{14}
a_{21}	x_{22}	x_{23}	x_{24}
a_{31}	x_{32}	x_{33}	x_{34}
a_{41}	x_{42}	x_{43}	x_{44}
(1)	(2)	(3)	(4)

(1) Write down the first column from the given matrix and

$$x_{12} = a_{12}/a_{11} \qquad x_{13} = a_{13}/a_{11} \qquad x_{14} = a_{14}/a_{11}$$

(2)

$$\begin{aligned} x_{22} &= a_{22} - a_{21}x_{12} \\ x_{32} &= a_{32} - a_{31}x_{12} \\ x_{42} &= a_{42} - a_{41}x_{12} \end{aligned}$$

(3)

$$\begin{aligned} x_{23} &= (a_{23} - a_{21}x_{13})/x_{22} \\ x_{33} &= a_{33} - a_{31}x_{13} - x_{32}x_{23} \\ x_{43} &= a_{43} - a_{41}x_{13} - x_{42}x_{23} \end{aligned}$$

(4)

$$\begin{aligned} x_{24} &= (a_{24} - a_{21}x_{14})/x_{22} \\ x_{34} &= (a_{34} - a_{31}x_{14} - x_{32}x_{24})/x_{33} \\ x_{44} &= a_{44} - a_{41}x_{14} - x_{42}x_{24} - x_{43}x_{34} \\ D &= a_{11} \times x_{22} \times x_{33} \times x_{44} \end{aligned}$$

Example—Value of a Determinant

Given Matrix

27.948	– 6.2992	– 5.2125	8.1643
– 84.522	174.46	19.412	– 9.8742
– 6.3428	4.5542	3.9844	12.748
7.1932	– 10.764	20.398	115.35

Auxiliary Matrix

27.948	– 0.22539	– 0.18651	0.29212
– 84.522	155.41	0.023472	0.095337
– 6.3428	3.1246	2.7281	5.2428
7.1932	– 9.1427	21.954	– 0.98007

$$D = 27.948 \times 155.41 \times 2.7281 \times - 0.98007 = - 11613$$

b. Symmetrical.

Let the determinant and auxiliary matrix be

Given Matrix

a_{11}	a_{12}	a_{13}	a_{14}
a_{12}	a_{22}	a_{23}	a_{24}
a_{13}	a_{23}	a_{33}	a_{34}
a_{14}	a_{24}	a_{34}	a_{44}

Auxiliary Matrix

a_{11}	x_{12}	x_{13}	x_{14}
a_{12}	x_{22}	x_{23}	x_{24}
a_{13}	x_{32}	x_{33}	x_{34}
a_{14}	x_{42}	x_{43}	x_{44}
(1)	(2)	(3)	(4)

The steps are:

(1) Same as for the unsymmetrical matrix.

(2)
$$x_{22} = a_{22} - a_{12}x_{12}$$
$$x_{32} = a_{23} - a_{13}x_{12} \qquad x_{23} = x_{32}/x_{22}$$
$$x_{42} = a_{24} - a_{14}x_{12} \qquad x_{24} = x_{42}/x_{22}$$

(3)
$$x_{33} = a_{33} - a_{13}x_{13} - x_{32}x_{23}$$
$$x_{43} = a_{34} - a_{14}x_{13} - x_{42}x_{23} \qquad x_{34} = x_{43}/x_{33}$$

(4)
$$x_{44} = a_{44} - a_{14}x_{14} - x_{42}x_{24} - x_{43}x_{34}$$
$$D = a_{11} \times x_{22} \times x_{33} \times x_{44}$$

EXAMPLE—EVALUATION OF A DETERMINANT

Given Matrix

1.2643	0.98724	− 0.40312	1.5734
0.98724	1.4396	2.0937	− 0.9682
− 0.40312	2.0937	0.87326	2.0431
1.5734	− 0.96820	2.0431	2.6114

Auxiliary Matrix

1.2643	0.78086	− 0.31885	1.2445
0.98724	0.66870	3.6017	− 3.2855
− 0.40312	2.4085	− 7.9300	− 1.3188
1.5734	− 2.1970	10.458	7.2271

$$D = -48.453$$

2. Simultaneous equations.

Suppose that the equations are

$$a_{11}X_1 + a_{12}X_2 + a_{13}X_3 = a_{14}$$
$$a_{12}X_1 + a_{22}X_2 + a_{23}X_3 = a_{24}$$
$$a_{13}X_1 + a_{23}X_2 + a_{33}X_3 = a_{34}$$

We set up the given matrix and calculate the auxiliary matrix.

Given Matrix

a_{11}	a_{12}	a_{13}	a_{14}
a_{12}	a_{22}	a_{23}	a_{24}
a_{13}	a_{23}	a_{33}	a_{34}

Auxiliary Matrix

a_{11}	x_{12}	x_{13}	x_{14}
a_{12}	x_{22}	x_{23}	x_{24}
a_{13}	x_{32}	x_{33}	x_{34}
(1)	(2)	(3)	(4)

(1) Same as in evaluation of determinants.

(2) $$x_{22} = a_{22} - a_{12}x_{12}$$

$$x_{32} = a_{23} - a_{13}x_{12} \qquad x_{23} = x_{32}/x_{22}$$

$$x_{24} = (a_{24} - a_{12}x_{14})/x_{22}$$

(3) $$x_{33} = a_{33} - a_{13}x_{13} - x_{32}x_{23}$$

(4) $$x_{34} = (a_{34} - a_{13}x_{14} - x_{32}x_{24})/x_{33}$$

Then

$$X_3 = x_{34}$$

$$X_2 = x_{24} - x_{23}X_3$$

$$X_1 = x_{14} - x_{12}X_2 - x_{13}X_3$$

EXAMPLE—SOLUTION OF SIMULTANEOUS EQUATIONS

Given Matrix

947.17	– 20.834	272.76	694.96
– 20.834	414.23	– 354.00	79.648
272.76	– 354.00	630.00	407.00

Auxiliary Matrix

947.17	– 0.021996	0.28797	0.73372
– 20.834	413.77	– 0.84105	0.22944
272.76	– 348.00	258.77	1.1080

$X_3 = 1.1080$

$X_2 = 0.22944 - (-0.84105 \times 1.1080) = 1.1613$

$X_1 = 0.73372 - (-0.021996 \times 1.1613) - (0.28797 \times 1.1080) = 0.44019$

3. Calculation of Gauss multipliers and partial regression and correlation coefficients from a correlation matrix.

Original Matrix

a_{11}	a_{12}	a_{13}	a_{14}	a_{15}	a_{16}	1	0	0	0	0	0
a_{12}	a_{22}	a_{23}	a_{24}	a_{25}	a_{26}	0	1	0	0	0	0
a_{13}	a_{23}	a_{33}	a_{34}	a_{35}	a_{36}	0	0	1	0	0	0
a_{14}	a_{24}	a_{34}	a_{44}	a_{45}	a_{46}	0	0	0	1	0	0
a_{15}	a_{25}	a_{35}	a_{45}	a_{55}	a_{56}	0	0	0	0	1	0
a_{16}	a_{26}	a_{36}	a_{46}	a_{56}	a_{66}	0	0	0	0	0	1

Auxiliary Matrix

	a_{11}	a_{12}	a_{13}	a_{14}	a_{15}	a_{16}	1					
	a_{12}	x_{22}	x_{23}	x_{24}	x_{25}	x_{26}	y_{21}	y_{22}				
	a_{13}	x_{32}	x_{33}	x_{34}	x_{35}	x_{36}	y_{31}	y_{32}	y_{33}			
	a_{14}	x_{42}	x_{43}	x_{44}	x_{45}	x_{46}	y_{41}	y_{42}	y_{43}	y_{44}		
	a_{15}	x_{52}	x_{53}	x_{54}	x_{55}	x_{56}	y_{51}	y_{52}	y_{53}	y_{54}	y_{55}	
	a_{16}	x_{62}	x_{63}	x_{64}	x_{65}	x_{66}	y_{61}	y_{62}	y_{63}	y_{64}	y_{65}	y_{66}
Steps	(1)	(2)	(3)	(4)	(5)	(6)						

b Matrix

b_{61}	b_{62}	b_{63}	b_{64}	b_{65}	
b_{51}	b_{52}	b_{53}	b_{54}		b_{56}
b_{41}	b_{42}	b_{43}		b_{45}	b_{46}
b_{31}	b_{32}		b_{34}	b_{35}	b_{36}
b_{21}		b_{23}	b_{24}	b_{25}	b_{26}
	b_{12}	b_{13}	b_{14}	b_{15}	b_{16}

c Matrix

c_{11}	c_{12}	c_{13}	c_{14}	c_{15}	c_{16}
	c_{22}	c_{23}	c_{24}	c_{25}	c_{26}
		c_{33}	c_{34}	c_{35}	c_{36}
			c_{44}	c_{45}	c_{46}
				c_{55}	c_{56}
					c_{66}

r Matrix

r_{12}	r_{13}	r_{14}	r_{15}	r_{16}
	r_{23}	r_{24}	r_{25}	r_{26}
		r_{34}	r_{35}	r_{36}
			r_{45}	r_{46}
				r_{56}

$$r^2_{1.23456} = a^2_{16} + x_{62}x_{26} + x_{63}x_{36} + x_{64}x_{46} + x_{65}x_{56}$$

Calculation of Auxiliary Matrix

(1) Enter first row and column from original matrix.

(2)

$$x_{22} = a_{22} - a_{12}a_{12}$$

$$x_{32} = a_{23} - a_{13}a_{12} \qquad x_{23} = x_{32}/x_{22}$$

$$x_{42} = a_{24} - a_{14}a_{12} \qquad x_{24} = x_{42}/x_{22}$$

$$x_{52} = a_{25} - a_{15}a_{12} \qquad x_{25} = x_{52}/x_{22}$$

$$x_{62} = a_{26} - a_{16}a_{12} \qquad x_{26} = x_{62}/x_{22}$$

$$y_{21} = - a_{12}/x_{22}$$

$$y_{22} = 1/x_{22}$$

(3)

$$x_{33} = a_{33} - a_{13}a_{13} - x_{32}x_{23}$$

$$x_{43} = a_{34} - a_{14}a_{13} - x_{42}x_{23} \qquad x_{34} = x_{43}/x_{33}$$

$$x_{53} = a_{35} - a_{15}a_{13} - x_{52}x_{23} \qquad x_{35} = x_{53}/x_{33}$$

$$x_{63} = a_{36} - a_{16}a_{13} - x_{62}x_{23} \qquad x_{36} = x_{63}/x_{33}$$

$$y_{31} = (- a_{13} - x_{32}y_{21})/x_{33}$$

$$y_{32} = (- x_{32}y_{22})/x_{33}$$

$$y_{33} = 1/x_{33}$$

(4)

$$x_{44} = a_{44} - a_{14}a_{14} - x_{42}x_{24} - x_{43}x_{34}$$

$$x_{54} = a_{45} - a_{15}a_{14} - x_{52}x_{24} - x_{53}x_{34} \qquad x_{45} = x_{54}/x_{44}$$

$$x_{64} = a_{46} - a_{16}a_{14} - x_{62}x_{24} - x_{63}x_{34} \qquad x_{46} = x_{64}/x_{44}$$

$$y_{41} = (- a_{14} - x_{42}y_{21} - x_{43}y_{31})/x_{44}$$

$$y_{42} = (- x_{42}y_{22} - x_{43}y_{32})/x_{44}$$

$$y_{43} = (- x_{43}y_{33})/x_{44}$$

$$y_{44} = 1/x_{44}$$

(5)

$$x_{55} = a_{55} - a_{15}a_{15} - x_{52}x_{25} - x_{53}x_{35} - x_{54}x_{45}$$

$$x_{65} = a_{56} - a_{16}a_{15} - x_{62}x_{25} - x_{63}x_{35} - x_{64}x_{45} \qquad x_{56} = x_{65}/x_{55}$$

$$y_{51} = (- a_{15} - x_{52}y_{21} - x_{53}y_{31} - x_{54}y_{41})/x_{55}$$

$$y_{52} = (- x_{52}y_{22} - x_{53}y_{32} - x_{54}y_{42})/x_{55}$$

$$y_{53} = (- x_{53}y_{33} - x_{54}y_{43})/x_{55}$$

$$y_{54} = (- x_{54}y_{44})/x_{55}$$

$$y_{55} = 1/x_{55}$$

etc.

Calculation of c Matrix

(1)

$$c_{16} = y_{61}$$
$$c_{15} = y_{51} - x_{56}c_{16}$$
$$c_{14} = y_{41} - x_{45}c_{15} - x_{46}c_{16}$$
$$c_{13} = y_{31} - x_{34}c_{14} - x_{35}c_{15} - x_{36}c_{16}$$
$$c_{12} = y_{21} - x_{23}c_{13} - x_{24}c_{14} - x_{25}c_{15} - x_{26}c_{16}$$
$$c_{11} = 1 - a_{12}c_{12} - a_{13}c_{13} - a_{14}c_{14} - a_{15}c_{15} - a_{16}c_{16}$$

(2)

$$c_{26} = y_{62}$$
$$c_{25} = y_{52} - x_{56}c_{26}$$
$$c_{24} = y_{42} - x_{45}c_{25} - x_{46}c_{26}$$
$$c_{23} = y_{32} - x_{34}c_{24} - x_{35}c_{25} - x_{36}c_{26}$$
$$c_{22} = y_{22} - x_{23}c_{23} - x_{24}c_{24} - x_{25}c_{25} - x_{26}c_{26}$$

(3)

$$c_{36} = y_{63}$$
$$c_{35} = y_{53} - x_{56}c_{36}$$
$$c_{34} = y_{43} - x_{45}c_{35} - x_{46}c_{36}$$

etc.

Calculation of b Matrix

General formula

$$b_{ij} = \frac{c_{ij}}{c_{ii}}$$

(1) Calculate reciprocals for c_{11}, c_{22}, $\cdots$, c_{66}, giving d_{11}, d_{22}, $\cdots$, d_{66}.

(2)

$b_{61} = d_{66}c_{16}$ $\quad b_{62} = d_{66}c_{26}$ $\quad b_{63} = d_{66}c_{36}$ $\quad b_{64} = d_{66}c_{46}$ $\quad b_{65} = d_{66}c_{56}$

(3)

$b_{51} = d_{55}c_{15}$ $\quad b_{52} = d_{55}c_{25}$ $\quad b_{53} = d_{55}c_{35}$ $\quad b_{54} = d_{55}c_{45}$ $\quad b_{56} = d_{66}c_{56}$

etc.

Calculation of r Matrix

General formula.

$$r_{ij} = \frac{c_{ij}}{\sqrt{c_{ii}c_{jj}}}$$

(1) Calculate

$$g_{11} = \frac{1}{\sqrt{c_{11}}},\ g_{22} = \frac{1}{\sqrt{c_{22}}},\ \cdots,\ g_{66} = \frac{1}{\sqrt{c_{66}}}$$

(2) $\quad r_{12} = c_{12}g_{11}g_{22}$ $\quad r_{13} = c_{13}g_{11}g_{33}$ $\quad$ etc.

Example—Calculation of Gauss Multipliers, Partial Regression and Correlation Coefficients, and Multiple Correlation Coefficient

Original Matrix

1.0000	− 0.4589	− 0.5612	− 0.3947	− 0.3123	0.6412	1	0	0	0	0	0
− 0.4589	1.0000	0.3114	0.0429	0.2861	− 0.3190	0	1	0	0	0	0
− 0.5612	0.3114	1.0000	− 0.0655	0.1467	− 0.4462	0	0	1	0	0	0
− 0.3947	0.0429	− 0.0655	1.0000	0.1882	− 0.3511	0	0	0	1	0	0
− 0.3123	0.2861	0.1467	0.1882	1.0000	− 0.3092	0	0	0	0	1	0
0.6412	− 0.3190	− 0.4462	− 0.3511	− 0.3092	1.0000	0	0	0	0	0	1

Auxiliary Matrix

1.0000	− 0.4589	− 0.5612	− 0.3947	− 0.3123	0.6412	1					
− 0.4589	0.7894	0.06824	− 0.1751	0.1809	− 0.03135	0.5813	1.2668				
− 0.5612	0.05387	0.6814	− 0.4074	− 0.05622	− 0.1243	0.7776	− 0.1002	1.4676			
− 0.3947	− 0.1382	− 0.2776	0.7069	0.1051	− 0.1935	0.9774	0.2084	0.5763	1.4146		
− 0.3123	0.1428	− 0.03831	0.07433	0.8667	− 0.1094	0.2151	− 0.2310	0.01545	− 0.1213	1.1538	
0.6412	− 0.02475	− 0.08467	− 0.1368	− 0.09486	0.5407	− 0.7525	0.05450	0.3784	0.3366	0.2023	1.8495

b Matrix

0.4069	− 0.0295	− 0.2046	− 0.1820	− 0.1094	
− 0.1129	0.1913	− 0.0483	0.0718		− 0.1720
− 0.5494	− 0.1630	− 0.4323		0.0568	− 0.2261
− 0.5757	0.0041		− 0.3616	− 0.0319	− 0.2126
− 0.4489		0.0054	− 0.1794	0.1664	− 0.0403
	− 0.2248	− 0.3795	− 0.3028	− 0.0492	0.2787

c Matrix

2.7004	0.6070	1.0247	0.8178	0.1328	− 0.7525
	1.3522	− 0.00724	0.2426	− 0.2250	0.05450
		1.7800	0.6435	0.05685	0.3784
			1.4886	− 0.08448	0.3366
				1.1759	0.2023
					1.8495

r Matrix

− 0.318	− 0.467	− 0.408	− 0.073	0.337
	0.005	− 0.171	0.178	− 0.034
		− 0.395	− 0.039	− 0.209
			0.064	− 0.203
				− 0.137

$$r^2_{1.23\cdots6} = 0.6412^2 + (0.03135 \times 0.02475) + (0.1243 \times 0.08467)$$
$$+ (0.1935 \times 0.1368) + (0.1094 \times 0.09486) = \mathbf{0.4593}$$

$$r_{1.23\cdots6} = 0.678$$

Index

Abbreviated Doolittle solution, 139
Abnormality, flatness, 33
  measures of, 34, 42, 43
  peakedness, 34
  skewness, 33
  types of, 33
Acceptance number, 428
Accuracy in experimental design, 194
Addition theorem, 305, 362
Adjustments to treatment means, factorial experiments, 236, 239
  lattice experiments, 273, 279, 284, 287
Algebraic functions, 8
Aliases in fractional replication, 247
α_3, α_4 (alpha), binomial distribution, 42
  normal distribution, 35
  Poisson distribution, 43
Analysis, of balanced lattice, 274
  of covariance, 153
    application to the control of error, 155
    calculation of sums of products, 159
    corrections to means, 157
    example, 160
    principles of, 153
    standard errors of corrected means, 157
    tests for heterogeneity of regression, 158
    tests of significance in, 162
  of cross-over designs, 212
  of Latin squares, 203, 216
  of linear regression, 102
  of non-linear regression, 166
  of non-orthogonal data, 304
  of quadruple lattice, 260, 275, 280
  of randomized blocks, 196, 214
  of split-plot experiments, 223
  of ungrouped experiments, 195
Analysis, of variance, balanced lattice, 274
    cross-over designs, 212
    fundamental principles, 64
    Latin squares, 203, 216
    limitations of, 97
    linear regression, 107
    non-linear regression, 167
    non-orthogonal data, 317
    quadruple lattice, 260, 275, 280
    randomized blocks, 196, 214
    test of significance in, 69
    three-fold classification, 94
    two-fold classification, 73
    ungrouped experiments, 196
Arbitrary origin for calculation of standard deviation, 25
Arithmetic mean, 16

Balanced lattice, 261, 274
  analysis of, 274
  calculation of sums of squares, 274, 285
  outline of analysis, 271
  variances for mean differences, 275, 287
  variety corrections, 273, 275, 287
Basic experimental designs, 192
  cross-over design, 212
  Graeco-Latin square, 209
  Latin square, 203, 209, 216
  randomized blocks, 196, 214
  ungrouped randomized, 195
Bias, freedom from, in experimental design, 193
  test for, 47
Binomial, α_3, α_4 for, 42
  expansion, 7, 354
  in goodness of fit tests, 354
  in sequential sampling, 341
Binomial distribution, 38

Binomial sequential sampling, 430
Binomial theorem, 7
Biological assay, 394; *see also* Probit analysis

c_2 (for average standard deviation), 419, 445
Calculation, of control limits, 420
  of correlation coefficient, 131
  of partial correlation coefficient, 145, 454
  of partial regression coefficient, 136, 454
  of regression coefficient, 113, 116
  of sample means for control charts, 419
  of standard deviation, 24
  of standard deviations for control charts, 419
  of sums of products, 125
    in covariance analysis, 159
  of sums of squares, 82
    balanced lattice, 274, 285
Chi-square (χ^2), definition, 361
  genetic ratios, 366
  goodness of fit tests, 361
  heterogeneity test, 362
  ratios with multiple classification, 364
  table of, 444
Chi-square (χ^2) tests, for goodness of fit, genetic ratios, 366
    multiple classification, 364
    two or more classes, 359
    twofold classification, 353
  for independence, in $r \times c$ tables, 370
    in $r \times 2$ tables, 371, 375
    in 2×2 tables, 372
Class intervals for frequency table, 32
Class values, selection of, 22
Coding, 105
Coefficient, of correlation, 125
  of multiple correlation, 138, 144, 147, 150
  of partial correlation, 135
  of partial regression, 135
  of variability, 25
Combinations, formulas for, 6
Complete confounding, 230, 237
  in a 2^3 experiment, 230, 237
  principle of, 230
Completed values, 307, 316, 322
Confounding, complete, 230, 237
  in a 3^2 factorial experiment, 250
  in a 3^3 factorial experiment, 253
  in factorial experiments, 230
  in 2^n experiments, 243
  partial, 235, 240
Consumer's risk, 428
Control chart, 418
  calculations, 423
  control limits, for the mean, 419
    for the standard deviation, 420
  correction to standard deviation of sample mean, 419
  examples, 420, 422
  illustration, 418
  sample means, 419
  setting up, 418, 423
  standard deviation, 419
  summary of technique, 423
Control of error by analysis of covariance, 155
Corrections, for adjustment of average standard deviation, 445
  for block effects in confounded experiments, 236, 242
  for continuity in χ^2 tests, 358
  Sheppard's, 22
  to treatment means, in factorial experiments, 236, 239
    in lattice experiments, 266, 272, 279, 284
    in standard deviation of sample means, 419
Correlation, 122
  definition, 122
  measurement, 124
  positive and negative, 123
  scatter diagrams, 123
  surfaces, 123
Correlation coefficient, 125
  calculation, 131
  fiducial limits, 131
  partial, 144
  range and interpretation, 126
  sampling distribution, 129

Correlation coefficient, test of significance, 130
 z transformation, 130
Covariance analysis, 153
 applications in the control of error, 155
 calculation of sums of products, 159
 correction to means, 157
 example, 160
 principles, 153
 standard errors of corrected means, 157
 test for heterogeneity of regression, 158, 163
 tests of significance, 162
Covariance technique for estimating missing values, 324
Covariation, 122
Cross-over design, 212
 outline of analysis for, 212
Cubic response, 167

Defining contrast, definition of, 247
 in fractional replication, 247
Degrees of freedom, 20
 in tests of independence, 370
 individual, 87
 partitioning of, 71, 87
Deletion of a variable in partial regression analysis, 142
Derivation, of partial regression equation, 135
 of regression equation, 102
Determinants, 11
 evaluation of, by matrix calculations, 451
  symmetrical, 452
  unsymmetrical, 451
Differentiation of soil types by discriminant function, 380
Discriminant function, 378
 applications, 385
 applied to differentiation of soil types, 380
 assigning weights, 387, 390
 example, 388
 plant selection, 385, 388
 principles, 385
 test of significance, 385
Disproportionate sub-class numbers, 326
 considerations arising out of, 328
 effect of presence or absence of interaction, 329
 methods of analysis, 333
  $r \times c$ table, by fitting constants, 339, 346
   by weighted squares of means, 350
  $r \times 2$ table, by fitting constants, 336, 341
   by weighted squares of means, 338, 345
  2×2 table, by fitting constants, 333
   by weighted squares of means, 335
 multiple classification, 327
 single classification, 326
Distribution, of means of samples, 37
 of tolerances, 394
Distributions, binomial, 38
 normal, 29
 Poisson, 42
Doolittle solution, abbreviated, 139
Dosage-mortality experiments, 413
Double sampling, 429

Efficiency, in experimental design, 214
 in Latin square experiments, 217
 in randomized block experiments, 200, 213
Empirical probits, 399
Enumeration data, 353
Equations, logarithmic, 173
 polynomials, 173
 simultaneous, 9
Error, experimental, 74
 selecting a valid, 90
Error control, in covariance analysis, 155
 selection of a variable for, 159
Errors, first kind, 48
 second kind, 48
Estimation of missing values, *see* Missing values
Evaluation, determinants, 11, 451
 simultaneous equations, 9, 452

Exact test for independence in 2×2 table, 372
Experimental design, accuracy, 194
efficiency, 213
in probit analysis, 415
Experimental designs, basic, 192
cross-over design, 212
Graeco-Latin square, 209
Latin square, 203, 209, 216
randomized blocks, 196, 203, 214
ungrouped randomized, 195
Experimental error, 74

F, correction for lattice experiments, 280
table, 446
test, 70, 76
Factorial experiments, 220
complete confounding in, 230, 237
confounding in, 221, 230
confounding in 2^n experiments, 243
correction for block effects, 236
design and analysis of simple, 221
design for 3^3 experiments, 253
fractional replication, 221, 246
partial confounding, 235, 240
principles, 220
split plot, 222
standard errors, 225
2^n designs in one replication, 245
Feeding trials, analysis of, 99
Fiducial limits, correlation coefficients, 131
goodness of fit ratios, 358
means, 59
regression coefficients, 107, 114, 117
Fitting constants, analysis with disproportionate sub-class numbers, $r \times c$ table, 339, 346
$r \times 2$ table, 336, 341
2×2 table, 333
equations for, 313
non-orthogonal data, 310
Fitting curves, non-linear regression, 172
normal, 30
reasons for, 172
Fitting orthogonal polynomials, 181
Fitting polynomial equations, 174

Formulas, for α_3, α_4, binomial distribution, 42
normal distribution, 35
Poisson distribution, 43
for combinations, 6
for permutations, 5
for sequential sampling, binomial, 431
Poisson, 433
Fractional replication, 246
an alias in, 247
confounding, 248
defining contrast, 247
outline of analysis, 249
principal block in, 247
principle of, 247
Frequency distributions, *see* Distributions
Frequency polygon, 24
Frequency table, 20
graphical representation, 23
setting up, 21
Functions, algebraic, 8

$g_1 = k_3/(k'_2)^{3/2}$, $g_2 = k'_4/(k'_2)^2$ (measures of abnormality), 36
standard errors of, 36
Gauss multipliers, 139
in matrix calculations, 454
Genetic ratios, goodness of fit tests, 366
Goodness of fit, 353
multiple classification, 364
9:3:3:1 ratio, 366
two or more classes, 359
χ^2 test of heterogeneity, 362
twofold classification, numbers moderate to large, 356
numbers small, 353
Graeco-Latin square, theory of, in experimental design, 209

Heterogeneity, of regression, in probit analysis, 401, 406, 411
tests for, 158, 163
of variation, 63
Histogram, 23, 30

Incomplete block experiments, 257
an elementary type, 257
lattice experiments, 259

Incomplete block experiments, missing values, 300
principles, 257
Incomplete blocks, meaning of, 257
Independence, tests of, degrees of freedom, 370
$r \times c$ tables, 370
$r \times 2$ tables, 371, 375
2×2 tables, 372
χ^2 test, 374
exact test, 372
nature of, 369
Individual degrees of freedom partitioning, 87
Inspection, 418
and verification, 418
sampling for, 427
Interaction, effect with disproportionate sub-class numbers, 329
first order, 77
higher order, 80
Introductory concepts, 1
Invariance, 157

k_1, k_2, k_3, k_4 (k statistics), 35

Latin square experiments, 203
analysis, 216
efficiency, 204, 217
estimation of missing values, 209
outline of analysis, 210
randomization, 205
standard errors, 217
Lattice designs, 259
balanced, 261, 274, 285
corrections to variety means, 266, 272, 279, 284
lattice squares, 288, 299
partially balanced, 260, 275, 280
standard errors, 270, 274, 280, 284, 287
theory, 262
with groups repeated, 280
with 2–p groups, 271
Lattice experiments, 259
balanced, 261, 274, 285
corrections to variety means, 266, 272, 279, 284
diagrammatic representation of data from, 268
Lattice experiments, partially balanced, 260
groups repeated, 280
quadruple, 260, 275
simple, 260
triple, 260
2 to p groups, 271
standard errors, 270, 274, 280, 284, 287
Lattice squares, 288
inaccuracies of weighting, 299
type $r = \frac{1}{2}(p + 1)$, 288
type $r = p + 1$, 296
L.D. 50 (median lethal dose), 397
Least squares method for deriving regression equations, 104
Limitations of analysis of variance, 97
Linear regression analysis, both variables subject to error, 108
calculation, regression table, 110
ungrouped data, 109
general observations, 102
graphs, 103, 106, 110
test, for deviations from, 111
of significance, 107, 117
Linear response, 167

Mathematical concepts fundamental to statistics, 3
Matrices, 13
Matrix, 13
Matrix calculations, 451
evaluation of determinants, 451
partial regression and correlation coefficients, 454
solution of simultaneous equations, 452
Mean, arithmetic, 16
calculation of, 24
geometric, 126
of samples, distribution of, 37
Mean square, 69
Measurement data, 353
Measures of abnormality, 34
α_3, α_4, normal distribution, 35
binomial distribution, 42
Poisson distribution, 43
g_1, g_2, normal distribution, 36

Missing values, effect of, 305
estimation, 318
covariance technique, 324
incomplete block experiments, 300
Latin square, 209
lattice experiments, 300
randomized blocks, 203
$r \times c$ table, 318
more than one missing value, 320
one missing value, 318
$2 \times c$ table, 307
standard errors, for experiments with more than one missing value, 323
for experiments with one missing value, 320
Multiple correlation, 144
calculation, 138, 144, 148
coefficient, 138, 144, 147, 150
interpretation, 146, 150
significance, 150
Multiple measurements in discriminant function, 378
Multiple regression, 134
analysis, 150
equation, 135
interpretation, 146, 150
problem, 134
special applications, 150
test of significance, 150

Non-linear regression, 166
analysis of components, 166
analysis of regression components, 168, 171
analysis of variance, 167
basic factors, 171
selecting a regression equation, 173
Non-orthogonal data, analysis of variance, 317
treatment by fitting constants, 310
2×2 table, 306
Non-orthogonality, 304
meaning, 304
owing to disproportionate sub-class numbers, 326
Normal curve, 30
equation, 30
fitting, 31
Normal curve, histogram, 30
table of ordinates, 442
Normal distribution, 28
α_3, α_4, 35
experimental derivation, 28
histogram, 30
Normal equations, linear regression, 104
non-linear regression, 175
orthogonal polynomials, 176
Null hypothesis, 59

Objective in experimental designs, 194
Ordinates of normal curve, table, 442
use of, in fitting, 29
Original values, 307, 316, 322
Orthogonal polynomials, fitting by Fisher's summation method, 181
fitting with Fisher and Yates' tables, 186
test of significance, 184
Orthogonality, 70, 304
effect of missing values, 305

Paired values, regression analysis for, 113
regression table, 114
t test, 57
Parameters, 19
Partial confounding, 235
in a 2^3 experiment, 235, 240
principle of, 235
Partial correlation, 144
coefficient, 144
calculation, 145, 454
Partial regression, 134
analysis, 146
coefficient, 135
calculation, 136
different sets of Y values, 138
Gauss multipliers, 139, 454
standard error, 142
test of significance, 145
deletion of a variable, 142
methods, 134
Partially balanced lattice, 260
analysis, 271
correction to F test, 280
outline of analysis, 272
quadruple, 260, 275, 280

Partially balanced lattice, simple, 260
standard errors in, 280
triple, 260
variety corrections, 272
Partitioning, of error components, 200
of sums of squares and degrees of freedom, 71, 87
Permutations, formulas for, 5
Plant selection, example, 388
use of discriminant function for, 385
Poisson distribution, 42
applications, 43
verification trials, 436
basic principles in verification trials, 437
formulas for α_3, α_4, 43
sequential sampling, 433
Polynomial equations, 173, 175
fitting, 174, 186
example, 177, 181, 188
Population, concept of, 15
homogeneous, 65
Principal block, definition, 248
in fractional replication, 247
methods of writing, 247
Principles, covariance analysis, 153
experimental design, 192
Probability, basic rules, 4
definition, 3
of acceptance, 44
of rejection, 44
Probability integral, 30
table of, 441
Probit analysis, 394
data appropriate for, 394
determination of relative potency, 408
experimental design, 415
graphical methods, 414
heterogeneity in, 401, 406, 411
practical applications, 397
regression coefficient, 397
fiducial limits, 401
test of significance, 401
Probit regression line, 398
fitting a provisional, 398
fitting by maximum likelihood, 404
weighting coefficients, 398
Probit transformation, 395
Producer's risk, 429

Quadratic response, 167
Quadruple lattice, 260, 275
Quality control, 418
definition, 418
examples, 420, 422
setting up control chart, 418, 423
Quantity of information, 157

Random numbers, 450
Randomized block experiments, 196, 214
analysis, 196, 214
efficiency, 200, 213
estimation of missing values, 203
outline of analysis, 196
partitioning error components, 200
standard errors, 197, 201, 215
tests of significance, 215
variance components, 198
Range, table of range/standard deviation, 21
Regression, deviations from linear, 106
goodness of fit, 106, 398
testing for heterogeneity, 158, 163
Regression analysis, linear, 102
general observations, 102
paired values in regression table, 114
series of paired values, 113
tests of significance, 107
Regression coefficient, fiducial limits, 107, 114, 117
probit analysis, 397
test of significance, 107, 401
testing heterogeneity of series of, 158, 163
Regression components, 166
analysis of, with Fisher and Yates' tables, 167
cubic and higher degree, 167
example of analysis, 168
linear, 167
quadratic, 167
Regression equations, derivation, 102, 104
Regression table, 118
calculation, 112
Relative deviate, 357
Relative potency, determination in probit analysis, 408

Response, cubic, 167
  linear, 167
  quadratic, 167

Samples, 16
Sampling, inspection, 426
    double, 429
    sequential, 430
    single, 427
Sampling distribution, correlation coefficient, 129
Scope, sufficiency in experimental design, 195
Selecting a valid error, 75, 90
Sequential sampling, 430
  binomial distribution, formulas, 431
    graphs, 435
  Poisson distribution, formulas, 433
    graphs, 435
  principle, 430
Sheppard's corrections, 22
Significance, tests of, *see* Tests of significance
Simple lattice, 260
Simultaneous equations, evaluation by matrix calculations, 452
Single sampling, 427
Skewness, 33
Split plot experiments, 222
  example, 225
  outline of analysis, 223
  plan, 222
  standard errors, 224, 243
  sums of squares, 224
Square yard plots, table of yields, 26
Standard deviation, 17
  calculation, 24
  control charts, 419
  control limits, 420
  of a mean, 53
  sample mean, correction to, 419
  unbiased estimates of, 19
Standard error, experiments with missing values, 323
  Latin square experiments, 217
  lattice experiments, 270, 274, 280, 284, 287
  of a mean, 20
  of estimated Y, 108
Standard error, randomized block experiments, 197, 201, 215
  split plot experiments, 224, 243
Standard regression coefficients, 144
Statistic, definition of, 16
Statistics, introductory concepts, 1
Sterling's approximation, 361
Summation method of fitting orthogonal polynomials, 181
Sums, of products, calculation, 125
    in covariance analysis, 159
  of squares, calculation, k groups, n not the same for each group, 82
      of n variates each, 82
    $(m \times n)$-fold table, 84
    non-orthogonal data, 316, 323
    split plot experiments, 224, 227
    three factor interaction, 85
    two factor interaction, 84
    $(2 \times n)$-fold table, 82
    (2×2) table interaction, 78

t, table of, 443
t test, 50
  logic of, 47
  variances different, 58
  variates not paired, 55
  variates paired, 57
Table, of c_2 (for average standard deviation), 445
  of chi-square (χ^2), 444
  of F, 446
  of ordinates of normal curve, 442
  of probability integral, 441
  of random numbers, 450
  of range/standard deviation, 21
  of t, 443
Tests, of independence, degrees of freedom, 370
    nature of, 369
    $r \times c$ tables, 370
    $r \times 2$ tables, 371, 375
    2×2 tables, 372
      χ^2 test, 372
      exact test, 372
  of significance, analysis of covariance, 153
    correlation coefficient, 130
    distribution of t, 50

Tests, of significance, heterogeneity of regression coefficients, 158, 401
logic of, 47
mean difference, 50, 56
multiple correlation coefficient, 150
partial regression coefficient, 145
probit analysis, 401
randomized blocks, 215
regression coefficient, 107, 401
Theoretical frequency distributions, 27
normal, 28
derivation by sampling random numbers, 28
equation, 30
histogram, 30
Theory of lattice designs, 262
Threefold classification of variates, 94
Tolerances, distribution of, 394
Transformations, fractions of percentages, 98
inverse sine, 98
logarithmic, 98
small whole numbers, 98
square root, 98
whole number counts with a wide range, 98
Triple lattice, 260
Twofold classification of variates, analysis of variance, 73
goodness of fit tests, 353
Types of abnormality, *see* Abnormality

Ungrouped randomized experiments, 195
calculation of sums of squares, 195
outline of analysis, 195

Variance, analysis, 63
limitations, 97
test of significance, 69
definition, 20
for mean difference, balanced lattice, 275, 287
Variance components, randomized block and ungrouped experiments, 198
Variates, continuous, 27
discontinuous, 27
threefold classification, 94
twofold classification, 73
Variation, 15
assignable causes, 419
heterogeneity of, 63
Verification trials, application of Poisson distribution, 436
basic Poisson distribution for, 437
definition, 436
limits of accuracy, 439

Weighted squares of means for analysis with disproportionate sub-class numbers, $r \times c$ table, 344, 350
$r \times 2$ table, 338
2×2 table, 335
Weighting coefficients in probit analysis, 398
Wireworm counts, analysis of, 101
Working probit, 404

$z = \frac{1}{2} \log_e (V_1/V_2)$, 69
test for differences between correlation coefficients, 131
transformation for correlation coefficient, 130